ZOOLOGY

for Intermediate Students

G. *Chapman*

M.A., Ph.D.

Professor of Zoology in the University of London,
Queen Elizabeth College

W. B. *Barker*

M.A., Diploma in Agriculture (Cantab.)

Formerly Senior Biology Master, King's College School,
Wimbledon

LONGMANS

LONGMANS, GREEN AND CO LTD
48 Grosvenor Street, London W.1

*Associated companies, branches and representatives
throughout the world*

*Printed in Great Britain by
Western Printing Services Ltd, Bristol*

ZOOLOGY
FOR INTERMEDIATE STUDENTS

Contents

I INVERTEBRATE ANIMALS

II VERTEBRATE ANIMALS

III THE WORKING OF THE ANIMAL BODY

IV THE DEVELOPMENT OF THE INDIVIDUAL

V THE EVOLUTION OF ANIMALS

ACKNOWLEDGEMENTS

For permission to base illustrations on figures in other publications we are indebted to the following:

The American Physiological Society for Fig. 24.4 from *Physiological Reviews*, **15**; Balfour Library for Fig. 36.4A from Sedgwick, *Monograph on genus Peripatus*, **4**; Ernest Benn Ltd. for Figs. 17.2 and 36.4B from Norman, *A History of Fishes*; The Trustees of the British Museum (Natural History) for Fig. 36.1 from *Short Guide to the Exhibition Galleries*; Cambridge Philosophical Society for Figs. 34.7 and 34.24 from *Biological Reviews*, **15**; Cambridge University Press for Figs. 8.14 and 9.20 from Borradaile, Eastham, Potts and Saunders, *Invertebrate Zoology*, Fig. 10.2 from Shipley and McBride, *Zoology* and Fig. 35.13 from Bateson, *Mendel's Principles of Heredity*; William Collins, Sons & Co. Ltd. for Fig. 17.2 from Hardy, *The Open Sea*, II and Figs. 31.1 and 31.2 from Matthews, *British Mammals*; The Company of Biologists Ltd. for Fig. 14.32 from Gray, *J. Exp. Biol.* **X**, 1933, Fig. 6.15 from Gray, *J. Exp. Biol.* **XVI**, 1939, Figs. 14.27 and 14.28B from Pumphrey and Lowenstein, *Symp. Soc. Exp. Biol.* **4**, 1950 and Fig. 9.21B from Dethier, *Symp. Soc. Exp. Biol.* **16**, 1962; Elsevier Publishing Company for Fig. 6.3B from R. Reed and K. M. Rudall, *Biochim. Biophys. Acta*, **2** (1948), 7; VEB Gustav Fischer Verlag for Fig. 2.4 from *Arch. Protistenkunde*, **82**; Holt, Rinehart and Winston, Inc., for Figs. 33.7, 34.12, 34.16, 34.20(1), 34.30 and 34.31B from Kellicott, *Outlines of Chordate Development*; Macmillan & Co. Ltd. for Figs. 7.1, 8.2A, 8.10 and 9.14 from Parker and Haswell, *Textbook of Zoology*, Fig. 9.23C and D from Lulham, *An Introduction to Zoology (Invertebrates)* and Figs. 14.13, 14.17C and D, 14.22, 14.29B, 15.17, 15.18, 15.20, 15.21 and 15.26, from Lockyer and Crofts, *Practical Zoological Illustrations*; The Macmillan Company, New York, for Fig. 36.3 from Gregory, *Evolution Emerging*; Masson et Cie for Figs. 6.14, 13.6, 13.10–13.13, 13.15–13.20 from Grassé, *Traité de Zoologie*; McGraw-Hill Book Company for Fig. 4.14 from Hyman, *The Invertebrates*, 1951; Methuen & Co. Ltd. for Figs. 9.3, 9.4, 9.19D and 9.21A from Imms, *Outlines of Entomology* and Fig. 26.1 from Wigglesworth, *Insect Physiology*; Oxford University Press for Figs. 2.12 and 2.22 from Mackinnon and Hawes, *An Introduction to the Study of Protozoa*, Fig. 6.6A from Stephenson, *The Oligochaeta*, Figs. 8.2B, 8.15C, 9.6, 9.11, 9.12, 16.37, 34.17 and 34.20(2) from Borradaile, *Manual of Elementary Zoology*, Fig. 9.23A and B from Dakin, *The Elements of General Zoology*, Fig. 13.5 from Young, *Life of Vertebrates*, Fig. 14.9 from *Quart. Journal of Micro. Sci.* **63**, Fig. 30.2 from *Quart. Journal of Micro. Sci.* **89**, Fig. 15.12 from De Beer, *The Development of the Vertebrate Skull* and Fig. 28.4 from Young, *Life of Mammals*; Penguin Books Ltd. for Figs. 3.7 and 14.1 from *New Biology*; Routledge & Kegan Paul Ltd. for Figs. 8.6, 8.8A, 8.11–8.13A and B and 8.15A and B–8.17 from Huxley, *The Crayfish*; W. B. Saunders Company for Fig. 16.28C from Romer, A. S., *The Vertebrate Body*. Ed. 3. Philadelphia, 1962; University of California Press for Fig. 2.3B from *Univ. of Calif. publications in Zoology*, **39**; University Tutorial Press Ltd. for Fig. 3.4 from Grove and Newell, *Animal Biology*; Wistar Institute of Anatomy and Biology for Figs. 33.4 and 34.1–34.6 from E. G. Conklin. *J. Morph.*, **54**. Fig. 2.3F is taken from *Biol. Bulletin*, **91**; Fig. 6.13 from *Biol. Bulletin*, **106**, Fig. 19.10D from *Endeavour* and Figs. 18.6 and 33.2A(2) from *Scientific American*.

Preface

THIS book is an attempt to supply in a reasonable compass the present-day needs of the G.C.E. 'A' level candidate in Zoology. It begins with descriptions of the structures and functions of selected types of invertebrate and vertebrate animals, followed by a general account of the physiology of the animal body and of its cellular structure. Concise descriptions of the mode of development of selected types and of the processes of evolution and heredity, together with an elementary scheme of classification, complete the volume. The argument for choosing this order of presentation is that at least an elementary acquaintance with a certain number of animals is necessary before they or their bodily features can be compared structurally and functionally, and also that the teaching of zoology as a practical subject is most conveniently conducted in the first instance animal by animal rather than function by function or system by system. Though this approach follows the historical development of the subject, it fails by itself to produce in the mind of the student any real concept of the underlying unities in the animal world, but it is hoped that the later sections of the book will to some extent at any rate supply the remedy.

So complex is the animal kingdom and so varied are the activities of its members – whether independent or interrelated – that zoology has never shown clearly defined boundaries, and this is still true. Nor can the employment of a small number of simple, related concepts produce that unification of the many aspects of this subject which is the aim of scientific explanation. The most far-reaching concept so far developed – that of evolution coupled with genetics – is not sufficient by itself to produce this unification, nor has the time yet come to base the teaching of zoology entirely on the chemistry and physics of the living cell. It therefore still remains necessary for the student to acquire a considerable body of factual knowledge of the animal kingdom – much of which is descriptive and morphological – and it is difficult to envisage a time when such knowledge can be dispensed with, even if the basis of teaching undergoes radical changes in the future. Any so-called 'principles of zoology' that have been enunciated directly or stated by implication in this book must be regarded not as equivalent to the powerful generalizations in the realms of physics and chemistry but rather as lesser unifying agents subject to future change or displacement as research throws more and more light on the nature of life and living organisms.

It is a pleasure to acknowledge the help received from Mrs Cynthia Clarke who drew almost all of the illustrations, from Miss R. H. Matthews who typed the manuscript, and from many colleagues whom we consulted about various points and who assisted with the loan of specimens.

G. C.

March 1964

W. B. B.

I. INVERTEBRATE ANIMALS

1. *Introduction*

ZOOLOGY is the meeting place of many peoples' interests and many branches of scientific knowledge. The amateur bird-watcher or butterfly collector, the veterinary surgeon or doctor, the oil geologist, pharmacist or gamekeeper, all require to know something of some part of the animal kingdom and all have something to contribute to the study of animals. The boundaries of such a subject are obviously difficult to define and have changed with advances in knowledge. From ancient literature, particularly that of the Greeks, we learn that from the early days of civilized mankind human anatomy has been studied by those who sought to understand the working of the body in order to cure disease, although such knowledge was mixed up with much that was believed to be supernatural or was imaginary. Interest was not confined to man alone, as is shown by the works of Aristotle dealing with natural history and the classification of the animal kingdom. Very slowly during the Middle Ages, but with increasing speed after the Renaissance, scientific knowledge accumulated and the centre of interest changed firstly to human anatomy, then to collection and classification, then to evolution. A hundred years ago zoologists were chiefly employed in the study of comparative anatomy, whereas today comparative physiology (i.e., the study of the functions of animals) is of greater importance and is now being superseded as the centre of advance by that of cell physiology.

It is clear, too, that any biological science leans very heavily on physics and chemistry since it employs these disciplines in the investigation of living processes. Biochemistry for example is the application of chemical methods to the study of animal and plant products and processes, and some knowledge of it is necessary to the student of zoology that he may understand how animals work. The scientific study of the earth, geology, is closely linked with zoology in the study of fossil animals, and botany and zoology are often studied together by students of natural history or ecology. These few examples will be enough to show how difficult it is to draw a line round the subject of zoology and to say that beyond the boundary lies something else. They also show the great interest of the subject

3

as a meeting point for various studies. It can also readily be understood that living animals present a tremendous challenge to man in his attempts to understand their structure, working and evolution – one might say 'to explain' them in a scientific manner.

The characteristic method of the natural sciences is 'induction', i.e. the collection of observations and the results of experiments and the drawing of a general inference from them so that all the facts 'hang together'. Such an induction should suggest further experiments which can be made and which, it is hoped, will also fit in with the induction. When this takes place the diverse phenomena are said to have been explained. For example, the idea that evolution has taken place is a kind of explanation of many diverse facts, such as the presence of certain fossils in rocks and the way in which animals can be grouped together by anatomical similarities. Evolution has only rarely been *seen* to take place and actually produce a new species which does not breed with members of the species from which it arose, but there is little doubt nowadays that the evolution of the animal kingdom as we know it today has actually taken place during many millions of years. This idea, which serves to link together many diverse observations, is thus a type of explanation. Such an explanation is essentially a simplification of the same kind as the laws of motion of bodies which can be expressed in terms of mass and velocity. Very few biological facts can be put so simply as to be expressible numerically as can many physical facts, but nevertheless the same type of induction can be made from biological data and the fitting of the results of new experiments into this framework is described as explaining them. Observations are described as inexplicable when they do not fit the inductions which are currently held. For example, the linkage of characters in inheritance did not fit Mendel's original 'laws' and was not explained by them, but the discrepancy led to experiments being made which ultimately threw much more light on the whole mechanism of inheritance and led to a modification of the original 'laws' to fit the newly discovered facts.

It will readily be understood that the type of scientific explanation which has just been described serves only to relate certain types of observation and experiment and that many of man's activities lie outside its present scope. Nevertheless the method of science which uses the collection of data and the drawing of an inference from the data – again in turn to be tested by further experiment leading to confirmation of the original inference or to its modification or rejection – has been successful in producing a unified picture of the world where it has been rigorously applied. Its gradual extension to wider fields of experience may be confidently awaited.

The study of animals can be compared to a stone with many facets each of which may be looked at closely so that it appears to be the whole. Seen from further off it is quite apparent that the whole stone has many facets and that although not of equal size, they are all essential to describe the true shape of the stone. So zoology includes the study of animal form and animal function, the study of behaviour, and of evolution and of the relation of animal species to one another and to other living things. Each of these divisions may be an engrossing study but all must be borne in mind if a complete picture of animal life in the world is to be obtained. In this book we shall first examine a number of different animals that are typical or representative of the chief divisions of the animal kingdom and shall see something of their structure and functioning. After this we shall look more closely at the cells of which they are composed and see how much the diverse animals have in common when their activities are analysed at a cellular level. This will lead to a discussion of the functioning of animals in general terms and a comparison of the ways in which different animals perform the same type of activity.

A unique property of living organisms is their power to reproduce themselves. The way in which new organisms develop merits a separate section, as does a description of the theory and working of evolution. Finally, a brief survey of the animal kingdom is given so that the impression need not be formed that zoology begins with amoeba and ends with the rabbit.

It will become apparent that there are in zoology many items of knowledge which simply have to be learned and which cannot be worked out from one or two laws as the position of image and object can be worked out from the formula

$$\frac{1}{v} + \frac{1}{u} = \frac{1}{f}$$

for a convex lens. Or, in other words, there are many experiments and observations which cannot be clearly linked by any induction. Nevertheless there are some general principles, one of which, the theory of evolution, has the widest validity. The generalizations embodied in the classification of animals are no less real scientific achievements for being expressed verbally instead of in symbols and numbers. If these considerations are borne in mind, zoology or the study of animals will be found to have so many facets that its students can be as varied in their interests as the animals themselves are varied.

The term 'living matter' is frequently used instead of living animals or plants, but it is best avoided because the word 'matter' is so often used in science to denote that which is inanimate or non-living and because the property which we call life is found only in the complex and highly organized bodies of various organisms. But there is one type of living thing to which the term 'living matter' could aptly apply and which illustrates how other types of living thing are better referred to as living organisms or as animals and plants.

The viruses, of which the species giving the blotchy leaved mosaic disease of tobacco plants was first used for experiments, can be crystallized and kept in a bottle like an 'ordinary' chemical substance. A small portion can be injected in solution into a tobacco plant. After a time far more of the virus can be extracted than was used to inoculate the plant. The virus has grown and increased in bulk in the same way as do larger and more familiar organisms but once extracted and crystallized this power of growth stops although it is not lost for it is immediately shown in the right environment, which is the inside of a tobacco plant cell. We might well describe such a living thing as 'living matter'. The study of viruses is not strictly in the province of zoology, although, as will be seen on page 425, all biologists will be interested in the relationships between viruses and cell nuclei.

The organisms with which the zoologist has to deal are more complex than viruses and they cannot be crystallized, bottled, stored and restarted at will although there are some which can retreat into a resting condition in which their activity is at a minimum and in which they can remain for many years. This is true of the eggs of the 'brine shrimp' *Artemia* and of many rotifers.

Living organisms are characterized by a number of 'properties' such as the power of movement, of responding to stimuli, of feeding, respiring, excreting, growing and reproducing, but this list omits what is perhaps the most important aspect of living things, namely, their ability to maintain themselves as entities in spite of the effects on them of their environment. This seems easy to do because it is familiar in men who have thick skins and wear clothes, but it is a striking ability in *Amoeba*, which is a mere speck of jelly bounded by a cell membrane so thin that it cannot be seen under the highest powers of the microscope. It is true that man can withstand very much greater changes in his surroundings than can *Amoeba* and might be expected to have survived for a longer geological period, but it is very probable that minute organisms like *Amoeba* have been in existence for many hundreds of millions of years since remains of the shells of related animals are found as fossils. In other words, even a tiny organism like *Amoeba* can, somehow, resist adverse environmental changes sufficiently to live, grow and reproduce during a vast period of time. All the amoebae in the world have at no time been entirely overcome by their surroundings but have contrived to admit them sufficiently to supply themselves with food, oxygen and salts.

This continuity of life and its evolution into many different forms is wonderful in the extreme, and while we strive to understand it or to translate it into physical and chemical terms (and hence to make it 'hang together' with the physical sciences) we have to admit that the self-maintenance of living organisms is of such complexity that it cannot at present be expressed in physical and chemical terms. It can be described by saying that the activities of organisms are such that they maintain themselves against the molecular forces which disrupt them. It is also true that some self-maintaining activities are exceedingly complex while others are relatively simple. Thus the learning of a trade by a man in order to earn money in order to buy food is a self-maintaining activity of great complexity compared with the pumping out of surplus water in a contractile vacuole from the body of an *Amoeba*. Although the power of self-maintenance is a characteristic of every living thing, the ability to maintain the state of the body varies during life from a phase of construction during development to a gradual failure of the ability in old age. The causes of these changes in the life of the individual organism are not understood.

In the chapters which follow we shall first describe the structure, functioning, reproduction and life histories of a variety of animals typical of the various stages of complexity into which the animal kingdom has evolved. These are so frequently dubbed 'types' that the meaning and usefulness of the method is forgotten. 'Types' are useful simply because there are so many species of animals that it would be impossible to learn and to remember details of all of them. Some sort of 'essence' or 'extract' has to be obtained which will summarize or embody the essential features of a large variety of slightly different animals and this the 'type' does, just as John Bull is supposed to typify the physical and mental characters of the

Englishman and Uncle Sam those of the men of the United States. You have only to look at your fellow citizens in the streets to realize that they are not all John Bulls any more than all fishes are dogfish. If such limitations of the 'type system' are clearly understood it is obviously a very convenient method of study, but if they are forgotten it can give only an extremely limited view of the animal kingdom. In an attempt to offset this risk we shall look in Section III at the way in which animals in general carry out their life processes. We shall have to call upon information set out in Sections I and II but we shall no longer be thinking of the excretory structures and processes of the crayfish, for example, but of excretion in general and of why it is necessary and how it is carried out in relation to the environment; we shall not think of the movements of the frog but of how the molecular structure of muscles enables them to contract and move the animal.

Throughout these descriptions of types of animals and of the functioning of animals it should be apparent that their activities seem to be directed towards or aimed at their own maintenance in a living state or at the maintenance of the species. We shall understand the animal kingdom best if we attempt always to explain the workings of animals in terms of physics and chemistry while at the same time realizing that their complexity is so great as to make explanation partial at present, although possibly complete in the remote future.

2. Protozoa

Introduction

SINCE the clear emergence in the middle of the nineteenth century of the idea that the animal body is generally divided into compartments or *cells* the Protozoa have been looked upon as the simplest animals because in them the living protoplasm is *not* divided into separate cellular units. For this reason they are often referred to as single-celled animals or, more accurately, as non-cellular animals. The term non-cellular is to be preferred because it does not imply a comparison between the *whole body* of a protozoan and a *single cell* of the body of a multicellular animal but rather a comparison between the whole body of the protozoan and that of the multicellular animal. The multicellular animals include all members of the animal kingdom that are not Protozoa and are referred to collectively as the Metazoa. An account of some of them forms the bulk of chapters 3 to 17 but in the present chapter we are concerned with the Protozoa. They are, of course, all small animals but nevertheless they show a tremendous range of structure and habitat for they are found in the sea, freshwater and soil, their spores may be carried in the air and very many are parasitic, living in the bodies of other organisms where they frequently cause disease. From the enormous number of species of Protozoa, *Amoeba proteus* is often chosen for study because it is representative of one large group of the Protozoa, because it is easily obtained and because it is a transparent creature which is relatively simple in structure. Although it appears simple at first sight it is, unfortunately, not always possible to give a clear explanation of the way in which its life processes work, partly because they are very complex and partly because its small size makes it a very difficult creature on which to perform chemical tests or experiments, although the essential features of its structure can easily be seen and understood. *Amoeba* is usually bought from a dealer when required but is found naturally occurring in the stagnant or slowly moving water of ponds, lakes and ditches. It can be kept in the laboratory in small covered dishes containing one or two boiled wheat grains. These provide food for the growth of bacteria on which other micro-organisms feed and which in turn serve as food

9

10   *Protozoa*

for the *Amoeba* with which the culture is started. From time to time
it is necessary to start a new culture with fresh wheat grains and with
a few *Amoeba* from the old culture.

Amoeba

Structure

The appearance under the microscope of *Amoeba proteus*, a large,
but not naturally very common species of *Amoeba*, is shown in

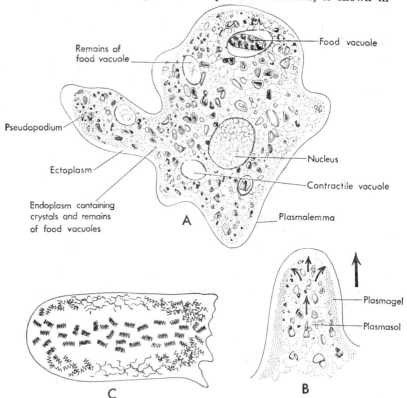

Fig. 2.1. *Amoeba.*

A Drawing of a specimen of *Amoeba* from life. In the food vacuole
is a recently-captured flagellate, probably Chilomonas.

B Diagram to illustrate the forward movement of a pseudopodium.
The arrows within the pseudopodium show the direction of movement
of the endoplasm.

C Diagram to illustrate a theory of amoeboid movement. Each
protein molecule is represented by zigzag lines. These are compact
and free in the centre; they expand and form cross links in the plasmagel region. They contract again posteriorly, still cross-linked, but
become free in the central plasmasol.

Fig. 2.1 A. It may grow to about 0·5 mm. in length and is therefore visible to the unaided eye. Its most striking attribute when alive is its constantly changing shape. Blunt projections, the *pseudopodia*, can be put out in any direction and into the main one of these the animal 'flows'. This type of locomotion is known as '*amoeboid movement*' and is described on page 14. There appears to be a thin cell membrane or *plasmalemma* outside the protoplasm but it is doubtful if this is really a 'skin' about 0·25 μ thick as it appears to be.* Probably the protein molecules, forming one of the chief constituents of the protoplasm, become more closely and regularly arranged the nearer they lie to the surface and on the outside of them there is an arrangement of fat molecules. Minute droplets of oil can be made 'to cap' the pseudopodium of *Amoeba* in a way that makes it appear that the outer surface is made up of fatty molecules or at least contains them. Just inside the plasmalemma there is a clear layer of protoplasm free from granules and of variable thickness, being thickest at the advancing tip of each pseudopodium. It is known as the *ectoplasm* or *hyaline* layer. Inside the hyaline layer the endoplasm can be distinguished into an outer layer, the *plasmagel* and a more fluid layer, the *plasmasol* (Fig. 2.1 B). These are not sharply marked off from one another, and both contain, beside salts and food substances in true solution, various particles and crystals of different sizes and little 'liquid bubbles' or *vacuoles* containing food in the process of digestion.

The *nucleus*, which in life is seen as a clear refractive vesicle of biconcave shape, is found in the endoplasm as is also the *contractile vacuole*, a clear, water-filled vesicle. This 'little organ' or *organelle* helps to maintain a constant composition of the fluid endoplasm.

Feeding

The feeding of *Amoeba* is a simple process when seen under the microscope. The animal simply flows round a suitable speck of material or a minute living organism such as the flagellate *Chilomonas* and the particle is engulfed together with a drop of water. What is not understood, however, is the way in which *Amoeba* perceives that one particle is suitable for food and that another one is not, and how, having perceived this, its ordinary locomotion by the putting forward of pseudopodia is modified to enable it to engulf a particle and form a *food vacuole*.

* 1 μ = 0·001 mm. = 10,000 Å (Ångstrom units).

Digestion

Once the food vacuole is inside the *Amoeba* it circulates with the movements of the endoplasm and receives digestive juices which act at different pH values. By using food dyed with a harmless indicator it can be seen that the contents of the vacuole become first acid and later alkaline. Digestive fluids are undoubtedly secreted into the food vacuole and they have the effect of splitting up the molecules of the food material until they are small enough to diffuse rapidly and can thus be taken up into the protoplasm surrounding the food vacuole. Any undigested material which remains in the food vacuole is left behind when the erstwhile food vacuole comes near to and breaks through the surface of the *Amoeba* as the protoplasm circulates.

Respiration

Respiration is little understood in *Amoeba* but it is clear from the known rate at which dissolved oxygen molecules can diffuse through water and watery protoplasm, and from the small size of *Amoeba* that the diffusion of dissolved oxygen is quite sufficient to provide all that is necessary for respiration. No respiratory organelles are necessary and no respiratory pigments or other substances with an affinity for oxygen have been found. Oxygen reaches the interior and carbon dioxide leaves it, simply by the random movement of molecules to which diffusion is due. It may be pointed out that this process is assisted by the circulation of the protoplasm which takes place as the animal moves and which has the effect of bringing internal material near to the surface from time to time.

Excretion

The nitrogenous waste products of metabolism, such as ammonia which is formed when proteins are oxidized or otherwise degraded, are likewise lost by diffusion over the general surface of the protoplasm. There is no evidence of a high concentration of nitrogenous waste in the contents of the contractile vacuole or that more nitrogenous matter passes out in the vacuolar fluid than would be obtained by diffusion over an area of external body surface corresponding to that of the vacuole wall.

Osmoregulation

The outer layer acts like a semi-permeable membrane (see Chapter 27, p. 539), so that water accumulates in the body when the osmotic pressure of the endoplasm is greater than that of the surrounding medium, but the regulation of the body volume and osmotic concentration of the protoplasm is clearly carried out to a great extent by the working of the contractile vacuole. This empties and fills less frequently when a freshwater amoeba is placed in dilute salt solution; on the other hand, some marine amoebae, which lack contractile vacuoles when living in their natural habitat, form them if the sea water is diluted. It is probable that the osmotic concentration of the protoplasm of marine amoebae is about the same as that of the sea in which they live and consequently there is little tendency towards any net gain of water molecules by their diffusion to and fro across the surface of the ectoplasm. On the other hand, the osmotic concentration of fresh-water amoebae such as *A. proteus* is about equivalent to that of 0·01 M KCl and is therefore above that of the water in which they live. The semipermeability of the cell surface therefore results in a net gain of water molecules and would result in a swelling of the organism were the water not removed as fast as it enters. This is done by the contractile vacuole and, since it involves a separation of water from a solution, it also involves the consumption of energy. Chemical substances such as potassium cyanide which poison the respiratory mechanism of the organism by removal of the source of energy therefore destroy the ability to control the osmotic concentration of the protoplasm with the result that water accumulates in the animal which swells, becomes vacuolated or bubbly in appearance and dies.

Sensitivity

No organelles can be seen in *Amoeba* by which the effects of light, heat, gravity, mechanical disturbance or the presence of chemical substances may be perceived. Nevertheless *Amoeba* does behave in a way which shows that it perceives changes in the world outside it.

In bright light *Amoeba proteus* moves away from the direction whence the light comes. This it is believed to do by the direct effect which the light has in increasing the gelation of the ectoplasm so that pseudopodia are less easily formed in the side exposed to the light.

No reactions to temperature gradient or to gravity have been described in *Amoeba* but the animal is sensitive to mechanical disturbances and shaking the dish in which a culture of animals is kept causes them to withdraw their pseudopodia and to become rounded and free from the substratum.

Gentle touch causes the formation of a pseudopodium directed towards the stimulus but stronger stimulation causes the withdrawal of the pseudopodium.

It seems likely that *Amoeba* can perceive the presence of various chemical substances because it reacts even to very low concentrations by the withdrawal of pseudopodia and ultimately by movement away.

These aspects of the behaviour of *Amoeba* are not very striking nor easy to observe, partly because the animal's rate of movement is very slow. The reactions of a protozoan to changes in its environment – stimuli – are much better seen in another type, *Paramecium*, whose locomotion is much more rapid. (See p. 21.)

Movement

The movement of *Amoeba* has been intensively studied because, although apparently simple, it is, in fact, difficult to explain and because amoeboid movement is seen in some cells of almost all animals, including those of the 'highest', the mammals, where it occurs in the white blood corpuscles.

The movement of the protoplasm in an advancing pseudopodium, as revealed by the path of the protoplasmic granules, may be likened to that of sand flowing from a burst sack. It was thought that fluid endoplasm – or plasmasol – streamed forwards in the interior of the pseudopodium, spreading out forwards over the side of the advancing tip of the pseudopodium and there gelating (Fig. 2.1 B). At the 'posterior' end solation of the protoplasm occurred and it began to stream forwards. This explanation is obviously too simple and various modifications have been made to it. While the phenomenon of amoeboid movement is not yet fully explained, it seems likely that an explanation will be possible in terms of the structure of the protoplasm. This contains, among many other constituents, protein molecules which may consist of straight chains or of very much folded chains of linked atoms. The unfolded chains are thought to form a more rigid colloid than the folded chains and are believed to be more plentiful in the plasmagel than in the plasmasol. It is thought that, during locomotion, unfolding of the long protein molecules takes place near the tip of the advancing pseudopodium and brings about an increase in the rigidity of the protoplasm while folding of the molecules takes place at the posterior end and allows the now more fluid material to flow forwards (Fig. 2.1 C). It is not clear how the energy for these changes could be provided but at least it is known that molecular interaction is the basis of muscular contraction and is probably brought about by a substance which does take part in the cycle of respiratory changes by which sugar is oxidized (see p. 503). It may well be that similar events take place in *Amoeba* and that contractile processes of all types are fundamentally similar.

Growth and Reproduction

Amoeba grows in size by the synthesis from its digested foods of proteins and other substances which are characteristically its own. This growth in the amount of living matter does not continue indefinitely and when the organism reaches a certain size, which again is characteristic of the species or type to which it belongs, it divides, forming two so-called *daughter* amoebae. The division of *Amoeba* is preceded by the division of the nucleus by a mitotic process (see p. 429) but it differs from the mitosis of the cells of higher animals in two ways. There are a very large number of very small chromosomes and the halves appear not to be pulled apart after longitudinal fission but to be pushed apart by the expansion of the middle region of the spindle. Some species of *Amoeba* (but probably not *A. proteus*) can secrete a tough coating outside the protoplasm and remain alive within this in conditions of drought and temperature which are, at least, more unfavourable than those which a naked animal can withstand. At the end of encystment multiple division of the animal takes place and many swarm spores emerge. These are similar to the 'adult' but often possess more 'spiky' pseudopodia and in some species even have flagella. They soon feed and grow into creatures like their parents. No sexual reproduction is known in *Amoeba*.

Paramecium

Introduction

Eight species of *Paramecium* are recognized today but the one which is commonly described is *P. caudatum*. Individuals vary in length from 170 μ to nearly 300 μ, i.e. many are about ¼ mm. long and therefore visible to the naked eye (subtending an angle of about 4′ at a distance of 10 inches). They are found in nature in stagnant or slowly moving fresh water especially where bacteria abound, as in places where there is abundant decaying organic matter. *Paramecium* is easily cultured in a hay infusion prepared by boiling for 20 minutes a few grammes of cut hay in a litre of water. When the infusion is cold it can be left standing to collect bacteria from the air and then inoculated with water containing *Paramecium*. A culture rich in *Paramecium* but containing also other protozoans is usually the result. If, after a time, the vigour of the culture diminishes it can be restored by sub-culturing, i.e. inoculating a fresh hay infusion with a few *Paramecium* from the old culture. It is also possible to make a pure line culture derived from a single individual by inoculating a boiled hay infusion with a single specimen of *Paramecium*. A single specimen can be isolated by taking up a drop of the culture fluid in a fine capillary tube and checking under the microscope that only one individual *Paramecium* is present in the liquid in the tube with which the fresh culture is inoculated. Such pure line cultures are useful in conjugation experiments (see p. 23).

Structure

Unlike *Amoeba*, the shape of *Paramecium* is fixed except when it squeezes through a small hole. Its appearance is illustrated in Fig. 2.2

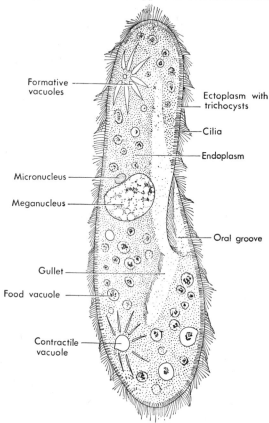

Fig. 2.2. *Paramecium caudatum* as seen in life.

where its resemblance to a slipper shows how it gained its old popular name of 'slipper animalcule'. The heel of the slipper is anterior during locomotion and corresponding with the opening of the slipper is a wide shallow groove, the oral groove, leading into a blindly ending tube or gullet. At the base of the gullet there is a modified region of the pellicle and cytoplasm where food vacuoles are taken into the body. This is sometimes called the *cytostome*.

The pellicle of *Paramecium* is more rigid than the outer layer of *Amoeba* and is sculptured in a geometrical pattern which can easily be demonstrated by mixing a drop of *Paramecium* culture with a drop of 0·5% aniline blue on a microscope slide and leaving to dry (Fig. 2.3 A.). On mounting the dry film in Canada balsam and examining under the high power of the microscope (preferably using a $\frac{1}{12}$ in. or 2 mm. oil immersion objective) the patterned pellicle of the animals can be seen. More refined methods demonstrate that each cilium arises from a basal granule situated in the middle of a pellicular compartment and that the cilia are connected by fine fibrils which may have the function of co-ordinating the ciliary beat. These threads are called *kinetodesmata* (sing. *kinetodesma*).[1]

Embedded in the ectoplasm and arranged to touch the pellicle on the ridge of the pattern are carrot-shaped bodies, the *trichocysts*, which can discharge in the form of fine threads (Fig. 2.3 B and F). These threads, which are of a protein probably like collagen (q.v.) were thought to act as a means of defence or of anchoring but neither their origin in the cytoplasm nor their function in the life of the animal is clearly understood. They provide little or no defence against *Paramecium's* chief protozoan enemy, *Didinium*, and against large predators which feed by filtering planktonic organisms, they are, likewise, clearly useless.

The *cilia* with which the external surface is covered are cytoplasmic processes, each arising from a basal granule and consisting, when seen in the electron microscope, of eleven fibrils surrounded by a sheath (Fig. 2.3 C and D). The nature of the contractile process is not properly understood but the way in which the cilia beat and by means of which the animal is driven through the water is described on p. 22.

The ectoplasm, in which are embedded the trichocysts, the basal granules of the cilia and the kinetodesmata (Fig. 2.3 B and E) connecting them, is relatively thick and like that of *Amoeba* is clear when seen in the living animal, although a striated appearance, owing to the

[1] The concept of *neuronemes* as fibrils connecting the bases of cilia has now been superseded.

presence of the trichocysts, can sometimes be seen in a tangential view. The endoplasm contains the nuclei, food vacuoles, contractile vacuoles and numerous granules and circulates, carrying with it the granules and food vacuoles, on a definite path. This movement of the endoplasm and vacuoles is called 'cyclosis'.

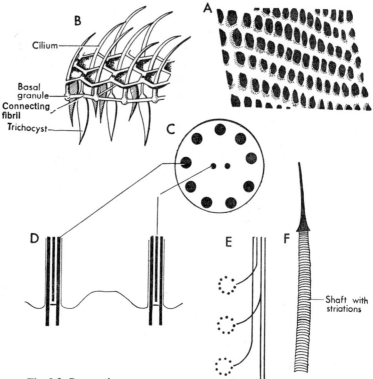

Fig. 2.3. *Paramecium.*

The fine structure of *Paramecium*: *A* The sculpturing of the pellicle drawn from a slide. *B* The arrangement of cilia and trichocysts. (After *Lund.*) *C* Diagram showing the arrangement of the nine peripheral and two central fibres of a cilium seen under the electron microscope. *D* The insertion of the cilia into the body of *Paramecium* as seen under the electron microscope. *E* Diagram of the connexion between the cilia and Kinetodesmata. *F* A discharged trichocyst as seen under the electron microscope. (Based on *Jakus* and *Hall.*)

The nuclei are two in number, a larger *macronucleus*[1] and a smaller *micronucleus* situated close to it. Although the nuclei appear to be identical in chemical composition, their behaviour during the sexual reproduction of the animals is very dissimilar and it may be supposed

[1] Often called the *meganucleus.*

that they play different roles in heredity, if not in the normal working of the cell.

The contractile vacuoles are two in number and occur in definite places in the cytoplasm. Each vacuole is fed by a number of radial canals which remain in the cytoplasm, collect the vacuolar fluid, and discharge it into the vacuole which in turn discharges to the exterior through an outlet pore. Thus each vacuole system may appear at a particular instant as a full vacuole, as fine radiating canals, or as swollen radial canals just about to empty into a small vacuole. In general the vacuolar cycles of the anterior and posterior vacuoles are out of step.

Feeding and Digestion

The food of *Paramecium* consists largely of bacteria or of very fine organic particles which it takes into its body as it moves through the water with the oral groove and gullet pointing in the direction of movement. The oral groove is ciliated like the rest of the outer surface of the body but in the gullet there are specialized cilia, four longitudinal rows of long cilia and eight closely set rows of short cilia which have the appearance in life of an 'undulating membrane' (Fig. 2.4). These play a part in wafting particles down the gullet for

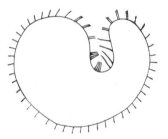

Fig. 2.4. *Paramecium.*
Transverse section of *Paramecium* in the region of the gullet to show the arrangement of the cilia. The four rows of long cilia are shown to the right and the duplicated rows of four short cilia to the left. (Based on *Von Gelei.*)

ingestion or in rejecting those which are unsuitable. Food particles are taken into the cytoplasm at the bottom of the gullet in tiny drops of water and immediately begin to circulate through the cytoplasm as food vacuoles (Fig. 2.5). As can be shown by feeding *Paramecium* on dried milk stained with Congo Red, these vacuoles become at first acid and then return to neutrality and may even become alkaline. On the change from neutral to acid there is a decrease in size and later an increase on changing back to neutrality. Evidence suggests that digestion occurs mainly during the alkaline phase.

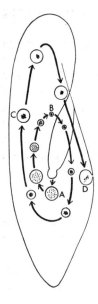

Fig. 2.5. *Paramecium.*
Diagram to illustrate the intake and course of food vacuoles. When they are first formed at the base of the gullet, they are large (*A*). They diminish by the absorption of water and the contents are coagulated (*B*). Digestive enzymes are secreted and they increase in size (*C*). The undigested residue is eliminated (*D*).

Proteins can certainly be digested to amino-acids, starch can probably be digested but the digestion of fat is more doubtful, although fat globules may be ingested in food vacuoles. After the circulation of the vacuoles around their regular path (see Fig. 2.5) the undigested remains are voided through a permanent weak place in the pellicle, the 'anus', which is situated posteriorly on the oral side of the body.

Respiration

As in *Amoeba*, no special respiratory structures or pigments are known in *Paramecium* and there is no doubt that its surface provides a sufficient area for the inward diffusion of oxygen and the outward diffusion of carbon dioxide to meet the needs of the animal.

Excretion

Excretion of nitrogenous waste from protein metabolism probably takes place all over the body surface and doubtless, to some extent, in the large volumes of water which are expelled by the contractile vacuoles, but analysis of their contents has failed to detect any high concentration of nitrogen compounds. The culture medium in which *Paramecium* is kept comes to contain uric acid, urea and ammonia but it is likely that urea is the main nitrogenous excretory product.

Osmoregulation

The chief function of the contractile vacuole is the regulation of the hydrostatic pressure within the pellicle and the maintenance of a constant body volume. In pure water it takes only 15 minutes or so for the contractile vacuoles to discharge a volume of water equal to that of the body but in 0·5% NaCl it takes 45 minutes and in 1·0% NaCl about 6 hours. Water is taken in both osmotically over the body surface and also in the food vacuoles during feeding. The way in which the radial canals of the vacuoles collect fluid from the cytoplasm and discharge it into the contractile vacuole which in turn discharges to the exterior has already been described.

Sensitivity and Behaviour

Paramecium, being a more active animal than *Amoeba*, is correspondingly better for the observation of behaviour, which has been much studied.

In general it may be said that *Paramecium* swims forwards in its normal spiral path until it meets some change in the environment (some stimulus) to which it is receptive and to which it responds by alteration of its ciliary beat. For example, when it encounters a solid object or a noxious chemical substance it stops, backs, alters its direction and moves forwards again (Fig. 2.6). This so-called

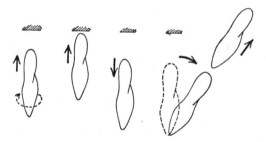

Fig. 2.6. *Paramecium.*
Diagram of the 'avoiding reaction' of *Paramecium.*

'avoiding reaction' is the basis of its behaviour and by this process of trial and error, this avoidance of stimuli to which it is subject, it behaves as if it seeks to remain in its preferred environment. In this way the individuals of a culture of *Paramecium* presented with a choice of, say, temperature, concentration of carbon dioxide or light intensity, soon collect in their optimum environment.

There is no doubt that *Paramecium* is sensitive to a wide variety of stimuli including mechanical contact, gravity, light, temperature, electric potential, pH and the presence of various chemical substances.

Movement

Movement of *Paramecium* through the water is produced by the co-ordinated but not simultaneous beating of the cilia. Each one beats backwards stiffly by bending near its base but recovers its upright position in a limp fashion. The down beat is thus the effective stroke and tends to drive the animal forwards while the return stroke offers as little resistance to the water as possible. As we have seen, the cilia arise in pits of the pellicle arranged in lines running spirally round the animal. This causes the animal to rotate as it swims through the water. Each cilium beats a little in advance of the one posterior to it and in the line, the cilia being said to beat in *meta-*

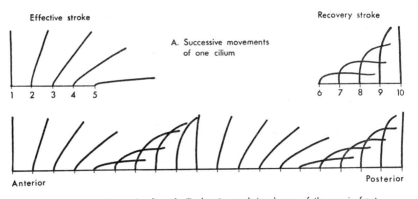

Effective stroke   A. Successive movements of one cilium   Recovery stroke

1 2 3 4 5   6 7 8 9 10

Anterior   Posterior

B. Instantaneous picture of a line of cilia beating, each in advance of the one in front

Fig. 2.7. *Paramecium.*

Diagrams illustrating the movements made by cilia. At *A*, stages in the movement of a single cilium are shown, the numbers 1–10 indicating *successive* instants of time. At *B*, a line of cilia is shown at *one* instant of time. It will be seen that each cilium is at a stage of its beat which is slightly in advance of the one anterior to it.

chronal rhythm (Fig. 2.7). As a result of this, waves of ciliary activity appear to pass along the animal from front to rear. The cilia can be stopped, reversed in direction and started again according to the external circumstances and, no doubt, according to the internal conditions too.

Reproduction

Binary fission as in *Amoeba* is the common method of reproduction of *Paramecium*. Before division occurs the animal stops feeding, the body becomes thicker in the middle and the oral groove disappears. The micronucleus then increases in size and forms a spindle (see p. 429). Very small chromosomes appear, undergo the normal mitotic division and the daughter nuclei move to opposite ends of the dividing animal, remaining for a time connected by a thin portion of the spindle (Fig. 2.8). The macronucleus divides by an amitotic division.

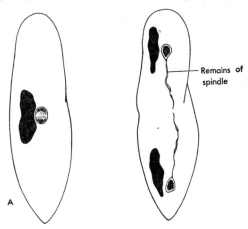

Fig. 2.8. Diagram of binary fission in *Paramecium*.

In *A*, the meganucleus is beginning to constrict and the micronucleus is completing its mitosis. In *B*, both nuclei have divided and constriction of the cytoplasm has begun.

The cytoplasm divides and eventually the two daughter individuals separate, the anterior one possesses the anterior contractile vacuole and the posterior one the other vacuole. A new oral groove and gullet is formed in each, the basal granules of the cilia divide and a complete covering of cilia is formed as the animal increases in size.

Under very favourable conditions binary fission can take place two or three times in 24 hours, about 30 minutes being all that is required for the operation.

In addition to binary fission *Paramecium* possesses a form of sexual reproduction involving the conjugation of two individuals. These, which should normally be of different lines of descent, come together by their oral surfaces where they fuse together. In each, the macronucleus begins to degenerate and disappear, the micronucleus divides by a reduction division first into two, then into four daughter nuclei. Of these, three degenerate, the remaining one divides to form two gametic nuclei, one of which migrates and fuses with the stationary one of the other conjugant (Fig. 2.9). The single effective nucleus

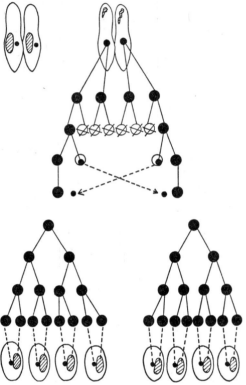

Fig. 2.9. *Paramecium.*
Diagram illustrating the behaviour of the nuclei of *Paramecium* during conjugation. Macronuclei shaded, micronuclei black.

now present in each conjugant begins to divide and eventually forms eight nuclei in each exconjugant. Four give rise to macronuclei and four remain as micronuclei. The exconjugants each divide twice so that eight individuals, each containing one macronucleus and one micronucleus, are ultimately formed as a result of the sexual process known as conjugation.

Conjugation does not normally occur between what may be called closely related animals, but in the species of *Paramecium* which has been most studied (*P. aurelia*), it occurs between individuals belonging to different *mating types*. When cultures of both mating types belonging to one of the eight varieties of *P. aurelia* are mixed, the animals clump together in a minute or two, separating after an hour or so into pairs of conjugants. The *mating reaction* is characteristic and the mating type to which an animal belongs is one of its inherited characteristics.

An aspect of inheritance in *Paramecium* which has recently been described and which is of great importance is the inheritance of characters by means of particles in the cytoplasm instead of in the nucleus. The best known character of this type is found in the

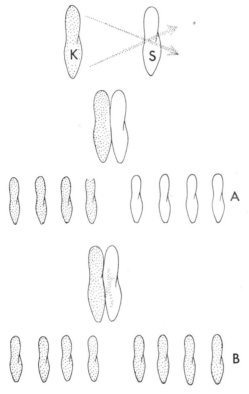

Fig. 2.10. *Paramecium.*

Diagram to illustrate the conjugation of 'sensitive' and 'killer' *Paramecium.* At *A*, conjugation has taken place quickly and no 'killer' particles have entered the 'sensitive' conjugant. Only half the exconjugants are therefore 'killers'. At *B* conjugation has taken a longer time and 'killer' particles have entered the 'sensitive' conjugant with the result that all the exconjugants are 'killers'. (Based on *Sonneborn.*)

'killer' strain of *Paramecium aurelia*. This strain liberates a poison which kills members of the 'sensitive' strain in about two days. Notwithstanding this, 'killers' and 'sensitives' can conjugate and by culturing separately the exconjugants it can be shown that 'killers' perpetuate 'killers' and 'sensitives', 'sensitives'. But if the conjugants stay together a long time and exchange cytoplasm, the 'sensitives' may give rise to a 'killer' strain (Fig. 2.10). It is now known that 'killer' *Paramecium* all contain small particles, 0·2–0·8 μ long in the cytoplasm which stain heavily with a nuclear stain but that these particles are absent from 'sensitives'. These '*kappa*' particles are probably similar in chemical constitution to nucleic acid and they may be known therefore as *cytoplasmic genes* or *plasmagenes* but they also share in their method of multiplication some of the properties of infective bodies like the viruses.

Paramecium is thus an important animal in biology for various reasons and it has been used in many studies of behaviour and inheritance.

CLASSIFICATION OF PROTOZOA

Before describing the structure, locomotion and life history of other Protozoa, a brief classification of them will be given. It will be noticed that the animals fall into groups which are distinguished chiefly by their methods of locomotion and that the two examples of the phylum already described are taken from different classes.

Phylum: Protozoa

Class: Flagellata (Protozoa which move by means of flagella), e.g. *Euglena, Polytoma, Peranema* and *Trypanosoma*;

Rhizopoda (Protozoa which move by means of pseudopodia), e.g. *Amoeba, Entamoeba*;

Sporozoa (Parasitic protozoa with many spores), e.g. *Monocystis, Plasmodium*;

Ciliata (Protozoa which move by means of cilia), e.g. *Paramecium, Vorticella.*

In addition to free-living forms, it is notable that the Phylum contains many parasitic members. Among the flagellates *Trypanosoma* is the best known, among the Rhizopoda, *Entamoeba*, while the class Sporozoa is entirely parasitic. Many ciliates which live in other animals are so well adjusted to their hosts that they are regarded as *commensals* or *symbionts* rather than harmful parasites. Sedentary or fixed forms such as *Vorticella* occur in the Class Ciliata.

Before considering those protozoa which are important parasites, some other free-living species of particular interest will be described. These comprise *Euglena, Peranema* and *Polytoma* among the Flagellata; *Vorticella* among the Ciliata will be mentioned at the end.

Euglena

Euglena possesses chromatophores, containing chlorophyll, and can synthesize its own food from CO_2, water and mineral salts like a plant; *Peranema* is similar in general structure to *Euglena* but possesses no chlorophyll and feeds holozoically like *Amoeba* and *Paramecium*, while *Polytoma* is capable of obtaining its nutritional requirements from a simple organic compound, sodium acetate, as a source of carbon together with mineral salts. All occur in fresh water.

Euglena viridis is a spindle-shaped creature covered with a thin, elastic, protein pellicle (Fig. 2.11 A). At the anterior end is a

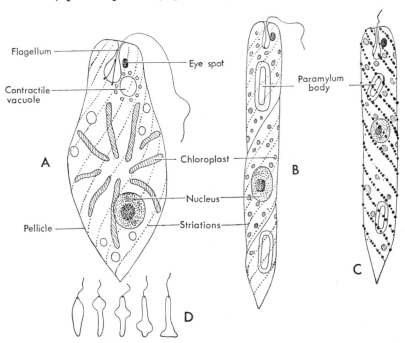

Fig. 2.11. *Euglena.*

A Euglena viridis. B Euglena oxyuris. C Euglena spirogyra. D Euglenoid movement. Diagram of a specimen of *Euglena viridis* performing its characteristic wriggling movement.

[Note that the figures of the species of *Euglena* are not all drawn to the same scale. *E. viridis* is about half the length of *E. spirogyra* and only a quarter that of *E. oxyuris*.]

permanent gullet into which a contractile vacuole opens. A long *flagellum* and a short one arise from two basal granules at the base of the gullet. These two flagella frequently unite. A spot composed of pigment granules (haematochrome) lies at the side of the gullet and according to the orientation of the creature shades an allegedly sensitive granule at the flagellar junction. The chlorophyll is contained in a group of slender chloroplasts arranged in radiating manner. Each may contain a pyrenoid which is enclosed in a paramylum or starch-like outer layer. The nucleus has a central portion which acts as a spindle during division. Other species of *Euglena* are shown in Fig. 2.11 B and C.

Euglena, possessing chlorophyll, is able to manufacture its carbo-

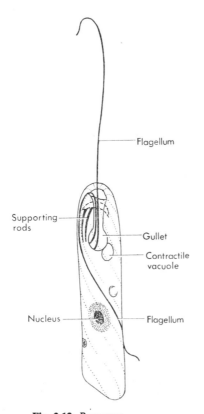

Fig. 2.12. *Peranema.*
A colourless, holozoic flagellate.
(Based on *Mackinnon* and *Hawes*.)

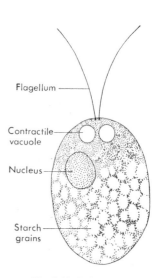

Fig. 2.13. *Polytoma.*
A colourless, saprozoic flagellate.

hydrate from CO_2 and water with the aid of light. It cannot live in the dark and the 'gullet' is not capable of taking in any food vacuoles. By way of contrast, *Peranema* (Fig. 2.12), which is similar in general appearance but which lacks chlorophyll and chloroplasts, does feed in a typically animal or holozoic manner by taking in food vacuoles at the base of the pharynx. It has a similar arrangement of gullet and contractile vacuole but there are two supporting rods alongside the gullet and it possesses two flagella, one of which adheres to the pellicle while the other one is free to vibrate.

Movement occurs in two ways, by the movement of the flagellum and by the wriggling of the body, a type of movement which is called 'euglenoid movement' or 'metaboly', and which is most easily understood from diagrams (Fig. 2.11 D). The type of movement due to the flagellum is quite characteristic when seen under the microscope and contrasts with the slow flowing of *Amoeba* and with the smooth rapid motion of ciliates.

The animal swims with the flagellar end forwards but with the flagellum trailing. Undulations pass along the flagellum from base to tip at about 12 per sec., causing the organism to move forwards and at the same time to rotate on its axis and to describe a spiral path through the water.

Polytoma (Fig. 2.13), on the other hand, has lost the power of taking in solid particles and the power of synthesizing its own food with the aid of chlorophyll, but it can live on very simple organic molecules and will thrive if supplied with sodium acetate in addition to mineral salts. All three reproduce by longitudinal binary fission.

Trypanosoma

Trypanosoma gambiense (Fig. 2.14) is the cause of the disease known as African sleeping sickness and is found in the blood of infected men in the early stages of the disease and later invades the central nervous system; it causes fever, anaemia, lethargy and death. The parasite is taken from an infected man by a blood-sucking tsetse fly *Glossina* and given to a new victim when the fly bites him (Fig. 2.15).

A trypanosome is small, spindle-shaped and simple in structure. It contains a nucleus, a basal granule or blepharoplast from which the flagellum arises. Near to this lies the kinetoplast which contains chromatin. The flagellum is attached to the body by a thin film of protoplasm, the undulating membrane, for most of its length but the anterior end is free. When the blood of an infected animal is seen

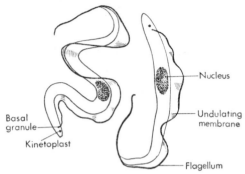

Fig. 2.14. *Trypanosoma gambiense.*

The flagellate responsible for causing the disease of African sleeping sickness.

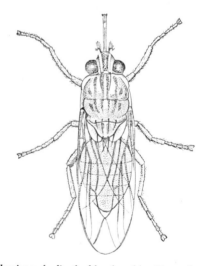

Fig. 2.15. *Glossina palpalis*, the blood-sucking Tsetse fly as seen at rest.

This insect is responsible for transmitting *Trypanosoma gambiense* from one host to another.

in the fresh state under the microscope the trypanosomes can most easily be picked out by their rapid and constant wriggling which convulses the whole body although it is doubtless the motions of the flagellum which bring this about.

Reproduction occurs only by means of binary fission, which involves the nucleus, blepharoplast and kinetoplast, followed by the cytoplasm. One daughter cell retains the old flagellum, the other forms a new one. When the blood of an infected man is taken in by the tsetse fly the trypanosomes undergo rapid fission in the fly's stomach for a few days and give rise to slender forms of diverse size which migrate to the salivary glands after about 10 or 12 days. Here they change their appearance and become so-called *crithidial* forms in which the flagellum runs only half-way along the body, its basal granule lying anterior to the nucleus. These crithidial forms multiply and after a few days give rise to trypanosome forms which are infective to man when transferred by the bite of the insect. Thus the trypanosome shows a degree of polymorphism, differently shaped forms succeeding one another in the life cycles. Polymorphism of this type is typical of the trypanosomes and is seen even better in *T. lewisi*, a non-pathogenic trypanosome of the rat. Infection occurs when fresh faeces of the rat flea *Ceratophyllus fasciatus* containing the organism are licked up by the host. After an incubation period in an unknown part of the body, the trypanosomes appear in the blood and multiply rapidly by binary fission and multiple fission for one or two weeks until antibodies developed by the rat suppress the trypanosome.

Trypanosomes sucked up by the rat flea during the multiplicative phase (Fig. 2.16) enter the cells of the stomach where they multiply and later infect the rectum where another phase of multiplication produces a variety of short forms which eventually give way to trypanosome-like forms. These pass out from the gut in the faeces, ready to begin the cycle of infection again.

It will be noticed that in both *T. gambiense* and *T. lewisi*, transmission of the parasite from its old host to a new one is brought about by the agency of another animal, i.e. the tsetse fly or the rat flea. This animal is known as a vector and it will also be noticed that the trypanosome must be able to live in the conditions of temperature and osmotic concentration provided both by the vertebrate host and by the vector, which is an invertebrate and hence very different in its chemical make-up. This power of adaptation is remarkable in view of the fact that many parasites are otherwise highly specific, i.e. capable of living in only one species of host animal but incapable of existence even in closely related forms.

Little is known of the nutrition or respiration of trypanosomes apart from the fact that they absorb all the food and oxygen which they require over the body surface. They live in a medium containing readily available nutritive substances, of which they are believed to use chiefly sugar.

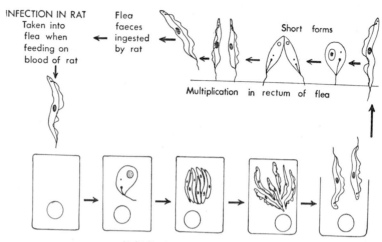

INFECTION IN RAT
Taken into
flea when
feeding on
blood of rat

Flea
faeces
ingested
by rat

Short forms

Multiplication in rectum of flea

Multiplication in stomach cells of flea

Fig. 2.16. Part of the life cycle of *Trypanosoma lewisi*, a non-pathogenic trypanosome from the rat.

The part of the life-cycle shown takes place in the intermediate host, a rat flea, which becomes infected when feeding on the blood of an infected rat. Multiplication of the trypanosome occurs in the stomach cells of the flea and also in the gut cavity while attached to the wall of the rectum.

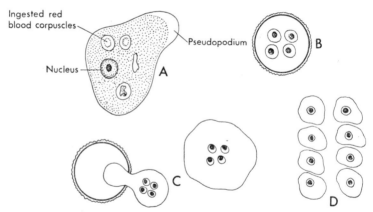

Ingested red
blood corpuscles

Pseudopodium

Nucleus

A

B

C

D

Fig. 2.17. *Entamoeba histolytica*, the cause of amoebic dysentery.

At *A*, the amoeba is shown with a typical blunt pseudopodium and ingested red blood cells which it obtained from the damaged wall of the intestine. At *B*, the amoeba is shown encysted and with the nucleus having formed daughter nuclei. At *C*, the amoeba is emerging from its cyst. The eight daughter amoebae which are subsequently formed are shown at *D*.

Entamoeba

The majority of Rhizopoda are free living but *Entamoeba histolytica* (Fig. 2.17 A) is a parasite living in the intestine of man and giving rise to amoebic dysentery. In a severe infection the parasites may spread beyond the gut to other viscera and even to the brain. The amoeba lives on and in the epithelial cells and ingests fragments of cells and blood corpuscles. It is a small amoeba, simpler in structure than most of the free-living forms, having only blunt pseudopodia and possessing no contractile vacuoles. Reproduction in the host is by binary fission. In addition, encystment takes place after preliminary division in which the size of the amoeba is reduced (Fig. 2.17 B). During the encysted stage the nucleus divides into four and when the cyst is transferred to a new host a tetranucleic amoeba emerges (Fig. 2.17 C) which soon divides to produce eight small trophozoites (Fig. 2.17 D). Infection of new hosts is by the direct ingestion of the encysted amoebae passed out with the faeces and hence occurs chiefly in conditions of primitive sanitation.

Monocystis

All the members of the class Sporozoa are parasitic and many have very complicated life cycles. *Monocystis* (Fig. 2.18) is a parasite of the common earthworm, living in the vesiculae seminales, and *Plasmodium* is the parasite of man which causes malaria. *Monocystis lumbrici* is chosen as a type for study because it is readily obtainable, since most earthworms are infected with it. It has the disadvantage that its exact mode of transmission from one host to another is unknown. The malarial parasite is of great importance because of its widespread distribution in warm countries where it causes untold suffering and because the discovery of its life history and the subsequent elaboration of methods of control are of great biological interest. *Monocystis lumbrici* is a small, spindle-shaped animal found in the seminal fluid of the earthworm (Fig. 2.18 A). Its protoplasm is little differentiated, but a pellicle, ectoplasm, endoplasm and nucleus can be distinguished and although there are no obvious motor organelles, contractile longitudinal fibrils in the cytoplasm, the myonemes, give the animal the power of making slow wriggling movements. This particular type of movement is peculiar to members of the Order Gregarinida to which *Monocystis* belongs and is known as gregarine movement.

The animal propagates its kind by the formation of resistant bodies containing spores. Two adult forms (*trophozoites*, or feeding

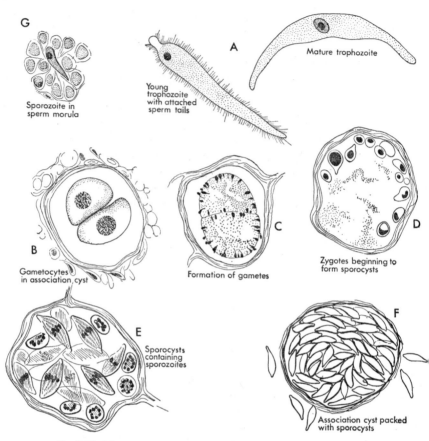

Fig. 2.18. *Monocystis.*

Stages in the life cycle: *A* Young and mature trophozoites. *B* Association of two mature trophozoites (now called gametocytes). *C* Formation of gametes by nuclear division. *D* The gametes fuse in pairs and each zygote secretes a cyst wall around itself, the sporocyst. *E* Within its sporocyst each zygote divides to form eight sporozoites. *F* Sporocysts filling an old association cyst. *G* A liberated sporozoite in a clump of sperm-forming cells. (*A–F* from slides.)

individuals) come together and secrete a cyst wall around themselves (Fig. 2.18 B). They are now known as *gametocytes* and are contained in an *association cyst*. The nucleus of each divides until many daughter nuclei are present (Fig. 2.18 C). These migrate to the periphery of the cytoplasm and each becomes detached together with a small portion of cytoplasm, leaving a residual mass which plays no further part in reproduction. The gametes fuse in pairs, those formed from one gametocyte almost certainly fusing with those from the other (Fig. 2.18 D). The zygotes thus formed secrete a boat-shaped, resistant cyst known as a *sporocyst*. Within this the zygote divides into eight *sporozoites* (Fig. 2.18 E and F). It seems unlikely that the cyst is transferred from one worm to another during copulation since the sporocysts are not known to occur in the spermathecae of earthworms. This implies that they do not escape from the vesiculae seminales when seminal fluid is transferred from one worm to another and hence the only way out must be that provided by the death and decay or digestion of the worm in birds when the sporocysts are ultimately set free in the soil where they are ready to be consumed by another earthworm. When the sporozoites are liberated from the sporocyst they make their way to the seminal vesicles where each one enters a bunch of developing sperms, a sperm morula (Fig. 2.18 G). It is believed that the young feeding forms, the trophozoites, secrete enzymes which digest some parts of the sperm morula but it does not entirely prevent the sperm from differentiating, for in the end trophozoites become covered with attached sperm tails. These are lost before the trophozoite becomes a gametocyte. It is uncertain how much of the nutritional requirements of the animal are derived from the substance of the sperm rendered soluble and diffusible by secreted enzymes, for the creatures are floating in the highly nutritious seminal fluid by which the metabolic requirements of the developing sperm are supplied in an already soluble and diffusible state. Since, however, the sperm heads attached to the trophozoite do not become mature, it is believed that they are absorbed by the parasite.

Thus the parasite is in a situation where it needs merely absorb soluble food substances and oxygen over its surface and excrete waste products in the same way. It is in an osmotically stable and suitable environment and hence needs no contractile vacuole. It needs practically no movement to secure its food. On the other hand the hazards involved in propagating the species are very great and are overcome only by the production of large numbers of infective forms. It is thought that, as a rule, 64 gametes are produced by each gametocyte and since each zygote divides into eight sporozoites, there are 512 infective bodies formed from each original trophozoite. It would appear that since there is no other known multiplicative phase in the life cycle of the parasite, the chances of a sporozoite finding a sperm morula are greater than 1:256, otherwise the parasite would die out.

This figure of 1:256 would seem to compare very favourably with the wastage rates of other parasites, both protozoan and metazoan. It also shows that much soil must be passed through the bodies of earthworms if they come upon the infective stages at random.

Monocystis does not appear to be very harmful to its host, since almost all common earthworms are infected and yet the species continues in vigorous life. It can hardly be described as a symbiont since it cannot conceivably confer any benefit on the earthworm. It does harm to the worm in small measure since it consumes a certain amount of the nourishment which would otherwise be available to the developing sperm and it also destroys some of the sperms. Thus it can only be described as a parasite but it appears to be one that is so little offensive to its host that it is tolerated.

Plasmodium

In contrast to *Monocystis*, *Plasmodium vivax* is a parasite which causes the terrible disease of malaria in man. The disease has been recognized since Greek and Roman times and during the Middle Ages was known as ague. It was for long thought to be due to the 'bad air' emanating from swampy regions. The malarial parasite was not seen in human blood until 1880, when the French doctor Laveran discovered it while working in Algeria. Seventeen years later Ross, at Manson's instigation, demonstrated the parasite in an anopheline mosquito in India. Soon after this, the Italians Grassi and Bignami described the life cycle of the parasite in the mosquito, and a little later Sambon and Ward proved that malaria cannot be transmitted from one man to another except by the bite of a mosquito. Finally, Manson and Warren allowed themselves to be infected with malaria in London by the bites of infected mosquitoes sent from Italy. The cause of the disease and its mode of transmission was thus known about a half a century ago. It remained to devise methods of control to combat the disease which could be carried out on a large scale instead of relying on empirical measures such as treatment with cinchona bark, which had been known for a long time. It was introduced into Europe from Peru in 1640 and was known as a cure for fevers, but the active substance, quinine, was not extracted until the early part of the nineteenth century. It has now been largely replaced by synthetic drugs including daraprim nivaquin and paludrin. This provided a means of preventing infection if taken regularly and a partial cure if taken after the onset of the disease, but it is clear that one of the best hopes of controlling the disease is the elimination of the mosquito vector which transmits it.

LIFE HISTORY (Fig. 2.19). The life cycle begins in man when the slender sporozoites are injected from the female mosquito's salivary glands into a blood vessel, when the insect 'bites' to obtain its blood

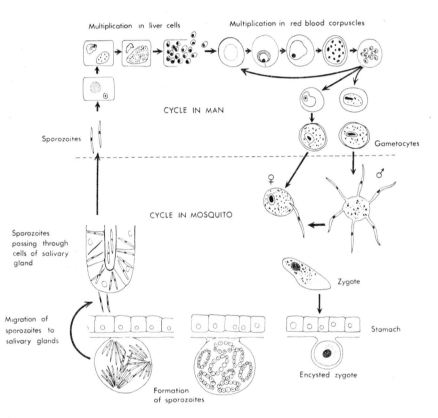

Multiplication in liver cells   Multiplication in red blood corpuscles

CYCLE IN MAN

Sporozoites

Gametocytes

CYCLE IN MOSQUITO

♀   ♂

Sporozoites passing through cells of salivary gland

Zygote

Migration of sporozoites to salivary glands

Stomach

Encysted zygote

Formation of sporozoites

Fig. 2.19. Diagram of the life cycle of the malaria parasite, *Plasmodium vivax*.

meal for egg production. Although the blood in the immediate vicinity of the insect's proboscis is drawn up into its gut, many of the infected forms are rapidly swept away from their point of entry and into the general circulation. They pass to the liver and enter the liver cells where they remain for about 12 days. During this time no stage of the malarial parasite is present in the blood and although the man 'has malaria' he is not a source of infection for fresh mosquitoes. After the 12 days have elapsed, during which time the parasite has multiplied by multiple fission in the liver cells, many so-called *schizozoites* are liberated into the blood and each enters a red blood corpuscle. It becomes ring-shaped, feeds, grows and undergoes division to form many more schizozoites (= *merozoites*) which are somewhat shorter and thicker than the sporozoites. These are liberated into the plasma by the rupture of the old red cell envelope. This occurs together in a large number of individual parasites every 48 hours for *P. vivax*, and corresponds with the characteristic bouts of fever which recur every third day.

After a time a sexual phase begins in man but is not completed until the gametocytes are taken into the gut of a suitable mosquito. The gametocytes develop within the red blood cells from schizozoites which, instead of dividing after they have grown in size, remain in the erythrocyte until they are taken up by an anopheline mosquito. If this does not happen they degenerate.

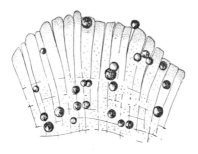

Fig. 2.20. Part of the stomach of a mosquito with cysts of *Plasmodium* on the outside. (From a slide.)

Those which are taken into the gut of a mosquito develop into male and female gametes after their liberation from the erythrocytes, the female by accumulation of food reserves and the male by division into a number of slender gametes and a mass of residual cytoplasm. A male gamete fuses with the female and the zygote bores through the stomach wall of the mosquito and forms a cyst on its outer side (Fig. 2.20). This grows in size and very many nuclear divisions of the zygote nucleus take place. Each nucleus eventually separates off with a small portion of the cytoplasm and forms a sporozoite. The bursting of the cyst on the stomach wall liberates the mass of sporozoites into the insect's haemocoele, from which the sporozoites migrate and pass through the cells of salivary glands into its lumen and hence to the exterior. When the mosquito 'bites' another man, sporozoites are injected into his blood system and the man has contracted malaria.

CONTROL OF MALARIA (Fig. 2.21). When the malaria parasite is present in the blood, it is suppressed by quinine but this drug has no effect on the liver stage. The parasites which are in the liver cells provide a reserve that persists for a long while, so that a relapse or recurrence of the fever may take place some time after a cure has

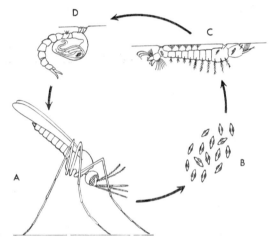

Fig. 2.21. The life history of an anopheline mosquito.

A Resting position of adult; *B* Eggs laid separately, each with a pair of flotation chambers; *C* The larva attached to the surface film of the water for feeding and respiration; *D* The pupa, also attached to the surface film by its respiratory trumpets.

apparently been effected. Destruction of the anopheline mosquitoes which spread the disease can be done in many different ways. The stagnant water in which they breed can be drained, it can be covered with a film of oil which kills the surface-dwelling larvae by blocking their breathing tubes or the larvae can be devoured by fishes introduced for that purpose. The adults can be killed with persistent insecticides such as D.D.T., especially during the winter hibernation. Biting can be prevented by wearing suitable clothing and by sleeping under mosquito-proof netting, and insect repellants can be applied to the exposed parts of the skin.

Vorticella, a sessile ciliate

The Ciliata are the most highly organized protozoa, showing the greatest range of form and the most complex organelles. A number of sedentary forms, such as the genus *Vorticella*, are included in the group in addition to free-swimming and symbiotic species.

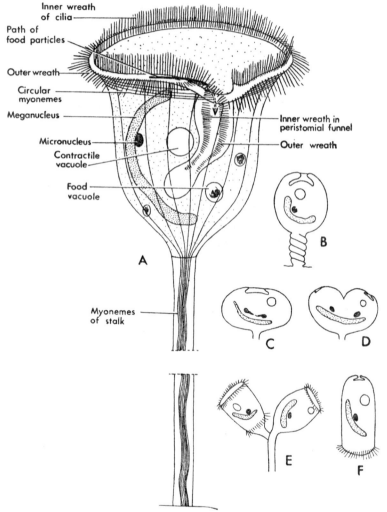

Fig. 2.22. *Vorticella.*

A Individual with stalk extended. *B–F* Stages in binary fission. In *B*, the stalk is shown contracted as are also the circular myonemes at the top of the bell. (Based on *Mackinnon* and *Hawes*.)

The bell-shaped body of *Vorticella campanula* (Fig. 2.22) is attached to the substratum by a stalk in which run contractile fibrils or *myonemes* by means of which the creature can suddenly retract. Myonemes also run round the disk and their contraction can cause it to be covered. The cilia are confined to the peristomial region and consist of an inner upstanding and an outer horizontal row. Both rows are continued into the gullet but on opposite sides. Food particles are wafted into the gullet by the action of the cilia and are taken into food vacuoles in the cytoplasm. There is a macronucleus and a micronucleus and a contractile vacuole.

Reproduction is by binary fission, the two daughter bells adhering temporarily to one stalk until one develops an additional wreath of cilia and swims away to settle elsewhere. Conjugation also occurs but only after several fissions of some of the bells have produced smaller forms which become attached to ordinary bells with which the nuclear exchange takes place, the associated nuclear changes being similar to those of conjugating *Paramecium*.

3. *Coelenterata*

Introduction

As HAS been mentioned, there is a clear distinction between the non-cellular Protozoa and the cellular Metazoa. It is true that sponges are intermediate in position to a certain extent in that they consist of cells which behave almost like a collection of Protozoa, but the cells do act together to some extent; for example, in the secretion of mineral spicules and during reproduction. They are, in fact, true Metazoa although the characteristics which we think of as typically Metazoan are more clearly shown by the Coelenterata. The name of this phylum implies that they are hollow animals and moreover that their only body cavity is a gut cavity. Although some species may be large and bulky, the cellular layers are only one cell in thickness and there are only two layers of cells. They are known from this feature as *diploblastic* animals. They may be thought of as having an outer layer of cells, the *ectoderm* in which the individual cells are specialized for various functions such as protection, movement, perception, conduction, secretion, defence and replacement, and an inner layer of cells, the *endoderm*, specialized for digestion, absorption and assimilation of food. These features are illustrated by the two kinds of coelenterate commonly chosen for study, namely *Obelia* and hydra, although many members of the phylum are larger and a true picture of the group can hardly be obtained without a glance at a few other forms. Of the genus *Obelia*, the species *geniculata* is a common one found on the fronds of large seaweeds, on piers and on rocks where it forms a growth of an inch or so in height which, like many apparently fragile organisms, can stand up to considerable wave action. In its habit of growth it resembles a plant and can easily be mistaken for one at a glance. Animals like *Obelia* were earlier referred to as zoophytes because of this resemblance and their sedentary habits, but the term has now dropped out of use. *Obelia* is a marine coelenterate, as are the majority of the members of the group, although the one which is most commonly used as a type in the study of biology is the somewhat atypical freshwater polyp hydra. (See p. 52.)

General structure of *Obelia*

A colony of *Obelia* is a branching growth consisting of zooids of different types united by a common stem or axis called the *coenosarc* (Fig. 3.1). Both this and the bodies of the zooids are made up of the two layers of cells, outer ectoderm and inner endoderm, separated by a thin middle layer or *mesogloea* which shows a fine fibrous

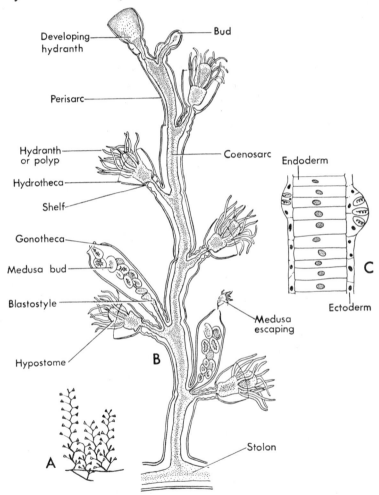

Fig. 3.1. *Obelia.*

  A A small colony as it appears to the unaided eye. *B* A portion of a colony with hydranths and blastostyles (*magnified*). *C* A portion of a tentacle showing ectoderm and solid core of endoderm. (*B* and *C* drawn from a stained preparation.)

structure under the microscope but from which cells are absent. This common stem or coenosarc has a basal anchoring portion or *stolon* which is parallel to the substratum and attached to it and from which the branches of the colony are given off at right angles.

Each feeding polyp or *hydranth* consists of a squat cylindrical body and a *manubrium* or *hypostome* in which the mouth lies, a circlet of many tentacles occurring at the junction of the two regions. The polyps, which are borne alternately on the axis of the colony, are connected to the rest of the colony by a tube of coenosarc. In the axils of the lower hydranths of a mature colony modified polyps, with a narrow body ending in a disc, are found bearing buds from which small, free-living jellyfish or *medusae* develop. These modified polyps are called *blastostyles* and lack both a mouth and tentacles.

The whole colony is covered by what may be called a loose cuticle, the *perisarc*, which is stated to be composed of chitin, the chief constituent of which is a highly polymerized amino-sugar, glucosamine. It is in contact with the ectoderm only during its formation by that layer in growing regions and irregularly elsewhere. The perisarc is a smooth tube except where it surrounds the polyp stems, where it is annulated, and also where it is expanded into a cup-shaped vessel or *hydrotheca* to accommodate the hydranth. This sits on a shelf near the base of the cup and can be completely retracted into it. Each blastostyle is enclosed by and does not project from a cylindrical, narrow-mouthed expansion of the perisarc, the *gonotheca*.

Detailed structure

As we have said, the arrangement of the cells of the body as two distinct layers, ectoderm and endoderm, is spoken of as a diploblastic arrangement. This type of organization is found only in the coelenterates in which the two layers are separated by a mesogloea, which may be thin and non-cellular, as it is in *Obelia*, or it may be very bulky and may contain a few cells as it does in some jellyfish. The mesogloea is not regarded as constituting a third layer of the body because it does not appear regularly as a separate cell layer during development and because it is essentially either free from cells or made of a matrix or ground-substance in which cells, originating in the ectoderm or endoderm, are scattered. The two cell layers and the mesogloea together make up the body-wall which surrounds the simple gastrovascular cavity or *enteron*, continuous throughout the entire colony.

The ectoderm is made up of a single layer of cells which are columnar in shape and which have their bases drawn out into contractile processes or *muscle tails* parallel to the longitudinal axis of the polyp. In between them lie small, undifferentiated reserve cells or *interstitial cells* and sensory cells connected with those of the nervous system. Special stinging cells, chiefly used in the capture of prey, are found in batteries on the tentacles and more sparsely elsewhere. They are known as *nematoblasts* or *cnidoblasts* and each produces a small stinging capsule or *nematocyst*, details of which, in hydra, are given on p. 56. Those of *Obelia* are not so well known, but are similar, although smaller, and are chiefly of a type similar to the glutinants of hydra.

The cells of the endoderm are columnar in shape. Their bases are also drawn out into muscle tails but these are arranged transversely to the long axis of the polyp, i.e. circularly. Their free ends, where they line the enteron, are either flagellate or amoeboid, so that they either assist in the circulation of the fluid which fills the gastrovascular cavity or are able to ingest minute particles of food and to complete the process of digestion within a vacuole of the cell as does *Amoeba*. In addition they secrete digestive enzymes which act on protein in the food. The endoderm everywhere lines the enteron. The tentacles, however, lack a branch of this cavity as (cf. hydra) having a solid endodermal axis made up of a line of large vacuolated cells.

Nerve cells are present, usually lying between either cell layer and the mesogloea. By means of its processes each one links up with neighbouring nerve cells to form a network which covers the whole animal, but which is better developed in some regions than elsewhere, e.g. in the tentacles. The nerve net in turn is linked with receptor or sensory cells in the ectoderm, small spindle-shaped elements which, where they have been described in other coelenterates, have been shown to have a fine sensory process projecting beyond the free surface of the ectoderm. For the functioning of the nerve net in coelenterates see p. 558.

Feeding and Digestion

The food of *Obelia* consists of small animals which are caught by nematocysts of the tentacles and swallowed whole. Cells of the endoderm secrete proteolytic enzymes into the enteron, which, together with muscular movements of the animal, cause the food to be rapidly broken into small pieces. These are then taken in by the cells of the endoderm just as *Amoeba* forms food vacuoles, and the process of digestion is completed intracellularly. All regions of the body, including the coenosarc tubes, are near to a supply of food material, and since there exists a circulation of the contents of the enteron throughout the colony, produced by the flagellated cells, there is no need of special organs to circulate the digested food and, in fact, none is present. The body wall of a coelenterate, despite the appearance which it assumes when contracted, is nowhere thicker than two cell layers so that nowhere is any cell far removed either from a source of food or from the external environment.

Respiration

The rate of living of the coelenterates is not high and as we have seen, no cell is far removed either from a source of food or from the outside, so that just as food material diffuses across the cell layers, so oxygen can diffuse across the short distance from the outside to the endoderm. No special organs or cells are set apart for respiration and no system of oxygen-carrying compounds or pigments is known. CO_2 can diffuse out in like manner.

Excretion

No organs or cells are recognized as performing this function, the waste products of nitrogenous metabolism simply diffusing out of the cells into the surrounding water.

Osmoregulation

The power of regulation of the osmotic pressure of the cells and the contents of the enteron is slight in *Obelia* and the animals soon die when placed in diluted or concentrated sea water. It is likely that the inorganic composition of the cells and of the enteric fluid is much the same as that of the sea water.

Sensitivity

Little more is known of the workings of the sensory and nervous system than that given in the section on structure above. The polyp reacts to most stimuli, other than that provided by food organisms, by withdrawing into the hydrotheca. More highly differentiated sense organs occur on the medusa (see p. 50).

Movement and Locomotion

The movements which the polyp makes in its daily existence are neither great nor varied. The body can be withdrawn into the hydrotheca by the contraction of the longitudinal muscle tails and protruded again by the contraction of the circulars. The mouth can be opened and closed and the hypostome is somewhat mobile, but the greatest mobility resides in the tentacles. Since they possess no extension of the enteron but have a cellular axis, they can alter but little in dimensions but can be bent by the contraction of the longitudinal muscles of one side. They are thus bent over in feeding and in the rapid withdrawal into the hydrotheca that follows a noxious stimulus.

Growth and Reproduction

The growth of the *Obelia* colony takes place only in the warmer months of the year when there is a plentiful supply of zooplankton on which it feeds. Then growth, which is rapid, occurs at the apices and the colony attains its full size and begins to produce blastostyles on which the medusae arise. When the temperature falls in the autumn and the supply of zooplankton is reduced, the colony becomes moribund, apart from the basal portion which may survive until the next year. Although some hydranths may remain, a search for a good, vigorous colony of *Obelia* in winter is usually fruitless.

An *Obelia* colony does not reproduce itself directly in a sexual way but gives rise to small free-swimming medusae which bear germ cells.

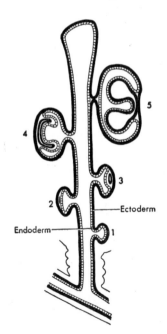

Fig. 3.2. Formation of a medusa.

Diagram illustrating successive stages in the formation of medusae on a blastostyle. At 2 the ectoderm which will line the sub-umbrella has just become separated; at 3 it is hollow; at 4 the manubrium is forming and at 5 the medusa bud is nearly complete.

These medusae, as has been mentioned, are formed on the blasto-styles and appear first as simple outpushings of the two cell layers, ectoderm and endoderm, separated, as elsewhere in the animal, by mesogloea (Fig. 3.2). These medusa buds become bell-shaped by the growth of an inpushing formed from the outer side, but they remain attached to the blastostyle by a stalk on their convex side until they are almost perfect medusae. A mouth opens at the tip of a protrusion, the manubrium, in the centre of the concave side of the bell, a fringe of tentacles develops on the free edge of the bell and four branches of the enteron grow towards the edge of the bell to form the radial canals. These finally become linked by a ring canal before the medusa is complete and ready for liberation. When ready, the organism – for a unit having an independent existence may be so termed – breaks the strand of ectoderm still holding it to the blastostyle and eventually squeezes out of the entrance to the gonotheca, and swims away.

Structure of the medusa

The medusae of *Obelia* (Fig. 3.3) are tiny free-living jellyfishes vary-ing in size from a diameter of about 0·1 cm. when first liberated to about 0·5 cm. when mature. Each is umbrella shaped, the position of the handle on the concave side, or subumbrella, being occupied by the manubrium at the end of which the mouth opens. The convex side is termed the exumbrella. At the edge of the bell is a fringe of tentacles, resembling those of the polyp in most respects but differing in bearing a swelling at the base packed with developing nemato-cysts and known as the tentacular bulb. Although most medusae related to *Obelia* have an inwardly projecting shelf, the *velum*, which narrows the opening of the subumbrella, it is only rudimentary in *Obelia*, which is therefore atypical in this respect. The mouth opens into the enteron from which four radial canals run to the bell margin where they join a ring canal. A section taken through the interradius, between two radial canals, shows that the endoderm is not confined to the radial canals but that there is a thin endoderm lamella spread out between the canals and separating the mesogloea of the ex-umbrella from that of the subumbrella. This endoderm lamella lies nearer to the subumbrella than to the exumbrella.

Microscopical structure of the medusa

The cells composing the ectoderm and endoderm of the medusa are similar to those of the polyp except that the muscular portions of the

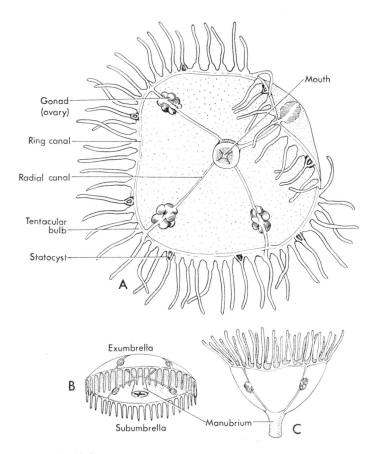

Fig. 3.3. *Obelia.*

A Fully-grown medusa with gonad. (From a stained preparation.)
B and *C* Two positions of a medusa during swimming; at *B* the circular muscles have contracted and are beginning to relax; at *C* the animal is completely relaxed and sinking between bursts of swimming.

ectoderm cells are better developed and enable more rapid and powerful muscular movements to be made. The muscles of the bell are almost entirely ectodermal and consist of muscle tails of musculoepithelial cells arranged radially on the subumbrella side. In addition, there is a ring of well-developed separate striated circular muscles lying towards the edge of the bell on the subumbrella side. The use of these muscles in swimming is described below (p. 50).

Whereas the polyp possesses no sense organs other than isolated sensory cells, the medusa has eight clearly defined *statocysts*. In addition there is a concentration of cells of the nerve net at the edge of the bell. Each of the statocysts, which lie between the radial canals and below the base of a tentacle, consists of a small ectodermal, fluid-filled vesicle into which project sense cells, the other ends of which are connected to the lower nerve ring (Fig. 3.4). These sense

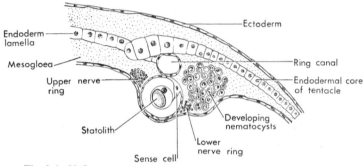

Fig. 3.4. *Obelia.*
  Radial section through the edge of the bell and a tentacle-base bearing a statocyst. (Based on *Grove* and *Newell.*)

cells bear fine processes which are embedded in or stimulated by a small calcareous body, the *statolith* secreted by and enclosed in a lithocyte cell. These statocysts have been regarded as organs of balance or equilibrium, but it seems more probable that they act as centres to stimulate the nervous system, for medusae from which they have been removed may lose the power of swimming spontaneously. The nervous system consists, like that of the polyp, essentially of a sub-ectodermal nerve net but it is better developed along the inner margin of the bell above and below the rudiment of the velum, as the upper and lower nerve rings. This nerve ring ensures the co-ordination of the subumbrella circular muscles used in swimming.

The swimming of the medusa, which is important in keeping the animal suspended in the zone where its food is found as well as in catching its food, takes place chiefly by the rapidly alternating contraction and relaxation of the muscles of the subumbrella, especially those at the edge of the bell. The alteration of the shape of the medusa from a shallow saucer to a globular form drives the animal aborally forwards through the water chiefly by the expulsion of water from the diminished volume contained in the subumbrella. Swimming is not usually continuous for a long time, but the swimming movements are repeated rapidly many times, after which the animal drifts with tentacles outspread, the manubrium hanging down and frequently with the exumbrella concave in shape (Fig. 3.3). After a rest the swimming movements begin again, swimming movements and rest periods alternating.

As the medusa lives its free life floating in the sea, it feeds by collecting small organisms on to its tentacles as these are waved through the water during its swimming movements. It grows and the four gonads, which are simply accumulations of sex cells lying beneath the radial canals between the ectoderm and the mesogloea, arise from interstitial cells of the ectoderm. The medusae are either male or female. Many flagellate spermatozoa are formed in the male medusa by the usual process of spermatogenesis (see p. 611) but in the female medusa only a few eggs mature. Many interstitial cells may start on the way to becoming ova, but only a few actually mature, the others serving to nourish the successful ones which may engulf them. Eggs and sperm are both shed into the sea water where fertilization takes place and where each zygote develops into a ciliated *planula* larva which, after swimming about, finally settles down to form another polyp colony. The chance of egg and sperm coming together seems very small indeed in the sea, but it must be remembered that the colonies of *Obelia* and hence the medusae which they liberate occur chiefly around the coasts rather than in the open ocean so that the population of *Obelia* medusae in a given volume of water is rather greater than would appear at first sight. Nevertheless, the life of the species can only be continued in this way at the cost of the enormous wastage entailed in the formation and liberation of many medusae. These have the value that they are not sessile like the polyps and therefore can serve to distribute the species by water currents.

Life history

Obelia then possesses two clearly defined phases in its life cycle: a fixed hydroid phase and a pelagic medusoid phase, the first serving to overwinter and to give rise to the medusae by an asexual budding process. The medusae reproduce sexually and disperse the species. This type of life cycle involves the possession of two distinct types of individual, the polyp and the medusa which alternate with one another. The so-called Alternation of Generations in the life of *Obelia* which this involves is only analogous to that which is shown in plants where a haploid gametophyte alternates with a diploid sporophyte. In *Obelia* there is no nuclear difference between the two generations. An alternative name for the phenomenon shown by *Obelia* is *metagenesis*.

Hydra

Introduction

Unlike *Obelia*, hydra is found attached to the leaves and stems of plants as a solitary polyp in fresh water but never in sea or brackish water. There are three common species of fresh-water hydras in Britain, which are now known as *Chlorohydra viridissima*, the green hydra; *Pelmatohydra oligactis*, the brown hydra; and *Hydra attenuata*. These are most easily distinguished by their colour and by the larger size and longer tentacles of *P. oligactis* which frequently hangs upside down with its tentacles extended for a distance of several inches. The green hydra is the one which is most commonly used for practical classes, often under its old name of *Hydra viridis* (Fig. 3.5), but the brown hydra is equally suitable and has the advantage of being somewhat larger. All are colloquially referred to as hydras.

Structure

In its expanded state the polyp of hydra is more nearly columnar than that of *Obelia*, and the projection, the hypostome, at the top of which the mouth opens, is conical in shape and is often spoken of as the oral cone. At the end opposite to the oral cone the animal is attached to the substratum by its basal disc, in which it is said an opening may sometimes be seen, particularly during certain phases of the animal's locomotion.

The tentacles are fewer in number than are those of *Obelia*, commonly ranging from four to eleven with more animals possessing six than any other number. They are hollow and very mobile, being, in *P. oligactis*, fine and hair-like in extension and mere knobs on extreme contraction.

Budding from the side of the column is common in well-fed hydras which may bear all stages from small replicas of the parent, with mouth and tentacles and ready for liberation, to mere outpushings of the body wall which are formed at the beginning of the process. Thus a flourishing hydra may look almost like a colonial organism but it is nevertheless described correctly as a solitary polyp because the buds leave the parent when ready to lead an independent life.

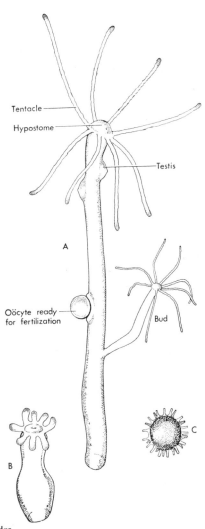

Fig. 3.5. Hydra.

The green hydra (*Chlorohydra viridissima*) in expanded (*A*) and contracted (*B*) states. (Drawn from life.) *C* Fertilized egg in protective case. (From a slide.)

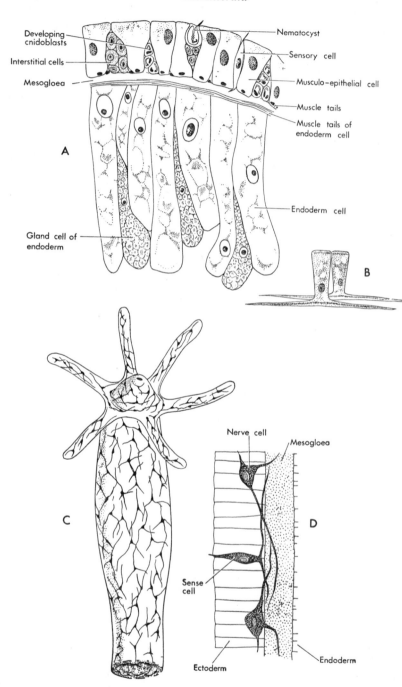

Developing cnidoblasts

Interstitial cells

Mesogloea

Nematocyst

Sensory cell

Musculo-epithelial cell

Muscle tails

Muscle tails of endoderm cell

A

Endoderm cell

Gland cell of endoderm

B

C

Nerve cell

Mesogloea

Sense cell

D

Ectoderm

Endoderm

The buds may themselves start to bud before they leave the parent polyp.

No trace of a perisarc occurs in adult hydra.

Detailed structure (Fig. 3.6)

The diploblastic structure described in *Obelia* is found also in hydra; the two layers, ectoderm and endoderm, separated by a thin layer of mesogloea, retain their own identity (which can be distinguished by the types of cell found in them) even when subjected to very drastic changes. For example, if a hydra be turned inside out, the cells migrate back into their original positions, endoderm inside and ectoderm outside.

Seven types of cell are found in the ectoderm, viz. musculo-epithelial, interstitial, nerve, sensory, secretory, sex and cnidoblast cells. The mesogloea, like that of *Obelia*, is non-cellular and thin, and contains fibres which can be demonstrated by silver impregnation and other techniques. The endoderm is composed largely of amoeboid or flagellate cells in which the functions of enzyme secretion and absorption are combined. In addition there are some recognizable glandular cells. In the green hydra the endoderm cells are packed with the small single-celled green alga *Zoochlorella* (or *Zooxanthella* in the brown hydra) which lives in harmony with the animal. This association of two organisms for their mutual benefit is known as symbiosis. The example of hydra and *Zoochlorella* is one of the best known. (See also p. 66.)

The musculo-epithelial cells are conical in shape and are arranged with the base outwards and forming the outer surface of the animal. The apical part of the cone bears a contractile process, muscle tail, lying on the mesogloea and orientated in a longitudinal direction. Interstitial cells are small, rounded, undifferentiated cells which are chiefly packed in the spaces between the musculo-epithelial cells and which are said to be able to differentiate into any of the other types

Fig. 3.6. Hydra.

A Transverse section of the body wall of *Hydra attenuata* showing the main types of cell to be seen in the ectoderm and endoderm. (Based on *Brien*.)

B Two musculo–epithelial cells, somewhat diagrammatically drawn.

C Diagram of the way in which the nerve cells of hydra are generally believed to be arranged.

D Two nerve cells and a sense cell.

of cell but which are probably mainly used in the replacement of nematocysts (see below).

Sensory cells of the type already described in *Obelia* are present and connect with the nerve cells of the nervous system. With good fortune these nerve cells can be revealed in the living animal by staining with reduced methylene blue when they can be seen to have relatively longer processes and smaller cell bodies than is shown in the customary diagram. In other coelenterates, e.g. the sea anemone *Metridium* and the jellyfish *Aurelia*, nerve cells can be demonstrated microscopically rather more easily than they can in hydra, both in the living tissue and by silver impregnation, when they can be seen to extend for a distance of up to 1 cm.

Glandular cells are present in the ectoderm of the basal disc where they secrete a mucus by which the animal sticks to its support. Germ cells are formed from interstitial cells and occur as local accumulations of sperm or oocytes (see p. 61).

Cnidoblasts are derived from interstitial cells and they in turn elaborate the nematocysts within. Although most nematocysts occur and are used on the tentacles, it is believed that they are formed in the lower part of the column, are extruded into the enteron, taken up again in the tentacles and passed out to the ectoderm where they are grouped in batteries. There are four distinct types of nematocyst found in hydra, the penetrant, the volvent and the large and small glutinant (Fig. 3.7). Each is situated in its formative cell; this bears a fine protoplasmic process or *cnidocil* which is thought to act like a trigger in the discharge of the stinging capsule. The capsule itself is of a proteinaceous nature and when discharged consists of an oval bladder from which a fine hollow tube projects. This may be straight and bear spines as it does in the penetrant, it may be spirally coiled as it is in the volvent, straight and smooth as in the small glutinant, or it may bear fine hairs as in the large glutinant. The exact mechanism by which the thread is discharged from its internal position in the undischarged nematocyst has been the subject of controversy. While it may be that not all nematocysts discharge in the same way, studies on a variety of coelenterates make it probably true to say that in many the nematocyst discharges by the eversion of a fine tube which is turned inside out in the undischarged capsule. The thread can clearly be seen coiled up inside many nematocysts and can be seen to bear spines inside, which, after discharge, are outside. Recent measurements indicate that the tube changes its dimensions on discharge in such a way as to suggest that an intrinsic swelling

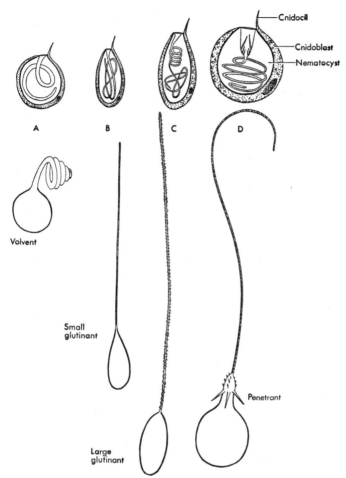

Volvent

Small
glutinant

Large
glutinant

Penetrant

Fig. 3.7. Hydra.
A–D The four types of nematocysts found in *Chlorohydra viridissima* shown in their undischarged state in their formative cells
(*top row*) and after discharge (*bottom row*). (Based on *Ewer*.)

mechanism of the tube itself is the cause of the discharge. It is
generally believed that an increase in internal pressure in the capsule,
probably caused by uptake of water, is responsible for initiating the
discharge of the thread but it is not clearly understood how this
occurs.

Whatever may be the mechanism of discharge it seems certain
that no nervous control is involved, nematocysts being known as

independent effectors. Both a chemical and a mechanical stimulus are necessary to bring about the discharge of penetrant and volvent nematocysts of hydra. Neither prodding with a fine glass rod alone nor the presence of protein substances in the water alone will bring about the discharge, but prodding with a glass rod coated with mucus will do so. The glutinant nematocysts are not discharged in these circumstances but probably respond to a particular type of mechanical stimulation, are used for attachment when the animal is moving and are inhibited by the presence of protein.

The endoderm cells of hydra are more uniform than those of the ectoderm and like those of *Obelia* may be flagellate or amoeboid. They undergo a cycle of changes so that the appearance of the endoderm cells in section is variable, some being in a resting phase, some being distended with secretory products and some containing particles of food undergoing intracellular digestion. Each cell has a muscle tail at its base next to the mesogloea arranged transversely to the longitudinal axis of the body and may contain many symbiotic unicellular algae (p. 55).

Feeding

The feeding of hydra resembles that of *Obelia*. When hungry the tentacles are extended and remain so until suitable prey e.g. *Daphnia* bumps against them. Then the nematocysts are discharged and the prey is held by the volvents and paralysed by the penetrants and attached by them to the tentacles, which shorten and bend towards the mouth. This opens, and the prey is engulfed and the mouth closed.

Digestion

Hydra, like *Obelia*, secretes enzymes which rapidly digest protein so that the prey is soon made into broth from which fragments are picked up by the endoderm cells. After a meal, protein granules can be recognized in the cells and fat droplets can sometimes be seen to have been engulfed. No enzymes are provided for the digestion of carbohydrates but insoluble granules such as glycogen may be taken up.

Respiration

As in *Obelia*, no special organs are present and no oxygen-carrying pigments have been recognized. Gaseous exchange is brought about entirely by diffusion.

Osmoregulation

The osmoregulation of hydra is not properly understood. Like *Amoeba* and *Paramecium*, it lives in fresh water, the osmotic content of which is below that of its cells, but unlike them it has no obvious osmoregulating organelles. It is not known by what mechanism it extracts its necessary salts from the low concentration in which they occur in its surroundings, nor is it known how it prevents endosmosis.

Growth

Growth in hydra takes place continuously in the uppermost third of the column, probably by the differentiation of interstitial cells which are plentiful there but almost absent from the basal third of the column which is continually undergoing retrogression. By this means the cells are continuously renewed and there is evidence that this renewal can take place indefinitely above about 10°C. so that, like *Amoeba* in which sexual reproduction does not occur, hydra may be said to be potentially immortal given proper culture conditions.

Sensitivity

It has been seen in the discussion on nematocysts that hydra responds to the appropriate combined mechanical and chemical stimuli by the discharge of (a) the independent effectors, the nematocysts, and (b) muscular movements of the tentacles and mouth to bring about feeding. Hydras can be said to respond somewhat sluggishly to light in that they tend to accumulate in light of medium intensity in the course of their phases of slow locomotion. Otherwise hydra shows no clearly differentiated reaction to stimuli, the general response being a contraction. (See also p. 558.)

It is surprising – and unexplained – that they do not respond to the movement over their surface of the two common epizoic protozoa, *Trichodina* and *Kerona*, which run rapidly over the surface apparently stimulating the cnidocils of the nematoblasts mechanically yet without causing discharge of the nematocysts. How this immunity has been derived and its effectual mechanism in the hydra is not understood.

Movement and Locomotion

The movements of hydra which are brought about by the longitudinal ectodermal and circular endodermal muscle tails suffice for food catching and feeding. Being hollow, the tentacles are capable not only of bending but of changing their size by the flow of their fluid contents into and out of the main enteron.

In addition to these movements, hydra can change its point of attachment by slow looping movements. The column is bent over and the tentacles are attached to the surface, the foothold is released and then regained in a fresh position. The process is repeated and slow locomotion thereby accomplished.

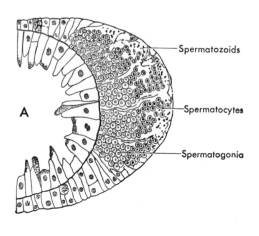

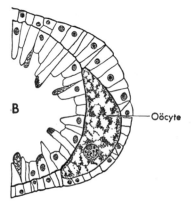

Fig. 3.8. Hydra.

Transverse sections through region of testis (*A*) and developing ovary (*B*). In *A*, the outer cells are fully-formed spermatozoids; in *B*, the oocyte is in an early stage of development and will increase in size and become rounded before it is ready for fertilization as in Fig. 3.5 (*C*). (From slides.)

Reproduction

Reproduction in hydra takes place in an asexual manner by budding, as already mentioned. This occurs in the middle zone of the column when the animal is well fed. In times of poor nutrition, buds already formed may be absorbed and no new buds arise.

Especially towards the autumn, sexual reproduction takes place and results in the formation of resistant encysted bodies which can remain dormant for several months. Testes or spermaries are first formed on *C. viridissima* in the upper part of the column by the accumulation, between the ectoderm and the mesogloea, of cells which differentiate from interstitial cells into spermatozoa (see p. 611) and which form a bulge (Fig. 3.8) that eventually opens by a nipple by which the spermatozoa escape to fertilize the oocytes.

Usually only one egg comes to maturity at a time in the hermaphrodite *C. viridissima*, although many interstitial cells enlarge and begin developing into oogonia. These occupy a lower zone of the column than the testes, and although at first oogonia occur all round the body, finally only one is covered by a distended ectoderm to form the ovary. This wall breaks but the oocyte usually remains attached by mucus to the base of the ovary until it is fertilized, when it begins its division and drops to the bottom of the pond to complete its development. In the process a rough resistant chitinous covering is secreted by the developing embryo, which may remain dormant for some time (see Fig. 3.5). Cleavage of the zygote gives rise at first to a hollow ball of one layer of cells, the blastula, which is converted

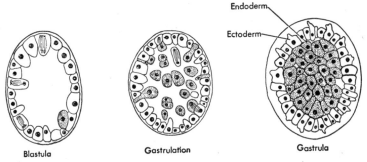

Blastula   Gastrulation   Gastrula

Fig. 3.9. Hydra.

Stages in the formation of the two-layered embryo which hatches to give a planula larva. The inner layer of cells, the endoderm, is formed partly by the inward migration of cells of the blastula and partly by tangential cell division. Both methods of formation are shown.

into a two-layered embryo or gastrula by the migration inwards of certain cells from all points and the cutting off of others by tangential division. This mixed immigration results in the formation of a non-ciliated planula larva with a solid core of endoderm (Fig. 3.9). When the larva is liberated from its theca, an enteron is formed in the endoderm and the creature soon settles down by one end, develops a mouth and tentacles, and begins to feed and to grow into an adult hydra.

Other Coelenterata

The phylum Coelenterata is divided into three classes:
Class: Hydrozoa, e.g. *Obelia* and hydra
  Scyphozoa, e.g. *Aurelia* (the common jellyfish);
  Anthozoa, e.g. *Actinia* (the beadlet sea anemone).

The majority of the Hydrozoa are small, and like *Obelia* have a hydroid and a medusoid generation, although the medusa may not always be liberated from the polyp as it is in *Obelia*. In *Aurelia*, a scyphozoan, on the other hand, the medusa is the most conspicuous phase in the life history, measuring up to 12 inches across, and although the polyp is an essential stage, it is small and difficult to find. The structure of an adult medusa is shown in Fig. 3.10, where it can be seen to resemble in shape the medusa of *Obelia*, having a bell with a fringe of tentacles and a manubrium with oral arms. It differs in that the enteron forms a series of radiating and branching channels connecting the stomach with the ring canal. The gonads are of endodermal origin and are present as four opaque horseshoe-shaped ridges projecting into the enteron. Eight sense organs are borne round the edge and are of a more complex type than those of *Obelia*, combining an eye spot and a type of statocyst.

The sexes are separate. Eggs are liberated into the enteron; sperm are drawn in with the ciliary currents which are generated in the enteron by the cells lining it and fertilization takes place, leading to the formation of planula larvae. These larvae become embedded for a time in folds in the oral arms but are eventually freed, settle down and grow into small polyps which can bud to form others and which divide up by constrictions at right angles to the long axis (Fig. 3.11). These constrictions cut the polyp, which is called a *scyphistoma*, into a series of small medusoid larvae (*ephyrae*) by the process known as *strobilization*. The larvae, which are liberated one at a time, swim away, feed and grow into adults during the summer months. *Aurelia*

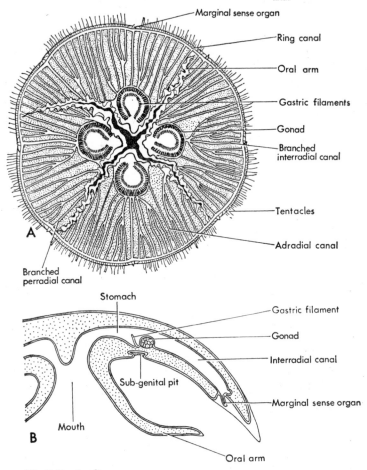

Fig. 3.10. *Aurelia.*

A Subumbrellar view of the whole animal. (From a specimen.)
B Diagram of a radial section through an adradial canal and marginal
sense organ.

feeds chiefly on small floating animals which strike against its tentacles to which they are caused to adhere by the discharge of nematocysts. The prey is wiped off from the tentacles by the oral arms.

By contrast, the Anthozoa have no medusoid phase. Instead,
sexual reproduction leads directly from one polyp generation to the
next. *Actinia equina*, the beadlet anemone (Fig. 3.12), is one of the
commonest British species and is found in rock pools and in crevices

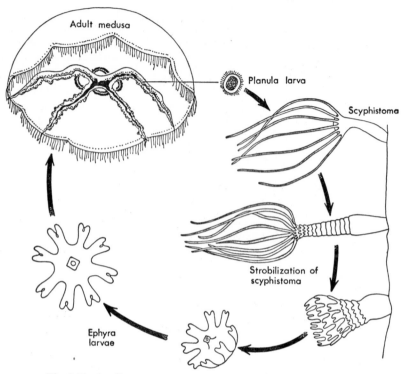

Fig. 3.11. *Aurelia.*

The life cycle. The adult medusa is shown with planula larva embedded in the oral arms. These larvae give rise to a polyp stage which
may survive for some years giving off annual crops of ephyra larvae.

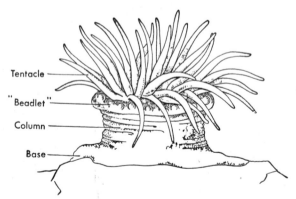

Fig. 3.12. *Actinia.*

The beadlet anemone seen in expanded condition. The 'beadlets' are
bright blue, contain nematocysts, and contrast with the olive green or
dark red of the rest of the animal. (Based on *Stephenson.*)

between tide marks. As often seen when the tide is out, it is a rounded
red or green object shaped like a bee skep but when expanded the
numerous tentacles, which are borne on a disc, are seen surrounding
the mouth which is at the base of an intucking or *stomodaeum* lined
by ectoderm instead of being borne on a protuberance or hypostome
as it is in hydra and *Obelia*. The mouth leads into a large enteron cut
into segments by partitions or *mesenteries* which project radially
from the body wall into the interior (Fig. 3.13). These are numerous

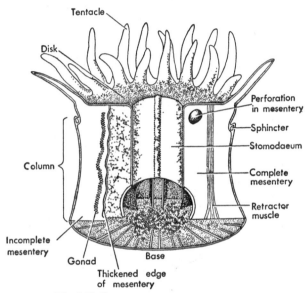

Fig. 3.13. Sea anemone.
Stereogram to show internal structure.

in mature anemones and are arranged in several series of different
sizes. Each has a thickened edge composed of ciliated cells and glandular cells which secrete digestive enzymes. The muscular system is
well developed for a coelenterate and consists largely of separate
plain muscle fibres derived from the endoderm. These form a
circular layer around the column, especially well developed as a
sphincter just below the disc, and longitudinal strands in the mesenteries. Contraction of these in response to stimulation withdraws the
disc and its tentacles, and contraction of the sphincter closes the
animal completely so that only the side walls of the column are
exposed. The endodermal gonads are borne on the mesenteries.

As in *Aurelia*, the sexes of sea anemones are separate and both eggs and sperm are shed into the sea where fertilization leads to the development of a planula. This settles down and develops directly into a polyp which grows into a mature sea anemone. In *Actinia*, however, the eggs are sometimes retained by the female and fertilized in the enteron by sperm entering with the sea water. They develop in the enteron into miniature anemones before being liberated by the parent.

Like hydra and *Obelia*, *Actinia* is dependent for food on suitable living or dead animals striking the tentacles, whereupon the nematocysts are discharged causing the prey to adhere. The tentacles bend towards the mouth, which opens to receive the prey.

Near relatives of the sea anemones which are of great importance, are the true or stony corals, chiefly colonial forms which rapidly secrete a calcareous exoskeleton on which they live. They occur in such quantities in warm seas that they form reefs of great extent surrounding the land and are also responsible for the building of islands such as the numerous coral atolls of the Pacific Ocean.

Symbiosis and Commensalism

Parasitism involves a close association between a parasite and its host from which the parasite *only* obtains benefit. Symbiosis is an equally close relationship between two organisms to their *mutual* benefit, examples of which are common among coelenterates. A well known instance is that of hydra and the zoochlorellae found in the endodermal cells. For a long time it has been *assumed* that the hydra obtains nutrients from the alga which receives CO_2 and waste nitrogenous compounds in return, but recently it has been demonstrated by using radioactive CO_2 that the hydra does in fact receive carbon compounds synthesized by the alga. Most corals possess symbiotic zooxanthellae and these have been shown to use up waste nitrogen and phosphorus compounds excreted by the coral and greatly to enhance its rate of growth. It has also been shown that the symbiotic algae belong to a genus of flagellates of the subclass Phytomastigina which are found living independently. Commensalism is the association of two organisms with a certain degree of mutual benefit. An oft-quoted example is that of the sea anemone *Calliactis* seated on the empty shell housing a hermit crab. The sea anemone may acquire scraps of food from the crab's 'table' while affording the hermit crab protection from predators by means of its nematocysts. Hermit crabs may be found without sea anemones on their shells and *Calliactis* is often found by itself also.

4. *Platyhelminthes*

Introduction: Triploblastic animals

IT HAS been seen how differentiation of the animal body in the non-cellular Protozoa has taken place during the course of evolution and has given rise to *organelles* such as contractile vacuoles and flagella which perform definite, and different, functions. In the Coelenterata the animal body is cellular and the *cells* are differentiated into distinct types such as nerve cells and musculo-epithelial cells which also perform separate functions but which are not aggregated into groups of similar cells. It is also true that the living part of the coelenterate body is nowhere very thick, almost all the cells being spread out over the mesogloea in a layer one cell deep. They are arranged in two layers, one on each side of the mesogloea, and although this may contain cells derived by migration from the ectoderm, only the two layers, ectoderm and endoderm, are distinguishable in the embryo. For this reason the Coelenterata are known as diploblastic – or two-layered animals. On the other hand, the Platyhelminthes are known as *triploblastic* forms because another layer of cells lying between the ectoderm and endoderm is recognizable early during development, being produced in some forms from cells which are marked out from early cleavage of the egg to give rise to this *mesoderm*. But although the Platyhelminthes have the three layers of ectoderm, mesoderm and endoderm, the elaboration or complication which the mesoderm undergoes is not very great. Much of it remains as a loose packing tissue, the *parenchyma*, but some muscle fibres are differentiated in it and it gives rise also to the generative organs. It does not, however, form a differentiated transport or vascular system, and hence the size and shape of the body are, to a large extent, determined by the need to keep all parts of it near to a supply of food and oxygen. In all forms the body is flat, thereby giving a relatively large surface for a given volume and requiring nowhere a long path for oxygen to travel to the innermost cells. In those forms which have a gut, it is a very much branched organ ramifying throughout the greater part of the body. These points of construction should be borne in mind when considering the platyhelminths and they will help to make their structure understandable. Also the flatworms may be looked upon as triploblasts in which the mesoderm is not sufficiently highly differentiated to play a part of great importance in the day-to-day life of the animal.

The phylum contains three clearly defined classes:

Class: Turbellaria (free-living flatworms), e.g. *Polycelis, Dendrocoelum*;
Trematoda (parasitic flatworms with gut, but without strobilization), e.g. *Fasciola, Schistosoma*;
Cestoda (parasitic flatworms without a gut, but with strobilization), e.g. *Taenia, Dibothriocephalus.*

A Turbellarian

Introduction

Dendrocoelum lacteum is a common turbellarian which is white in colour and therefore more suitable for study than the pigmented opaque species such as the common *Polycelis nigra*. It is between 10

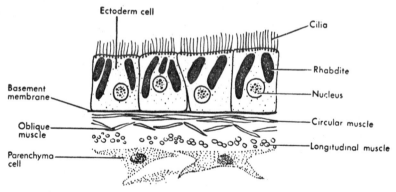

Fig. 4.1. A planarian.

Transverse section of the superficial layers of a planarian to show the ciliated epidermis and muscle layers.

and 20 mm. long and 2 and 5 mm. wide. The short description which follows would apply almost as well to other freshwater turbellarians as to *Dendrocoelum* since they differ from one another only in such details as pigmentation and the number and placing of the eyes. All are bilaterally symmetrical.

The bulk of the worm consists of the so-called parenchyma, a tissue which is a spongelike mass in which the boundaries of the constituent cells are almost impossible to make out. It is formed by the vacuolation and linking of the cells in the middle of the body so that, although nuclei are present in the fully formed parenchyma, the correspondence between nuclei and cells is not clear. Presumably the interstices between the fine strands of the spongy parenchyma, which can be seen in fixed and stained preparations, are filled in life with a watery fluid.

In the parenchyma are embedded the gut, reproductive organs, an excretory system and a nervous system. Towards the outside of the parenchyma there are three layers of muscles – an outer circular, a middle diagonal and an inner longitudinal – and in addition strands cross from the dorsal to the ventral side (Fig. 4.1). The animal is covered with a simple epidermis of ciliated cells containing characteristic rod-shaped bodies or *rhabdites* whose function is unknown. The rhabdites are formed in cells lying in the parenchyma.

Gut and Digestion

The gut has only one opening, at the end of a muscular pharynx, which is normally retracted but which can be extruded for feeding.

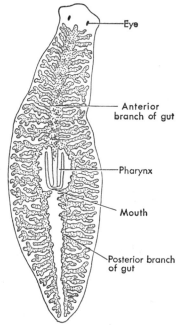

Fig. 4.2. *Dendrocoelum.*

The gut as seen in a specimen recently fed on clotted blood. (From life.)

The gut has a single anterior and two posterior main branches, each of which has many diverticula so that it spreads out over a large part of the animal (Fig. 4.2). Its wall consists of little more than a layer of endoderm cells adjacent the parenchyma, which is thus in close contact with it. Animal food is preferred and mostly dead material is eaten, but small living worms or crustacea may be captured. Digestion takes place partly in the lumen of the gut but is largely intracellular, small particles being taken into the vacuoles in the endoderm cells in an amoeboid fashion.

Excretory system

The excretory system, as it is often called, consists of special cells, known as *flame cells* scattered in the parenchyma. Each is hollowed out and connected to a fine duct leading eventually to a tubule opening to the exterior by a series of excretory pores (Fig. 4.3). A group of cilia lies in the hollow of the cell; their beating would agitate the liquid in the lumen and would help to drive towards the

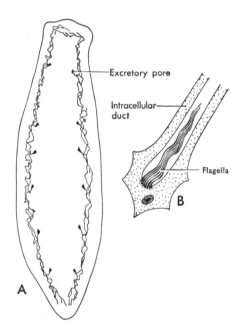

Fig. 4.3. *Dendrocoelum.*
 A The excretory canal system. (After *Wilhelmi.*) *B* A flame cell.

outside any fluid secreted into the lumen of the cell. It is thought that soluble excretory matter is eliminated in this way.

Osmoregulation

Little is known about the osmotic regulation of *Dendrocoelum* or indeed of freshwater turbellarians in general, but it is believed that the flame cell system plays a part in ridding the body of excess water. Any separation of water from the more concentrated protoplasm takes place as a result of energy expended during respiratory activities, the cilia merely keeping the fluid contents of the flame cell in motion. It is possible that the ectoderm also plays a part in osmotic control by being selectively permeable to different substances in the environment but how such control is exercised is not understood.

Nervous system and Sense organs

The nervous system of a turbellarian consists of a network of nerve cells and fibres underlying the epidermis, together with aggregations forming two longitudinal nerve cords. These cords run into anterior aggregations of nerve cells known as the *cerebral ganglia* (Fig. 4.4). These are closely connected with the chemical and mechanical receptor cells which are especially numerous at the anterior end of the animal and with the eyes which also occur there. A turbellarian eye consists of a cup of pigmented cells in the hollow of which lie receptor cells with their sensitive ends against the pigment. They thus constitute a primitive inverted retina and, since they are shielded from light except in the direction of the opening of the cup, they have some rough discrimination of the direction of the incident light.

It will be seen that the main concentration of nerve cells and receptor cells lies at one end of the animal, the anterior end, which always goes first when the animal is moving. The anterior end can hardly be described as a 'head' but nevertheless the evolution of a distinct head (the process of *cephalization*) may be said to have begun in the platyhelminths. The 'head region' not only bears the most receptor cells for the reception of stimuli arising in the outside world and goes first during locomotion, but it is the region of most active metabolism, is most resistant to poisons like potassium cyanide, and dominates the rest of the body so that the animal acts as a co-ordinated whole.

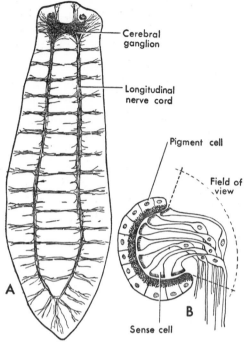

Fig. 4.4. A turbellarian.

Diagram to illustrate the nervous system: *A* The cerebral ganglia and main nerve cords; *B* An eye as seen in section. (Based on *Hesse*.)

Locomotion

Dendrocoelum looks rather like a small, animated leaf which can crawl over the bottom or in the surface film and which can also swim in mid-water. Locomotion at a surface is carried out by waves of contraction of the muscles which lie just below the epidermis. The waves pass from head to tail and drive the animal forwards. It will readily be seen that a wave of contraction passing backwards down a continuous band of muscle fibres will have the effect of propelling the animal forwards if there is greater frictional resistance between the ground and the animal at the wave than there is posterior to it. Shortening of the muscles and their consequent bulging bring about this increased pressure on the substratum at the locus of the wave. In addition, the cilia with which the epidermis of the animal is covered are also capable of moving the creature slowly through the water or over the substratum.

Behaviour

Turbellarians are fairly active creatures but they may remain motionless for some time after feeding. Usually they are moving about and changing their direction of movement in an apparently random manner. However, the angle through which their direction of movement turns in a given time is known to depend upon the intensity of light falling on them. In bright light they alter their direction by a greater amount than in dim light which causes them to remain longer in shade than in light. They thus appear to 'prefer' dim light and tend to accumulate in it.

Turbellarians are suitable animals for the study of the behaviour of simple forms and, since the freshwater ones may easily be procured and kept, they have been extensively used for experiments on behaviour.

Reproduction and Growth

The reproductive system is hermaphrodite and consists not only of the gonads and their ducts, but of various accessory organs. The arrangement of the ovaries, testes and accessory glands is shown in Fig. 4.5, in which it will be noticed that the ducts from both testes and ovaries open into a common genital atrium. The *vas deferens* discharges via a muscular *penis*. The female duct receives the products of many *vitelline* or yolk glands before opening into the atrium. A muscular gland organ of unknown function also opens into the atrium as well as a flask-shaped receptacle for sperm, the *bursa copulatrix*. Cross-insemination occurs when two animals come together ventrally and the extruded penis of each is inserted into the genital atrium of the other. This action shuts off the opening of the oviduct into the atrium so that the seminal fluid of each partner is taken into the bursa copulatrix of the other. After cross-insemination the animals separate and the received sperms travel up the oviduct to fertilize the eggs as they leave the ovary. The eggs receive yolk and shell from the vitelline glands after fertilization and are deposited on vegetation in a cocoon formed in the genital atrium.

Turbellarians have also been used for experiments on the regeneration of the whole animal from isolated parts, for experiments on growth when fed and 'degrowth' when starved and also on the gradient of metabolic activity which occurs along their length and which can be demonstrated by the different susceptibilities of the anterior and posterior regions to poisoning by potassium cyanide.

Platyhelminthes

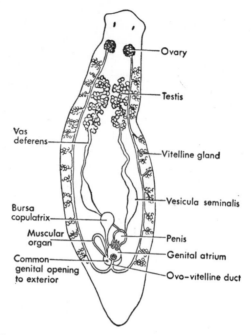

Fig. 4.5. *Dendrocoelum.*
Reproductive system. (From a stained preparation.)

Trematoda

General structure of Fasciola – the Liver fluke

An important group of parasitic platyhelminths is the Class Trematoda or the 'flukes', of which the species that causes liver rot in sheep, *Fasciola hepatica*, is an important and common member.

The adult is a leaf-like animal measuring between 20 and 50 mm. long and 5 to 13 mm. at its widest part, and is found living in the bile duct of the sheep and, less commonly, in other domestic animals and in man (Fig. 4.6). It resembles a turbellarian in being bilaterally symmetrical and in having a complex generative system, flame cells and a diffuse nervous system resembling that of a planarian, but differs in being covered externally by a cuticle with spines instead of a ciliated epidermis, in the possession of suckers and in the lack of an eversible proboscis. The cuticle is a strong outer covering resting on a basal membrane. It bears backwardly directed spines. The

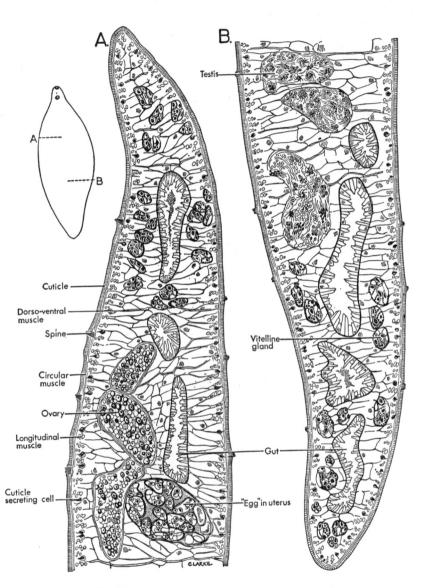

Fig. 4.6. *Fasciola.*
General structure. *A* Transverse section through region of ovary.
B T.S. through region of testes. (From a stained preparation.)

Platyhelminthes

method of its formation is not certain but it is thought to be a secretion of mesodermal cells rather than cells of the ectoderm, for these degenerate during development so that the adult animal lacks an epidermis (Fig. 4.6). The muscles of the body consist of circular fibres just below the basal membrane and of diagonal and longitudinal layers lying deeper. There are also fibres running from the dorsal to the ventral side, and radial and semicircular muscles occur in the suckers.

Gut

The gut opens by a terminal mouth surrounded by an oral sucker. There is a small muscular pharynx after which the two main caeca run

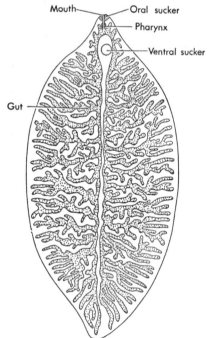

Fig. 4.7. *Fasciola.*
The gut. (From a stained preparation.)

nearly the length of the body and give off numerous side branches (Fig. 4.7). *Fasciola* is believed to feed on tissue cells and tissue fluids from the smaller branches of the bile duct system and may migrate back to the bile duct and gall bladder when satiated, returning to the liver when 'hungry'. There is no doubt that it ingests liver cells as it burrows through the liver during the wandering of the young stages.

Respiration

The respiration of material derived from the food is largely anaerobic. It is thought that glycogen is the chief substrate metabolized and this is split into carbon dioxide and fatty acids. The rate of CO_2 production is little affected by the presence or absence of oxygen, and although oxygen is taken up when it is present, there is no relationship between the oxygen uptake and carbon dioxide output.

Reproductive system

The male generative organs comprise a pair of testes from each of which the sperm is led by a *vas deferens*. The two vasa deferentia join at the *vesicula seminalis* which leads to the *cirrus* (an eversible

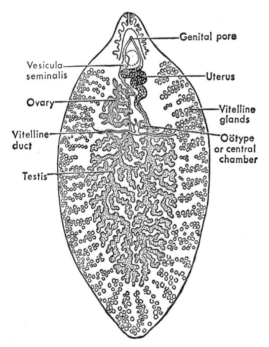

Fig. 4.8. *Fasciola.*
General arrangement of the reproductive system. (From a stained preparation.)

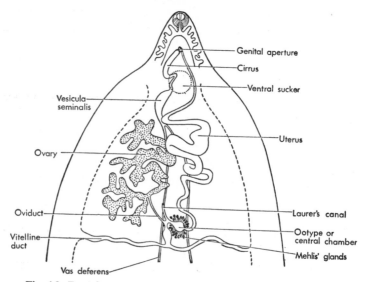

Fig. 4.9. *Fasciola.*
The arrangement of the anterior part of the reproductive system.

intromittent organ). This in turn opens to the exterior at the common genital pore and can be protruded through it by eversion (Figs. 4.8 and 4.9).

The female generative organs include a single ovary on the right side which has a continuous duct leading to the outside at the common genital pore. Where the duct first leaves the ovary it is known as the oviduct. This is short and leads to a region known as the central chamber or *ootype* into which open many small glands (Mehlis' glands). From the central chamber the duct becomes wide and twisted and is known as the uterus. It leads to the common genital pore. Opening into the central chamber region are two other ducts, one is the vitelline duct leading from the mass of vitelline or yolk glands on either side of the animal and the other is Laurer's canal which opens to the exterior at its other end on the dorsal side of the animal. Copulation has been observed in *Fasciola* and it is thought that cross fertilization usually occurs, the cirrus of each co-copulant being inserted into the common genital pore of the other and not into Laurer's canal as was at one time believed. The sperm must make their way nearly as far as the ovary because fertilization and egg capsule formation occur in the central chamber which imparts to the capsule its characteristic shape. Eggs are released from the ovary, probably one at a time, are fertilized and pass to the central chamber where they become associated with yolk cells from the vitelline glands. The shell is formed from droplets of secretion released by the vitelline cells in the central chamber. It forms a covering to the 'egg cell + yolk cells' of protein tanned in a leather-like fashion. The secretion of Mehlis' gland is not known to play any part in the formation of the egg or shell but may serve to lubricate the passage of the egg capsules. From the central chamber the egg capsules pass into the uterus where they collect for a time while development of the larva takes place before they are released.

Life history

Release of the egg capsules from the parent fluke is the beginning of a complex life cycle involving three larval stages and the infection of a secondary host, most commonly the pond-snail, *Limnaea truncatula* (Fig. 4.10). Early in the cleavage of the fertilized egg a so-called *germ cell* or *propagatory cell* is set aside which continues to divide and some of whose cell progeny give rise to the various larval forms. Thus there is a line of cells which can be followed in each larva and which can be traced back to the original propagatory cell cut off early in development. The first of these larvae is the *miracidium*, which emerges by pushing aside the cap or operculum at the top of the egg capsule. It is covered by 21 ciliated cells arranged in five tiers covering a pear-shaped body (Fig. 4.10B). Within this epithelium and the thin underlying body-wall there are a 'brain' and two eye spots, rudiments of an excretory system and gland cells which aid in the entry of the larva into its host. The posterior region of the body is filled with the cell progeny of the propagatory cell which include little aggregations of cells known as germ balls. The miracidium is viable for only 24 hours, after which it dies unless it penetrates the body of a suitable pond-snail. It bores its way through the epidermis into the body cavity and generally comes to lie in the digestive gland. Here it loses its cilia and changes to a spherical shape and is known as a *sporocyst*. As the sporocyst grows it becomes distended with larvae, one of which is formed from each germ ball. These larvae, known as *rediae*, are liberated within the snail by rupture of the sporocyst. Each is a cylindrical larva equipped with a simple gut and flame cell system, and circular and longitudinal muscles by means of which it can move. Eyes are lacking but the redia contains germinal cells like those of the sporocyst, from which

80   *Platyhelminthes*

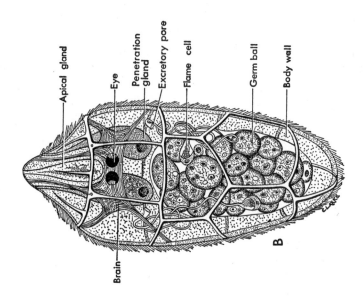

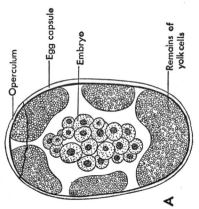

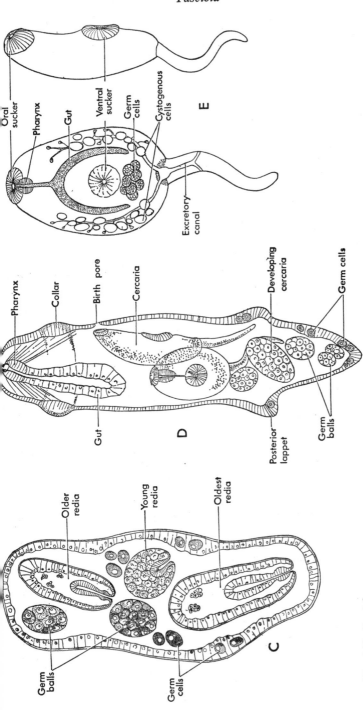

Fig. 4.10. *Fasciola.*

Diagrams of the stages in the life cycle: *A* Developing egg; *B* A trematode *miracidium* larva after hatching from the egg (that of *Fasciola* is similar to the diagram but not exactly like it in all details); *C Sporocyst* formed from miracidium within tissues of snail; *D Redia* larva formed from the sporocyst; *E* Ventral and lateral views of a *cercaria* larva as liberated from snail. (After various authors.)

Labels in E:
- Oral sucker
- Pharynx
- Gut
- Ventral sucker
- Germ cells
- Cystogenous cells
- Excretory canal

Labels in D:
- Pharynx
- Collar
- Birth pore
- Cercaria
- Gut
- Developing cercaria
- Germ cells
- Posterior lappet
- Germ balls

Labels in C:
- Older redia
- Young redia
- Oldest redia
- Germ balls
- Germ cells

are derived firstly more rediae and later *cercaria* larvae, both of which escape through an anterior birth pore.

The redia is an activa larva and can move about in the tissue of the snail by the action of its muscles, especially those of the anterior collar and posterior lappets. Anterior circular muscles contract and the larva elongates, the lappets providing purchase at the posterior end. The anterior longitudinal muscles then contract, the collar thickening and gripping the side of the 'burrow' while the posterior part is drawn up. In this way the redia can burrow through the soft tissues of its host.

The cercaria larva, with many of which the rediae eventually become filled, has a flattened disc-like body and a posterior tail by the wriggling of which it can swim. It possesses a ventral sucker, a mouth with oral sucker and a bifid gut, an excretory system and cellular rudiments of the reproductive system in the form of germ or propagatory cells like those found in the other types of larvae. Near the anterior end there are gland cells which secrete a cyst in which the cercaria can remain when it has escaped from the body of the snail and has emerged from the water in which the snail lives. It encysts on herbage near the water whence it came by the secretion of a wall which hardens round the body and nips off the tail. It remains encysted as a *metacercaria* until eaten by a sheep and is viable for many months in moist conditions. The cyst wall is unaffected by gastric digestion but is dissolved in the intestine. The metacercaria which are liberated mostly penetrate the gut wall and pass into the liver by way of the coelom. The young flukes live and feed in the tissue of the liver and eventually reach the bile duct, about seven weeks from the time of infection, as adults already containing egg capsules in the uterus.

The life history can be represented diagramatically:

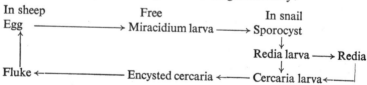

Control of infection

The life history of *Fasciola hepatica* is typical of that of many trematodes in which a vector serves to convey the larval stages from one host to another. It is clear that the control of the infection is not easy, as the bile duct is an inaccessible place into which to introduce drugs. Nevertheless, carbon tetrachloride is administered to sheep which are liable to infection and is fairly effective in killing stages of the parasite in the liver. It is better to prevent the infection by control of the vector and this is achieved by filling in ponds and by drainage of the pasture on which sheep graze, thereby reducing in amount the habitat preferred by the snails.

The structure and life history of the liver fluke is well known, but the physiology of this and other parasites is much less well understood, chiefly owing to the difficulty of keeping the animals outside their hosts in a situation where they may be observed and used in experiments.

Cestoda

Taenia—the tapeworm

Introduction

The Cestoda differ from the Turbellaria and Trematoda in having a growth region of the body from which a string of similar *proglottids* or 'segments' is budded off. Each proglottis contains a set of reproductive organs and as it passes back along the chain of segments (or *strobila*) by the growth of the active region it increases in size, the reproductive organs mature, fertilized eggs develop and finally the proglottis drops off at the end of the strobila (Fig. 4.11). The *scolex* (or holdfast) remains attached to the gut wall by hooks and suckers and may live until its host dies.

Taenia solium, the human tapeworm, is the species frequently described as a type of the Cestoda and although its life history is well known, it is so rare in Britain today that material for study is difficult to procure and other species of *Taenia* or related genera are commonly used for practical work. They do not differ greatly in structure and the description of the structure of *Taenia solium* (but not the life history) will apply fairly closely to them. The other common species of *Taenia* is *T. pisiformis*, whose primary host is the dog and whose larvae are distributed by rabbits and hares. *Taeniarhynchus saginata* is the beef tapeworm which infects man and whose secondary host is the ox.

General structure

Taenia solium has a scolex which bears four suckers and a crown of hooks. The suckers are equipped with muscles which enable them

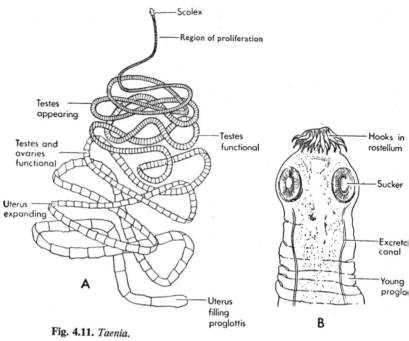

Fig. 4.11. *Taenia.*

A An entire animal. *B* The scolex. (From a stained preparation.)

to anchor themselves to projections of the gut wall; the attachment of the scolex is aided by the presence of the hooks which become embedded in the host's tissue. Although the holdfast is tiny compared with the size of the whole strobila, it attaches the worm so effectively that it resists dislodgment even when the gut is thrown into violent muscular spasm by the action of vermifuge drugs. These may cause the strobila to break so that a large portion of the worm is evacuated but rarely succeed in ridding the host of the tiny scolex and neck. The region just behind the scolex is a region of active cell division and from there a chain of proglottids is generated. These are small at first but gradually grow in size as they absorb nutriment and are pushed backwards by the addition of fresh proglottids in the neck region. A large part of each proglottis comes to be occupied by hermaphrodite reproductive organs but portions of the nervous and excretory systems are also present (Figs. 4.12 and 4.13).

As in the Trematoda, the ectoderm cells are lost early in development and the external covering of the body is the cuticle, probably secreted by mesodermal cells lying below it. This is smooth in the

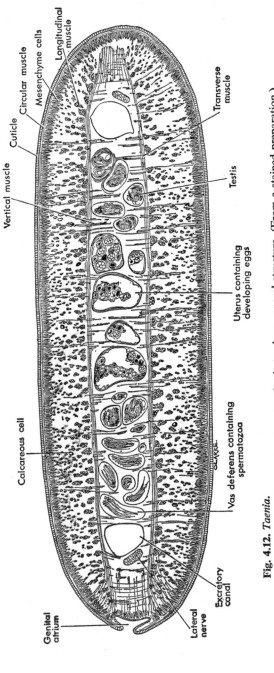

Mesenchyme cells
Longitudinal muscle
Circular muscle
Cuticle
Transverse muscle
Vertical muscle
Testis
Calcareous cell
Uterus containing developing eggs
Vas deferens containing spermatozoa
Genital atrium
Excretory canal
Lateral nerve

Fig. 4.12. *Taenia.*
Transverse section of a mature proglottis to show general structure. (From a stained preparation.)

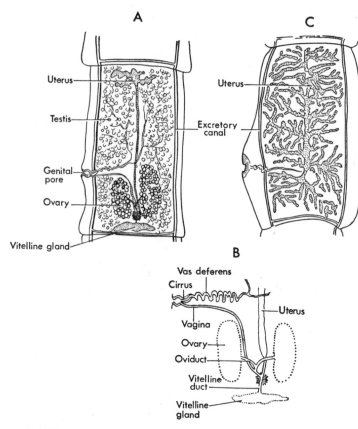

Fig. 4.13. *Taenia.*

The reproductive system:

A The arrangement of the organs in a mature segment; the uterus is just beginning to expand (from a stained preparation).

B Diagram to show the relations of the ducts.

C A 'ripe' proglottis in which the expanded uterus, packed with oncospheres, has nearly filled the whole proglottis.

Cestoda and does not bear spines. Muscle fibres are arranged as follows. There is a thin layer of circulars lying just below the basal layer of the cuticle. The longitudinals occur in bundles in the parenchyma from just below the circular layer to the transverse muscle layer. They are least numerous towards the outside where there are a few interspersed with the layer of mesodermal cells and most numerous near the transverse muscle layer. This layer divides the body into inner and outer regions and encloses the reproductive organs. There are also vertical fibres traversing the parenchyma, especially that of the inner reproductive region, in a dorso-ventral direction.

A noticeable feature of the parenchyma of the tapeworm is the occurrence of 'calcareous cells', each containing a concretion of calcium and magnesium phosphate and carbonate. These cells often stain heavily and may be conspicuous. Their function is unknown.

Digestion and Respiration

There is no doubt that since *Taenia* does not possess a gut, all food material must be taken in by diffusion through the surface layers. If these are sufficiently permeable to allow the diffusion of food molecules and the gas molecules involved in respiration, then it might be expected that the surface would be vulnerable to attack by the host's digestive enzymes. But this is not so, for the animals live and flourish in the gut so they must be protected in some way. It is believed that the cuticle is possibly akin in nature to chitin and is impregnated with fatty material so that it is resistant to waterlogging, and it seems unlikely that the animals do, in fact, produce anti-enzymes to counteract the effects of the host's digestive juices.

Food material is readily available as small molecules resulting from the action of the host's digestive processes and is absorbed through the cuticle, but there is also evidence from experiments made on rats infested with tapeworms and fed on a protein deficient diet that the parasite can continue to flourish even though the host is suffering from protein lack. The tapeworm, presumably, derives its protein from the host's tissues. Tapeworms have a high content of glycogen which is presumably synthesized from glucose absorbed from the gut. It is used in respiration, which is chiefly anaerobic, carbon dioxide and various acids such as lactic and some higher fatty acids being formed.

Excretion and Osmoregulation

The excretory system consists of two excretory canals, one on either side parallel with nerve cords and joined by a transverse canal at the hinder end of each proglottis. Into these canals lead numerous flame cells embedded in the parenchyma. Next to nothing is known about the excretory processes of tapeworms or about the osmotic relation between a tapeworm and its environment.

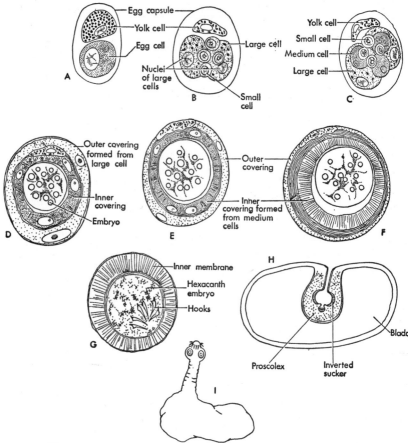

Fig. 4.14. *Taenia.*

Diagrams illustrating the life-history of *Taenia*:

A Fertilized egg cell and yolk cell enclosed in a thin eggshell.

B The egg cell has divided into two large cells and four small ones. The large cells have received yolk from the yolk cells and will eventually form coverings for the embryo.

C The large cell has further divided, producing medium cells, which give rise to the inner covering of the embryo.

D The small cells have aggregated and further divided, and are beginning to form an embryo. This is enclosed by an inner and an outer layer formed from the medium and large cells.

E The inner layer is becoming a hard case round the embryo while the outer layer is becoming reduced.

F The inner layer is increasing and forming a striated hard case containing the embryo. The outer layer is further reduced and the yolk cell has almost disappeared.

Nervous system and Behaviour

The functioning of the nervous system has also been very little studied. The animal is responsive to touch and can contract to a third of its extended length quite quickly, the whole worm being involved in the process. This might be expected from the continuity of its lateral nerve cords which run the whole length of the chain of proglottids and join in a nerve collar in the scolex.

Reproductive system and Life history

The male reproductive organs consist of testes, vas deferens and a cirrus which is eversible and opens at a common genital pore on one side of the proglottis. The female organs comprise the bilobed ovary, the oviduct and the *vagina* which opens at the common genital pore. Arising at the point where the oviduct becomes the vagina is a side tube, the *uterus*, which receives the fertilized eggs and enlarges enormously in the later stages of the life of the proglottids. In addition there are vitelline glands which provide yolk cells and egg capsule and a cluster of small Mehlis' glands round the junction of the uterus and oviduct (the ootype) (Fig. 4.13). These may secrete a fluid which holds the fertilized egg cell and vitelline cells together while the capsule is formed from a secretion of some of the vitelline cells.

Oocytes from the ovary are fertilized in the ootype and pass into the uterus. Each becomes attached to a yolk cell from the vitelline gland and the whole is soon surrounded by a thin capsule probably formed from droplets of secretion from the vitelline cells. The fertilized egg divides into large, medium and small cells, the small ones giving rise to the embryo while the medium and large ones form the inner and outer coverings of the embryo respectively, as shown in Fig. 4.14. The yolk cell yields its reserve material to the large cells

---

G The inner layer is complete and encloses the hexacanth embryo. Little structure is visible in this except the 6 hooks from which it derives its name. The whole structure consisting of embryo and 'eggshell' is termed an onchosphere. The 'eggshell' being derived from some of the cells set aside during the division of the fertilized egg is not properly an eggshell but a hardened or chitinized embryonic membrane.

H Cysticercus or bladder worm consisting of a fluid-filled bladder containing a pro-scolex which develops as an invaginated or 'inside-out' structure.

I Bladder with everted scolex after liberation from secondary host tissues.

(Based on various authors.)

during the early stages of cleavage. It is not certain whether a proglottis is cross-fertilized or selfed. In general the testes of a proglottis mature before the ovaries and it is thought that the cirrus of the anterior segments may be used for the insemination of posterior proglottids although this has not been seen directly. Other observers believe that seminal fluid is liberated into the surrounding gut fluid and makes its own way into the appropriate vagina.

As the developing eggs accumulate in the uterus this grows in size and branches as the other parts of the reproductive system are consumed until, when all the eggs have been discharged from the ovary, the uterus has come to occupy almost the whole proglottis and is packed with 30,000 to 40,000 embryos which may be squeezed out into the faeces by muscular movements of the segment. Each *hexacanth* embryo is enclosed in a resistant spherical capsule, the whole forming an *onchosphere*. The embryo is characterized by the possession of six hooks equipped with muscle fibres and set in a mass of cells in which little differentiation is ordinarily visible but which have been shown to include flame cells and probably germinal cells similar to those of trematode miracidia. When the hexacanths are freed from their capsules in response to the stimulus provided by the host's digestive juices, they actively bore their way through the gut wall and are carried by the blood to the muscles where they lodge, since they are about 35 μ in diameter and the capillaries are much smaller. Here, chiefly in the muscles, each develops into another larval stage, the *bladder worm* or *cysticercus*. This is formed from a hexacanth by rapid growth into a parenchymatous mass surrounded by a cuticle. The centre of this becomes hollowed out to form a bladder and from the periphery a thickening invaginates and develops into an inverted scolex. At this stage the animal remains until it is eaten by a man before it has been killed by proper cooking. In the gut of the primary host the wall of the cyst breaks down and the scolex turns inside out and attaches itself to the gut wall by its hooks and suckers and starts to generate proglottids at the rate of seven or eight a day. At the end of three or four months the first-formed proglottids, filled with oncospheres, drop off from the end of the strobila and are ready to begin the life cycle again.

A table is given opposite of a few common tapeworms with their alternate hosts and a few of their important features.

Measures for the control of tapeworm infections in both man and animals are usually aimed at interrupting the life cycle either by measures which prevent the secondary host from becoming infected

Genus and species	Primary host	Secondary host(s)	Features
Moniezia expansa	Sheep	A mite	Common sheep tapeworm. Two sets of reproductive organs per proglottis.
Echinococcus granulosus	Dog	Domesticated animals. Man	Bladderworm stage forms hydatid cyst up to 6 in. diameter in liver, kidney, lungs, brain. Many scolices formed in each cyst.
Taeniarhynchus saginatus	Man	Cattle	Common 'beef' tapeworm of man. Lacks rostellum and hooks. Larger than *T. solium*, up to 40 ft., 2,000 proglottides. Bladderworms chiefly in jaw muscles, heart and diaphragm. Cosmopolitan but especially Abyssinia.
Multiceps multiceps	Dog	Sheep	Bladderworm size of hen's egg, usually in brain of sheep causing staggers. Many scolices formed internally and also daughter bladders budded off.
Taenia pisiformis	Dog	Rabbit	The common dog tapeworm. Cosmopolitan.
Hymenolepis nana	Man	None	The only tapeworm completing life cycle in one species. Direct infection through ingestion of faecal matter containing embryos. Common in S.-E. United States.
Dibothriocephalus latus	Man	*Diaptomus* (a copepod crustacean). Freshwater fish, esp. pike, perch	The 'fish' tapeworm of man. Two flabby suckers. Europe and elsewhere, esp. parts of Russia.

or preventing access by the primary host to the infected secondary host. Thus the disposal of human faeces by sanitary measures prevents pigs having access to them and ingesting hexacanth embryos. Alternatively the life cycle of *T. solium* may be interrupted by thorough cooking of all pork for human consumption, thus ensuring the destruction of the bladder worm stage.

It will be seen that ordinary sanitary measures would not interrupt the life cycle of *Dibothriocephalus* since sewage disposal usually takes place in rivers where the secondary hosts occur. Here it is necessary to ensure that all freshwater fish eaten are thoroughly cooked.

5. *Nematoda*

THE members of this phylum form a very numerous group whose ubiquity has been compared to that of the bacteria. Nematodes are found in the soil, in water or in the alimentary canals, body cavities or tissues of higher animals, exhibiting various degrees of parasitism. Some are parasitic on plants. Owing to their cylindrical form and circular cross-section, nematodes are commonly known as thread or round worms, or, in some cases, as 'eelworms' on account of their wriggling movements. Their structure is remarkably uniform and is exemplified by that of *Ascaris megalocephala*—a large nematode found in the intestine of the horse.

Ascaris megalocephala

External features

The sexes are separate, the male when fully grown being roughly seven inches long and the female rather more than twice that length. In both the body is cylindrical with pointed ends. The surface of the body is smooth and covered by a thick elastic cuticle composed of protein. It has a collagen-like structure and contains many fibres arranged in layers running in various directions. At the anterior end is the mouth, which is triangular in section and bordered by three lips furnished with sensory papillae, while the anus is situated at the posterior end, slightly on the ventral side. Just behind the mouth and also on the ventral side is an excretory pore. The posterior end of the male is more curved than that of the female and displays two horny spines protruding from the anus, adjacent to which is the genital aperture. In the female, the genital aperture lies on the ventral side about one-third of the way along the body from the mouth (Fig. 5.1).

Internal structure

The body is hollow and within the single, continuous fluid-filled cavity lie the alimentary canal and the reproductive organs. The outer body wall consists of three layers: the cuticle, the ectoderm which secretes the cuticle and an inner muscular coat. The ectoderm is

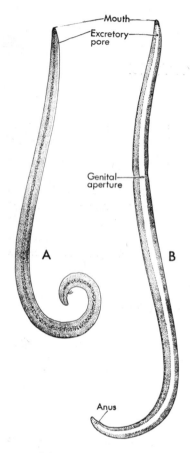

Fig. 5.1. *Ascaris megalocephala.*
A male, *B* female.
(Drawn from specimens.)

syncytial, no cell boundaries being visible and the nuclei are concentrated mainly in four longitudinal internal ridges which divide
the muscular coat into four longitudinal bands. One of these ridges
is in the mid-dorsal line, another in the mid-ventral while the remaining two are lateral, one on each side. The muscle bands are made up of
elongated cells in which contractile fibres occur in the peripheral
regions of the outer portion of each cell. In structure these muscle
cells appear to be intermediate between the musculo-epithelial cells
of hydra, with their muscle 'tails' (Fig. 3.6B) and the plain muscle
'fibres' of the annelids (p. 117). It is by means of the alternating
contractions and relaxations of the muscle bands that the undulating
movements of the animal in a dorso-ventral plane are produced
The internal structure is illustrated in Fig. 5.2.

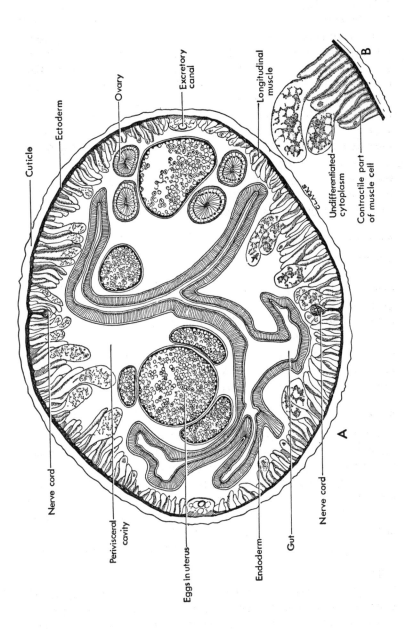

Fig. 5.2. *Ascaris.*
A T.S. of the body of a female *Ascaris* (drawn from a stained preparation). *B* The longitudinal muscle cells enlarged.

Feeding and Digestion

The alimentary canal is a straight tube. The mouth leads into a short stomodaeum called the oesophagus (or pharynx), lined by inturned ectoderm and cuticle. Its walls are largely composed of radially arranged muscles, giving it a suctorial function. Succeeding the oesophagus is a long narrow tube called the intestine (mid-gut) whose wall consists of a single layer of endodermal cells covered externally by a thin cuticle and forming an absorptive organ. Finally the gut ends in a short proctodaeum, similar to the stomodaeum in that it is lined by ectoderm, and whose external opening is the anus. The food of the worm is the digested food of its host ingested via the mouth by the suctorial action of the oesophagus, which also forces it into the intestine against the high pressure of the fluid in the body cavity. This pressure may be as high as 225 mm. Hg.

Excretion and Osmoregulation

The excretory system consists of two longitudinal canals embedded in the lateral ectodermal ridges and uniting at the anterior end to form a single tube leading to the excretory pore. Actually these canals are formed from a single large branched cell, their cavities being intracellular. Associated with them are four large phagocytic cells with many fine processes which have been shown to ingest carmine particles injected into the body cavity. It is not known if they have any excretory function. Recent work suggests that the canals are osmoregulatory and that nitrogenous excretion occurs via the anus.

Nervous system

The nervous system is formed of a nerve ring encircling the oesophagus and containing the cell bodies of nerve cells whose nerve fibres form six nerves running forward and six running backward. Two of the latter form the main nerve cords seen in the dorsal and ventral ectodermal ridges in the transverse section. Other nerve cells occur scattered along the nerve cords. There are no certain sense organs apart from the sensory papillae of the lips. The muscle cells are connected by cytoplasmic fibres to the nerves (see Figs. 5.2 and 5.3).

Reproduction

The reproductive system in the male is a much coiled tube which is blind at its inner end. The inner portion of the tube forms a syncytial testis producing non-flagellate, amoeboid sperm which pass down into the outer portion or vas deferens. The external opening of

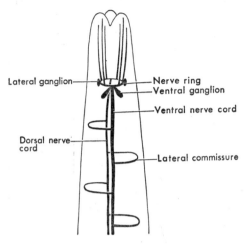

Lateral ganglion

Dorsal nerve cord

Nerve ring
Ventral ganglion

Ventral nerve cord

Lateral commissure

Fig. 5.3. *Ascaris.*
Diagram of the nervous system. (Based on various authors.)

this is in a cloaca-like depression formed by its union with the procto-daeum. In the female is a pair of coiled tubes also blind at their inner ends. These unite to form a short tube known as the vagina, which leads to the genital pore. The inner portion of each tube forms a syncytial ovary which produces oocytes. These pass into and collect in the outer portion of the tube called the uterus prior to coition. When this occurs the horny spines of the male are inserted into the genital aperture of the female to distend the vagina to enable the sluggish amoeboid sperm to be injected into it and hence into the uteri to fertilize the eggs. These are then provided with a cyst secreted by the walls of the uteri. When the eggs are laid they pass out of the host with the faeces. Within the cysts, the eggs develop into larvae, subsequently to be swallowed by a fresh host grazing on grass contaminated with them. Inside the alimentary canal of the new host the larvae are liberated from their cysts. They pass through the walls of the canal into the blood and tissues, eventually reaching the lungs. Here they are coughed up and reswallowed. By this time the larvae have reached the adult, sexually mature stage and continue the life cycle in the intestine. (See Fig. 5.4.)

A special note is needed concerning the nature of the body cavity. In *Ascaris*, though not in all nematodes, it contains large vacuolated cells. These constitute a parenchyma and the cavity is presumably

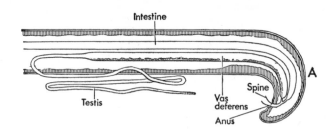

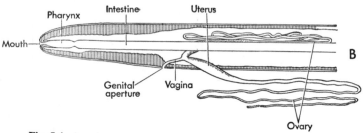

Fig. 5.4. *Ascaris.*

Reproductive systems: *A* L.S. of male *Ascaris* to show reproductive organs; *B* L.S. of female *Ascaris* to show reproductive organs.

formed by the coalescence of vacuoles of adjacent cells. The cavity is therefore not regarded as a coelom since it is not bounded by two distinct layers of mesoderm but is by reason of its origin more akin to a haemocoelic space. It is sometimes referred to as a pseudo-coele.

In free-living nematodes, e.g. *Rhabditis*, which is a common nematode in the soil, gaseous exchange for respiration occurs through the cuticle, oxygen diffusing in and carbon dioxide out, but for *Ascaris* the supply of oxygen in the intestinal fluids is limited. *Ascaris*, however, stores a considerable amount of glycogen in its cells, including the muscle cells, and the anaerobic breakdown of this to lactic acid provides the energy necessary for movement. In the absence of oxygen, more energy is liberated by the conversion of lactic acid to simple fatty acids, and hence *Ascaris* can obtain all the energy it needs without employing oxygen although it can respire aerobically if oxygen is available.

A peculiar feature of *Ascaris* and of all nematodes is that the final larval stage contains the same number of cells as the adults. Growth is produced by enlargement of the cells unaccompanied by the further cell division which is the normal mode of growth in animals. It is for this reason that many of the cells of the nematodes are so large. During the growth of the larvae the cuticle is moulted four times. In the case of parasitic nematodes, after the second moult the larvae can remain in a dormant state within the shed cuticle and dispersal often occurs at this stage. After the third moult the larvae frequently wander for a time before settling down in their final habitat (vide the migration of the larvae of *Ascaris* from the intestine to the lungs).

Parasitic nematodes

A large number of different species of *Ascaris* are found inhabiting the alimentary canals of mammals including *Ascaris lumbricoides*—a much smaller species than *Ascaris megalocephala*—which occurs in man; a similar species (*A. suis*) occurs in the pig. In addition to depriving the host of nourishment, the presence of these parasites produces nervous irritability, and young farm animals—pigs, sheep and cattle—lose condition and fail to develop satisfactorily. Farmers therefore administer certain vermifuges to their young stock to rid them of these pests. Kittens and puppies are also treated in this way. Young poultry often suffer from 'gapes' due to the presence of nematodes in the larynx. Far more serious parasites are those nematodes which actually damage the tissues of their hosts. Examples of these are given below.

Ancylostoma duodenale—the hookworm—feeds on the villi of the intestine of man, causing haemorrhage and ulceration. It occurs in warm climates and is also known as the miner's worm, since in certain mines, notably in tin mines in Cornwall in this country, the workers are liable to infection by it. The larvae gain entrance to the body by burrowing through the skin.

Wuchereria bancrofti occurs in the tropics, particularly in Africa. The larvae are transmitted by mosquitoes from one human host to another. The adults occur in the lymphatic system, causing pronounced swelling of the limbs and other parts of the body—a condition known as elephantiasis. The larvae show a peculiar adaptation in migrating to the cutaneous blood vessels during the late hours of the day when mosquitoes are liable to 'bite' and retreating next morning to the deeper tissues.

Dracunculus medinensis—the Guinea worm—is found in the Middle East in the countries bordering the Red Sea and in Ethiopia. The larvae are found in a small copepod called *Cyclops* in fresh water. If water containing these is drunk by man, the larvae enter the body and eventually the female, whose body is several feet long, is found in the subcutaneous tissues with the head of the worm often situated near the ankle. Here a blister forms which on bursting liberates the eggs produced by the worm. In this way the eggs may reach fresh water, particularly if, as in the case of the Egyptian fellaheen, the infected persons work in flooded fields. In this way the larvae are able to infect the copepods. The native remedy is to remove the worm from an infected person by slowly coiling the anterior end of the worm around a stick and by further twisting to withdraw the worm. Should the worm break, the part remaining under the skin dies and mortifies, producing septicaemia which may prove fatal.

Trichina spiralis. This occurs in the pig and other mammals. The adult stage reproduces in the intestine and the viviparously produced larvae migrate to the muscles where they encyst. Should this 'measly' pork be eaten in a semi-cooked condition by man, the life cycle is repeated. Serious inflammation, often fatal, is caused by the migrating larvae. Pork infected with the encysted bladderworms of *Taenia* is also known as 'measly'.

Eelworms attacking plants cause damage to farm and garden crops. Clover, potatoes and wheat are all liable to be damaged by them.

Tylenchus scandens—the Corn-Cockle worm—forms galls where the grains should be. The deformed foliage and crippled stems often seen in Phlox plants are due to eelworms attacking the base of the stems.

6. *Annelida*

Introduction

THE Annelids are the 'ringed' worms and are so-named because typical members, e.g. earthworms and lugworms, have elongated cylindrical bodies consisting of a linear series of segments indicated externally by constrictions of the body wall between the segments (see Fig. 6.3, the earthworm). In an ideally primitive annelid each segment would have a structure identical with that of the others so that the various organs would be repeated throughout the body, each segment possessing, for example, its own excretory and reproductive organs, blood vessels and muscles. Such a repetition of segments or *metameres* constitutes what is known as *metameric segmentation* and is laid down while the animal is still in the embryonic state so that although the animal may grow in bulk for a considerable period of its life, no new segments are formed. While metameric segmentation is clearly shown by annelids in general, it is never complete in the sense of affecting equally all the organ systems owing to the tendency displayed to confine certain organs, particularly the reproductive ones, to certain segments of the body only.

It will be obvious that metameric segmentation such as is shown by the Annelida is quite different from the strobilization of the tapeworm. In this creature the proglottids are continually being produced and hence are of different ages, sizes and degrees of sexual maturity. Although they have common nerve cords and excretory ducts, there is little integration of the parts and the ripe proglottids are shed from time to time. This is in contrast to the condition of the annelids, as will readily be seen, and it is best to distinguish the two types of organization by different words, the bodily division of the tapeworm being known as strobilization and that of the annelids as metameric segmentation.

As we have seen, both the platyhelminths and the nematodes are triploblastic animals since they have a cellular mesoderm formed during development and lying between the ectoderm covering the animal and the endoderm lining the gut. The nematodes are triploblastic and also have a body cavity but this was shown not to be

101

lined with an epithelium but merely to have been formed by the
breakdown of a cellular mass. The annelids, on the other hand, are
not only triploblastic but are also *coelomate*. The mesoderm arises
as a series of fluid-filled pouches or sacs, the outer wall of which,
lying against the ectoderm, becomes part of the body wall and is
called the *somatic layer*, while the inner layer lies against the endoderm and forms the muscular wall of the gut and is called the

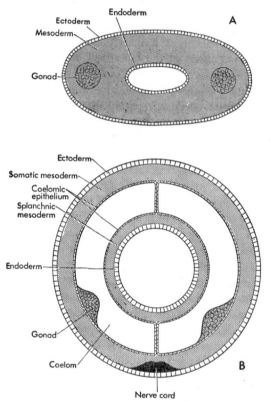

Fig. 6.1. Diagrams to illustrate the essential features of non-coelomate
(*A*) and coelomate (*B*) animals, as seen in cross-section.

splanchnic layer. The fluid-filled cavity or *coelom*, in between the
somatic and splanchnic layers of the mesoderm, is lined with coelomic
epithelium and thus separates an inner tube, the gut, from an outer
tube, the body-wall.

Both ectoderm and endoderm are one cell only in thickness but the mesoderm is many cells in thickness and is differentiated into various tissues such as muscle tissue, connective tissue and blood tissue. Between the segments there are vertical partitions, or *septa*, of connective tissue plus some muscle fibres. The coelom is thus divided up into annular spaces. The fact that the coelomic spaces are filled with liquid (the coelomic fluid) has several results. Owing to its incompressible nature the coelomic fluid acts as an endoskeleton in the

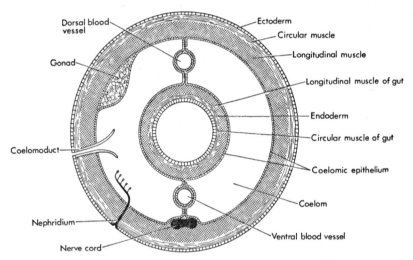

Fig. 6.2. Diagram to illustrate the essential features of an annelid worm as seen in transverse section.

transmission of the force generated by the contraction of the muscles of the body wall. Since in life the muscles maintain a slight, persistent contraction or tonus, the body of the worm is somewhat turgid (see also Movement, page 116). Secondly, the separation of the body wall from the gut wall allows gut movements to take place independently of those of the body wall and for movements of the body wall to be made with little effect on the gut. Thirdly, the coelomic fluid separating the outer body wall from the gut would provide the only means of transport between the gut and body wall were there not a blood vascular system consisting of a set of tubes or vessels in which blood circulates and transports food, oxygen, carbon dioxide and excretory products. In small, sluggish animals the coelomic fluid alone might suffice for transport but it is characteristic of the annelids to have a well-developed blood system which, since the blood is confined to definite blood vessels, is known as a *closed* one.

Substances such as food materials pass out of the blood through the walls of the finer vessels (capillaries) and so reach the cells by diffusion through the intercellular fluid which bathes them. Substances excreted by the cells diffuse in the same way into the blood and are carried away. The circulation of the blood is brought about by waves of contraction passing along the muscular walls of the larger vessels.

The nervous system consists of a solid double nerve cord lying ventral to the gut and connected to two so-called cerebral (or brain) ganglia lying above the anterior end of the gut by two cords (commissures) encircling it. Paired nerves connect the nerve cord to various parts of the body.

Leading from the coelomic spaces in the segments are pairs of tubules which serve to eliminate excretory products or to convey reproductive cells from the coelom to the exterior. There are two types of these: (1) the *nephridia* formed as ingrowths of the ectoderm and (2) *coelomoducts* which are of mesodermal origin. The nephridia in certain primitive annelids end blindly in the coelom in a tuft of cells resembling the flame cells of platyhelminths but in the majority they open into the coelom by a ciliated funnel known as the *nephrostome*. The coelomoducts do not necessarily occur in every segment of the body and in many annelids are few in number.

The epidermis secretes a thin non-living layer known as the cuticle. This presents little obstruction to the passage of gases and hence gaseous exchange can take place at the surface of the body.

All the above-mentioned features are well illustrated by the earthworm which will be described below. The earthworm, of course, possesses those features which are common to all annelid worms but it is nevertheless a creature which is specialized for life in a particular environment. It is adapted to living, feeding and mating in burrows in the soil. There are many other annelids which are less specialized than *Lumbricus* and in some ways it would be best to study those first. However, the earthworm is a familiar and easily obtained creature and its structure is easier to apprehend from dissection and the examination of sections than is that of the less specialized annelid worms such as the polychaete *Nereis*. This animal and the medicinal leech *Hirudo* will therefore be described after the earthworm.

The Earthworm
Lumbricus terrestris

General structure

The 'Common Earthworm', being one of the largest of the British species, is commonly used for study. It may reach a length of ten inches and is of nearly uniform cylindrical shape but is flattened at

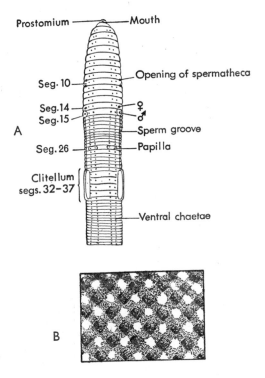

Fig. 6.3. *Lumbricus.*

A The external features of the earthworm as seen in ventral view. Only the ventral chaetae are shown.

B A view of the cuticle drawn from an electron micrograph showing the sub-microscopic fibres arranged in a diagonal pattern.

(*A*, from a specimen; *B*, from *Reed* and *Rudall*.)

the tail end and tapers in front. It is bilaterally symmetrical and is clearly marked externally into about 150 rings which correspond with the internal division into segments (see annulation of leech, page 135). Each segment except the first and last bears four pairs of

protrusible bristles or *chaetae* situated in the ventral half of the
animal which is lighter in colour than the dorsal side. The mouth
opens ventrally in the first segment or *peristomium* but a non-
segmental lobe, the *prostomium*, precedes and overhangs it. The anus
opens in the last segment, the *pygidium*. In the grooves between segments a series of sphinctered openings occurs. These are the dorsal
pores. The nephridia open by nephridiopores which lie anterior to
the ventral pair of chaetae. The female genital openings occur in
segment 14 and the male in segment 15. From both of these openings
grooves can be seen in preserved specimens running back to the
clitellum. This is a thickened region of the epidermis which obscures
the annulation dorsally between segments 32 to 37. The openings of
the spermathecae occur between segments 9 and 10, and 10 and 11.
Enlarged genital chaetae and associated glandular tissue can be seen
in mature worms in the clitellar segments and also in segments 10, 11
and 26. (See Fig. 6.3A.)

The body wall of the earthworm is composed of epidermal and
mesodermal layers. The epidermis is made up chiefly of columnar
cells interspersed with mucus-secreting and albumin-secreting gland
cells and with sensory or receptor cells. It is covered with a cuticle
secreted by the epidermis and composed of extremely fine collagen-
type fibres arranged in a spiral pattern in which the helices are both
left and right handed so that a lattice pattern is formed (Fig. 6.3B.)
Below the epidermis there is a plexus of fine nerve fibres which are
the ultimate branches of deeper lying nerve cells.

Feeding and Digestion

The gut of the earthworm is a straight tube running from mouth to
anus distinguishable into different regions both structurally and
functionally. The buccal cavity into which the mouth opens is thin
walled and is succeeded by the pharynx. This has a muscular wall and is
connected to the body wall by strands of muscle running across the
coelom. These strands on contraction serve to enlarge the bore of
the pharynx and to enable it to suck food material or soil into the
alimentary canal. The food of the animal consists chiefly of vegetation
and is collected from the ground adjacent to its burrow. Leaves are
collected and are taken into the burrow narrow end first. They are
gripped between the prostomium and the peristomium or, alternatively, the pharynx is pushed forwards inside the body, the mouth
placed over the leaf and the pharynx retracted, thereby causing the
leaf to adhere by suction. The pharynx is followed by the narrow

oesophagus which dilates at its hinder end to form the crop. The oesophagus bears a pair of oesophageal pouches in segment 10 and two pairs of calciferous glands in segments 11 and 12. The glands secrete calcium carbonate and probably serve to rid the body of the excess of this material which has been absorbed from the food and soil. Why, if this is so, they should be situated at the anterior end of the body so that their secretion has to pass along the length of the

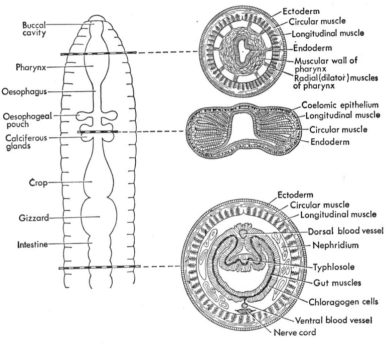

Fig. 6.4. *Lumbricus.*
Diagrams illustrating the regions of the gut and their main features as seen in transverse section. (Based on specimens.)

alimentary canal and presumably run the risk of reabsorption is a mystery.

The crop can store a little ingested material while the gizzard which follows grinds it up before passing it on to the intestine. The gizzard has a thick muscular wall and a hard cuticular lining. The intestine stretches from segment 20 to the hind end of the body. It has a relatively thin wall and is lined with columnar epithelium which secretes digestive enzymes and is also absorptive. The area of epithelium is increased by the infolding of the dorsal wall of the intestine to form the *typhlosole*. The lining or *peritoneum* covering the coelomic side of the intestine gives rise to a layer of loose yellow cells, the *chloragogen*, the function of which is uncertain. Food is forced backwards along the gut by waves of contraction of the gut wall muscles (peristalsis). Soil and undigested food residues are egested via the anus.

The Blood Vascular System and Respiration

The blood vascular system of the earthworm is well developed and contains blood in which the haemoglobin is present in the plasma and not contained in the corpuscles. The haemoglobin molecules are, however, about 40 times larger than those of the mammals owing to the pigment group being linked with a larger protein molecule. Its haemoglobin confers on the blood of the earthworm a high oxygen capacity which is probably of the order of 6 vol. per 100 vol. of blood instead of that of water which is less than 0·5 vol. per 100 vol. of water. (See p. 518.)

Two main vessels run along the body, one above the gut and one below; a third vessel, the subneural, runs beneath the ventral nerve cord. The blood is moved forwards in the dorsal vessel by contractions of its walls starting at its hinder end. Along most of its length it receives in each segment two pairs of efferent vessels from the intestine and a pair of efferent vessels running from the subneural vessel. Most of the blood which passes forwards is pumped into the ventral vessel by the hearts, a pair of which occurs in each of segments 7 to 11. The hearts contain valvular flaps on their inner walls which ensure that the blood passes onwards when the vessels contract. A small forward continuation of the dorsal vessel supplies the pharynx. The ventral vessel is the main channel of distribution of the blood to the body. In each segment a vessel passes to the gut and paired vessels pass to the nephridia and body wall. Blood returns by vessels connecting with the dorso-subneural vessel. Stereograms illustrating the layout of the main vessels and the direction of blood flow are given in Fig. 6.5.

In the body-wall and organs of the body the blood vessels divide up into very small vessels known as *capillaries*. The capillary loops which occur in the body wall are noteworthy, for these lie close to the surface of the body and penetrate between the cells of the epidermis so that they are in a very favourable position for the occurrence of gaseous interchange between the blood and the air. Although the earthworm has a blood vascular system filled with blood containing haemoglo-

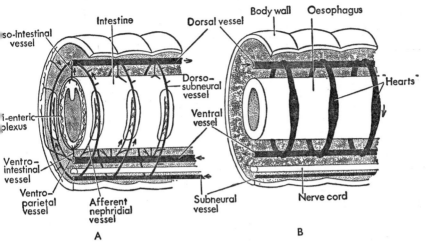

Fig. 6.5. *Lumbricus.*
Stereograms of the arrangement of the principal blood vessels. Arrows indicate the direction of blood flow. *A* Region of intestine; *B* Region of oesophagus. Anterior to the right.

bin, it is not entirely dependent upon the respiratory pigment for the carriage of oxygen because even if the haemoglobin is eliminated by saturation with carbon monoxide, respiration can still continue.

Excretion and Osmoregulation

It has been seen that the excretory system of the acoelomate platyhelminths consists of ducts which end internally in flame cells. In some annelid worms the excretory system consists of similar ectodermal ducts or nephridia opening into the coelom instead of being embedded in parenchyma. In addition, the nephridia become differentiated along their length into recognizable regions and acquire a good blood supply. In *Lumbricus*, a pair of nephridia occurs in each segment except the first three and the last one, and each nephridium opens by a nephrostome into the coelom in one segment, the nephrostome being situated on the septum near the mid-line. It leads to a narrow intracellular tube which passes through the septum into the segment behind. Here follows the middle tube, wide tube and muscular tube before the organ opens to the outside by a sphinctered nephridiopore placed anteriorly to the lower chaetae, the sphincter being a ring of muscle, the contraction of which can close the nephridiopore. (See Fig. 6.6.)

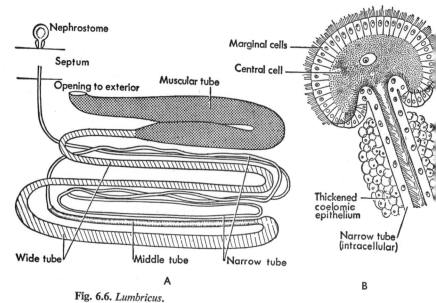

A

B

Fig. 6.6. *Lumbricus.*

A Diagram of the nephridium of an earthworm. *B* The nephrostome enlarged.

The nephrostome is covered with cilia and parts of the intracellular narrow tube are ciliated too but the rest of the tube is not. The beating of the cilia seen under the microscope when the nephridium is removed from the earthworm and mounted in normal salt solution gives the impression that coelomic fluid must be continuously passing down the tube but it must be remembered that a sphincter is present to close the nephridiopore. Nevertheless, the fluid which accumulates in the wide muscular tube or bladder can be collected at the rate of about 0·5 cu. mm. per nephridiopore per hour or say 0·15 ml. per worm per hour. Although this fluid has been shown to contain ammonia, urea and creatinine, these substances are present in little greater concentration in the urine than they are in the coelomic fluid. On the other hand, the concentration of various salts and protein is much less in the urine than it is in the body fluids. It seems likely that the fluid excreted by the nephridiopores may be coelomic fluid from which certain salts and protein have been largely removed during its passage down the nephridial tube. On the other hand, protein is nowhere known to be easily absorbed across a cellular membrane. Also nephridia which do not open into the coelom are present in some worms which yet produce copious urine. An alternative explanation of urine formation in earthworms is that the blood plasma minus its protein is filtered off from the blood flowing in the capillaries covering the tubular portion of the nephridium, in a way similar to that by which the formation of urine is begun in the vertebrate kidney, but it would seem that the blood pressure of the worm, equal to some 7 cm. of water, is hardly sufficient to cause very rapid ultrafiltration against the colloid osmotic pressure of the blood. The colloid osmotic pressure of mammalian blood is of the order of 40 cm. of water but there is little doubt that that of the earthworm is considerably less and it may be that the hydrostatic pressure of the blood exceeds that of the colloid osmotic pressure so that ultrafiltration can occur.

At present there seem to be no clear-cut experiments which make it possible to decide which of these two views is correct or if the explanation lies in a combination of them, but there is no doubt that the process of urine formation results in the production of a hypotonic fluid and that, along the length of the nephridium, it is in the wide tube that the osmotic concentration falls below that of the coelomic fluid.

The function of the chloragogen was at one time thought to be excretory. There is little doubt that the cells of this fluffy yellow tissue, proliferated from the peritoneum, drop off into the coelom, but it is not clear that the yellow granules which they contain are of an excretory nature, nor is it clear how they are eliminated. It seems most likely that they are taken up by amoebocytes in the coelomic fluid and are stored at the posterior end of the worm as 'brown bodies' lying in the coelom.

Nervous system and Sense organs (Fig. 6.7)

The cerebral ganglia lie above the pharynx in segment 3 and are joined by the circumpharyngeal connectives to the subpharyngeal ganglia which lie in segment 4. From there the ventral nerve cord extends backwards along the entire length of the body and is regarded as a double structure, the two halves of which are fused together, and swell somewhat in each segment. The bodies of the nerve cells are not confined to the swellings, but are found distributed along the whole length of the cord and also occur outside it, both along the course of the segmental nerves and in the enteric and epithelial plexuses.

The cord lies freely in the coelom and is covered with a layer of peritoneum below which lies a layer of longitudinal muscle fibres and inside this the epineurium of fibrous connective tissue. Except in the first three segments, the cord is connected with the rest of the body in every segment by three pairs of nerves. Each pair of these segmental nerves runs into the body wall and continues along a circular course between the longitudinal and circular muscles, giving off branches to the muscles and to the epidermis. The first pair of nerves of each segment is given off just posterior to each septum from the narrower region of the nerve cord. The other two pairs arise more posteriorly from the enlarged ganglionic region. A small branch supplying the septum arises from the posterior segmental nerve of each segment.

The prostomium receives its innervation from the cerebral ganglia, segments 1 and 2 chiefly from the nerves arising from the circumpharyngeal commissures and segment 3 from three pairs of nerves arising from the subpharyngeal ganglia in segment 4. Since these ganglia also have the set of nerves appropriate to segment 4, they are regarded as consisting of two sets of fused ganglia.

The branches from the segmental nerve rings which run towards the epidermis join a fine sub-epidermal plexus, fibres from which end between the cells of the epidermis. Other branches from the nerve rings run to the longitudinal muscles. Branches from the segmental nerves also supply the circular muscles.

A sub-epithelial plexus also occurs in the wall of the gut and is connected to the central nervous system by small nerve fibres which join the circumpharyngeal connectives.

The nerve cells (*neurons*) of the central nervous system are situated chiefly in the ventral part of the cord. Above them are chiefly nerve fibres, together with supporting cells and fibres (the so-called *neuroglia*). Towards the dorsal side lie three prominent giant fibres of which the central one is the largest. These run from the subpharyngeal ganglia and are joined by processes from unipolar nerve cells lying in the ventral region of the nerve cord. The lateral giant fibres also have small cross connexions with the central one. The lateral fibres each give off branches to the body which leave the cord in the middle of the three nerves of each segment. Each giant fibre appears to be a composite structure made up of a closed compartment to each segment separated from its fellows by slanting partitions which presumably have the properties of a synapse. Since the rate of transmission of an impulse along a nerve fibre depends on, among other factors, the diameter of the fibres, the chief feature of

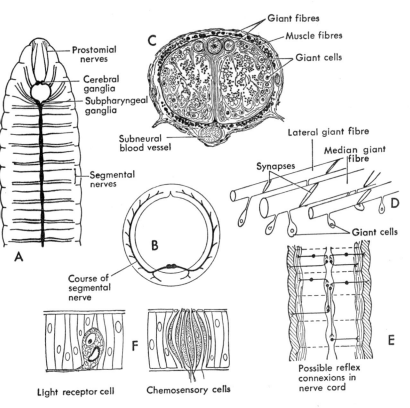

Fig. 6.7. *Lumbricus.*

Diagrams illustrating the structure of the nervous system:

A The arrangement of the ganglia and segmental nerves.

B The course of a segmental nerve around the body.

C A transverse section of the nerve cord showing the giant fibres and cells.

D The arrangement of cells and synapses in the giant fibres.

E Diagram showing some of the possible arrangements of nerve cells in the nervous system making up reflex arcs which could be used in the alternate contractions of the circular and longitudinal muscles.

F Diagram of the photoreceptor cells and epidermal sense organs. (Based on various authors and on specimens.)

the giant fibres which is of physiological importance is the rapidity of their conduction compared with that of other elements of the nervous system.

The only recognized receptor cells of earthworms are the *light receptors* and the *epidermal sense organs*. Both of these can be recognized microscopically but it is not clear how, or to what stimuli, the epidermal sense organs respond. In addition, there are free nerve endings among the epidermal cells. Each photoreceptor cell is made of cytoplasm containing a nucleus and an optic organelle which is more highly refractive than the rest of the cell and which may vary in shape from one cell to another, frequently being globular or in the shape of a short straight or bent rod. The photoreceptor cells are about half as tall as the epidermal cells and are situated on the basement membrane just above the nerve plexus. Nerve fibrillae from the plexus enter the photoreceptor cell and are believed to be continuous with a system of fine fibrillae in the cells which, in particular, surround the optic organelle. The photoreceptors are most numerous in the prostomium and first segment, and also in the last segment.

Each epidermal sense organ consists of an aggregation of receptor cells which are slightly taller than the epidermal cells and which are prolonged into hair-like processes passing through minute pores in the cuticle. The receptor cells are interspersed with some non-nervous cells which are termed supporting cells. Each receptor cell has a nerve fibre passing from its base into an epidermal branch of a segmental nerve. Like the photoreceptors, these sense organs are most numerous at the anterior end of the earthworm. Whether they respond to more than one type of stimulus is not certain but they show some structural similarity to the organs of chemical sense in vertebrates and also, it must be admitted, to neuromast organs which are known to respond to mechanical disturbances (see page 296). No definite evidence is available to indicate their function with certainty but it is likely that they, together with the free nerve endings in the epidermis, serve to apprise the animal of both tactile and chemical stimuli, since earthworms show a distinct preference for some substances as food and can, for example, distinguish between onion leaves, which are preferred, and those of other plants. Earthworms are also known to respond to vibrations of the ground.

Receptors which are sensitive to the degree of extension of the structures in which they occur or to their mechanical deformation in other directions are known as *proprioceptors* (see also page 585). None has been identified histologically in the earthworm but nerve impulses passing along the nerves have been recorded electrically when the animal was stretched and are therefore believed to have originated from internal stimuli. It is concluded that nerve endings somewhere in the body are proprioceptive. The impulses which they initiate are of importance in locomotion and are believed to act together with the stimuli which the worm receives from outside in the regulation of locomotory movements. Further understanding of the nervous control of muscular actions is also made possible by a description of the way in which neurons are connected with each other in the central nervous system.

The cell bodies of *sensory* neurons are found in the side of the nerve cord which their fibres enter but, by contrast, fibres from *motor* neurons run to both sides of the body whether they are situated in the right or the left halves of the nerve cord. Intermediate neurons link sensory cells with motor cells supplying both sides of the body, and also link sensory cells with motor cells of successive segments. Pathways are thus available for incoming impulses to be connected to a number of motor tracts. A particular pathway of this type constitutes a *reflex arc* which, in its simplest form, consists of an *afferent* or sensory neuron, an intermediate or *internuncial* neuron, and an *efferent* or motor neuron.

Although it is difficult to demonstrate an arrangement like this in a simple transverse section, there is little doubt that it represents the basic arrangement of neurons and will go a long way towards accounting for the muscular movements which are made during locomotion.

The propagation of waves of muscular contraction down the body depends partly on reflexes which are believed to act in the following way. The stretching of the longitudinal muscles of one segment by the contraction of those anterior to it stimulates the proprioceptors of the segment. When proprioceptor impulses are received in the central nervous system the reflex arc is completed by the passage of impulses from the motor nerves to the muscles, which contract in response to these impulses. The wave of contraction of longitudinal muscles is thus passed down the body by a series of reflex actions. This can be demonstrated by cutting a worm in half and tying the two halves together with cotton. Such a preparation can still crawl and the wave of contraction of the longitudinal muscles can still pass the gap in the continuity of the worm's tissues without there being any nervous connexion between the two parts. This is believed to be due to the initiation of a stretch reflex in the posterior half when the longitudinal muscles of the anterior half pull upon it.

But this use of a chain of reflexes in the propagation of the muscular wave is not the complete story, as can be seen from another experiment. If a worm be almost cut in half and only the nerve cord left intact, no stretch reflexes can pass the point of injury because the nerve cord is too weak to transmit them. Nevertheless the backwards passage of a peristaltic wave is unimpeded, which shows that a means of exciting the muscles, in addition to the stretch reflex, must exist since this cannot pass the cut body-wall. The experiment implies that nerve impulses entering the cord anterior to the cut can, in their turn, serve to excite motor neurons several segments posterior and that these in turn may initiate normal waves of muscular contraction. The motor neurons behind the point of injury are thus brought into play by excitation which can pass for some distance down the cord without the intervention of segmental reflexes.

Movement

It might, perhaps, have been better before discussing the way in which the movements of locomotion are co-ordinated to describe the muscles and the movements themselves, but that would have meant breaking into the section on the nervous system. Everyone knows that an earthworm crawls, but in this section we must see exactly how the process takes place and what is the arrangement of muscles and bristles that provide the mechanism.

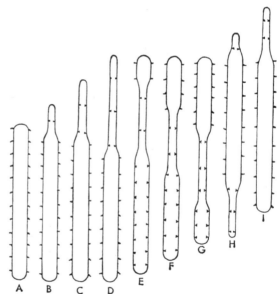

Fig. 6.8. *Lumbricus.*

Diagram to illustrate the contractions of the longitudinal and circular muscles of the earthworm and the co-ordinated movements of the chaetae made during crawling (see text).

The musculature of the body wall consists of an outer layer of circularly arranged fibres and an inner one of longitudinal fibres. As seen in transverse section, the latter are arranged in nine blocks, each block being made up of a surrounding sheath of connective tissue and crossed radially by partitions of connective tissue to which the muscle fibres are attached. This arrangement presents a characteristically feathery appearance in section and provides space into which the fibres can expand when they thicken on contraction. The muscle fibres are non-striated and average over 4 mm. in length. Since each contains only one nucleus, not many nuclei are seen in any one transverse section. The innermost layer of the body-wall is the layer of peritoneum bounding the coelom.

Each chaeta is housed in a pit lined by intucked epidermis, at the base of which lies the large formative cell responsible for its secretion. Protractor muscles originating below the epidermis and inserted into the chaetigerous sac can, by contraction, cause the chaeta to project while retractor muscles running between the two pairs of chaetae on each side cause their withdrawal.

Almost all the parts of the body-wall play a part in the animal's movement. An earthworm can crawl over the surface of the ground and even over smooth surfaces and up window panes, but little of its time is normally passed that way. Most of its locomotion takes place in its burrow, the construction of which is an important aspect of its life. However, the basis of all the movements which it makes is the action of the longitudinal and circular muscles which work in opposition or antagonism to one another. Contraction of the longitudinal muscles shortens the animal and, at the same time, because the coelomic fluid is incompressible, thickens it and therefore stretches the relaxed circular muscles. Contraction of the circulars again exerts a pressure on the coelomic fluid which results in the stretching of the longitudinal muscles and elongation of the worm. In life, control over the actions of the muscles is exercised by the nervous system which co-ordinates the actions of the circular and longitudinal muscles with the actions of those which move the chaetae.

The type of locomotion which it is easiest to observe is that of crawling over the ground. This takes place by the contraction of circular muscles at the anterior end, with the withdrawal of chaetae in that region to produce the forward extension of the anterior part of the body. This phase is followed by the protrusion of the anterior chaetae and the contraction of the longitudinal muscles so pulling up the hinder parts. The passage backwards down the body of alternate waves of contraction of circular and longitudinal muscles results in the forward movement of the animal (Fig. 6.8).

More than one region of the body may be in longitudinal contraction at the same time, since a peristaltic wave may be initiated at the front end before the previous one has reached the rear. The propagation of the waves of muscular contraction down the body depends on the nervous co-ordination that has been described above.

Burrowing into the soil is accomplished by the insertion of the anterior end into a crack between soil particles, with the contraction of the longitudinal muscles to bring about a widening of the crevice. This is followed by further extension and a repetition of the process. In this way a burrow with firm walls of packed earth bound together with mucus secreted by the epidermal cells is formed. If the soil is very hard and compact, the worm can actually eat its way through for a short distance at least, at any rate sufficient to insert its anterior end so that it can get sufficient grip to advance by the usual method.

Nothing much seems to be known about the locomotion of the worm in its burrow but there can be little doubt that it progresses by a type of peristalsis, gripping the sides of the burrows by its chaetae, as can be seen from the marks which they leave.

In distinction to the slow backwards progression of waves of contraction, another type of movement can be performed. In this the longitudinal muscles shorten quickly all together, usually in response to a noxious stimulus. This response is brought about by three large nerve fibres, the 'giant fibres', which run the length of the nerve cord and which connect in every segment with motor nerve cells supplying the muscles. Thus the longitudinal muscles can be brought into action practically simultaneously and in about one-sixtieth of the time taken by the usual series of reflexes to spread along the nerve cord. Since the centre giant fibre conducts impulses from head to tail and the two lateral fibres conduct from tail to head, a stimulus at either end of the worm can be effective in eliciting this movement of rapid withdrawal. The action can be seen very clearly when a worm is suddenly illuminated at night, as it is foraging with its anterior end while its posterior end remains in its burrow. It disappears in one movement with great rapidity.

The mucus secreted by the epidermal cells minimizes the friction between the earthworm and the ground when the posterior part of the body is being drawn up but would diminish the hold obtained by the anterior region were it not for the action of the chaetae. It may be surmised that the cuticle protects the epidermal cells from friction and adds somewhat to the strength provided by the connective tissues of the body wall.

Reproduction

The reproduction of the earthworm involves the copulation of two hermaphrodite individuals for exchange of sperm and the subsequent laying by both of fertilized eggs enclosed in a cocoon. Both the testes and the ovaries shed the cells which develop into gametes into the coelom, whence they travel by coelomoducts to the exterior. These ducts are not serially repeated along the body like so many of the organs of the earthworm but are confined to a short region at the anterior end. Moreover, although the developing ova are shed into the coelomic cavity of segment 13, the spermatogonia which drop off the testes are contained in a special enclosed portion of the coelom (forming the *testis sacs* and the *seminal vesicles*). These contain a fluid differing in composition from the general coelomic fluid by the addition of nutrients for the developing sperm. The way in which the gonads and their ducts are arranged is shown in Fig. 6.9. There is a pair of testes present in segment 10 and another in segment 11. They are small branched bodies and are difficult to find by dissecting mature worms since they have shed into the testis sacs most of the cells of which they were originally made. These sacs are the enclosed ventral portions of the coelom of segments 10 and 11 and are enlarged by possessing three pairs of outgrowths, or diverticula, the anterior and median and the posterior seminal vesicles. Two pairs of ciliated rosette-like funnels open into the testis sacs and are connected by *vasa efferentia* to the *vasa deferentia* along which the seminal fluid travels to the exterior. Each of these male ducts opens separately on a small papilla on segment 15.

The ovaries are flattened pear-shaped bodies situated ventrally and attached, one on each side, to the anterior wall of segment 13. Each consists of a connective tissue and peritoneal covering surrounding the developing eggs, those near the tapering, free end being the most mature. They pass to the outside by way of an oviducal funnel on the posterior wall of segment 13. This funnel is continuous with a short oviduct which opens to the exterior on segment 14. A small *ovisac* forms a shallow diverticulum in the duct at its junction with the oviducal funnel and in this the eggs collect until required for passing into the cocoon.

In addition to the gonads and their ducts, there are a number of

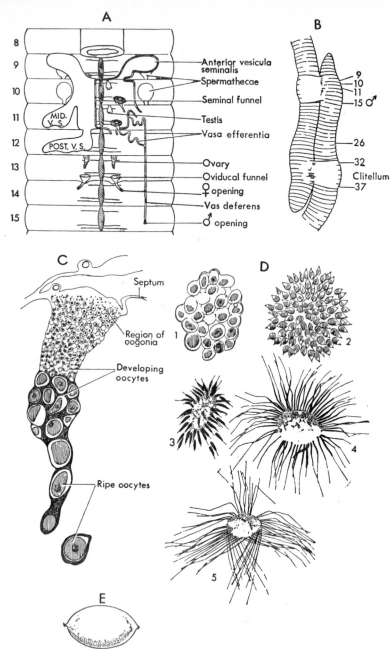

Fig. 6.9. *Lumbricus.*

The reproductive system: *A* Arrangement of the organs; *B* Anterior ends of two worms during copulation; *C* Section of an ovary; *D* Stages in the formation of sperm as seen in a stained smear of the contents of the vesiculae seminalis; *E* A cocoon. (*C* and *D* from specimens.)

accessory structures connected with reproduction. The *spermathecae* are two pairs of muscular sacs situated in segments 9 and 10, and opening ventrally in the grooves between segments 9 and 10 and 10 and 11. They receive and store the seminal fluid from the other member of a copulating pair of worms. The clitellum is a thickened region of the epidermis of segments 32-37 which obscures the external segmentation of the worm and which has three types of glandular cells, secreting respectively mucus, the egg cocoon and a nutritious protein-containing fluid. The chaetae of segments 10, 11 and 26 as well as those of the clitellar region are longer and more slender than the others and there are glands in the chaetal sacs which secrete an adhesive material. The *arciform* muscles of either side are a series of strands of muscle which lie within the thickness of the body wall and do not cross the coelom. Each is inserted at the base of the epidermis below the seminal groove and at another point ventral to it. Their contraction on each segment causes two tiny depressions to appear where they are inserted into the epidermis. The dorsal series of these depressions constitutes the seminal grooves seen in hardened specimens.

The formation of the ripe spermatozoids of the earthworm takes place in the nutrient fluid of the testis sacs and the seminal vesicles from the special cells or spermatogonia which are shed from the testis. These divide to form clumps or *morulae* of numerous cells. During the production of sperm a process of maturation occurs which is essentially the same as that accompanying the general formation of male germ cells and which is described on page 611. The fully formed spermatozoids are long, flagellated cells composed, apart from the tail, mainly of nuclear material.

The oocytes are shed from the tip of the ovary and begin their maturation divisions during their passage to the exterior.

Reproduction begins by the exchange of seminal fluid during the copulation of two animals which emerge from adjacent burrows on to the surface of the ground. It occurs only on fairly warm, still nights when the humidity is high. It takes three or four hours to complete and results in the spermathecae of each worm being filled with the seminal fluid from the other. The worms lie head to tail with segments 9 and 10 opposite the clitellum of the partner. Each one secretes a continuous envelope of mucus around itself from about segment 8 to segment 31, but the two worms are attached to each other by the secretions of the clitellum and by the insertion of the long genital chaetae (see above) into the body wall of each other. The secretion of the glands of these chaetal sacs forms an additional attachment which helps to keep the animal in place. When attachment is complete, sperm passes from the *vesiculae seminales* down the vasa deferentia and along the sperm grooves of each partner. It flows between the mucus tube and the body wall and is caused to pass backwards by the contraction of the arciform muscles of each segment in turn from anterior to posterior. This series of muscular contractions results in the accumulation of seminal fluid between the bodies of the two earthworms in the clitellar region where they are not enclosed in separate mucus tubes. The seminal fluid passes into the spermathecae of the partner, possibly by being pumped in by muscular ripples passing from the dorsal to the ventral side of the clitellar region.

When the exchange of sperm is completed, or before if the worms are disturbed, the partners separate and withdraw into their burrows. The formation of cocoons containing fertilized eggs begins after an interval of about a day and may go on for several months without further copulation since enough seminal fluid can be stored in the spermathecae to fertilize the eggs laid in many cocoons.

The cocoons are secreted by cells of the clitellum and it is thought that the eggs may be passed backwards from the female openings along egg grooves, formed at the point of insertion of the ventral ends of the arciform muscles, under cover of a mucus tube like the one formed during copulation. Each cocoon is passed forwards from the clitellum by a wave of contraction of the longitudinal muscles of the body-wall, which increases the diameter of the worm behind the cocoon and pushes it forwards. Seminal fluid enters the cocoon as it passes the openings of the spermathecae and the eggs are fertilized by the spermatozoids which it contains. After the head of the worm has been withdrawn from the elastic cocoon, its ends close up. Several eggs are laid in one cocoon but, after a period of development which lasts about 12 weeks, only one young worm (or occasionally two) hatches from the cocoon. Cocoons are produced at a variable rate throughout the year, depending upon the soil temperature and the food supply, the rate being greatest in the late summer months.

Natural history of earthworms

Although *Lumbricus terrestris* is the earthworm usually studied, there are about two dozen different species found in the British Isles. *L. terrestris* is by no means the commonest, but it is one of the largest. It is easily collected at night when, in damp weather, it is foraging or pairing. If approached quietly with a dim light and grasped firmly before it has time to retreat into its burrow, it can be withdrawn by a steady, gentle pull. Other common species include *Allolobophora longa*, an earthworm about the size of *L. terrestris* but of a browner colour, *A. chlorotica*, a small greenish form which coils up on being disturbed. *A. caliginosa*, a small light-coloured worm which can tolerate a wide variety of soil conditions, *Eisenia foetida*, the Brandling worm which is found in manure and compost heaps and frequently in rural drains; it can be easily recognized by its transverse stripes of red and cream and was esteemed by Izaak Walton and other anglers as the best worm for bait.

All the earthworms burrow in the soil in much the same way, but if the soil is too compact for the anterior end to be inserted between the soil particles, the animals may literally eat their way through. The normal method of feeding of *L. terrestris* does not, however, consist of taking in soil and extracting the small amount of nutrient material which it contains but of selecting leaves on the surface within reach and drawing them into its burrow. There they may be moistened with a secretion containing digestive enzymes and subsequently, as it were, nibbled away. Since earthworms generally forage only over the ground which they can reach while still keeping the tail within the burrow, scarcity of food necessitates the making of more burrows in order that the feeding areas may be increased.

Soil is always found filling the gut of earthworms, and considerable quantities are eaten in the course of burrowing and feeding, as can be seen by the inspection of worm casts which are deposited on the surface of the ground by some species, chiefly *Allolobophora longa*. On the other hand, *Lumbricus terrestris*, like the majority of earthworms, casts its faeces within the soil so that its occurrence is not revealed by the presence of worm casts on the surface. Those species which cast on the surface are particularly effective in bringing deeper soil to the top, and they thus play an important role in natural soil formation. In addition, all species are continually moving the soil and, by making burrows in it, serve to aerate and drain it.

Earthworms are found in all types of soil except the most acid ones, but they occur in smaller numbers in heavy clay than in lighter soils. There may be as many as one to three million per acre and they may have a total weight of up to 15 cwt. per acre in forest soils which are rich in humus. The conditions which favour their survival are the presence of plentiful vegetable matter for food, moist but not waterlogged soil, and a moderate temperature. Nevertheless, they can tolerate a wide variety of conditions and can remain totally immersed in aerated water for months without suffering adverse effects. They can withstand considerable loss of water but in nature, when the topsoil dries out, they descend to greater depths and may pass into a state of inactivity in a mucus-lined chamber. Like most invertebrates they can survive for many weeks without food. *Lumbricus terrestris* has been kept in captivity for six years but it is probable that in nature its normal life span is much shorter.

Classification of Annelida

The main features of the phylum Annelida were briefly described earlier in the chapter. A more detailed account of one member, the common earthworm, followed. But the phylum includes many different sorts of 'ringed' worms in addition to the earthworms, and is classified as follows:

Class CHAETOPODA Annelids with chaetae

  Order *Polychaeta*. Marine annelids with numerous chaetae arising from lateral projection of the body called *parapodia*. Usually with head appendages. Sexes separate.
e.g. *Nereis* (ragworms),
Arenicola (lugworms).

  Order *Oligochaeta*. Freshwater or terrestrial annelids with few chaetae and those not on parapodia. Hermaphrodite.
e.g. *Lumbricus* (earthworms), *Tubifex*.

Class HIRUDINEA Annelids with a relatively small fixed number of segments, with anterior and posterior suckers and without chaetae. Hermaphrodite.
e.g. *Hirudo* (leeches).

Nereis

General structure

By reason of their living in a marine habitat and by virtue of the simplicity and serial repetition of their gonads and ducts and their unisexual nature, the Polychaeta are usually considered to be the most primitive living annelids. *Nereis diversicolor*, whose external appearance is shown in Figs. 6.10 and 6.15A, is an example of a bristle worm which shows well the characters of the polychaetous annelids. It is common in mud and muddy sand, especially of estuaries where it

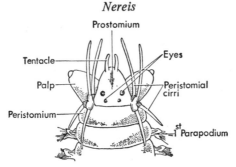

Fig. 6.10. *Nereis.*
The head region in dorsal view. (From a specimen.)

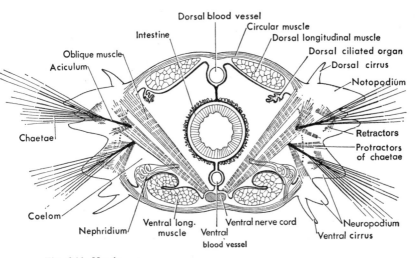

Fig. 6.11. *Nereis.*
Diagram of a transverse section to show the main structural features.
(Based on a specimen.)

lives in a burrow or under stones. It will be seen from Fig. 6.11 that
one of its salient features is the possession of four tufts of large
chaetae on each segment. These are inserted into flat projections
from the side of the body known as *parapodia*, each of which is
divided into an upper chaetigerous region, the *notopodium*, and a
lower chaetigerous region, the *neuropodium*. The dorsal and ventral
cirri are the names given to two additional outgrowths of the parapodium. The two groups of chaetae are inserted deeply into the parapodium and disposed round upper and lower skeletal rods, the

acicula. Muscles are attached to these structures which can retract and push out the two groups of chaetae.

The head region is much more complex than that of the earthworm, chiefly by virtue of the sensory organs that it carries. These include a dorsal pair of fine tentacles and a ventral pair of stout conical palps borne on the prostomium and four pairs of long mobile cirri borne on the peristomium. The prostomium also bears four eyes which, although they may be termed simple eyes since they are composed of light receptor cells arranged round a simple vesicular lens, are nevertheless much larger and more complex than those of the earthworm.

The body-wall of *Nereis* resembles that of the earthworm in having an outer cuticle with its underlying epidermis and in having the basic circular and longitudinal muscle layers. These are disposed somewhat differently, however, for the large parapodia interrupt the continuity of the circular muscles over part of the length of each segment so that in sections a complete ring of circular muscle is not readily seen. The longitudinal muscles are split up into four blocks, two dorsal and two ventral. In addition to these, strands of muscle run obliquely across the coelom, the two main ones originating in the region of the nerve cord and being inserted near the junction of the parapodia with the rest of the body-wall.

Gut and Feeding

Like that of *Lumbricus*, the gut runs straight from the mouth to the anus but is more complex at the anterior end than that of the earthworm. The mouth, situated on the peristomal segment, opens into a buccal cavity which is thin-walled and is succeeded by a muscular pharynx bearing a pair of cuticular thickenings acting as jaws. The buccal cavity and pharynx can be turned inside out by the pressure generated in the coelomic fluid by the contraction of the general body-wall muscles so that the anterior end of the pharynx and its jaws are exposed and ready to grasp food (Fig. 6.12). Other smaller cuticular teeth adorn the epidermis which lines the inside of the buccal cavity and pharynx and are also exposed when the 'proboscis' or bucco-pharynx is extruded by eversion. From the pharynx a narrow oesophagus leads to a muscular gizzard. A pair of glandular caeca arise at the junction of these regions of the gut. The gizzard is followed by a straight intestine constricted at the position of the septa so that it looks like a string of beads when seen in dissection.

Nereis diversicolor lives in a burrow through which it can maintain a

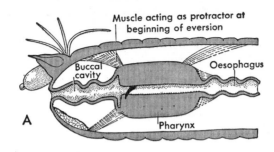

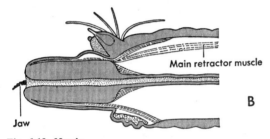

Fig. 6.12. *Nereis.*
    Diagrams to illustrate the eversion of the proboscis as seen in
sagittal section. *A* Retracted; *B* Extruded. (Based on specimens.)

current of water (see below). It has been shown to make a conical net
of mucus strands in the mouth of the burrow in which small organisms and particles become entangled. After a time it eats the net and
food which it has caught. Other species are not known to do this,
and probably feed by active foraging for living and dead animal
and plant matter which they take in by the action of their eversible
proboscis and jaws.

Blood vascular system and Respiration (Fig. 6.13)

The vascular system follows the same general plan as that of *Lumbricus*. There is a ventral vessel which communicates with the dorsal
vessel by two pairs of vessels in each segment. These run via the
parapodia where they break up into capillaries and rejoin before
reaching the dorsal vessel. Since the capillaries include many which
lie near the surface of the body, there is little doubt that gaseous
exchange takes place chiefly through the surface of the parapodia.
The blood, which contains haemoglobin in the plasma, is circulated
by peristaltic contractions of the muscular walls of the main vessels.

Branches from the segmental vessels supply the gut with blood which passes on into the dorsal vessel. A current of water can be maintained through the burrow by gentle undulations which pass down the body. This current serves chiefly to supply the animal with oxygenated water.

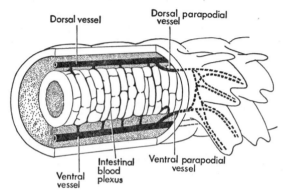

Fig. 6.13. *Nereis.*
Stereogram of the main blood vessels. (Based on *Nicol.*)

The excretory system

It is often stated that the possession of a pair of nephridia in each segment (except a few of the most anterior and posterior ones) provides the means for carrying out the function of excretion. The experimental evidence for this in *Nereis* is much less conclusive than it is for excretion by the nephridia of *Lumbricus*. Nevertheless, the structure of the organs is similar, the nephrostome providing a ciliated internal funnel, opening from the coelom into a long, twisted partly ciliated duct which opens to the exterior by a nephridiopore.

No separate functional coelomoduct is found in *Nereis*, although such occur in other polychaetes, e.g. the Capitellidae. The dorsal ciliated organs—small projections of the peritoneum lying lateral to the dorsal longitudinal muscle blocks—are regarded as being homologous with coelomoducts, but they lack openings to the exterior.

Osmoregulation

Nereis diversicolor, which is one of the commonest British species of the genus, is found chiefly in somewhat estuarine conditions and it can withstand considerable diminution in the salinity of the water in which it lives. In fact, it seems to prefer conditions where this is found. If placed experimentally in dilute sea water it can be shown that at first the animal swells owing to the uptake of water but that, after a time, salt leaks out and the internal fluids of the creature become once more nearly isotonic with the water in which it is living but yet remain of slightly higher osmotic concentration. Its ability to keep its internal concentration of salts a little above that of the environment is lost in the absence of calcium ions from the water, and if normal respiratory activity is poisoned by cyanide.

Nervous system

The nervous system of *Nereis* resembles that of the earthworm in consisting of a ventral chain of ganglionic enlargements joined by connectives to cerebral ganglia which lie in the prostomium.

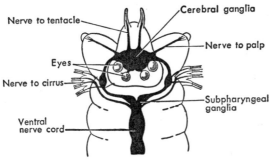

Fig. 6.14. *Nereis.*
Diagram of the anterior part of the nervous system. (Based on *Henry.*)

The appendages of the prostomium are supplied by nerves from the cerebral ganglia and the eyes are connected to them by short nervous tracts. The anterior peristomial cirri are supplied by nerves from the connectives and the posterior cirri by nerves from the subpharyngeal ganglion which also supplies the second segment. The peristomium may thus be seen to consist of two fused segments since its four pairs of appendages are innervated from two sources.

Nerves are given off from the ventral nerve cord segmentally. Giant fibres are present.

Movement and behaviour (Fig. 6.15)

The animal can crawl over the surface of the sand, chiefly using its parapodia in an oar-like fashion, each parapodium in turn making an effective (or propulsive) stroke in a backwards direction. It can swim by lateral flexures of its body which pass from tail to head and result in slow forward movement through the water. It begins to burrow by driving the head end into the sand by swimming movements but when the head is covered these give way to forceful extrusions of the proboscis which anchor the anterior end and allow the posterior

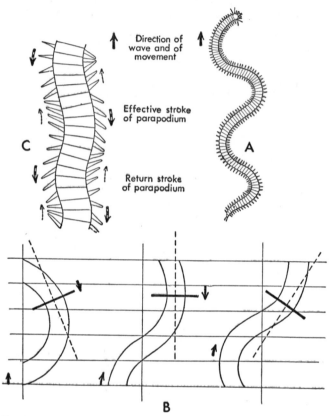

Fig. 6.15. *Nereis.*

Diagram illustrating the movements and locomotion of *Nereis.*

A The body form when swimming.

B This illustrates how the movement of lateral projections of the body (parapodia) is brought about by the forward passage of lateral flexures and how the effective backward stroke is made on the convex side of the flexure. Such movements are augmented by movements of the parapodia made by their intrinsic muscles.

C The disposition of the parapodia and the direction of movements which they make during the passage of the lateral flexures from tail to head. The large arrows indicate the propulsive stroke and the small arrows the return stroke. (Based on *Gray.*)

to be drawn up. This region can then grip the sand by its chaetae and thus permit the proboscis to be thrust again into the sand. By alternate body shortening and proboscis movements of this kind a burrow is made, the walls of which are held together by mucus secretions of the epidermis. It will be noticed that *Nereis* does not use the peristaltic type of locomotion found in the earthworm. It does not greatly change its length during the course of crawling and swimming movements and the longitudinal muscles and their nervous control are adapted to the production of lateral flexures in the body by the alternating contraction of the muscles on the two sides of the body. Only during burrowing and response to noxious stimuli are the longitudinal muscles of both sides contracted together and the body shortened.

Reproduction

In *Nereis* the sexes are separate and the sex cells are found packed in the coelom in most of the segments of the body. They are formed

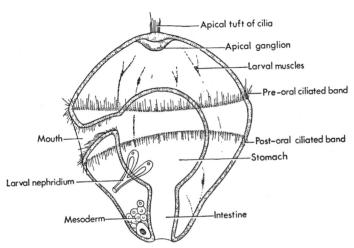

Fig. 6.16. Diagram of a trochophore larva of a polychaete.

from active regions of the coelomic epithelium which are hardly permanent enough in character to justify the application of the term gonads. When ripe, the gametes are shed into the sea water by rupture of the body wall, with the result that most of the parents die after spawning. During the proliferation, growth and maturation of the gametes, other extensive changes take place in the members of many species of *Nereis* (but not in *N. diversicolor*). The changes fit the animals for active swimming during the brief spawning period instead of for their usual life of crawling and burrowing. These changes result in the production of a *heteronereid* in which the posterior part of the body possesses enlarged parapodia with extra leaf-like outgrowths and larger oar-shaped chaetae. The eyes of the prostomium also become enlarged.

Spawning usually occurs over a short period of time in the early spring and a high concentration of eggs and sperm is ensured by the congregation of the mature heteronereids in the surface waters. After fertilization the zygote develops into a globular, pelagic or floating larva known as a *trochophore*. Again *N. diversicolor* differs from many other species of polychaetes in not having a trochophore which is pelagic but which develops in the surface layers of the mud inhabited by the adults. A typical trochophore is shown in Fig. 6.16.

The Lugworm

Arenicola

Another well known member of the Polychaeta is *Arenicola marina*, the lugworm, which makes the familiar castings seen on many sandy shores at low tide and which is extensively used by sea anglers for bait. The faeces which it deposits mark the tail shaft of a U-shaped burrow in which the worm lives, the head-shaft being marked on the surface of the sand by a shallow, conical depression. The worm feeds by taking in sand from the head-shaft which falls into the cone as it is removed at the bottom. This ensures that the animal eats sand coming chiefly from the surface, where the sand is richer in diatoms and microscopic animal life on which the worm feeds, than that of the deeper layers.

The creature looks, at first sight, much more like an earthworm than like a polychaete, but it can be seen on closer inspection to possess parapodia in the anterior region, from the notopodia of which arise long chaetae, though the neuropodia bear only short 'crotchets' which do not project very far from the surface of the body. Thirteen pairs of tufted gills lie dorsal to the notopodia in segments 7 to 19. The twentieth and succeeding segments constitute the tail and lack both chaetae and gills. The segments in the middle region of the body are each divided into five annuli, with which the segments should not be confused. The segmentation is clearly seen by reference to the parapodia. (See Fig. 6.17.)

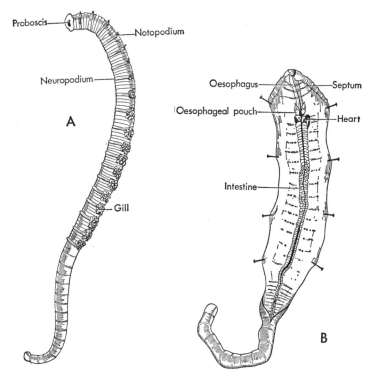

Fig. 6.17. *Arenicola.*

A The external features of the lugworm (*Arenicola*) with the proboscis partly everted.

B A dissection of the lugworm to show the gut, blood system and septa, of which there are three at the anterior end and many in the tail region. (Drawn from specimens.)

The characteristic eyes of polychaetes are absent from *Arenicola*, which also has no appendages on the first segment or on the prostomium. In the peristomium a pair of pits are found, the lining of which contains receptor cells. They are described as statocysts and contain a few fine sand grains: they are believed to respond to mechanical vibration or to apprise the animal of its orientation.

Gut and Feeding

The gut can be divided into an extrusible proboscis region consisting of a buccal cavity and pharynx armed with soft papillae but bearing no jaws. This is followed by an oesophagus with a pair of oesophageal pouches and is succeeded in turn by a digestive region which is divided into stomach and intestine. The gut of the tail region is thin-walled and serves for the accumulation of the very large bulk of faeces. It is known as the rectum. Digestion of the very small amount of nutritious matter which the sand contains is very rapid and the gut contents can pass through a worm in less than an hour. Some of the epithelial cells can engulf small food particles and digest them intracellularly but extracellular digestion in the lumen of the gut also occurs.

Blood system and respiration

The lugworm possesses a well-developed blood vascular system through which blood containing haemoglobin is pumped by two hearts, one lying on each side of the intestine. Each heart receives blood into its auricle from a very extensive plexus on the wall of the intestine. From there it passes to the ventricle and thence to a ventral vessel from which it is distributed to the body wall and gills. The blood is returned to the intestinal plexus and thence to the heart or to the dorsal vessel which connects with the plexus, but by-passes the heart and supplies the anterior part of the body. There is little doubt that a good deal of gaseous exchange takes place via the gills, for when the animal irrigates its burrow by the passage of waves of muscular contraction the gills are situated in the line of flow of the water.

Excretion

Six pairs of large, short nephridia lead from the coelom to the exterior in segments 3 to 8 inclusive. They possess large nephrostomes and short ducts and have the gonads attached to them.

Nervous system

The nervous system is essentially like that of the other annelids already described in that it consists of a ventral chain of ganglionic enlargements connecting with a pair of cerebral ganglia. Nerve tracts run from the connectives to the statocysts mentioned above.

Body-wall and movement

The body-wall resembles that of the earthworm in having clearly defined circular and longitudinal muscle layers but differs by the presence of oblique strands like those found in *Nereis*. The parapodia are small and their musculature is correspondingly weak. The animal can wriggle when left on the surface of the sand and it can burrow rapidly, chiefly by means of its proboscis, but it cannot swim in more than a feeble fashion by lateral flexures of *Nereis* type and it cannot crawl by peristalsis like the earthworm. It is only really at home in its burrow which it can, but does not often, leave. Here its time is spent in feeding, by taking in the sand from the bottom of the head-shaft, irrigating its burrow by the passage along its body of thickenings produced by waves of longitudinal muscular contraction, and voiding the sand which passes through its gut by ascending tail first to the hind end of its burrow and there depositing faeces on the surface.

Reproduction

The sexes, as in *Nereis*, are separate. Both male and female gonads shed the developing sex cells into the spacious coelom which becomes packed with them just before spawning time in October in the Thames Estuary. Both sperm and eggs probably leave the body through the nephridia and are pumped up the burrow by the worm on to the surface of the sand at low tide. After spawning many of the worms die.

Fertilization occurs when the eggs and sperm are mixed in the waters of the incoming tide and the zygotes, which tend to be carried on shore, develop into bottom dwelling larvae which stay in the surface layer of the sand. These gradually develop into young worms which eventually migrate seawards in the spring to repopulate the intertidal zone.

The Leech

Hirudo

The medicinal leech *Hirudo medicinalis* was common at one time in fresh water in Britain but is now rare and is usually imported from the Continent. Its use in medical practice for the withdrawal of small quantities of blood and pus was at one time very extensive but is now almost unknown.

The leech differs from the other annelids which have been described in lacking chaetae, in the possession of anterior and posterior suckers and in having a small, fixed number of body segments, most of which are clearly divided into a number of annuli varying from two in segment 3 to five in segments 8 to 22. The anterior sucker is a modification of the ventral part of the first four segments and surrounds the mouth, but the posterior sucker is regarded as additional to the twenty-six segments which are clearly distinguishable and may

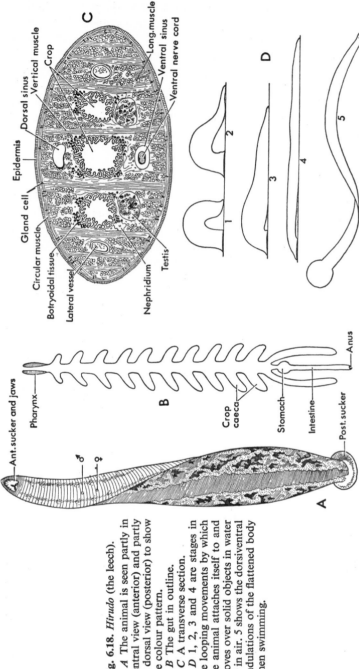

Fig. 6.18. *Hirudo* (the leech).

A The animal is seen partly in ventral view (anterior) and partly in dorsal view (posterior) to show the colour pattern.

B The gut in outline.

C A transverse section.

D 1, 2, 3 and 4 are stages in the looping movements by which the animal attaches itself to and moves over solid objects in water or in air. 5 shows the dorsiventral undulations of the flattened body when swimming.

represent seven more. It also has a very much reduced coelom which is confined to dorsal and ventral median sinuses. The gonads and internal ends of the nephridia lie in small sinuses connecting with the ventral sinus which also houses the ventral nerve cord. The two main lateral blood vessels, which are contractile, also communicate indirectly with the sinuses of the coelom.

Gut and Feeding

The gut comprises a short muscular pharynx provided with radial muscles running to the body-wall which enable it to suck blood from the wound made in the victim's skin by the three jaws. Unicellular glands secrete a saliva containing hirudin, a substance which prevents the blood from clotting in the leech's crop. The saliva also contains a vaso-dilator which, by acting on the victim's blood vessels, ensures a supply of blood to the leech during feeding. Blood passes from the pharynx to the very large crop which possesses eleven pairs of lateral caeca. Here the meal can be stored for many months or a year and is allowed to pass, a little at a time, into the stomach and intestine where digestion takes place. This is believed to result from the action of symbiotic bacteria, since no digestive enzymes produced by the leech itself have been found. A short rectum leads to the anus, which opens on the dorsal side of segment 26 above the posterior sucker. (Fig. 6.18 A, B and C.)

Excretory system

The nephridia, of which there are seventeen pairs, possess ciliated funnels lying in coelomic sinuses, which, in segments 12 to 21, also house the testes. The nephridia open to the exterior in segments 7 to 23 inclusive by nephridiopores in the 1st annulus (seg. 7) or the 2nd annulus (segs. 8–23).

Nervous system

The annelid pattern of cerebral ganglia and a ventral chain is found in *Hirudo* but the subpharyngeal ganglion can be shown to consist of four or five fused ganglia and the most posterior ganglion of seven. Around the margin of the anterior sucker lie five pairs of eyes. Each is a deep cup of pigment inside which lies a layer of photo-receptor cells like those which are found singly in the epidermis of the earthworm. Small segmental papillae occur on other body segments in a series which suggests that they are homologous with the eyes and are probably sensory.

The Body-wall and Movement

The body construction differs from that of other annelids by the great reduction of the coelom and the enlarged capacity of the gut. Its contents partly take the place of the coelomic fluid in its role as a hydrostatic skeleton, but this role is also played by the general connective tissue lying between the epithelium and the gut wall, which is of a parenchymatous type. Part of it is known as *botryoidal* tissue which is characteristic of leeches and is composed of large, darkly pigmented cells. The muscles comprise some outermost diagonal fibres, then circulars, inner longitudinals and also dorsiventral muscles. Some fibres run radially from the gut wall to the epithelium. (Fig. 6.18C.)

When the animal is floating freely in water the contraction of its dorsiventral muscles flattens it and it swims by undulations of its body made in a dorsiventral sense, but as soon as its anterior sucker touches a solid object swimming stops, the sucker adheres and the animal progresses by looping movements in which the posterior sucker is brought up behind the front one. When it has adhered the anterior sucker is released, the body extended and the anterior sucker attached again. (Fig. 6.18D.)

Reproduction

On each side of the body the ten (or nine) testes are continuous with their ducts (an unusual feature in the phylum Annelida) and discharge by means of a longitudinal vas deferens. Left and right vasa deferentia each coil before uniting in a muscular penis which opens in segment 10.

A pair of ovaries lie in segment 11 and are continuous with oviducts which join to form a single median vagina opening in segment 11.

Pairing results in sperm from one animal being deposited in the vagina of the other. A cocoon is formed from secretions of the epidermis of segments 9 to 12 (the clitellar segments) and this receives oocytes and spermatozoids as well as a protein secretion from the wall of the female duct. The cocoon is passed forwards over the body and is deposited in the mud.

7. Introduction to the Arthropoda

THE Arthropods form a most interesting and varied group of invertebrates. At the same time, they are the most successful in their conquest of the land habitat and show a wide range of *adaptive radiation* (see p. 194). The more primitive are aquatic but the more advanced are air-breathing.

The arthropods share certain basic features with the annelids, which are set out below.

(1) They are bilaterally symmetrical, triploblastic, coelomate metazoa.

(2) They display a high degree of metameric segmentation.

(3) The anus is situated in the posterior segment.

(4) The central nervous system is a double, ventral, solid nerve cord situated ventrally to the gut and connected to the 'cerebral' ganglia by two commissures encircling the anterior end of the gut.

(5) They possess a blood system.

As distinct from the annelids, the arthropods show the following characteristics.

(i) They possess pairs of jointed limbs. In primitive arthropods, there is one pair of such limbs attached to each segment of the body. Those in the neighbourhood of the mouth are modified to serve as *trophic* (feeding) organs known as *gnathites.*

(ii) The mouth is situated ventrally some way behind the more anterior segments and not, as in the annelids, right at the front.

(iii) They possess a chitinous exoskeleton which in some, e.g. the lobster, crab and crayfish, is very thick and impregnated with mineral matter, chiefly calcium carbonate. This serves as a supporting structure and also serves for the attachment of muscles to produce movements of the body. Owing to its impermeability to gases (unlike the cuticle of the annelids) special respiratory organs are needed and these take the form of gills in the aquatic types and of *tracheae* (internal air-transporting tubes) in insects and myriapods or *lung books* in the arachnids (e.g. spiders).

139

(iv) The muscles are *not* arranged as in the annelids in longitudinal and circular bands but exist in strands attached *internally* to the various parts of the exoskeleton, which are moved in relation to one another by the contraction of the muscles (see Fig. 7.2).

(v) The blood system incorporates a definite heart and is an *open* one, i.e. the blood vessels leading the blood away from the heart open into blood spaces which are known collectively as the *haemocoele*. The blood is therefore brought into direct contact with the tissues. The heart lies dorsally to the gut.

(vi) The nervous system is more highly developed than in the annelids and the cell-bodies of the nerve cells (*neurons*) are aggregated in swellings called *ganglia*, one pair of which occurs in each segment of the body in the primitive condition. In most annelids they are scattered along the ventral nerve cord and the only ganglia which are clearly distinguishable are the cerebral and the subpharyngeal ganglia (cf. *Nereis*).

(vii) The process of cephalization (head formation) is much more advanced than in the annelids and there is a concentration in the head of well-developed sense organs, e.g. eyes, statocysts and chemotactile organs (*antennae*). A corresponding enlargement of the 'cerebral' ganglia occurs since these have to deal with numerous impulses arriving from the sense organs. Removal of these ganglia produces more serious effects in arthropods than in the annelids in consequence.

(viii) Except in a very primitive group known as the Prototracheata, nephridia are absent though coelomoducts occur. In all arthropods the coelom is suppressed and confined mainly to the cavity of the gonads and the end sacs of the excretory organs of the Crustacea (e.g. lobsters, crabs), the main body cavity being the *haemocoele* (see (v) above).

(ix) Protrusible *chaetae* are not present as in the annelids, though bristle-like projections of the cuticle called *setae* occur. Cilia are also absent, and even the sperm are not motile.

The exoskeleton

Since the exoskeleton is so prominent a feature of the arthropods, it merits special attention. It consists of a cuticle secreted by the epidermis and composed of a substance called *chitin* (Fig. 7.1). Chitin is now considered to be a polysaccharide of acetyl glucosamine residues.

CH₂OH ... (chemical structure diagram)

In the primitive condition, each segment of the body has its own portion of the exoskeleton, consisting of a dorsal shield (*tergum*), a ventral plate (*sternum*) and two lateral portions (*pleura*) (Fig. 8.2, p. 146).

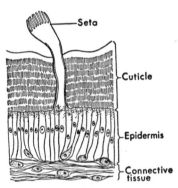

Fig. 7.1. Vertical section of the cuticle and epidermis of an arthropod (a lobster).

(After *Parker* and *Haswell*.)

The exoskeleton of one segment is attached to that of its neighbours by thin flexible cuticle which permits each segment to move in relation to its fellows (cf. the leather joints in a suit of medieval armour). The muscles which produce the movements of the segments are of the striped (or voluntary) type (page 459) and occur inside the exoskeleton connecting one segment to another. Those which produce bending (flexing) and straightening movements of the body run longitudinally, the flexing muscles by their contraction causing partial telescoping of the segments on the inside of the bend. The muscles exist in antagonistic pairs (see vertebrate limb and muscles, page 362) so that contraction of one pair (the *flexors*) will cause the body to bend, while that of the other pair (the *extensors*) will straighten the body.

The same type of movement occurs in the limbs, but in this case the 'free' ends of the muscles are attached to inward projections of the exoskeleton called 'tendons' (Fig. 7.2). The exoskeleton of the limbs forms a series of tubular segments called *podomeres*, joined by thin cuticle and moved relatively to one another by pairs of antagonistic muscles (Fig. 9.3, page 173).

The thickness of the cuticle varies in different parts of the body, being thinnest as previously indicated between the segments. It may be impregnated with calcium salts and coloured by various pigments. The terga of adjacent segments may fuse to form a continuous

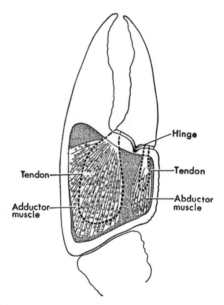

Fig. 7.2. Diagram to show the antagonistic muscles in the chela of a crayfish.

(From a specimen.)

covering extending over a number of segments, e.g. the carapace of the Crustacea (see below).

The phylum Arthropoda is divided into a number of classes. These are as follows:

I. The Crustacea, e.g. crabs, lobsters, crayfish and the smaller water fleas (e.g. *Daphnia* and *Cyclops*). These are recognized by the presence of two pairs of antennae. All are aquatic and breathe by means of gills or through the cuticle of the body, with the exception of the woodlice which have respiratory air-tubes in their abdominal limbs.

II. The Myriapoda (centipedes and millipedes) whose elongated bodies bear a pair of walking limbs on each segment of the body except the first three. They have one pair of antennae and breathe by means of tracheae.

III. The Insecta, e.g. the butterflies and moths, beetles, cockroaches, flies, bees, wasps and ants and many others. Insects are identified by their bodies being divided by constrictions into three parts: the head, the thorax and the abdomen, and by the fact that the thorax bears three pairs of walking legs while the abdomen is devoid of legs. Only one pair of antennae are present; there is a pair of compound eyes and the breathing organs are tracheae.

IV. The Arachnida, e.g. the spiders, harvestmen, bugs and mites, and scorpions. This is a very assorted group but its members agree in having no antennae and four pairs of walking legs. The body is never divided into more than two parts.

Two smaller classes also exist. These are: (a) The Onychophora. The chief genus is *Peripatus* (Fig. 36.4A, p. 692) a small slug-like creature with stumpy 'legs' which is a link between the annelids and the arthropods, possessing both nephridia and tracheae. (b) The Merostomata, or the King-Crabs (order Xiphosura), which inhabit the Caribbean Sea. They are animals of great antiquity and have features similar to those of the Arachnida.

8. *Crustacea*

The Crayfish

(*Astacus fluviatilis*)

THIS is a typical Crustacean, which is found in freshwater streams in limestone and chalky districts. Crayfish were formerly abundant in England in such areas but are now found only locally. While absent from the Thames in which they once flourished in large numbers,

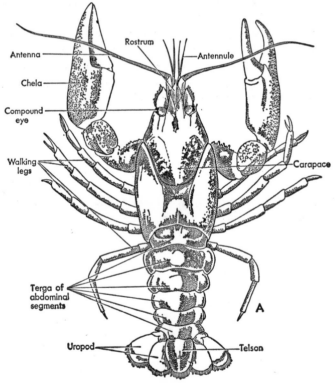

Fig. 8.1. *Astacus.* External features.

A Dorsal view; *B* Ventral view; *C* Side view. (Drawn from a specimen.)

144

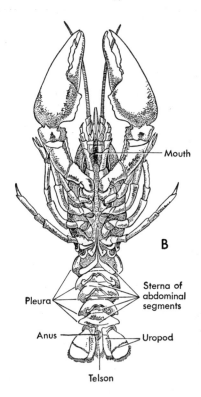

Mouth

Pleura

Sterna of
abdominal
segments

Anus

Uropod

Telson

B

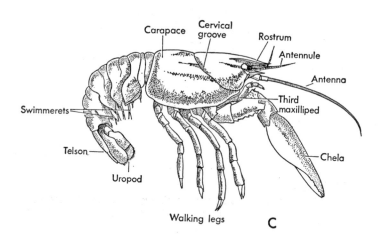

Carapace

Cervical
groove

Rostrum

Antennule

Antenna

Third
maxilliped

Swimmerets

Telson

Uropod

Chela

Walking legs

C

146 Crustacea

they are now found only in a few of its tributaries. Crayfish also occur in Derbyshire.

General structure

EXTERNAL FEATURES. The body is divided into an anterior region (the cephalothorax) and a posterior region (the abdomen). It consists of twenty segments, each segment except the first and the last having the exoskeleton composed of the dorsal tergum, the ventral sternum and the two lateral pleura, but this is apparent only in the posterior six segments which make up the abdomen. The terga of the anterior segments are fused to form an unjointed rigid *carapace* which has a beak-like projection at the front called the *rostrum*. The carapace is

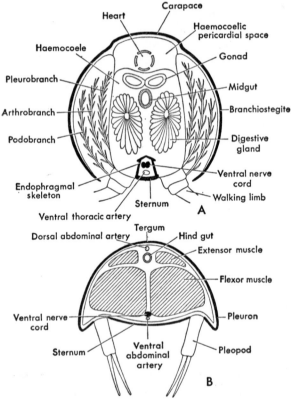

Fig. 8.2. *Astacus.*

A Diagram of a transverse section of the cephalothorax; *B* Diagram of a transverse section of an abdominal segment. (Based on *Parker* and *Haswell.*)

prolonged downwards on each side to form a cover for the gill chambers (the *branchiostegite*) within which the feathery gills lie hidden from sight. The branchiostegites curve inwards at their lower borders so that only the very narrow sterna and the appendages are visible from beneath. The pleura form the inner walls of the gill chambers and are, like the gills, hidden from view.

The whole of the exoskeleton apart from strips of cuticle between the segments of the abdomen and between the podomeres of the limbs is stiffened by deposits of calcium carbonate within the thick cuticle. The unstiffened strips of cuticle permit of the movement of one segment (or podomere) in relation to its neighbours.

Except for the first and last segments, every segment bears a pair of jointed appendages which are attached to the ventral side of the pleura by the *articular membranes* of thin flexible cuticle. The complete list of appendages and their appropriate segments is given below. (The pre-antennal segment bears no appendages and is not recognizable in the adult stage.)

Segment	*Appendages*
CEPHALOTHORAX	
Segment 1 (pre-antennal)	None
Segment 2	Antennules – probably olfactory organs
Segment 3	Antennae – tactile organs
Segment 4	Mandibles – 'jaws' with mouth between them
Segment 5	Maxillules
Segment 6	Maxillae
Segment 7	1st Maxillipeds
Segment 8	2nd Maxillipeds
Segment 9	3rd Maxillipeds
Segment 10	Great chelae – 'pincers'
Segment 11	1st walking limbs – chelate
Segment 12	2nd walking limbs – chelate
Segment 13	3rd walking limbs – non-chelate
Segment 14	4th walking limbs – non-chelate
ABDOMEN	
Segment 15	1st swimmerets (pleopods) – absent in ♀; modified in ♂
Segment 16	2nd swimmerets (pleopods) – modified in ♂
Segment 17	3rd swimmerets (pleopods)
Segment 18	4th swimmerets (pleopods)
Segment 19	5th swimmerets (pleopods)
Segment 20	Uropods
Telson	None – anus on ventral side

While two basically different types of crustacean limb exist (the *stenopodium* and the *phyllopodium*), both of which occur in the crayfish, it is sufficient at this stage to regard all the appendages as modifications to a greater or lesser extent of a *biramous* limb which is made up of three parts: the basal *protopodite* surmounted by an *exopodite*, and an *endopodite*, the latter being the nearer in position to the midline of the body. The protopodite may be divided into two podomeres (foot segments): the *coxopodite* (nearest the body) and the *basipodite* and attached to the coxopodite a flat projection called the *epipodite* along which lies a feathery gill.

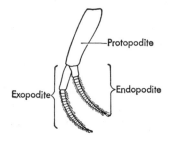

Fig. 8.3. Diagram of a biramous appendage of an arthropod.

In some of the limbs, e.g. the 3rd maxillipeds, all the above parts are present, but in others either the endopodite or the exopodite are missing. The epipodite is not present in all. The structure of each limb is modified for the particular function which it performs.

The structure of each appendage is shown in the accompanying figures which are self-explanatory but their functions are briefly described below:

1. *The antennules.* These bear many setae, particularly on the lower surfaces of the many-jointed prongs and these appear to have an olfactory function (i.e., they bear cells which are chemo-receptors) and enable the animal to recognize food. The basal joint contains a sac-like structure called the statocyst with a crescentic opening fringed with seta on the upper surface. This organ (the statocyst) is concerned with balance (see page 163).

2. *The antennae.* The long, jointed endopods have a tactile function. They can be waved about to touch surrounding objects but are often carried trailing towards the rear of the animal. On the under side of the coxopodite is a white rounded hump on which is the external opening of the excretory organ (the *green* gland) (page 159).

3. *The mandibles.* These form a pair of powerful jaws. The coxopodite of each has a serrated inner border and in order to grip the food each is moved inwardly towards its fellow by the action of the adductor muscles which are attached internally to the sides of the carapace and to the 'tendons' of the mandibles. More slender

abductor muscles pull the mandibles apart. Aided by the maxillipeds and great chelae, they shred the food into pieces small enough to enter the mouth which lies between them.

4. *The maxillules* are flattened leaf-like limbs with no apparent function.

5. *The maxillae.* These are also leaf-like but the exopodite of each has a flat, plate-like attachment called the 'baler' (*scaphognathite*). These limbs perform fluttering movements which cause the 'balers' to produce a current of water flowing over the gills (see page 158).

6. *The 1st, 2nd and 3rd maxillipeds.* These assist the ingestion of the food, particularly the 3rd maxillipeds which rake food towards the mouth and also serve to hold down the food while the mandibles tear off pieces.

7. *The great chelae.* The large jointed endopodite ends in a powerful pincer (*chela*). One claw of the pincer is fixed and the other is movable, being pivoted so that it can be moved towards the fixed one by the action of an adductor muscle. An extensor muscle opens the pincer. The great chelae are used to capture the prey.

8. *The four pairs of walking limbs* (*pereiopods*). These are used to enable the animal to crawl slowly along the bottom of the river or stream. Owing to the buoyancy provided by the water, they do not need to support the body to any great extent and so are slenderly built. The first two pairs have small chelae at their ends.

9. *The swimmerets* (*pleopods*). Owing to their small size, it is difficult to see what help these can give in locomotion, but when the animal is crawling they perform paddling movements. The anterior two pairs in the male are modified to assist in depositing sperm on to the eggs (page 167) while the young during their development hang on to the swimmerets of the female, which also help to aerate the eggs during their development by creating water currents around them, the eggs being 'glued' to the underside of the abdomen.

10. *The uropods.* Together with the telson, these form when spread out, the tail fan which is used to propel the animal rapidly backwards (see Locomotion).

Locomotion

Though the crayfish spends much of its time in a burrow which it has excavated by shuffling backwards into the muddy banks of the stream, it emerges to catch its prey or in order to mate during the breeding season. It crawls slowly forward by means of its walking limbs but, if disturbed, can shoot rapidly backwards by

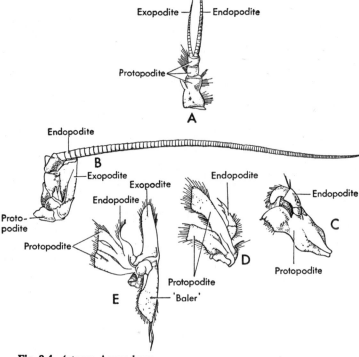

Fig. 8.4. *Astacus.* Appendages.

  A Antennule; *B* Antenna; *C* Mandible; *D* Maxillule; *E* Second maxilla; *F* First maxilliped; *G* Second maxilliped; *H* Third maxilliped; *I* Great chela; *J* First walking leg (pereiopod); *K* First pleopod of male; *L* Second pleopod of male; *M* Unmodified pleopod; *N* Uropod. (Drawn from specimens.)

repeated rapid flexings of its abdomen with the tail fan spread out. The muscles being of the striped (voluntary) type (page 459) are capable of much more rapid action than those of the earthworm which are unstriped.

  The powerful flexor muscles of the abdomen are attached at their front ends to the *endophragmal* skeleton which is formed by rafter-like ingrowths of the exoskeleton in the mid ventral region of the cephalothorax. The front ends of the smaller extensor muscles are also attached to the inner sides of the carapace. The hinder ends of the flexor muscles are attached to the sterna of the abdominal segments while those of the extensor muscles are attached to the terga.

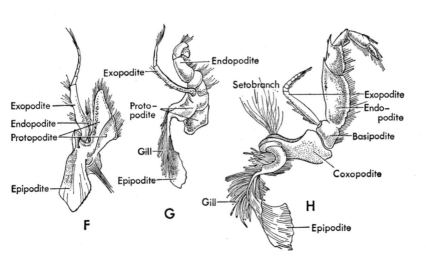

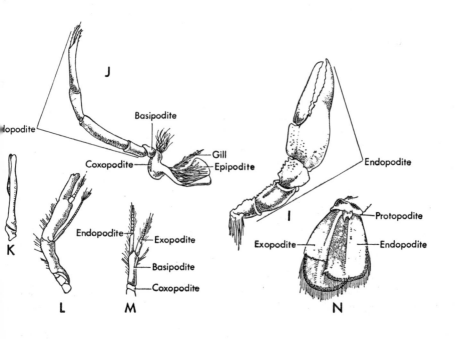

Contractions of the flexor muscles bend the abdomen forwards under the cephalothorax while those of the extensor muscles straighten it.

Feeding and Digestion

The crayfish is an omnivore, feeding on plant and animal matter either alive or dead. It is not at all adverse to carrion such as the dead bodies of fish, water voles, etc. The food is seized by the great chelae and pushed by them towards the mouth or raked in the same direction by the endopods of the maxillipeds. It is next shredded into small pieces by the mandibles and the finer pieces ingested, to be further ground up by the gastric mill (see below).

STRUCTURE OF THE ALIMENTARY CANAL (Fig. 8.5). The alimentary canal is divided into three regions: (1) The oesophagus and the *proventriculus* forming the fore-gut, (2) the mid-gut (*mesenteron*),

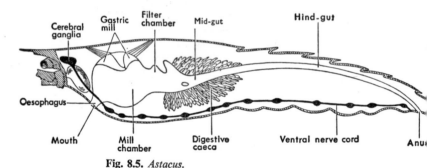

Fig. 8.5. *Astacus.*
Diagram of the alimentary canal. (After *Huxley*.)

(3) the hind-gut (or intestine). The fore-gut and the hind-gut are lined by inturned ectoderm and cuticle so that food is not absorbed in these regions. Only the mesenteron and its associated digestive caeca are lined by endoderm which, since it lacks a cuticle, allows digested food to be absorbed through it.

The proventriculus is a remarkable structure. It is divided into a mill chamber and a filter chamber. The mill chamber contains the gastric mill which grinds up the food into extremely fine particles, while in the mill chamber the food is acted upon by enzymes secreted by the digestive caeca. These pass forwards through the filter chamber into the mill chamber.

THE GASTRIC MILL. The walls of the mill chamber are lined internally by cuticle and parts of this in the dorsal region are thickened to form a set of plates hinged together and capable of movement. These plates or ossicles consist of (1) an anterior cardiac ossicle flanked by two ptero-cardiac ossicles, and (2) a posterior pyloric ossicle with a zygo-cardiac ossicle on either side. Between the cardiac and pyloric ossicles is a 'bridge' formed of a urocardiac and a pre-pyloric ossicle. These project downwards as shown in Fig. 8.6 and resemble a bent hinge, the lower end of which is serrated to form a

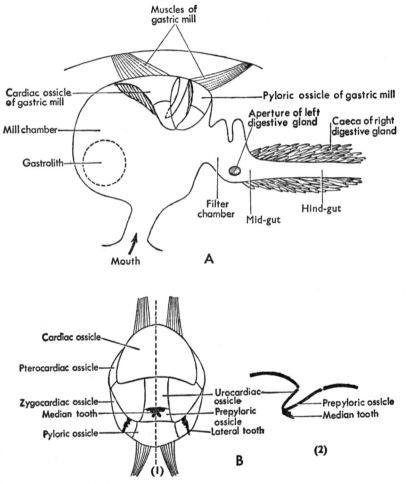

Fig. 8.6, *Astacus*.

A Diagram of the anterior region of the alimentary canal. *B* (1) Ossicles of the gastric mill seen from beneath. (2) L.S. along the dotted line in (1).

median tooth. Two similar lateral teeth occur on the inner sides of the zygo-cardiac ossicles. Attached to the upper side of the cardiac ossicle is a pair of muscle strands which run forwards and which are joined at their anterior ends to the inside of the carapace. A pair of muscular strands running backwards join the pyloric ossicle to the carapace. When these muscles contract, these two ossicles are moved apart causing the median tooth to move backwards. At the same time the deformation produced causes the lateral teeth to move inwards to grate against the median tooth, thus mincing up any food particles caught between them. When the muscles relax, the median ossicle moves forwards and the lateral teeth outwards. This operation is repeated until all the food is thoroughly ground up.

The filter chamber has a complex structure. Its lumen resembles an inverted Y and is crossed by inter-meshing setae which project from its sides to form a sieve which prevents all but the finest particles from passing on into the mid-gut.

The mid-gut is very short but its small surface for food absorption is compensated for by the very large total internal surface of the much branched tubular 'digestive' caeca which open into it on either side. These 'digestive' caeca are sometimes referred to as the ' *hepato-pancreas*' since they combine some of the functions of the liver and the pancreas of the vertebrates. Their cells secrete the digestive enzymes and also absorb the digested food, some of which is temporarily stored in them. The 'digestive' caeca lie in the haemocoele so that the blood can easily carry from them food to all parts of the body. (A calcareous body called a gastrolith occurs in the mill chamber. This disappears at each ecdysis and may serve as a store of calcium carbonate for deposition in the new cuticle.)

The blood vascular system and the circulation

The heart lies in a space called the *pericardial* space, which is part of the haemocoele situated under the dorsal side of the rear of the carapace. It is suspended in this space by strands called *alae cordis*. The wall of the oblong-shaped heart is muscular and has on each side three openings called *ostia*. These have inwardly directed flaps which act as valves. When the heart muscle is relaxed, blood flows into it through the ostia from the pericardial space but when the heart contracts the blood cannot be squeezed back again into this space since the flaps are forced outwardly to close the ostia. The blood then escapes through the arteries which lead from the heart to the front and rear of the animal, in a forward direction through the median

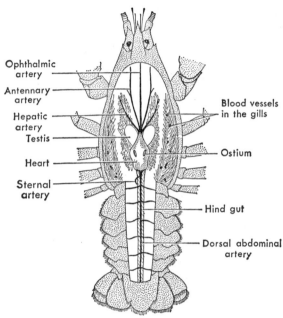

Fig. 8.7. *Astacus.*
Dorsal view of the heart and dorsal blood vessels. (Drawn from an injected specimen.)

ophthalmic artery and the two lateral antennary arteries, and in a backward direction by the dorsal abdominal artery. A median branch from the latter called the sternal artery runs downwards on the *left* side of the intestine to connect with the ventral thoracic and ventral abdominal arteries (see Fig. 8.9). After branching a number of times all the arteries open into the haemocoelic spaces to bathe the various organs of the body. By its direct contact with these, the blood is able to bring to them oxygen and food and to remove from them excreta (carbon dioxide and nitrogenous waste matter). The blood also passes through the limbs. Eventually the blood enters the ventral *sternal* sinus which lies under the endophragmal skeleton in the cephalo-thorax. From this sinus it is drawn up by the pumping action of the heart into the gills, and after circulating through these, the blood ascends by six lateral veins on each side into the pericardial space from whence it recommences its journey through the body.

The blood consists of plasma (a watery solution of various crystalloids together with colloidal protein). The respiratory pigment in it is

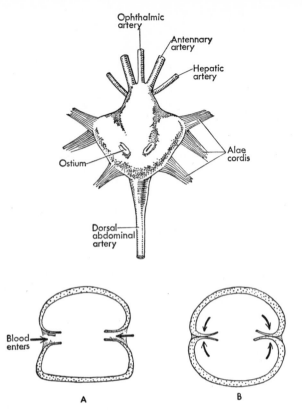

Fig. 8.8. *Astacus.*

Dorsal view of the heart (UPPER). (After *Huxley*.) Diagram to show the action of the valves of the heart (LOWER). *A* Heart relaxed (diastole); *B* Heart contracted (systole).

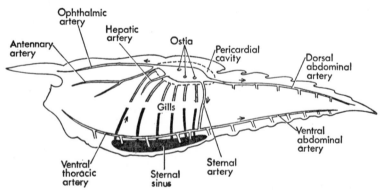

Fig. 8.9. *Astacus.*

Diagram to show the general course of the circulation.

156

called *haemocyanin*, which is a copper-containing compound, blueish when oxygenated and colourless when deoxygenated. Leucocytes are also present. The blood 'clots' very readily on coming into contact with ordinary fresh water. This enables the animal to lose a limb—which it can do by means of a special process when trapped (see page 167)—without excessive bleeding taking place. It should be noticed that the blood system, in addition to being an 'open' one, does not follow the metameric plan as in the case of the annelid blood system. This may be correlated with the fact that many of the muscles are also no longer disposed metamerically.

Respiration

Since the armoured cuticle over the greater part of the external surface of the body prevents the diffusion of gases into and out of the body, special organs of respiration are present. These are the feathery gills with their large external surface covered by the thinnest of cuticle which freely allows the passage of dissolved gases through it. The gills are not visible from the exterior, as previously stated, since they lie in a gill chamber covered by the branchiostegite (p. 147) on each side of the cephalo-thorax. They exist in three sets, (1) the *pleurobranchs*, which grow out of the pleura; (2) the *arthrobranchs*, which project from the articular membranes (the cuticle joining the limbs to the body); (3) the *podobranchs*. The last project from the basal joints of certain of the limbs and are attached to the epipodites of those limbs (see Fig. 8.4). The distribution of these gills is shown in the following table.

Thoracic segment	I	II	III	IV	V	VI	VII	VIII
Pleurobranchs	0	0	0	0	r	r	r	1
Arthrobranchs	0	1	2	2	2	2	2	0
Podobranchs	0	1	1	1	1	1	1	0
Epipodites	$\sqrt{}$	$\sqrt{}$	$\sqrt{}$	$\sqrt{}$	$\sqrt{}$	$\sqrt{}$	$\sqrt{}$	0
	1st max-illi-peds	2nd max-illi-peds	3rd max-illi-peds	great che-lae	walking limbs			

$\sqrt{}$ = epipodite present.   0 = epipodite or gill absent.   r = rudiment.
Setobranchs are filamentous gills occurring on the basal joints.

In the central axis of each gill is an ascending passage for the blood (afferent branchial vein) continuous at the upper end with a descending passage (the efferent branchial vein), the former being outermost. From these two passages, subsidiary ones run in the filaments (Fig. 8.10).

The blood from the sternal sinus (see below) flows through the gills on its way back to the heart as indicated in Fig. 8.9 and 8.10. The

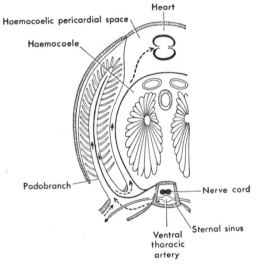

Fig. 8.10. *Astacus.*

Diagram of a transverse section of the cephalothorax to show the course taken by the blood from the sternal sinus to the heart.

dissolved oxygen diffuses into the blood from the surrounding water while carbon dioxide dissolved in the blood diffuses outwards. While the animal is walking the movements of the limbs produce backward and forward motions of the gills attached to the limbs and also of the epipodites. These movements are often sufficient to renew the water around the gills but when the crayfish is at rest, the 2nd maxillae are seen to flutter rapidly. This causes water to be baled out of the gill chambers in a forward direction by means of the 'balers' of the maxillae while fresh water enters between the legs. If a little Indian ink is injected into the water just beneath the posterior end of a gill chamber, in a few seconds 'puffs' of blackish water are seen to emerge from the region of the 2nd maxillae at the front.

Excretion and Osmoregulation

In arthropods part of the nitrogenous waste substances may be deposited in the cuticle and, since in the crayfish this is shed at intervals during the growing period (see ecdysis, page 167), it is possible that some nitrogenous excretion may occur in this manner. There are, however, a pair of organs known as the *green glands* which lie in the haemocoele anteriorly to the mouth. Each is a mesodermal structure

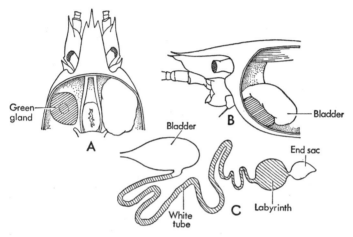

Fig. 8.11. *Astacus.*

A View of the green glands from above (bladder of left one removed). *B* Side view of green gland. *C* Diagram of green gland unravelled. (After *Huxley.*)

(coelomoduct) and consists of a looped tube ending blindly at the inner end and opening to the exterior at the summit of a whitish bump on the underside of the basal joint of the antenna. At the inner end is a small dilatation known as the end sac, whose cavity is coelomic and which opens into a wide greenish tube called the labyrinth. The internal structure of this labyrinth resembles that of a sponge, the spaces in it being lined by a glandular epithelium. Leading from the labyrinth is a narrower coiled tube with internally ridged walls (the white tube), and this in turn opens into a thin-walled dilated bladder which lies dorsally to the remainder of the tube and leads to the exterior by a short duct.

The presence of the thick cuticle over the greater part of the body presents an impervious barrier to the entry of water by osmosis into the haemocoele but the thin cuticle covering the gills allows water to be drawn continuously into the blood owing to the greater osmotic pressure of the blood as compared with that of the water bathing the gills. To maintain the necessary constancy of the osmotic pressure of the blood, the green glands act as osmo-regulatory organs and at the same time serve to remove nitrogenous waste substances (chiefly ammonium carbonate) from the blood. The hydrostatic pressure of the blood being greater than that of the osmotic pressure of the colloids in the blood causes water containing crystalloids (including ammonium carbonate) to be filtered off from the blood into the end sac whence it passes through the green gland to the exterior. On the way, selective reabsorption into the blood of useful crystalloids occurs through the cells lining the labyrinth and the white tube. This involves the use of energy and this energy is provided by respiration in these cells.

The nervous system and the Sense organs

In its basic layout the nervous system resembles that of the earthworm, in that it consists of a central nervous system (C.N.S.) linked to peripheral neurons, the C.N.S. taking the form of a nerve cord *ventral* to the gut apart from the supra-oesophageal ganglia (cerebral ganglia) joined to the nerve cord by two long commissures encircling the oesophagus. The ventral nerve cord differs, however, from that of the earthworm in being composed of a series of ganglia (one pair per segment) joined to their neighbours by double commissures though the double nature of these is apparent only in the thoracic region and there only for a certain distance (segments 9 to 14). The crowding together of the appendages behind the mouth is reflected by the fusion of the first five pairs of ganglia behind the mouth to form a single sub-oesophageal ganglion. The sternal artery passes between the commissures joining the ganglia in segments 12 and 13 in the thoracic region where the nerve cord lies in the sternal sinus within the endophragmal skeleton (page 150). The paired cerebral ganglia are relatively larger than those of the earthworm since the crayfish is a more complex animal, and shows a greater degree of cephalization together with the possession of definite sense organs housed in the head, such as the compound eyes and statocysts. In consequence the cerebral ganglia are considerably larger than in the earthworm and from them run nerves to the antennules, the antennae and the compound eyes.

The cerebral ganglia are in reality double structures, being composed of the *archicerebrum* (the ganglia of the pre-antennulary

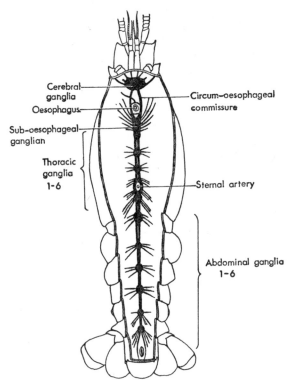

Fig. 8.12. *Astacus.*
The nervous system. (From a specimen.)

segment) and the *syn-cerebrum* (the fused ganglia of the antennulary and antennary segments).

Lateral nerves connect the ganglia of the ventral cord with the various segments and their appendages.

THE EYE. Each eye is a stalked structure surmounted by a black coloured hemisphere lying beside and slightly below the rostrum. It can be swivelled to some extent by muscles attached internally to the cuticle of the stalk. (If the rostrum is stroked by a glass rod, a reflex inward movement of the eyes occurs.) By means of these muscles the eye can be directed towards objects in view. The black hemisphere is composed of a large number of optical units known as *ommatidia*. Each ommatidium is shaped like an elongated cone with the apex

162 *Crustacea*

directed inwardly so that in section the ommatidia are seen to fit together like the rays of a fan. The surface of the hemisphere is therefore a mosaic made up of the square bases of the ommatidia fitted together. The ommatidium is a multicellular structure. At its outer

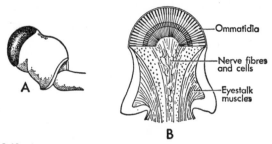

Fig. 8.13. *Astacus.*

A Eye – external view. *B* Eye as seen in a longitudinal section. (From various sources.)

end lie four flattened epidermal cells which secrete externally a transparent cuticle forming a cuticular lens. Beneath these are four tapering cells called *vitrellae* which combine to secrete and to surround a conical refractive lens (crystalline cone). Surrounding the tapered ends of the vitrellae are six retinular cells forming the *retinula* and enclosing a spindle-shaped transversely striped body called the *rhabdome*. These retinular cells are the photoreceptors and making contact with them are nerve fibres belonging to nerve cells lying in the optic ganglion. Surrounding the vitrellae and retinula are the outer and inner iris cells containing a black pigment (melanin) which optically isolates each ommatidium from its neighbours (Fig. 8.14).

VISION. Rays of light reflected from near-by objects which fall normally on the ommatidium pass directly through the cuticular lens and the crystalline cone to reach the retinula. Rays other than normal are refracted towards the retinula but, owing to the curtain of pigment in the iris cells, only rays near to normal reach it. Thus, each retinula receives rays from one small region of the object in view. It is assumed that all the images produced in the various retinulae fit together to form a composite image of the whole object. This is known as 'mosaic' vision. The images evoke nervous impulses which are relayed to the cerebral ganglia.

In dim light the curtains of pigment in the iris cells are withdrawn

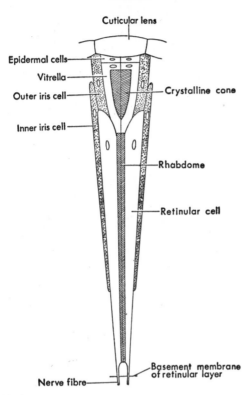

Fig. 8.14. *Astacus.*

An ommatidium in longitudinal section. (After *Borradaile, Eastham, Potts* and *Saunders.*)

upwards towards the surface so that rays received by one ommatidium can reach the retinulae of neighbouring ones. A mosaic of overlapping images is thus produced, with consequent lack of clear definition. Nevertheless, objects may be better discerned in dim light than would be the case otherwise. The eye in this condition of 'dark adaptation' is said to be a 'superposition' eye, while in bright light the eye with the curtains of pigment extending downwards is called an 'apposition' one.

THE STATOCYSTS. These organs are situated inside the basal joints of the antennules. Each is a sac produced by an ingrowth of the ectoderm and has a crescentic opening fringed by large setae on the upper surface of the joint. The cuticle inside the sac is thin and from it project into the cavity of the sac several rows of feathery hairs up the centre of which run nerve fibres. Inside the sac are found numbers of sand grains whose movements produced by those of the animal stimulate the nerve fibres of the hairs with which they come into contact. The nervous impulses evoked pass to the cerebral ganglia and are relayed to produce the reflex actions needed for the animal to maintain its normal equilibrium. When ecdysis occurs, the cuticle and contents of the statocyst are shed. It is therefore necessary for the crayfish to replace the sand grains in the statocysts and this

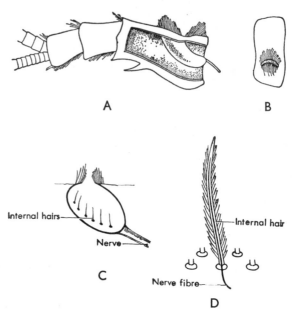

Fig. 8.15. *Astacus.*

   A Longitudinal section of basal joint of antennule to show statocyst.
B External opening of statocyst. *C* and *D* Internal sensory hairs of statocyst. (After *Borradaile*.)

it does by means of its chelae which it dips in the muddy sand of the river bed and then rubs across the openings of the statocysts.

   An interesting experiment was once performed to illustrate the mode of functioning of the statocysts. Young prawns were kept in filtered sea water and when ecdysis took place the animals were supplied with iron filings which they—in the absence of sand grains —duly deposited in their statocysts. The experimenter then held a magnet to one side of the prawn to attract the filings and to cause them to press on the side of the statocyst next to the magnet. The prawn then rolled in the opposite direction, thus making the same response as it would have done if the iron filings had been moved by gravity owing to the prawn tipping sideways.

THE CHEMO- AND TACTILE-SENSES. The setae of the outer branch of the antennules possess sensory nerve cells which respond to chemical substances in the water and which probably help the animal to recognize edible matter. Scattered about the surface of the body and on the limbs are setae with attached nerve cells which respond to contact with outside bodies and such setae are also found on the long antennae.

THE MODE OF OPERATION OF THE NERVOUS SYSTEM. The mode of operation is, like that of the earthworm, based on reflex arcs. The sensory cells of the eyes, statocysts, tactile and chemo-receptor organs are affected by various stimuli and respond by transmitting nervous impulses to the central nervous system where they are relayed by connector and motor neurons to the muscles to produce the appropriate response. In addition, the central nervous system is called upon to perform a higher degree of co-ordination than in the worm, since its muscles are more highly organized and limbs are present. Moreover, the concentration of the main sense organs in the head is reflected by the greater development of the cerebral ganglia. In consequence the removal of the cerebral ganglia in a living crayfish has a far greater effect than in the worm, the crayfish becoming passive and scarcely responsive to outside influence after the operation, whereas the worm is but little affected by it. As in the worm the ventral nerve cord contains dorsally three giant fibres which originate in the cerebral ganglia. These are concerned with the transmission of nervous impulses from the cerebral ganglia to the muscles of the abdomen in order to produce the rapid 'flicks' of the latter by which the crayfish escapes rapidly backwards when alarmed by visual or other impressions.

A visceral nervous system is present in the walls of the gut and is joined to a cross-connection behind the oesophagus between the commissures uniting the cerebral to the suboesophageal ganglia.

Reproduction

The sexes are separate and can be readily distinguished by the appearance of the anterior pleopods (swimmerets). The most anterior in the female is abortive, but in the male it and the next one posterior to it are modified to act as copulatory organs (Fig. 8.4K, L).

The ovary is a hollow sac-like organ lying just beneath the heart in the haemocoele. It is bifurcated in front and bulging from its walls can be seen the outlines of the developing eggs. In the breeding season (early autumn) these eggs pass to the exterior through two short wide oviducts, one on each side with an external opening on

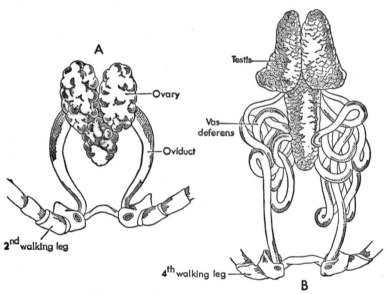

Fig. 8.16. *Astacus.* Reproductive organs.
A Female organs. *B* Male organs. (After *Huxley.*)

the ventral sides of the coxopodite of the second walking legs. On emerging, the eggs, which are heavily yolked and about 3-4 mm. in diameter, become attached to the swimmerets. The testis is similar in shape to the ovary and also lies just beneath the heart: its walls are smooth and leading from each side is a much-coiled vas deferens to open on the ventral side of the coxopodite of the fourth walking leg. The *vasa deferentia* act as seminal vesicles for the storage of sperm until they are required for fertilizing the eggs.

FERTILIZATION. Before the eggs laid by the female have become attached to her swimmerets, the male turns her over on to her back and sheds sperm on to the ventral side of her abdomen. The semen is a sticky fluid which when forced out by contractions of the walls of the *vasa deferentia* is deposited on the eggs by the aid of the modified first and second swimmerets of the male. The first swimmeret has its distal end twisted into a tubular form with a slot on one side in which the blade-like distal end of the second swimmeret can travel to force out the semen by a piston-like movement as it flows down the tube of the first swimmeret which is held against the male opening. The non-motile sperm are very peculiar. Their structure can be seen from the diagram (Fig. 8.17). When a sperm comes into

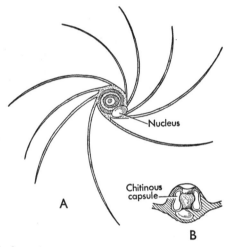

Fig. 8.17. *Astacus.*

   A A spermatozoon. *B* The central capsule of a spermatozoon in vertical section. (After *Huxley.*)

contact with an egg, the central capsule expands and forces the nucleus into the egg so that it can fuse with the egg nucleus. The development is direct, there being no true larval stage. After emerging from the eggshell of the egg, the young animals attach themselves to the pleopods of the female by their chelae. They resemble the adults except for the more rounded appearance of the cephalothorax and the presence of a dorsal spine on the carapace. From time to time they leave the shelter of the abdomen of the female to feed on scraps of food shredded by her mandibles and eventually leave her to start an independent life. While 'growing up', numerous ecdyses take place.

ECDYSIS. Since the skeleton is external to the body and once formed is incapable of further extension, an increase in the size of the body can only occur by a periodic 'moulting' (ecdysis) of the exoskeleton to allow for expansion. Growth is continuous in the young animal but increase in size is intermittent. When growth produces tension within the exoskeleton, a transverse crack appears dorsally at the junction of the cephalothorax and the abdomen, while the exoskeleton of the larger limbs splits longitudinally. First the anterior end of the body and then the posterior end emerges through the transverse split as the animal sheds its old exoskeleton. A new soft cuticle capable of expansion has already formed beneath the old exoskeleton before this is shed but after an increase in size has taken place, this new cuticle too becomes rigid by the deposition within it of calcium salts. A further ecdysis must therefore occur after an interval of growth.

AUTOTOMY. During an ecdysis or when trapped by an enemy, a crayfish can readily shed one or more limbs. The limb becomes detached by the transverse fracture of the basipodite where the exoskeleton is thin and constricted. The wound contracts rapidly and later a new limb is regenerated to replace the lost member.

9. *Insecta*

The Cockroach

THIS is a large insect and is the most suitable type with which to begin the study of insects owing to its size and the ease with which it can be reared. It is, moreover, comparatively unspecialized and in structure probably not far removed from the primitive forms. There are two well-known species: *Periplaneta* (*Blatta*) *orientalis* and *P. americana*. The American species is the larger one (1–1½ inches in length when adult) and differs from the Oriental species in that both sexes are winged whereas in *P. orientalis* the female is practically wingless. *P. americana* is reddish brown in colour but *P. orientalis* is much darker.

HABITAT. Cockroaches are found in dwelling houses hiding in crevices by day and emerging at night in search of food. They prefer warm situations such as kitchens and bakehouses.

General structure

EXTERNAL FEATURES. The body is segmented and covered by an exoskeleton (cuticle) and divided into three distinct regions: the head, the thorax and the abdomen, the head being separated from the thorax by a very narrow neck and placed at right angles to it.
THE HEAD. This is derived from six embryonic segments, but these are not discernible in the adult. The whole of the head is covered by an armour (the head capsule) composed of several plates (*sclerites*) with sutures between them (see Fig. 9.1D for names of these plates). On each side of the head is a large compound eye, and in front of these eyes is borne a pair of *antennae*. Each antenna consists of a long jointed *flagellum* set in a circular socket in a ring-like antennal sclerite and articulating by means of a thin membrane so that the antenna can be moved freely. Beneath and medial to the bases of the antennae are two white patches (*fenestrae*) which are regarded as rudimentary eyes (*ocelli*). The mouth is situated between the *labrum* and the *labium* (q.v.) and is flanked by two pairs of appendages: the *mandibles* and the first *maxillae* (see appendages, p. 172).

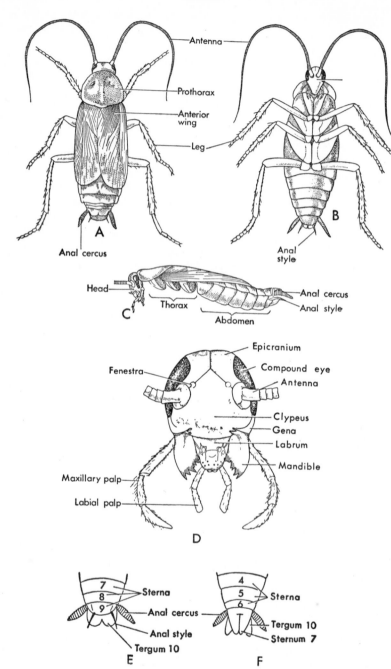

THE THORAX. This is composed of three segments known as the pro-, meso- and meta-thorax respectively. Each segment bears ventro-laterally a pair of walking limbs, while dorso-laterally the mesothorax and metathorax each bears a pair of wings folded backwards when at rest. The front pair are thicker than the hinder membranous pair and serve as wing-covers (*elytra*) to them. Each wing is a double membrane and running in this are 'nervures' or 'veins' containing blood sinuses and fine tracheae (breathing tubes).

THE ABDOMEN. This consists of ten segments though not all are visible externally (see below). It is devoid of appendages except for a pair of jointed *anal cerci* which project laterally, one on either side, at the posterior end.

EXOSKELETON. The exoskeleton (cuticle) is secreted by the epidermis and is composed partly of chitin and partly of protein rendered insoluble by a tanning process, the outer layer of which contains waxy substances to reduce water loss by evaporation through the cuticle. Except in the head where the cuticle consists of a number of plates (see page 169), each segment is covered by a dorsal *tergum* and a ventral *sternum* – slightly arched flexible plates joined at the sides by thin cuticle in which are embedded two very small lateral *pleura*. In each segment the hinder edges of the tergum and the sternum overlap the front edges of those of the segment behind.

The terga of the thoracic region are known as the *pronotum*, the *mesonotum* and the *metanotum*, the pro-notum projecting forwards over the neck. The tergum of the 7th abdominal segment overlaps those of the 8th and 9th segments so that only eight abdominal terga are visible. That of the 10th abdominal segment forms a backwardly projecting plate notched at the hinder end.

The sternum of the 1st abdominal segment is rudimentary. In the female only six sterna are visible, that of the 7th abdominal segment being a split structure resembling the prow of a boat directed backwards. Frequently an egg cocoon may be seen projecting from this. In the male, nine sterna are seen, the 9th abdominal sternum bearing a pair of anal styles.

Fig. 9.1. The Cockroach. External views.
A Dorsal view of male. *B* Ventral view of male. *C* Side view of male with legs removed. *D* Front view of head. *E* Underside of posterior end of the abdomen of the male. *F* Underside of posterior end of the abdomen of the female. (Drawn from specimens.)

Parts of the cuticle project inwards to serve for the attachment of muscles. In the rear of the head the internal projections of the cuticle form a girder-like structure spanning the region above the oesophagus.

The appendages

THE ANTENNAE. These are generally regarded as the first pair of appendages (for description see page 169 and Fig. 9.1). They have an olfactory function.

THE MOUTHPARTS. (a) The *labrum* or upper lip is a chitinous plate beneath the clypeus. On its inner side is a ridge called the *epipharynx*.

(b) The mandibles. Each mandible probably corresponds to the coxopodite of the basic arthropod limb and has an inner serrated border of thickened cuticle. It articulates by means of a condyle with the gena of the same side. The two mandibles can be opposed or separated by the adductor and abductor muscles attached to them and serve to shred the food.

(c) The maxillae. Behind the mandibles is a pair of first maxillae and in the rear of these the second maxillae, which are united to form the *labium* or lower lip. The maxillae resemble the basic biramous arthropod appendage in that each consists of a basal protopodite surmounted by a joined exopodite and a forked endopodite, though some consider that the true endopodite is missing and that the inner branch is an *endite*, i.e. an outgrowth of the protopodite. The names given to the various parts of these structures differ in the two maxillae, as shown in the following table:

	First Maxilla	Second Maxilla
Protopodite (a) proximal segment (b) distal segment	Cardo Stipes	Sub mentum Mentum
Exopodite	Maxillary palps (5 podomeres)	Labial palps (3 podomeres)
Endopodite (Endite)	Galea (outer prong) Lacinia (inner prong)	Paraglossa (outer prong) Glossa (inner prong)

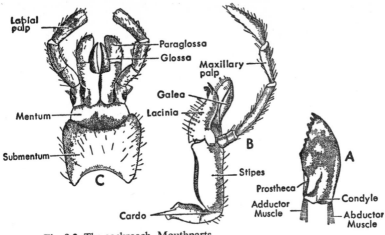

Fig. 9.2. The cockroach. Mouthparts.

A Mandible. *B* First maxilla. *C* Second maxillae united to form the labium. (Drawn from a prepared slide.)

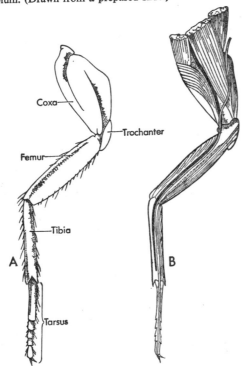

Fig. 9.3. The cockroach.

A External view of limb of an insect. *B* Arrangement of the muscles in the limb of an insect. (After *Imms*.)

173

The sharp point of the lacinia can emerge from the sheath-like galea to pierce and hold the food, while the mandibles are in action, and also help in the mastication of the food, by a scissor-like action between the lacinia and the galea. The labium appears to be function-less except for helping to retain the food in the 'mouth'.

(d) The hypopharynx. In the floor of the 'mouth' is a tongue-like chitinous structure called the *hypopharynx*, with two pointed lobes called the *superlingua*. It receives the saliva from the salivary duct and directs it on to the food.

THE WALKING LIMBS. These are jointed appendages terminating in claws. The names of the podomeres are shown in Fig. 9.3 and are derived somewhat inappropriately from those applied to various bones or regions in the pentadactyl limb of the vertebrates (q.v.). The three pairs articulate with the three segments of the thorax respectively.

TABLE OF SEGMENTS AND APPENDAGES

Segments	Appendages
HEAD	
1. Pre oral (Ocular)	None
2. Antennal*	Antennae Mouth
3. 2nd post oral (Intercalary)	None
4. 3rd post oral	Mandibles
5. 4th post oral	1st maxillae
6. 5th post oral	2nd maxillae (fused to form the labium)
THORACIC	
7. 1st thoracic (prothorax)	1st pair of walking limbs
8. 2nd thoracic (mesothorax)	2nd pair of walking limbs + anterior pair of wings
9. 3rd thoracic (metathorax)	3rd pair of walking limbs + posterior pair of wings
ABDOMEN	
10. 1st abdominal	None
11. 2nd abdominal	,,
12. 3rd abdominal	,,
13. 4th abdominal	,,
14. 5th abdominal	,,
15. 6th abdominal	,,
16. 7th abdominal	,,
17. 8th abdominal	,,
18. 9th abdominal	,,
19. 10th abdominal	,,

* This segment fuses with pre-oral segment during development so that the antennae come to lie in front of the mouth.

The internal structure

THE BODY CAVITY. The main body cavity is haemocoelic and is
divided by two horizontal muscular perforated diaphragms to form
the pericardial, perivisceral and perineural sinuses. In the perivisceral haemocoelic sinus lies a diffuse fat body which acts as a
store of food.

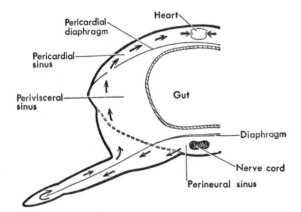

Fig. 9.4. The cockroach.

A vertical section of the body of an insect to show the body cavities
and direction of blood flow indicated by the arrows. (Diagrammatic –
after *Imms*.)

THE MUSCLES. Bending movements of the body and other movements concerned with respiration and flight are produced by muscles
lying in the haemocoele. They consist of the following:

(1) The longitudinal tergal muscles. These are attached to the
underside of the terga and run from one tergum to the next. On
contraction, they straighten the body.

(2) The longitudinal sternal muscles. These form flat transversely
segmented sheets extending from one sternum to the next. On
contraction these flex the body.

(3) The oblique tergo-sternal muscles. These flank the longitudinal
tergal muscles. These occur only in the abdomen.

(4) The flight muscles (see page 191). The wings are operated by
longitudinal and vertical muscles, which move the wings up and
down by producing distortions of the body in the thoracic region,
alternately causing the terga and sterna to approach and separate,
while other muscles move the wings sideways or alter their pitch.

To allow of these movements the wings have a hinge-like attachment to the articular membrane between the terga and sterna.

The limbs possess internal pairs of antagonistic muscles which produce movements of the podomeres relative to one another and are moved as a whole by muscles attached to the interior of the thorax and to the basal podomeres.

Feeding and Digestion

The alimentary canal is divided into three regions: (1) the stomodaeum (fore gut); (2) the mesenteron (mid gut); (3) the proctodaeum (hind gut). The stomodaeum and proctodaeum are lined by ectoderm and the thin cuticle secreted by the ectoderm. The mesenteron is lined by endoderm and alone is capable of absorbing the products of digestion.

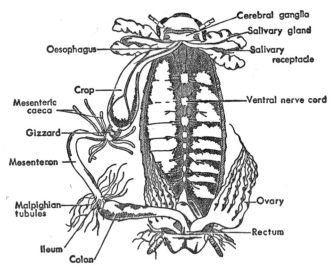

Fig. 9.5. The cockroach.

A female cockroach dissected to show the main organs after removal of the heart, muscles, tracheae and fat body. (From a specimen.)

THE STOMODAEUM. The mouth leads into a cavity succeeded by a narrow oesophagus passing from the head into the thorax where it dilates to form a wide, thin-walled extensible *crop*. Following this is a pear-shaped structure – the *gizzard* – in which the cuticle is thickened to form six longitudinal 'teeth' which can be opposed by the contraction of the muscular walls of the gizzard. Inwardly projecting

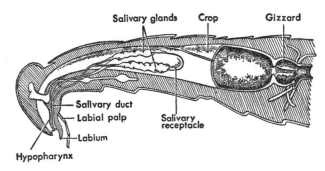

Fig. 9.6. The cockroach.

Diagram of the anterior region of the alimentary canal seen from the side, showing the interior of the crop and the gizzard. (After *Borradaile*.)

setae occur at the hinder end of the gizzard, where they act as a strainer to prevent all but the finest particles from passing into the mid gut.

THE MESENTERON. This is a short tube succeeding the gizzard. At the entrance are eight blind tubes projecting into the haemocoele, known as *mesenteric caeca.*

THE PROCTODAEUM. This is a coiled tube divisible into: (1) the ileum, (2) the colon, and (3) the wider rectum. From the walls of the ileum numerous fine tubules called *Malpighian tubules* project into the haemocoele. These are concerned with excretion (see page 181).

DIGESTION OF FOOD. The cockroach is omnivorous and feeds mainly on scraps of food and other organic matter (wool, fluff, or even paper). Lying on either side of and rather below, the crop is a pair of large salivary glands, each composed of two much branched secretory portions and a club-shaped diverticulum of the main salivary duct, which acts as a receptacle for the saliva. The ducts from both salivary glands enter the main duct which passes through the neck to open between the hypopharynx and the labium. Through this duct the saliva is passed on to the food. The saliva contains a diastatic enzyme which digests starch. After mastication and ingestion the food passes into the crop where it meets more enzymes secreted by the mesenteron and regurgitating forwards through the gizzard. These enzymes include proteolytic ones (trypsin and erepsin), lipase, invertase and maltase (see page 485). Further trituration

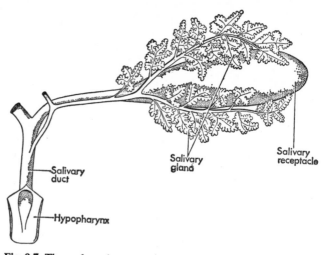

Fig. 9.7. The cockroach.
Salivary glands and receptacle of one side with the main duct. (After *Miall* and *Denny*.)

occurs in the gizzard and then the finely divided food passes into the mesenteron for final digestion and absorption of the productions of digestion. A thin membranous tube (the *peritrophic membrane*) which is secreted by the walls of the mesenteron and which is permeable to both the enzymes and the products of digestion. It probably protects the lining of the mesenteron from abrasion as the food passes through it. The enteric caeca increase the surface available for absorption and secretion of enzymes. The faeces are formed in the colon (where water is abstracted and absorbed from the indigestible residue of the food) and voided via the anus on the underside of the terminal segment of the abdomen.

The blood vascular system and the Circulation

As previously stated, the main cavity of the body is haemocoelic and divided into three regions (see Fig. 9.4). The blood is colourless, containing no respiratory pigment. Leucocytes are present in it. The blood is kept in circulation by the heart, which is an elongated tube with muscular walls lying dorsally beneath the terga in the pericardial space, the floor of which is a perforated diaphragm. In this lie twelve pairs of fan-like *alary* muscles attached by their narrow pointed ends to the terga on either side. Alternate contractions and relaxations of these muscles cause the diaphragm to rise and

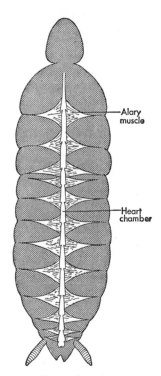

Fig. 9.8. The cockroach.

Dorsal view of the heart. (After *Miall* and *Denny*.)

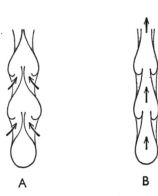

A   B

Fig. 9.9. The cockroach.

Diagrams to illustrate the action of the heart: *A* Heart chambers in diastole (relaxed); *B* Heart chambers in systole (contracted). The arrows show the direction of flow of the blood.

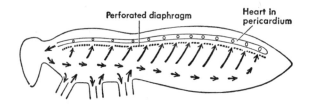

Fig. 9.10. The cockroach.

Diagram to show the main course of the circulation of the blood.

fall and so cause blood from the perivisceral haemocoele to flow upwards to replace that removed from the pericardial sinus by the heart as it 'beats'. The heart being attached to the diaphragm is also dilated each time the alary muscles contract and is thus enabled to 'suck in' more blood. The heart consists of thirteen chambers and though blind at the rear end, opens into the haemocoele at the anterior end. In the rear of each chamber a pair of valved ostia occur. These permit blood to enter the chamber when relaxed but prevent the blood from returning when the chamber contracts. The 'beating' of the heart consists of successive waves of contraction commencing at the rear end and passing forwards, followed by relaxations. The blood is kept flowing forwards in the heart by the presence of ventricular valves at the rear entrance of each chamber. The blood is thus kept flowing in a forward direction into the head region whence it returns backwards through the haemocoelic spaces to re-enter the heart. From the perineural sinus, the blood flows into the limbs and returns into the perivisceral sinus. It also flows out in the 'nervures' of the wings and returns likewise. The blood plays only a small part in respiration, being mainly concerned with the transport of food and excretory products.

Respiration

Respiration is effected by an elaborate network of tubes called *tracheae* which ramify through the haemocoele and allow air to penetrate throughout the body within these tubes. The tracheae are formed by ingrowths of the ectoderm which branch repeatedly and, except for the finest branches (called *tracheoles*), are lined by close spirals of chitin. The larger tracheae anastomose and communicate with the outer air by ten *spiracles* (or *sterigmata*) on each side, two pairs in the thorax (one between the pro- and the mesothorax and the other between the meso- and metathorax) and the remainder between the terga and sterna of the eight anterior segments of the abdomen. The finest tracheae end in tracheal cells and contain fluid.

Gaseous exchange occurs by diffusion between the air in the tracheae and the dissolved gases in the blood in the haemocoele, oxygen diffusing inwards and carbon dioxide outwards, though there is evidence to show that carbon dioxide also diffuses out through the cuticle. The main effect is that oxygen enters the spiracles, diffuses along the tracheae, dissolves in the fluid in the fine tracheoles and then enters the blood. To assist in this passage of oxygen into the body, certain respiratory movements occur. These take the form of

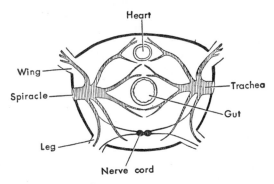

Fig. 9.11. The cockroach.

Diagram of a transverse section of the body to show the main tracheae. (After *Borradaile* from *Packard*.)

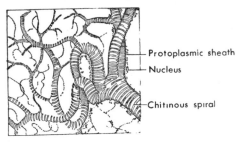

Fig. 9.12. The cockroach.

Magnified ends of tracheae. (After *Borradaile*.)

distortions of the profile of the body produced by muscular action and resulting in alternate compressions and relaxations of the main tracheae causing a certain amount of 'tidal' air to flow in and out (cf. mammalian respiration, page 516). Presumably the air entering the main tracheae is richer in oxygen and poorer in carbon dioxide than that which flows out.

Excretion and Osmoregulation

The cells of the walls of the Malpighian tubules (see Fig. 9.5) absorb nitrogenous excreta from the blood in the perivisceral haemocoele and excrete them in the form of uric acid and urates into the lumina of the tubules. This semi-solid waste passes into the proctodaeum to be voided with the faeces. (The excretion of solid uric acid and urates instead of a solution of soluble waste matter, e.g. urea, is an aid to the conservation of water within the body.)

The fat body also accumulates uric acid and a certain amount of nitrogenous waste may be shed in the cuticle during the periodic moultings which occur during growth.

The nervous systems and the Sense organs

THE NERVOUS SYSTEM. In the head is the 'brain' lying in front of and dorsal to the oesophagus. The 'brain' is a bilobed structure connected by nerves to the eye, and the antennae, and joined to a

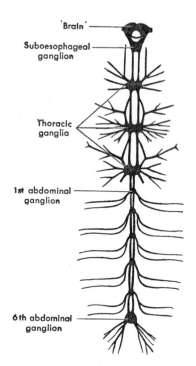

'Brain'

Suboesophageal ganglion

Thoracic ganglia

1st abdominal ganglion

6th abdominal ganglion

Fig. 9.13. The cockroach.
Diagram of the nervous system of the cockroach.
(After *Miall* and *Denny*.)

suboesophageal ganglion by two short commissures encircling the oesophagus. This ganglion is composed of three fused ganglia inner-vating the gnathites and the lining of the 'mouth' and joined by a pair of commissures passing through the neck to the first pair of ganglia of the ventral chain of ganglia lying in the perineural haemocoelic sinus. This chain consists of nine pairs of ganglia linked by double commissures, three in each of the thoracic segments and six in the abdomen. The last pair of abdominal ganglia is larger than the others in the abdomen and innervates the sixth and suc-ceeding segments of the abdomen. From all the ganglia paired segmental nerves are given off. A visceral nerve supply exists in connexion with the anterior part of the gut.

SENSE ORGANS. The eyes resemble those of the Crayfish but function solely as apposition eyes, since the pigment in the iris cells is not retractable. Chemo-receptors, tacto-receptors and, probably, sound receptors are found scattered in various parts of the epidermis. The receptors of the antennae are olfactory in nature.

Reproduction

The sexes are separate. In both sexes the gonads and accessory organs lie in the hinder part of the abdomen.

Embedded in the fat body of the male is a pair of lobed testes from each of which a *vas deferens* descends backwardly to unite with its fellow to form a short *ejaculatory duct* situated beneath the rectum and opening ventrally to the anus into the space above the ninth sternum. At the point of union of the two *vasa efferentia* is a so-called *mushroom gland* consisting of a large number of short blind tubes some of which serve to store the sperm. (The testes are functional in producing sperm only in the younger stages.) Surrounding the external aperture of the ejaculatory duct and of the club-shaped *conglobate gland* which lies beneath it are a number of small plates known as *gonapophyses*. The function of the conglobate gland is not known but its secretion may be used to form packets of sperm known as *spermatophores*.

In the female is a pair of ovaries, each of which consists of eight *ovarian tubules* tapering towards their inner ends and joined at their broader hinder ends to short oviducts. The two oviducts unite to form the *vagina*, which opens to the exterior beneath the anus into the genital bursa above the seventh sternum. The accessory female organs are (1) the unequally branched spermatheca, which lies above the vagina with a separate opening to the exterior and (2) the branched *colleterial glands*, which also open into the bursa. Projecting from the dorsal wall of the genital bursa is a complex structure of chitinous plates known as the *ovipositor*.

After pairing, sperms delivered by the male are stored in the spermatheca. The eggs are subsequently shed in batches of sixteen and are fertilized in the genital bursa by sperm from the spermatheca. After fertilization, each batch of eggs is surrounded by a brown case secreted by the colleterial glands. The gland on the left side secretes a protein which is hardened by the tanning action of the secretion

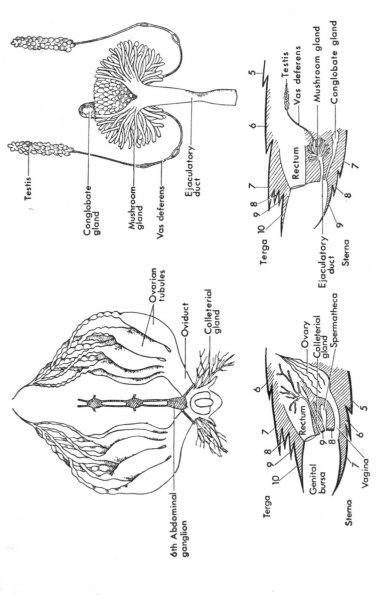

Fig. 9.14. The cockroach. The reproductive system.

A Female organs. Ventral view (ABOVE); vertical section (BELOW) to show the relative positions of the organs. Ovipositor omitted.
B Male organs. Dorsal view (ABOVE); vertical section (BELOW) to show the relative positions of the organs. Gonapophyses omitted.
(After *Miall* and *Denny.*)

of the gland on the right side. The egg case or *cocoon* is carried
about, protruding from the genital bursa until deposited in a suitable
hiding place.

GROWTH AND ECDYSIS. The young which hatch out from the eggs
are similar in form to the adults but lack wings. They are called
nymphs. During the growing period, a series of moults (ecdyses)
occur, since the exoskeleton is incapable of extension. In the final
stages of growth the wings appear.

GENERAL NOTES ON INSECTS

The insects may be classified as follows:

Sub-class 1. *The Apterygota* (Ametabola)—insects devoid of wings
and with direct development, i.e. the young are similar to the adults
in all but size and degree of maturity of the sexual organs.

Sub-class 2. *The Pterygota*—insects possessing wings in the adult
stage. These are further divided into two divisions.

(a) The Exopterygota (Hemimetabola) are insects in which the
wings develop as *external* projections of the body wall. The young
are known as nymphs and resemble the adults apart from the
possession of wings, i.e. there is an *incomplete* metamorphosis.

(b) The Endopterygota (Holometabola) are insects in which the
wings develop primarily as *ingrowths* of the ectoderm. The life history
displays a *complete* metamorphosis since the egg develops into a
larval form unlike the adult. When fully grown the larva enters
upon a dormant stage known as a *pupa* (or chrysalis in the
butterflies and moths) in which a reconstruction of the body takes
place and from which emerges finally the *imago* or *perfect* insect.
The larval stage is occupied in feeding and growing, while the
imaginal stage serves to reproduce and to disperse the species.

The sub-classes are further divided into orders. The following is a
list of the principal orders.

Apterygota
Order I: Collembola—the spring tails
Order II: Thysanura—the silver fish (*Lepisma*)

Pterygota
Division I: Exopterygota
Order I: Orthoptera—cockroaches, locusts, grass-hoppers,
             stick and leaf insects.

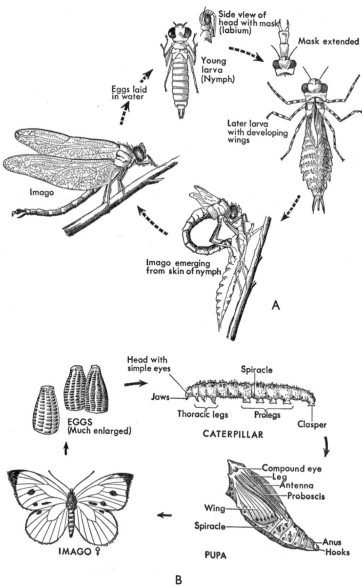

Fig. 9.15.

A Diagram of the life history of a Dragon-fly (*Aeschna*) – a representative of the Hemimetabola.

B Diagram of the life history of the Cabbage White Butterfly – a representative of the Holometabola.

Order II: Dermaptera—earwigs
Order III: Isoptera—termites
Order IV: Odonata—dragonflies
Order V: Hemiptera—bugs and aphids
Order VI: Ephemeroptera—mayflies

Division II: Endopterygota
Order I: Lepidoptera—butterflies and moths
Order II: Diptera—flies, including gnats and mosquitoes
Order III: Coleoptera—beetles
Order IV: Hymenoptera—bees and wasps
Order V: Neuroptera—lacewings, alder flies
Order VI: Trichoptera—caddis flies
Order VII: Aphaniptera—fleas

(In passing it may be noticed that the classification into orders is based largely on the wing characters from which the orders derive their names, e.g. Lepidoptera—scaly wings; Diptera—two wings, etc.)

1. The larva

The form of the larva varies in the different orders. In the Exopterygota it is called a *nymph* and differs from the adult mainly in

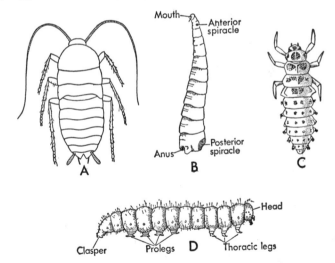

Fig. 9.16. Examples of insect larvae.

A Nymph of Cockroach; *B* Maggot of Blowfly; *C* Grub of Ladybird beetle; *D* Caterpillar of a Cabbage White Butterfly. (From specimens.)

the absence of wings, but in the Endopterygota the larva is markedly different from the imago. In the order Coleoptera, the larva is a *grub* possessing a distinct head with jaws and three pairs of thoracic walking legs, the abdomen being devoid of appendages; in the order Diptera it is a *maggot* lacking a head with jaws and also limbs, while in the order Lepidoptera and in some members of the Hymenoptera (the sawflies) the larva is a *caterpillar* which, in addition to possessing a distinct head with jaws and three pairs of thoracic walking legs, has a number of stumpy abdominal 'pro-legs' (five pairs or fewer in the Lepidopteran caterpillars, and more than five pairs in those of the sawflies). The larva in all cases undergoes a series of ecdyses (shedding of the cuticle) as it grows.

2. The pupa

This is the dormant stage in the life history of the Endopterygota, during which many of the internal organs break down while the tissues of the body become 'fluid', with the exception of the nervous

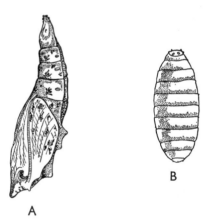

Fig. 9.17. Examples of pupae.
A Chrysalis of Cabbage White Butterfly; *B* Puparium of blowfly. (From specimens.)

system and the heart, and a wholesale reconstruction of the bodily structure occurs from 'imaginal buds' (small groups of cells found in the larval stage). In the silkworm moth, the pupa is enshrouded in a covering of silken fibres spun by the caterpillar when preparing to enter the pupal stage. The silk is secreted as a fluid, which hardens on exposure to the air, by a pair of glands called *spinnerets* situated in the labium. The majority of pupae, however, rely on the hardened cuticle for protection, any silken threads produced being used for attaching the pupa to its support. The pupae of many of the Diptera are also enclosed in the skin of the previous ecdysis, which is known as the *puparium*.

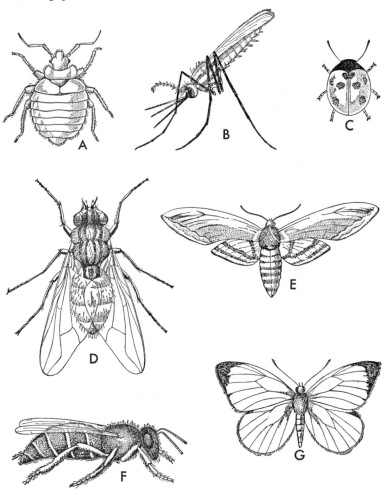

Fig. 9.18. Examples of insect imagos.

A Bed-bug (*Cimex*); *B* Mosquito (*Anopheles*); *C* Ladybird beetle (*Coccinella*); D House fly (*Musca*); *E* Hawk moth (*Sphinx*); *F* Honey bee (*Apis*); *G* Cabbage White Butterfly (*male*) (*Pieris*). (From specimens and various sources.)

3. The imago

The general features of the body of the imago are illustrated by the
cockroach. Variations are found in the mouthparts and in the wings.

MOUTHPARTS. The majority of insects have biting mouthparts
similar to those of the cockroach but modifications adapted to a
variety of feeding habits are found.

(a) Licking and biting mouthparts. These are found in the Hymenoptera. While the mandibles are used for biting (or moulding wax

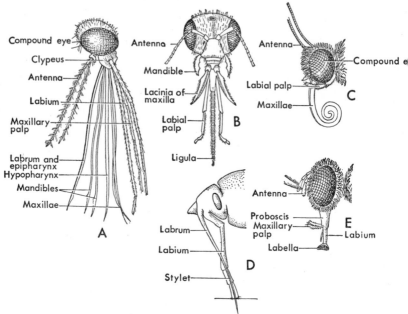

Fig. 9.19. Various types of insect mouthparts.

A Mosquito   (a dipteran);   *B* Honey bee   (a hymenopteran);
C Butterfly (a lepidopteran); *D* Bug (a hemipteran); *E* House fly (a
dipteran). (*D* after *Imms.*)

in the honey bee), the ligulae of the labium are drawn out to form a
licking organ to 'lap up' nectar in flowers.

(b) Sucking mouthparts. These occur in the Lepidoptera. The
mandibles are entirely lacking and the labium is much reduced. The
first maxillae form a long tube used for sucking up nectar, suction
being provided by a valved, dilatable oesophagus.

(c) Piercing and sucking mouthparts. (i) Diptera. In the majority
of the Diptera the labrum and second maxillae form a tube.

Within this tube are five fine stylets formed from the mandibles, the 1st maxillae and the lingua[1]. These are used to pierce the skin of the prey to enable the blood to be sucked up by the suctorial crop. In the house flies, the stylets are absent and the labium ends in a bilobed 'labellum' over the surface of which saliva flows on to the food. It is then ingested together with dissolved food. (ii) In the Hemiptera, the mouthparts here are also modified to form a jointed tube for sucking and piercing.

THE WINGS. The basic wing structure is a double fold of the integument (ectoderm and cuticle) in which lie a number of so-called 'nervures' whose number, arrangement and pattern varies widely among the different classes. Each 'nervure' consists of a haemocoelic canal surrounding tracheae and nerves.

The anterior pair of wings may serve as covers, called 'elytra', for the protection of the hinder pairs of membranous wings when not in use for flying. This is a feature in the cockroach (see page 171) but is more evident in the Coleoptera where the elytra are much thickened (as in the ladybird beetle). The members of one sub-order of the Hemiptera (bugs) have the front portions of the anterior pair of wings thickened, with the hinder portions membranous. The wings of the Lepidoptera are covered by overlapping scales containing urates and generally pigmented. (The iridescent colours of the wings of certain tropical butterflies are due to interferences of light reflected by a finely ridged surface.) The hinder pair of wings in the Diptera form small structures known as *halteres* which act as organs of equilibrium. The wings are hinged to the pleura between the terga and sterna, as shown in the following diagram (Fig. 9.20).

In the base of the wing are small axillary sclerites, to which are attached muscles. The movements of the wings are produced mainly by the indirect muscles, which cause the wings to rise and fall by movements of the terga relative to the sterna. At the same time, muscles attached to the axillary sclerites produce backwards and forwards movements and the combined effect of all the muscles is to cause the tips to perform a figure-of-eight movement accompanied by deflections of the wing membrane directed so as to produce propulsion.

The rate of movement is very high in the majority of insects. By causing the tips of the wings of a stationary fly to mark a rapidly moving smoked drum, it is estimated that the wings perform as many as 330 vibrations a second. These very rapid movements are due to the extreme efficiency of the insect's muscles, which are of the striped

[1] or *hypopharynx*.

T.S.

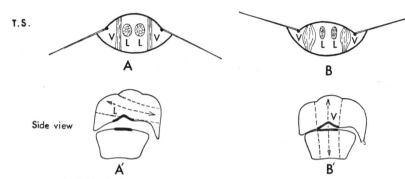

Fig. 9.20. Action of the muscles producing the up and down movements of the wings of an insect in flight.

*A, A*₁ Longitudinal muscles (L) contracted; vertical muscles (V) relaxed, causing elevation of the tergum and depression of the wings.

*B, B*₁ Vertical muscles (V) contracted; longitudinal muscles (L) relaxed, causing depression of the tergum and elevation of the wings. (Based on *Imms*.)

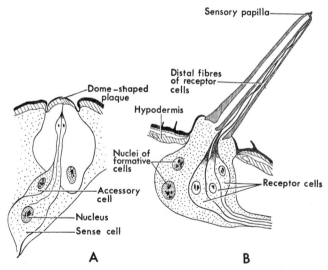

Fig. 9.21. Sensory cells of insects.

A Tactile campaniform sensillum of *Gryllus* (the cricket). (Based on *Snodgrass*.)

B Chemosensory hair of Blowfly. (Based on *Dethier*.)

variety. In Lepidoptera, the wing movements are much slower and the wings often act mainly as sails.

THE SENSES OF INSECTS. As mentioned in the chapter on the cockroach, the compound eyes of insects are similar in structure to those of the crayfish (see page 161). The day-flying insects have apposition eyes, while the nocturnal insects have superposition ones, though in many the eyes can function as both. The simple eyes (*ocelli*) found in the head region of many insects and their larvae more closely resemble the eyes of vertebrates in structure and have only one lens. Scattered about the cuticle are various nerve endings associated with sensory cells connected with hairs or plates. These consist of tactile organs and chemical receptors. The latter are usually concentrated on the mouth parts, the antennae and the tarsi of the walking limbs. The stimulation of the tarsi of the front limbs of a butterfly by means of a sugar solution is followed by the uncoiling of the proboscis. There is also distinct evidence that insects in certain cases possess a very acute sense of smell, the males being attracted from far and wide by the scent of females. Grasshoppers produce audible sounds by rasping file-like surfaces on the femurs of the hind limbs against the wings, while crickets 'chirp' by rubbing their wings together. These sounds are 'picked up' by special auditory organs on the first abdominal segments. The tapping sounds produced by the 'death watch' beetle are well known.

ADAPTIVE RADIATION. Insects, like mammals, show *adaptive radiation* as illustrated by the accompanying diagram (Fig. 9.23).

Insects are, indeed, remarkable for the high degree of adaptability shown by various genera and species in different environments. It is not surprising, therefore, that—coupled with their great fecundity and powers of dispersal—they form a large proportion of the fauna of any particular locality and constitute a source of food for higher animals, in particular for insectivorous birds, bats and mammals such as the mole, anteater and badger. On the other hand, they are man's most formidable competitors for food. So numerous are the insect plant depredators that every type of food crop is subject to attack, often by more than one type of depredator. For example, the cabbage is attacked at various stages in its development by (1) the turnip flea beetle which eats the cotyledons of the seedlings; (2) the larvae of the Cabbage Root Fly; (3) the caterpillars of the Cabbage White butterfly and of the Cabbage Moth.

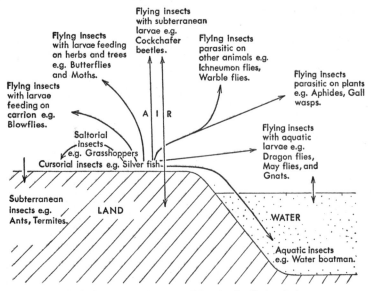

Fig. 9.22. Diagram to illustrate Adaptive Radiation in insects.

SPECIAL ADAPTATIONS: (a) MOUTHPARTS. These are modified to suit the food habits and have already been described on page 190. (b) AQUATIC INSECTS. These show adaptations which enable them to survive under water. Supplies of air may be carried down either in the tracheal system (e.g., in mosquito larvae) or trapped under the elytra as in the diving beetles, or as a film entangled in the covering of setae (e.g., in water boatmen). Alternatively, the oxygen dissolved in water may be utilized by allowing it to diffuse into the closed (apneustic) tracheal system of various aquatic larvae either through the skin (e.g., phantom fly larvae) or tracheal 'gills' (e.g., caddis fly) or a rectal basket of tracheae (e.g., dragon fly). In the larva of the harlequin fly (*Chironomus*) the blood contains haemoglobin capable of combining with the dissolved oxygen as it flows through projections of the body known as 'blood gills' (Fig. 9.23). (c) PARASITIC INSECTS. Well known parasites are bugs, lice and fleas, all with piercing and sucking mouthparts by which they obtain blood from their victims. The flea may be likened to a wingless dipteran which has a laterally compressed body to enable it to creep among the hairs or feathers of its hosts, and powerful limbs by which it can jump from one host to another. The aphids may be regarded

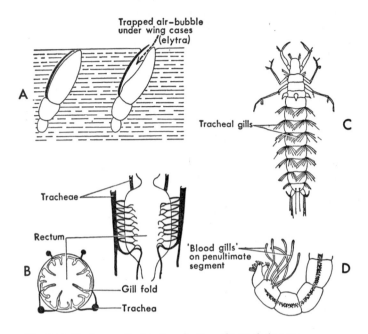

Fig. 9.23. Various methods of respiration of aquatic insects.

A Water beetle (*Dytiscus*); *B* Rectal 'basket' of Dragonfly (*Aeschna*) nymph; *C* 'Tracheal gills' of a Caddis fly larva; *D* 'Blood gills' of Harlequin fly (*Chironomus*) larva. (*A* and *B* after *Dakin*; *C* and *D* after *Lulham*.)

as plant parasites owing to their habit of sucking sap, unlike the plant depredators which eat the foliage, e.g. leaf-eating caterpillars, while the gall-forming insects (e.g. oak gall wasps) may also come under the same category. Even cases of insects parasitizing other insects occur, the best known example being that of the ichneumon wasps which lay their eggs in the caterpillars of Lepidoptera and on which the larvae feed after hatching.

SOCIAL INSECTS. Certain genera of the ants, the bees and the wasps live in colonies and display division of labour among the members. The honey-bee with its three castes, queens (egg layers), drones (males) and workers (sterile females), is a well-known instance. The varied tasks of the hive, e.g. nectar collecting, cell building, nurture and feeding of the young, cleaning of the hive and the evaporation of the nectar, are all performed by the workers at different periods of their

Fig. 9.24. 'Castes' of honey-bee.
A Drone; *B* Queen; *C* Worker.

lives. The workers in the ant colonies are more specialized in the performance of their tasks, and the highest degree of complexity of organization of the colony is found in the termites. In these occur a number of different 'castes': the 'reproductive caste', the 'worker caste' which perform many duties including the collection of food and the cultivation of fungi for food, and the 'soldier caste' which guard the hordes of workers when they sally forth from their 'hills' to collect food.

Economic importance of insects

So numerous and so formidable as competitors for food with man are the insects that they have been aptly named 'The Rival World'. The devastation caused by migratory swarms of locusts in Africa is well known but the depredations made on farm and fruit crops by insects in general, though not so marked as those produced by locusts, yet cause losses amounting to many millions of pounds the world over. Hence the very large amount of money spent annually by farmers, fruit growers and horticulturists in combating insect pests by means of poisonous sprays including D.D.T. and gammexane. Insects, too, may act as vectors of disease. The virus diseases of plants, e.g. that of the potato, are spread by aphids and other plant suckers, while the 'bites' of certain Diptera spread protozoan diseases of man and animals. Bubonic plague is spread by rat fleas, malaria by mosquitoes of the anopheline type, sleeping sickness and nagana disease of cattle by the tsetse flies. Contamination of food by harmful bacteria may occur through houseflies which carry them on their hairy bodies or deposit them in their saliva or faeces on to the food. Great damage to hides is often done by the 'bot' or 'warble' fly larva which causes a swelling beneath the skin. This eventually bursts and leaves a permanent hole in the skin.

On the credit side, insects—particularly bees, Lepidoptera and chrysomelid beetles—play a valuable part in the pollination of flowers as well as providing food for birds, Insectivora and Cheiroptera. The honey-bee has from very early times been domesticated by man for the sake of the honey and the wax provided by the bees, while the silkworm has been cultivated for centuries for the production of silk, the Chinese probably being the first to do so.

Finally, insects may be beneficial to man by preying on others which attack his cultivated plants, e.g. the ladybird beetle and the lacewing fly and their larvae feed on greenflies (aphids), wasps which feed on caterpillars and fly maggots, and ichneumon flies (Hymenoptera) which have larvae parasitic on injurious caterpillars such as those of the Cabbage White butterfly. Biological control of insect pests is well exemplified by the use of a parasitic insect (*Encarsia*) to exterminate the hemipteran white-fly (*Trialeurodes*), a greenhouse pest of tomatoes. Attempts have also been made to use insects to destroy obnoxious weeds, the outstanding example being the use of a moth (*Cactoblastis*) imported from South America into Australia to destroy the prickly pear (*Opuntia*).

10. *Arachnida*

THE CLASS Arachnida of the phylum Arthropoda is a heterogeneous one including such diverse types as the King Crab (*Limulus*) of the Caribbean seas, the scorpions of the tropics and sub-tropics, the ectoparasitic mites and ticks, the harvestmen and the spiders.

The Araneidae (spiders), though often popularly and erroneously regarded as insects, differ from the latter in the following ways: (1) The body is divided into two regions only—the cephalothorax (prosoma) and the abdomen (opisthosoma). (2) There are only two pairs of jaw-like appendages used for feeding: the *chelicerae* and the *pedipalpi*. The chelicerae are flat blades (gnathobases) with inner toothed borders and surmounted by a sharp fang perforated by a duct of a poison gland opening at its top. The fangs are used to pierce the prey and to paralyse it by injecting 'poison' into it. The pedipalps are more limb-like and terminate in claws for holding the prey. (3) Behind the pedipalpi are *four* pairs of jointed walking limbs also borne on the cephalothorax. (4) Antennae and compound eyes are lacking, there being usually eight simple eyes situated at the front of the cephalothorax. (5) In addition to possessing tracheae which are, however, unbranched (unlike those of the insects), spiders also respire by means of a pair of respiratory organs known as 'lung-books'. These are situated on the ventral side of the anterior region of the abdomen. Each lung-book is a cavity with a narrow opening to the exterior. From the wall of the cavity project a number of thin hollow shelf-like plates in which blood circulates and exchanges gases with the surrounding air, oxygen diffusing into the blood and carbon dioxide from the blood into the air.

The general internal anatomy of the spider can be seen from the accompanying figure (Fig. 10.2).

The majority of spiders are insectivorous, though a few of the larger tropical forms prey on small birds. The wolf spiders (*Lycosidae*) and jumping spiders (*Salticidae*) rely on the speed of their movements to catch their prey, but the members of many other genera spin various kinds of webs to trap insects. The webs are constructed of fine threads produced by the spinnerets situated at the hinder

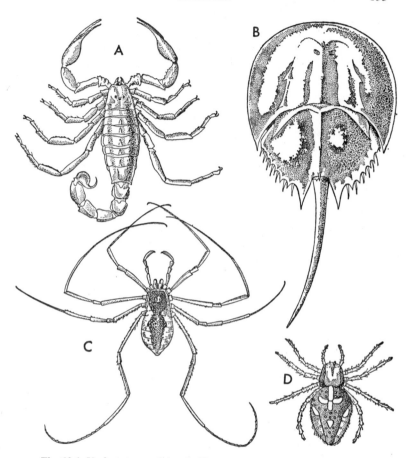

Fig. 10.1. Various types of Arachnida.

A Scorpion (*Scorpio*). *B* King Crab (*Limulus*). *C* Harvestman (*Phalangium*). *D* Garden Spider (*Epeira*).

end of the abdomen on the ventral side. Certain spiders such as the house spider (*Tegenaria*) form webs which are mere tangles of threads; others form tunnel-like webs leading into holes in the ground (e.g. the trapdoor spiders—*Avicularidae*), while the orb spinners (e.g. *Epeira*—the garden spider) spin flat webs consisting of spirals of viscid threads attached to a radiating system of spoke-like threads. The web spinners all remain motionless in the vicinity of their completed webs, ready to dart out of hiding to secure their prey when the vibrations of the web inform them that a victim has

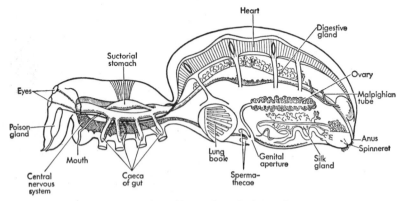

Fig. 10.2. L.S. of a spider to show the internal organs.
(After *Shipley* and *McBride* from *Warburton.*)

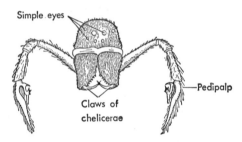

Fig. 10.3. Frontal view of a spider showing chelicerae and pedipalps.
(From various sources.)

become entangled in it. After capture, the spider proceeds to paralyse the prey by seizing it with the pedipalps and injecting poison
into it through the hollow fangs of the chelicerae. The prey is then
pressed against the mouth by the gnathobases of the chelicerae
while digestive fluids are exuded into it. In an hour or two, the
whole of the digestible matter of the insect undergoes external
digestion and the resulting fluid is sucked into the alimentary canal
of the spider by the suctorial 'stomach'. Eventually only the exoskeleton of the insect remains, the prey having been literally 'sucked
dry'.

The male spiders are usually smaller than the females and are
not uncommonly 'eaten' by the females after mating when the sperm
of the male are transferred with the aid of its pedipalpi to the spermathecae of the females, where they are stored until needed to fertilize

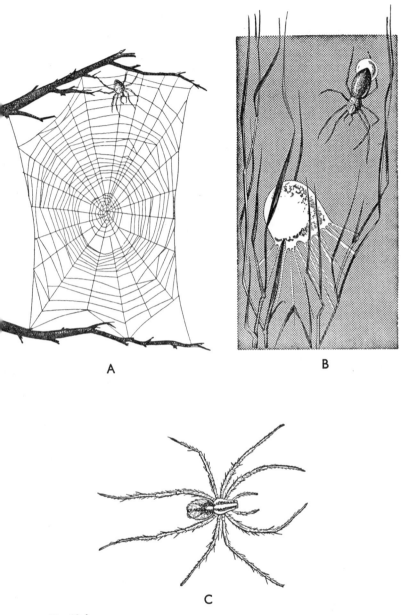

Fig. 10.4.
   A Epeira on its web. *B Argyroneta* (water spider). *C Lycosa* (wolf
spider). (Based on various authors.)

the eggs. These are laid in a cocoon of threads formed by the spinner-ets. After hatching, the young spiders—there being no metamor-phosis—are gregarious for a time, in the case of the web-spinners living within a tangle of threads. Eventually they disperse. To aid in dispersal, the young field spiders exude from their spinnerets a long thread (gossamer) which acts as a sail in the wind. After landing, these threads are abandoned. They may frequently be seen in late summer in the early morning, draping the grass in the fields and bespangled with dew which renders them visible. The female wolf spiders may often be seen carrying the egg cocoon attached to the rear of their abdomens until they deposit them under the shelter of dead leaves. The water spider (*Argyroneta*) is remarkable in spin-ning an underwater web to which it carries down air clinging to its hairy body. By repeated journeys to the web from the surface, a large bubble of air is collected and retained by the web. The spider uses this as a 'diving bell' while living beneath the water. It preys on insect aquatic larvae.

11. *Mollusca*

Introduction

THE MOST advanced invertebrate animals which we have so far considered are built on a segmental plan. One of the most interesting features of their biology is the way in which the primitive uniform segmental arrangement of limbs, ducts, nerves etc. has been altered

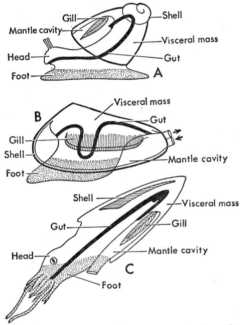

Fig. 11.1. Diagrams illustrating the body organisation of the three main classes of molluscs.

A a gastropod; *B* a bivalve; *C* a cephalopod.

in the course of evolution to fit the structure concerned for the performance of different functions. For example, the polychaete *Nereis* is either male or female, and the gametes are shed freely into the sea water. The oligochaete *Lumbricus* is hermaphrodite, the gametes are confined to limited regions of the coelom and are not shed freely but are exchanged during copulation, which is necessary because the animals live in the soil and not in an all-pervading aqueous medium.

The molluscs, such as the snail (*Helix*) and the swan mussel (*Anodon*) show no signs of segmentation or of any recent relationship to or derivation from segmented ancestors. However, the recent discovery of a very primitive mollusc *Neopilina* with some segmental features suggests that the mollusca may have sprung originally from a segmented ancestor but soon lost all traces of this type of arrangement. Instead, the molluscs have a characteristic body plan which distinguishes them from the animals of other phyla. This plan is shown by the snail, in which a *head, foot* and *visceral mass* are distinguishable. The head, of course, goes first during locomotion and bears sense organs and the mouth; the foot is the organ of locomotion and is a flat, muscular creeping structure. The visceral mass makes up the rest of the body and is housed in a spiral shell. As its name implies, the gut and digestive gland and the reproductive organs make up the largest part of it. This arrangement of parts is shown diagrammatically in Fig. 11.1.

Comparing *Anodon* with *Helix*, the most obvious feature is the shell, which is made of two parts or valves which can open and close. Inside the shell the body is soft, as is the body of *Helix*, and although a foot can be distinguished as a solid, muscular, ventral portion, there is no clearly marked head. The mouth opens in the anterior region between two pairs of soft flaps or palps, but although these may be sensory to some extent, sense organs like those of the snail are lacking. The visceral mass forms the soft tissue above the foot and between the shell valves and is extended on both sides as a lining to the shell. This is the *mantle*, which encloses the *mantle cavity*. The two large folded gills (*ctenidia*) lie in the mantle cavity, one on each side of the foot which is withdrawn into the mantle cavity when it is at rest but which can be protruded during burrowing.

A third group of the molluscs includes the squid and cuttlefish which are adapted to a pelagic life in the sea and which are superficially very unlike the two examples which we have just seen but which can be reconciled with the other molluscs by the possession of the head, foot and visceral mass with gills contained in a mantle cavity. These animals and the octopus belong to the Class Cephalopoda.

With the salient features of molluscan anatomy in mind, we can now examine the structure of *Helix* and *Anodon* in greater detail. In addition to the differences between annelids and molluscs which arise because the latter are non-segmented animals, there are other differences, the chief of which is the reduction of the coelom in the molluscs. In this they resemble the arthropods and, like some of them, have large blood spaces or haemocoeles which do duty for the coelom in that they contain some of the internal organs but the blood filling the haemocoele serves to carry food materials and also oxygen by virtue of its possession of a respiratory pigment. The coelom in the molluscs is reduced to the pericardial cavity, the cavities of the excretory organs and those of the gonads. The haemocoele (homologous with the blastocoele) is enormously enlarged and, in addition to some well defined blood vessels, consists of large tissue spaces.

Helix pomatia

The Roman or Edible snail, *Helix pomatia*, is the type frequently chosen for study and dissection on account of its large size. Among its external features may be noted its anterior ventral mouth, two pairs of retractile tentacles, the dorsal pair bearing eyes, reproductive

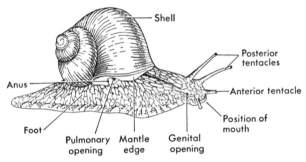

Fig. 11.2. *Helix.*
The external features of the snail (*Helix*). (From a specimen.)

aperture on the right side, *pneumostome* or opening into the mantle cavity which does duty as a lung, and the anus which opens near the pneumostome. The exposed surfaces of the animal are made slimy by the secretion of mucus which is especially copious on the ventral side or sole of the foot. This is applied to the substratum over which the animal crawls by forwardly progressing waves of muscular contraction. These can be seen by watching a snail crawling on a glass plate. It has been shown that in the regions where contraction of the longitudinal muscles occurs, the foot is lifted slightly off the ground and that portion moved forwards. In the regions where the longitudinal muscle is extended the foot is closely applied to the substratum and the foot is stationary.

Alimentary canal

Internally the mouth leads to a muscular buccal mass in the floor of which lies a ribbon-like rasping organ covered with fine horny teeth. This *radula* can be moved backwards and forwards against an upper jaw bar and used like a file to tear off small pieces of vegetation which it can also carry into the gut. The radula is gradually replaced by growth from a radula sac in which it originates. A pair of salivary glands opens into the buccal cavity. This leads into a large crop followed by a smaller stomach and an intestine lying in the visceral mass. The large digestive gland opens from the stomach and into its many fine tubules passes the ground-up food material, there to be digested intracellularly after some previous digestion has taken place in the crop. Here, probably by means of symbiotic bacteria, the snail can digest cellulose, thus liberating the contents of plant cells for intracellular treatment in the digestive gland. From the stomach, material passes into the intestine, the undigested portion to be formed into the copious faeces and passed out at the anus.

Reproductive system

The reproductive system is hermaphrodite and complex but consists essentially of a gonad, the *ovotestis*, which produces both eggs and sperm, and although the production of eggs is highly seasonal that of sperm goes on during the greater part of the year. These products both leave the gland by the single duct, the *hermaphrodite duct*. At the point where the hermaphrodite duct widens into the oviduct, the so-called *albumen gland* opens. This secretes not a protein but galactogen, a polymer of the *monosaccharide* sugar galactose. Also at this point, and partially embedded in the albumen gland, lies a small pouch, the *receptaculum seminis* where sperm from another snail can be stored to fertilize the oocytes as they descend from the hermaphrodite duct. The reproductive tract continues as the so-called oviduct with a line of secretory *prostatic tissue* attached to one side. This used to be known as the *sperm duct*, but it now seems unlikely that it is a hollow separate duct and that sperm pass along it in their passage from the hermaphrodite duct to the penis. Instead they, as well as the eggs, pass along the oviduct towards the end of which a sperm duct leads off as

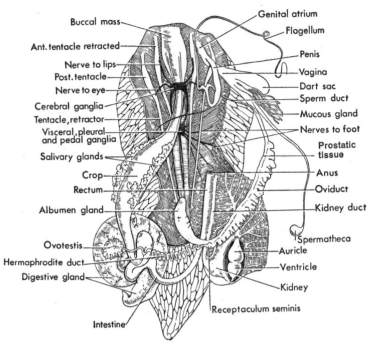

Fig. 11.3. *Helix.*

A general dissection of *Helix* to show the main structural features of the gut, reproductive and nervous systems. The shell has been removed, the mantle cavity and the body cavity opened, and the reproductive organs displaced to the right. (From a specimen.)

a continuation of the line of prostatic tissue, and this runs towards the bodywall to end in a muscular protrusible penis to which is attached a tapering hollow filament, the *flagellum.*

The female duct ends in a muscular vagina into which also open a *dart sac*, a mucous gland, and the duct of the spermatheca. Both the vagina and penis open into a genital atrium which in turn opens to the exterior by a common genital opening on the right-hand side of the foot just behind the head.

Cross fertilization of the eggs takes place after the exchange of sperm with another snail which is made during copulation. This occurs when two snails approach each other with the genital atria everted, thus exposing externally the openings of the penis and vagina. When the snails make contact, the calcareous dart contained in the dart sac is propelled into the body of the partner and provides a drastic form of stimulation. Later the penis of each snail is inserted into the vagina of the other and the packets of spermatozoa (or *spermatophores*) which are prepared in the flagellum travel up the duct of the spermatheca and are stored there. After this exchange of sperm the snails separate and eventually the spermatozoa in the spermatheca are liberated from the spermatophore in which they were transferred and make their way down the duct of the spermatheca and up the oviduct to the receptaculum seminis. Hereabouts they fertilize the oocytes as they come down the hermaphrodite duct, after which these become coated with a great thickness of galactogen and the secretions of the oviduct, the outer layer of which becomes somewhat calcified and forms a shell in which the egg is laid. This takes place in small holes in the soil in late summer. The eggs hatch in about a month.

Although the hermaphrodite reproductive organs are among the most conspicuous features of the viscera of the snail, other organ systems are represented.

Excretory system

The excretory system consists of a tube leading from the pericardial coelom by a small aperture and opening to the exterior adjacent the anus. It is seen in dissection as a brownish patch of tissue lying close to the heart. Its tubular nature is not clear to see owing to the folding of the walls but it can be shown to arise thus during development and to be essentially a coelomoduct.

Circulatory and Respiratory systems

The heart is the most conspicuous part of the circulatory system and consists of an auricle and ventricle lying in a coelomic space, the pericardial cavity near the left side of the mantle cavity. From the ventricle an aorta leads off and soon divides to give a main vessel to the head and another to the visceral mass. The arteries branch and the smaller branches discharge into the spacious haemocoele. The blood from this eventually collects in a channel surrounding the mantle cavity and from this it passes via the fine vessels which run in the wall of the mantle cavity to the pulmonary vein. This leads to the auricle. The circulation is thus an open one in that during part of its journey about the body the blood is contained in the haemocoele and bathes the various organs. Its movement is thus affected not only by the action of the heart but also by the body musculature which alters the shapes of the head and foot and hence affects the distribution of the blood. The blood is bluish in colour when oxygenated due to the presence in it of a respiratory pigment haemocyanin. This is a copper-containing compound of very high molecular weight (of the order of 6,000,000) which enables the blood to carry about one to two volumes of oxygen per 100 volumes of blood or about two to four times the amount that would dissolve in water under the same conditions. The blood is believed to be oxygenated as it passes through the fine vessels which form a network over the roof of the mantle cavity. This acts as a lung which possesses a mechanism for the renewal of air. The floor is muscular and can be flattened, thus drawing air into the pulmonary (or mantle) cavity. When the muscles relax the floor is raised and the pneumostome closed at the same time, thus raising slightly the pressure inside the lung and assisting in the uptake of oxygen. The opening of the pneumostome releases the excess pressure and the cycle continues in a somewhat irregular manner.

Nervous system

The central nervous system of *Helix* consists of a collar of nervous tissue in which five pairs of ganglia can be distinguished surrounding the oesophagus. These include the cerebral ganglia from which nerves run to the tentacles and buccal mass, and the pedal ganglia lying ventrally to the gut and supplying the foot. Posterior to these two pairs are three more pairs, namely the pleural, the pallial supplying the mantle, and the visceral ganglia. The central nervous system is thus compact but from the study of other gastropod molluscs it is believed that this state has been evolved from one in which the pallial and visceral ganglia were widely spaced from the others and were connected to them by long connectives.

The sense organs present are the eyes, borne at the tips of the dorsal retractile tentacles, and a pair of small statocysts adjacent the nerve collar. The ventral tentacles are believed to be chemosensory.

Asymmetry

The snail is a strikingly asymmetrical animal in its external appearance and in many of its organ systems. It is believed that this asymmetry is the result of the twisting of the visceral mass on the foot which has occurred during evolution and has affected the evolutionary development of other organ systems so that those on one side have disappeared. In addition to this twisting or torsion, the visceral mass has become elongated and coiled into a spiral or helix and fits into a shell of the same shape.

Shell

The shell is secreted by the ectodermal epithelium of the visceral mass and mantle, and is composed of three layers. The outer one is a protein known as conchiolin and forming the *periostracum*. The middle layer is largely calcium carbonate in the crystalline form calcite and is called the prismatic layer, while the inner layer is also calcium carbonate of different structure and forms the nacreous layer. The outer two layers are secreted by the cells lining a groove at the edge of the mantle cavity whereas the inner layer is secreted by the cells of the whole mantle and those covering the visceral mass. The spiral shell is, as it were, wound around a central axis, the *columella*, from which rigid central portion of the shell the columella muscle originates. This is inserted into the head and foot by a number of insertions and serves to retract those parts into the shell.

Hibernation

The snail hibernates during the winter in a dry position under leaves or in holes in walls and prepares for its suspension of bodily activities by blocking the aperture of the shell by a disk, the *epiphragm*, which is complete except for a small hole permitting sufficient gaseous exchange to take place as will keep pace with the greatly reduced metabolism.

Anodon

By comparison with the snail, the Swan Mussel, *Anodon cygnea*, is a sluggish animal living in mud on the bottom of ponds, lakes, and slowly moving streams. Consequently it is seldom seen except in the laboratory, when specially sought or when it is cast on the bank by dredging operations. The bivalve shell is brownish green in colour and marked by concentric lines indicating irregular stages of growth. The colour is that of the periostracum, as can be seen by looking at a piece of broken shell or at the oldest part of the shell, the *umbo*, from which the periostracum is usually missing. When tightly shut no part of the living animal can be seen, but if placed in water the valves of the shell open and in the natural state the foot is sometimes protruded and, by the movements which it makes, serves to drag the animal into or through the mud in which it lives. When the muscles which close the shell—the adductor muscles—have been cut, the valves gape because of the elastic nature of the *hinge ligament* which holds them together and which works in opposition to the adductor

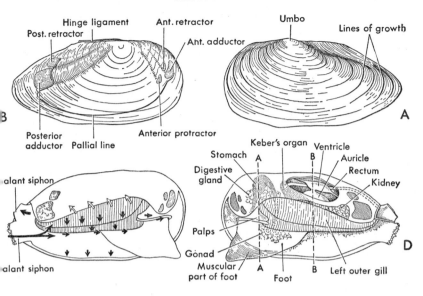

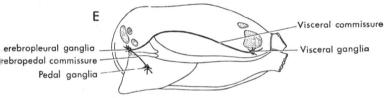

Fig. 11.4. *Anodon.*

Diagrams to illustrate the anatomy of the Swan Mussel (*Anodon*).
A External features of the left shell valve. *B* Interior view of left shell valve showing muscle scars. *C* Food collecting currents produced by cilia on gills and mantle as seen from the right side. Solid arrows denote currents in the mantle cavity: hollow arrows denote currents in the epibranchial chamber. The mouth lies between the labial palps. *D* The arrangement of the gut, heart, kidney and reproductive organs as seen from the left side. *E* The nervous system as seen from the left side.

muscles in the limited movements which the shell can make. The shell can be separated from the mantle which lines it, the hinge ligament broken and a valve removed, leaving the animal in the other valve. When seen in this way, the mantle lobe covers the animal with a translucent sheet of tissue through which the outlines of the foot and gills can be made out. The cut ends of the muscles stick through the mantle and the surfaces by which they were attached to the shell are exposed. Large anterior and posterior adductor muscles draw the shell valves together, anterior and posterior foot retractors lie on the inner sides of them; in addition there is a foot protractor muscle and a small dorsal muscle near the hinge ligament. The mantle lobes have thickened borders which secrete the two outer layers of the shell. These mantle edges are normally closely applied and make a water-tight cavity except at the opening of the *inhalant siphon* which leads from the outside into the mantle cavity and another dorsal opening (*the exhalant siphon*) which leads to the outside from a chamber lying above the gills. Removal of one mantle lobe reveals the inner and the outer gill lamina, the foot, the labial palps and the inner side of the other mantle lobe. (See Fig. 11.4.)

General organization

The mantle is joined to the rest of the body along a wavy line which marks the junction of the foot and visceral mass and which runs ventral to the adductor muscles and dorsal to the gills. The structure

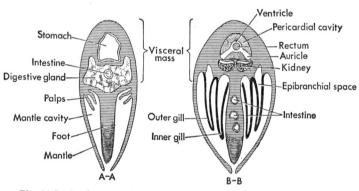

Fig. 11.5. *Anodon.*

Transverse sections of *Anodon* taken at the positions *A—A* and *B—B* in Fig. 11.4D.

of these very conspicuous organs is most easily understood by reference to their appearance in transverse section. The axis of each (left and right) gill, which is attached to the body along its length, bears folded filaments joined together in places. These form what appear to be two gills on each side but which are, in fact, two halves of a single gill. The line along which the filaments end lies parallel to the axis of the gill. Each gill thus consists of an inner and outer gill lamina composed essentially of folded filaments lying side by side and joined together by tissue bridges. The whole structure is heavily ciliated and by the beating of the cilia water is passed between the filaments, into the channels within the lamina formed by the folded filaments. These are all connected and the water finds its way to a canal (the *epibranchial chamber*) above each gill which unites with its fellow posteriorly to open by the exhalant siphon. The outer gill laminae are attached to the visceral mass along their outer edges but the inner edges of the inner laminae are attached to those of the opposite side, except in the region of the foot where they are free to allow for movements of the foot.

To the naked eye the gill appears to be horizontally striated but microscopic examination shows that the gill filaments run at right

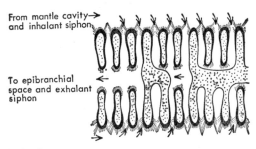

From mantle cavity→
and inhalant siphon

To epibranchial
space and exhalant
siphon

Fig. 11.6. *Anodon.*
Horizontal section of a gill of *Anodon* showing the gill filaments in transverse section with the tissue connexions between them. The main cilia are also shown.

angles to the long axis of the organ. The water current set up by the cilia of the gill brings in with it much suspended matter, both living and dead. Large particles tend to settle out in the mantle cavity and are conveyed to the exterior by the ciliation of the mantle but fine particles are captured in the mucus secreted by certain ectodermal cells of the gills and are transported to the free edges of the laminae by downwardly beating cilia. Here there is a groove in which the cilia beat towards the mouth carrying food strings in that direction. These are passed into the mouth aided by the *labial palps* which are, as it were, drawn out upper and lower lips with the aperture lying between them. The food strings pass by a short oesophagus to the stomach, into which opens the large digestive gland surrounding it. The stomach is extensively ciliated and considerable sorting of the food is believed to occur in it, the finer particles suitable for intracellular digestion being passed into the digestive gland, the large and the unsuitable particles being passed into the intestine which, after describing about two turns in the substance of the visceral mass, runs, as the rectum, in the dorsal part of the body to open into the common exhalant canal at the anus.

The rectum, along part of its length, is surrounded by one of the few remaining portions of the coelom, the *pericardium*. This subserves three main functions: it contains the heart, it gives access to the paired kidneys, and from its walls are formed Keber's organs which are believed to be excretory in function. Each kidney is a coelomoduct with complex walls lined by excretory cells and opening externally above the inner gill lamina by a small opening lying near the anterior border of the pericardium.

Circulatory system and respiration

The heart consists of a single ventricle which surrounds the rectum and into which paired auricles open. From the ventricle blood passes to the foot, mantle and viscera. It is collected into a pedal sinus from which some passes back to the heart but most returns via the kidney and ctenidia. The contraction of the ventricle can generate a pressure of from 3 to 4 cm. of water which is sufficient to drive the blood around the body when the animal is at rest, but the contraction of the foot musculature can generate a pressure of 30 cm. of water, which being much greater than the blood pressure would result in the squeezing of all the blood from the foot were it not for a valvular arrangement interposed in the circulation after the sinus in the foot. This can isolate the foot during its periods of activity, during which it is inflated with blood pumped into it by the heart. When the foot is retracted, much of the blood leaves it for other parts of the circulatory system, notably that of the mantle. This organ, being thin-walled and ciliated, acts as the chief region of gaseous exchange.

Excretory system

We have already seen that the excretory organs lead from the pericardium to the exterior. Each consists of a proximal bladder and a distal glandular part. It is believed that the fluid contents of the pericardium pass down the duct and that this fluid may have waste nitrogenous substance added to it. The pericardial fluid is probably produced by ultra-filtration through the wall of the heart. It has a slightly smaller salt content than the blood but the colloid osmotic pressure (owing to the presence of protein) is much less. It is probable that some more salt is absorbed by the kidney and some waste nitrogenous compounds added. Since the rate of urine flow and the concentration of salts in the urine are sufficient rapidly to deplete the salt reserves of the body even although these are being replenished from the food, it is thought that salts can be absorbed selectively from the environment over the body surface. It is indeed known that the swan mussel can absorb salts from very dilute solutions.

Reproductive system

The sexes are generally separate and the gonad occupies the upper portion of the foot around the intestine. The gonads discharge by ducts opening into the epibranchial space close to the apertures of the kidneys. The oocytes are fertilized *in situ* by spermatozoa from another animal taken in with the inhalant current. Development continues in the female parent, the eggs developing into larvae between the folds of the outer gill lamina. The *glochidia* so formed are tiny bivalves which are set free from the parent in the spring following the summer of their development. They do not feed and at first they possess no foot. In the ventral position they have a gland which secretes sticky protein threads, the *byssus* by which they can become attached to a fish. It is said that the proximity of a fish stimulates the larva to flap the shell valves and drive out the byssus which may adhere to the fish. If this occurs and the larva becomes attached to the fish by the teeth on its shell, the wound thus inflicted leads to local inflammation and the temporary parasite becomes embedded in the tissues of its host from which it absorbs nourishment. Eventually the inflamed tissue is replaced and sloughed off and the young mussel leads an independent existence, having by this time come to resemble the adult more closely in form. This remarkable life history is not typical of bivalve molluscs, which mostly have a free-swimming larva known as a *veliger*: it may be regarded as an adaptation to life in streams as providing a means of distributing the species without the risk of the larva being carried downstream and lost.

Nervous system

The nervous system of *Anodon* consists of three pairs of ganglia, the cerebropleural, lying one on each side of the oesophagus, the visceral, and the pedal. The pedal ganglia lie embedded in the foot at the junction of the ventral muscular with the upper portion containing the digestive gland and gonad. They are joined to the cerebropleural ganglia by short connectives. The visceral ganglia lie on the ventral surface of the posterior adductor muscle and are joined to the cerebropleural ganglia by long connectives. Sense organs are poorly developed but include the small statocysts lying near the pedal ganglia and the *osphradium* lying below the visceral ganglia and believed to be chemosensory. Receptor cells are present on the inhalant siphon, the mantle edge and elsewhere for the animal reacts to touch and to chemical stimuli.

12. *Echinodermata*

Asterias

THE COMMON starfish, *Asterias rubens*, is often seen in rock pools or stranded on the shore. It belongs to the phylum Echinodermata, an assemblage of sedentary or slowly moving animals having calcareous ossicles embedded in the dermis and spines protruding from the surface. Although they begin life as bilaterally symmetrical larvae, echinoderms metamorphose into radially symmetrical adults characteristically having a five-rayed (or *pentamerous*) plan. This is clearly seen in *Asterias* with its five arms arising from a small central region or disk. Patient watching shows that it can move with equal facility in any direction and this, together with other bodily activities, demonstrates that its morphological symmetry is also expressed physiologically.

External features

Since the side of the starfish which is uppermost is not the original dorsal side of the larva, it is named by reference to the side on which the mouth opens and is therefore called the *aboral* side. The mouth, in the centre of the *oral* side, is held against the ground and is normally obscured by spines and tube feet. The most conspicuous feature on the aboral surface of the disk is a small perforated calcareous plate lying between two of the arms, or, as one can say, between two radii. It is called the *madreporite*, is interradial in position and its pores lead into a very complex system of canals known as the *water vascular system* (see p. 220). Other noticeable features of the aboral side are the spines, which are short, rigid and irregularly placed, the *pedicellariae*, tiny pincer-like structures grouped round the spines and the pile or felt of thin-walled gills or *papulae* which cover the surface in between the spines. The mouth, lying in the centre of the oral side, is surrounded by longer spines than are found on the aboral side and these are continued as a row bordering a groove running along each arm. These *adambulacral spines* bear pedicellariae. The ambulacral groove is roofed by paired

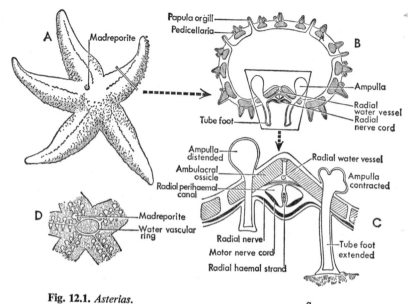

Fig. 12.1. *Asterias.*

A diagram of a starfish (*Asterias*) to show its external appearance; *B* a transverse section of an arm; *C* an enlarged view of the ambulacral region; *D* the water vascular system.

ambulacral ossicles embedded in the body wall and which cannot, of course, be seen from outside. Below this, and visible in the groove, lies the superficial radial nerve cord composed of receptors, nerve and supporting cells. On either side of the nerve cord lie the *tube feet*. These organs are peculiar to echinoderms and are used for many purposes including attachment, locomotion, feeding and gaseous exchange. When seen from the outside each consists of a tubular leg projecting from the body with a sucker at the tip. They are connected with the coelomic spaces mentioned above as the water vascular system. The tube feet of each arm are very numerous and lie in four rows, two on each side of the radial nerve cord. The unpaired terminal tube foot has no sucker but bears a red spot marking the position of a simple eye.

The internal structure of *Asterias* can be seen in two ways. Removal of the aboral half of the body-wall reveals the gut and gonads and parts of the water vascular system but the study of transverse sections of the arms is necessary to obtain a picture of the relation of the structures in the region of the ambulacral groove.

Alimentary canal

The mouth opens into a very short oesophagus which in turn opens into a large five-lobed stomach. This can be everted to surround the food and withdrawn by five pairs of retractor muscles inserted into its walls and taking their origin from the rows of ambulacral ossicles. The upper portion of the stomach is distinguishable from the lower portion by the openings of the five pyloric ducts. Each of these

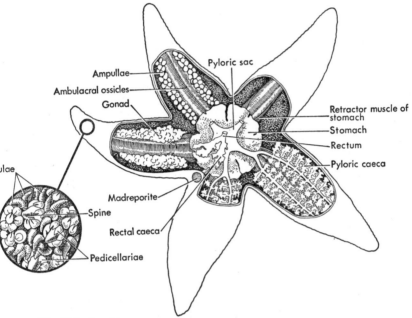

Fig. 12.2. *Asterias.*
 Dissection of *Asterias* to show the gut, gonads and parts of the water vascular system. Inset is an enlarged view of the external surface showing spines, pedicellariae and gills.

branches into a pair of pyloric caeca which run most of the way along the arms. These are thin-walled and are greatly sacculated. From the region of the pyloric ducts a short straight rectum runs to the tiny anus situated interradially on the aboral surface of the disk. A pair of small caeca also open from the rectum, forming an exception to the general radial arrangement of the organs.

Feeding

Asterias is a carnivore and feeds on living and dead animals of many sorts but its preferred diet is one of bivalve molluscs. It opens these by wrapping its arms round them with the opening of the shell directed towards the predator's mouth. The application of steady traction chiefly exerted by the tube feet which adhere to the mollusc shell opens the valves. The stomach is everted by contraction of the general musculature of the body-wall, the pressure of which is transmitted to the stomach wall by the coelomic fluid. The everted gut surrounds the soft parts of the mollusc, which it digests by the enzymes it secretes. When digestion is complete the stomach is withdrawn, the tube feet relax their grip and the empty shell is left. The fluid taken into the gut is wafted by ciliary currents into the pyloric caeca which are the chief sites of absorption.

Reproductive system

The gonads consist of a pair of strands in each arm from which the germ cells are proliferated so that they come to be contained in thin-walled sacs hanging in the coelom. They vary greatly in size according to the season and at maturity may occupy a considerable portion of the perivisceral space. The gonads of each arm discharge to the exterior by fine pores situated at the junction of the arms with the disk. The sexes are separate and approximately equal in numbers and the germ cells are discharged freely into the sea where fertilization takes place and leads to the formation of a characteristic larva. At first this is bilaterally symmetrical and relatively simple and is known as a *bipinnaria*. Later the bipinnaria develops very complex ciliated bands before settling down and metamorphosing into the adult radially symmetrical form.

Water vascular system

Parts of the water vascular system, the *ampullae*, have already been noticed projecting into the perivisceral cavity as rows of small bladders lying in the ambulacral position. Each ampulla is connected with a tube foot and each of these hydraulic units is, in turn, connected with a radial water vessel running along each arm. These vessels are joined by a ring vessel around the mouth, from which a single channel, the *stone canal*, leads to the madreporite. The water vascular system is thus open to the exterior by the pores in the madreporite but each functional unit of it (the tube foot-ampulla system) can be isolated from the whole by a valve in the connecting tube. The tube foot-ampulla system functions by the contraction of the muscles which are found in its walls. Those of the ampulla push fluid into the cavity of the tube foot and extend it. The tube foot has circular, non-extensible fibres of collagen and longitudinal muscle fibres in its walls. These muscles shorten the foot and work in antagonism to those of the ampulla. The sucker can be attached to the substratum, partly by means of mucus and partly by suction, and the direction in which the foot points can be altered also by its intrinsic longitudinal musculature. Contraction of the muscles of one side bends it in that direction. Contraction of all the muscles shortens it and drives the contained fluid back into the ampulla as the foot is withdrawn. By the co-ordinated extension, attachment, bending and retraction of the tube feet the animal can crawl slowly over the ground; by their traction it can open bivalves; and by circulation of the contained fluid brought about by movement and by virtue of the thinness of the walls they can act in the exchange of respiratory gases.

Nervous system

The nervous system of *Asterias* can be looked upon essentially as a nerve net with its receptor, association and motor cells distributed through and below the epidermis, the peritoneum and the gut epithelium. These parts of the nervous system are difficult to see but in certain places there is an aggregation of nervous tissue forming distinct nerve cords. The most conspicuous one is that already mentioned, namely the radial nerve cord which is a superficial strand lying between the rows of tube feet in the ambulacral groove and connected around the mouth by a circumoral nerve ring of similar composition. The radial nerve cord contains receptor and association neurones interspersed with supporting epidermal cells and gland cells and it is believed that its main function is reception and co-ordination. The main concentration of motor neurons is found separated from the radial nerve cords and lies on the floor of each *perihaemal canal*, which, with its fellow represents another separate portion of the coelom. It is believed that the dispersal of the receptor, association and motor neurons over the body as a nerve net confers a great deal of independence on the parts and certainly an isolated arm of the starfish can right itself when placed on its aboral side just as can the whole animal. The tube feet appear to be able to work independently of one another as can the pedicellariae. However, the radial nerve cords and circumoral nerve ring play a part in co-ordinating the activities of the whole animal, as can be seen by cutting them, when it is clear that correlation of the movements of tube feet of the arms is upset. Moreover, the whole animal can be seen to behave in a co-ordinated fashion with the activities of the parts subordinated to the activity of the whole as when it feeds on bivalve molluscs.

The only known sense organs present are the simple eyes borne on the end of the terminal tube feet of each row. Each consists of a cup lined by sensitive cells and containing a superficial lens-like transparent structure. Sensitivity of the animal to touch is believed to be generally distributed over the ectoderm, whereas sensitivity to chemical substances is confined to those tube feet lying towards the ends of the arms.

COELOM. The coelomic cavities of starfishes are complex. We have already seen that the coelom comprises a large perivisceral cavity and that the water vascular system represents another division of the coelom. Yet a third coelomic cavity is the perihaemal system, part of which can be seen in a section of the arms lying below the radial water vessel. These perihaemal cavities follow much the same course as the channels of the water vascular system and are associated with strands of 'haemal tissue'. This cannot really be likened very closely to the circulatory system, although it is believed that some of the amoeboid cells which it contains serve in the transport of food material from the gut, where the 'haemal' strands are also present, to other parts of the body.

GASEOUS EXCHANGE. We have seen how most of the functions of living animals are performed by *Asterias* and gaseous exchange has been mentioned as occurring through the tube feet. The papulae or gills also subserve this function and are found over the aboral surface of the body. At the papulae the ectoderm and coelomic epithelium are nearly adjacent so that the coelomic fluid is separated only by a thin layer of tissue from the sea water outside. Moreover, both ectoderm and coelomic epithelium are ciliated and keep the water adjacent them in motion.

EXCRETION. There are no separate excretory organs in *Asterias* and it is believed that soluble nitrogenous waste is lost by diffusion outwards through the gills and tube feet, mainly as ammonia but some as urea and amino-acids as well. The gills also provide thin places in the integument through which amoebocytes can migrate outwards, possibly carrying with them insoluble waste matter.

PEDICELLARIAE. It remains only to describe the little organs mentioned at the beginning: the pedicellariae. These are small pincer-like structures found in large numbers on the aboral surface and governed in the movements by the local region of the nerve net. They are capable of opening and closing by muscular action and they can

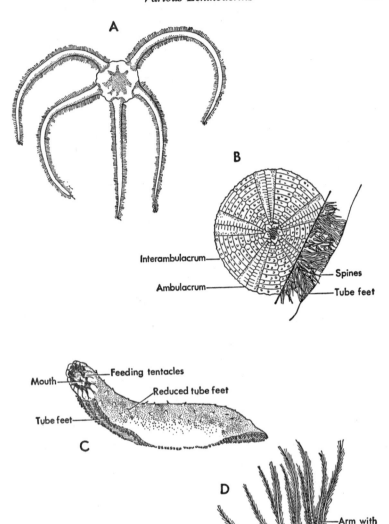

Fig. 12.3. Representations of the other classes of echinoderms.

A a brittle star (Ophiuroidea). *B* a sea urchin (Echinoidea). The left hand part of the test has been denuded of spines and tube feet to show the arrangement of the plates, the spine bosses and pores connecting the tube feet and ampullae. *C* a sea cucumber. (Holothuroidea) *D* a feather star (Crinoidea). (From specimens.)

capture and hold small organisms such as annelid worms and crustaceans which wander on to the animal's surface and they also help in keeping the aboral surface free from detritus.

Other Echinoderms

Asterias is a representative of one of the five classes, the Asteroidea, into which the phylum Echinodermata is divided. The other classes are the Crinoidea, the Holothuroidea, the Echinoidea and the Ophiuroidea.

The crinoids or sea lilies are mostly fixed, highly calcified deep-sea animals collecting their food by ciliary currents set up on their complex arms. *Antedon*, the feather star, is the commonest British form but instead of being fixed is free living and can swim slowly by movements of its arms. Tube feet are present only as small papillae on the sides of the ambulacral grooves.

The Holothuroidea are the sea cucumbers, the ossicles of whose dermis are much reduced when compared with those of *Asterias*. They feed on detritus which they take into the mouth by large modified tube feet surrounding it. The remaining tube feet resemble those of the asteroids and are used for fixation and locomotion and although there are five rows of them there is a bilateral symmetry about their distribution with respect to the long axis of the body.

Echinus, the sea urchin, is typical of many of the Echinoidea and has a rigid body wall or test composed of closely fitting calcareous plates embedded in the dermis. What is morphologically the oral surface by virtue of its bearing the tube feet is very large compared with the aboral surface. The mouth is surrounded by powerful jaws which can scrape off encrusting organisms from the rocks. The spines borne on the test are long and movable and are interspersed with pedicellariae. The numerous tube feet are very extensible and can be extended well beyond the spines.

The ophiuroids or brittle stars resemble the asteroids in having five arms and a disk, although the arms are much more sharply marked off from the disk. The tube feet lack suckers: movement and locomotion are effected chiefly by movement of the arms brought about by muscles which connect successive ambulacral ossicles. Ophiuroids are detritus feeders, having a capacious stomach but lacking any extension of the gut into the arms and lacking also an anus. Many bear long spines on the arms. Their common name refers to their habit of autotomizing their arms in response to slight stimulation. This loss is soon followed by the regeneration of the member.

II. VERTEBRATE ANIMALS

13. *Introduction to the Chordates and Amphioxus*

THE ANIMALS so far studied are representatives of many phyla, each phylum having a structural plan peculiar to itself and not shared by others to any great extent. The fact that animals fall into great groups or phyla makes possible their study through representative members or types. Were it otherwise, the task of the zoologist would be immeasurably more difficult. As it is, we have looked at representatives of the Protozoa, Coelenterata, Platyhelminthes, Annelida, Arthropoda, Mollusca and Echinodermata, members of each group having little in common with those of the other phyla. The chief phylum of which examples remain to be considered is the phylum Chordata. This, like the others, has a general plan on which its members are constructed and which is known and understood with much greater thoroughness than that of most invertebrate groups. There are several reasons for this. Man himself belongs to the phylum Chordata; many of the chordates are much bigger and more conspicuous than many invertebrates; fishes and domesticated mammals are economically important and have been associated with man from prehistoric times: and many features of the chordate plan are so constant and regular in their occurrence that the plan can be followed in great detail in the adult and to an even greater extent in the developing embryo.

The three main characters which separate the phylum Chordata from others are the possession of (1) a *notochord* or a vertebral column, (2) a dorsal tubular nervous system, and (3) a perforated pharynx. In addition, the mesoderm is primarily arranged in a series of blocks along the body. This segmentation is also shown by other anatomical features such as nerves, blood-vessels and kidney tubules. Although segmentation is a very important feature in the structure of chordates, it will be realized that they are not alone in being built on a segmental plan because this arrangement is characteristic of the arthropods and annelids.

The main features of chordate organization can be illustrated in

227

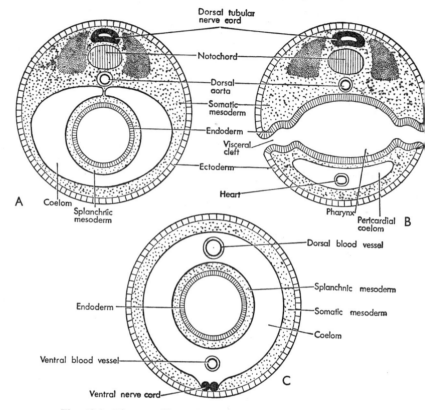

Fig. 13.1. Diagrams illustrating the chief structural features of a chordate (*A* and *B*) as seen in transverse section with those of a non-chordate (*C*) for comparison.

A is a section through the posterior region and *B* through the anterior, pharyngeal region. All are highly diagrammatic but that of the non-chordate is especially so since non-chordates include a great variety of animal types.

two ways, either by idealized diagrams or by the study of the simple chordate *Amphioxus*. This creature shows chordate structure in an almost diagrammatic way, having only a few special features or structural adaptations in which it differs from the type of animal believed to have been the ancestral stock of the higher chordates. The chief features of an idealized chordate are shown diagrammatically in Fig. 13.1, together with the transverse section of a non-chordate for comparison. The basic skeletal structure, the notochord, forms a stiff axis to the body. Above it lies the central nervous system in the form of a hollow tube; below it lies the main artery, the dorsal aorta. The gut is suspended in the coelom by a dorsal mesentery. The anterior region of the gut, the pharynx, instead of being separated from the outer body wall by the coelom, is connected to it by the walls of visceral clefts. These clefts are channels which run from the lumen of the pharynx to the outside of the animal and which have become adapted to perform different functions in different chordates in the course of evolution.

If to these features is added the arrangement of the muscles in segments, together with the blood vessels which supply them and the nerves by which they are innervated, then a basic pattern is completed, by the modification and adaptation of which fishes, amphibians, reptiles, birds and mammals have been derived.

In all higher chordates the notochord is replaced as the effective mechanical skeleton by a cartilaginous or a bony vertebral column. Animals possessing this feature are known as vertebrates or are said to belong to the sub-phylum Vertebrata. From their possession of a skeletal brain box or cranium they are also known as craniates.

In addition to the vertebrates or craniates there are three classes of animals which possess some but not all of the chordate characters and which are grouped together in the sub-phylum Acrania. These are (1) the Hemichordata ; marine worm-like animals having a pharynx with gill slits and a larva resembling that of the echinoderms (Fig. 13.2 (*A*) and (*B*)) ; (2) the Urochordata or Tunicata (Fig. 13.2 (*C*)), a group of sessile or pelagic animals, some solitary, some colonial, in which the pharynx is very highly developed as a food sieving organ. In the adult stage they would not easily be recognized as chordates but the larva possesses a notochord and a dorsal tubular nerve cord and it is due to these larval features that the group is considered to be classified with the Chordata. Finally, the last group (3) is called the Cephalochordata and comprises the lancelets of which *Amphioxus* is the best known genus. It is described in the next section.

The essential features of the chordates are the three characters already mentioned, namely the notochord, the dorsal tubular nervous system and the perforated pharynx. In addition to these, many—indeed most—chordates possess the following characters : an internal main skeleton, segmental mesoderm, dorsal and ventral roots to the segmental nerves, a ventral heart pumping the blood forwards in a ventral vessel, a hepatic portal system and a post anal tail.

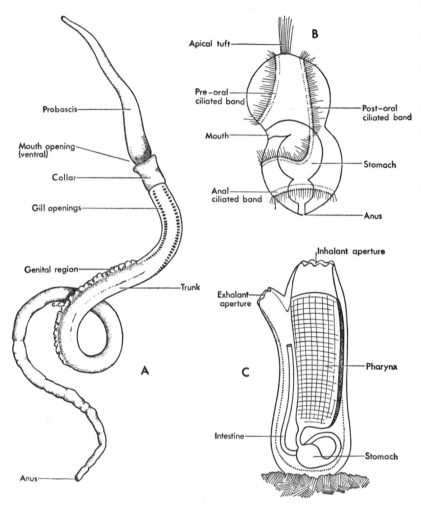

Fig. 13.2.

A A hemichordate, *Saccoglossus*, showing division of body into proboscis, collar and trunk with openings of numerous gill clefts.

B Diagram of larva of *Saccoglossus* resembling early larva of an echinoderm.

C An adult tunicate or sea-squirt, showing large perforated pharynx, the only chordate character still present in the adult.

Amphioxus

Introduction

Although at first mistaken for a small sea slug, *Amphioxus lanceolatus* (=*Branchiostoma lanceolatum*) is now recognized as a chordate of unique theoretical interest because it shows in an almost diagrammatic fashion the type of animal from which the chordates are believed to have sprung. One can only believe that it has persisted in an almost unchanging state for possibly 300,000,000 years. There is no fossil record of any certain chordate previous to that of the heavily armoured ostracoderms which are the relatives of the modern lampreys and which first appeared in the Silurian period, but the

Fig. 13.3. *Amphioxus* in its natural habitat.

It lies partly buried in shell gravel with its anterior end protruding.

fragmentary remains of an unarmoured creature, *Jamoytius*, have also been described from the Silurian. This animal was about six times the size of *Amphioxus* and, like it, was devoid of scales. It possessed muscle blocks of similar shape, but it also showed traces of eyes, which *Amphioxus* does not have. Its discovery does little to displace *Amphioxus* as the animal which almost perfectly illustrates the organization of the chordate body.

Amphioxus, so called from Greek words meaning pointed at both ends, lives in coarse sand of suitable grades in shallow seas in many parts of the world and is found in this country in shelly bottom deposits near the Eddystone lighthouse and in the Dogger Bank of the North Sea. When adult it is about 4 or 5 cm. long, and spear-point shaped, whence comes its common name of lancelet (a little lance). When alive it is translucent and covered by an iridescent but non-pigmented cuticle. It swims by rapid flexures of its body and burrows by the same movements, eventually settling in the bottom with its anterior above the sand, as seen in Fig. 13.3.

General structure

Its general appearance is shown in Fig. 13.4. The oral hood or buccal cavity is an open, funnel-shaped cavity leading to the gut (Fig. 13.7). The edge bears 20 or so oral cirri or tentacles. The gut ends at the anus, which is in a ventral position slightly to the left side near the beginning of the caudal fin. That portion of the body posterior to the anus is known as the tail and is short in the lancelet. Anterior to the anus there is another opening, the *atriopore*, which leads from a chamber called the *atrium* enclosing the pharyngeal portion of the gut and body-wall. The atrium is formed by the downgrowth of lateral folds and the ingrowth of a chamber which is enclosed by them and which surrounds the ventral part of the body in the pharyngeal region. Its formation can most easily be understood by referring to Fig. 13.15, where it will be seen that the atrium is a cavity which is morphologically 'outside the body' and is not a body cavity like the coelom or haemocoele.

There is a shallow fin running from tip to tail on the dorsal side, continuing round the tail as the caudal fin and ending ventrally just posterior to the atriopore. Anterior to that opening the *metapleural folds* are longitudinal ridges on the ventro-lateral surfaces of the body and merge into the wide ventral sides of the oral hood.

BODY WALL AND SKELETON. The outermost layer of the body is a single layer of columnar epidermal cells, the outer sides of which are slightly cuticularized (Fig. 13.5). The underlying connective tissue, corresponding to the dermis of the vertebrates, consists of an outer layer containing fibres and an inner, thick layer of a matrix with fewer fibres but containing connective tissue cells, blood vessels and nerves. The connective tissue underlying the epidermis is continuous with the web of connective tissue which separates the muscle blocks, surrounds the notochord and supports the dorsal and ventral fins. Its structure varies in different parts, either being fibrous or consisting of a gelatinous or cartilage-like matrix. Certain parts are of distinctive structure, however, and the fins are supported by skeletal nodules, four or five per segment enclosed in sheaths of connective tissue known as fin-ray boxes. Not being metamerically arranged and not having attached muscles, these are probably not homologous with the radials of the fins of fishes.

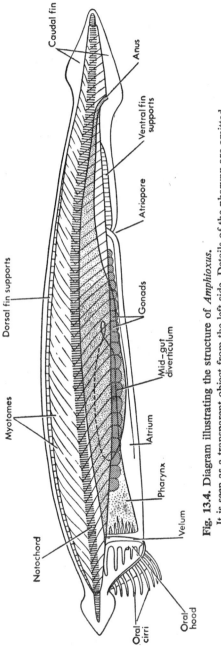

Fig. 13.4. Diagram illustrating the structure of *Amphioxus*. It is seen as a transparent object from the left side. Details of the pharynx are omitted.

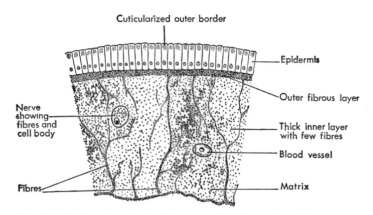

Fig. 13.5. Epidermis and underlying connective tissue of *Amphioxus*.

The epidermis consists of a single layer of cells. (From *Young* after *Krause*.)

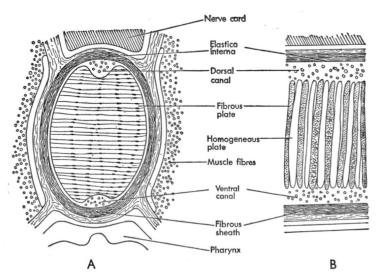

Fig. 13.6. The structure of the notochord of *Amphioxus* as seen in transverse section (*A*) and longitudinal section (*B*). (After *Pietschmann*.)

The main skeletal structure of the body is the notochord (Figs. 13.4 and 13.6) which runs from end to end below the nerve cord and which consists of an outer fibrous connective tissue sheath and a thin internal layer (the *elastica interna*) enclosing a fluid material containing small cells. Actually not much of the volume enclosed by the notochordal sheath is made up of this fluid, since it only fills in the spaces between a series of alternating, fibrous and homogeneous plates, each made by the enlargement of a single cell. This series of plates, like a pile of pennies, together with the fluid matrix in between them, provides an incompressible filling for the connective tissue sheath, so that the only changes which the notochord can readily undergo are bending movements requiring only slight changes of size of the elements of the notochordal sheath. Although it is made of soft materials (as distinct from a rigid skeletal material like bone), the notochord can thus act to prevent the body shortening when the muscles contract. When this takes place, first on one side and then on the other, the body is bent laterally.

The muscles which bring about movement are arranged with their fibres longitudinal and parallel to the long axis of the body, but they are cut up into about 60 blocks or *myotomes* on each side by connective tissue septa or *myocommata* (singular, myocomma). When seen from the side these myotomes are V-shaped and so several are seen in a transverse section. A phase of contraction starts at the anterior end of one side and progresses rapidly backwards, so bending the animal to that side. Before the contraction has reached the tail end another has started at the front on the opposite side, bending the animal in the opposite sense. The propulsion of animals by these lateral flexures, an essentially fish-like method of progression, will be dealt with in greater detail in the chapter on the dogfish.

The gut, feeding and digestion

The food channel of *Amphioxus* consists of a number of parts performing different functions. These parts are the oral hood, the pharynx, the oesophagus, the mid-gut and diverticulum and the intestine. The oral hood or buccal cavity (see Fig. 13.7) is lined with ciliated ectoderm tracts which have longer cilia and are called the *wheel organ* from their shape and apparent motion owing to the beating of the cilia during life. The oral cirri or tentacles at the free edge of the oral hood are sensory. The buccal cavity is separated from the pharynx by a constriction, the *velum*, in the centre of which is an aperture, the *enterostome*. This is fringed by the velar tentacles

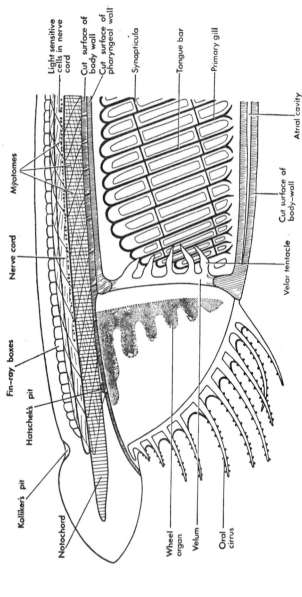

Fig. 13.7. Diagram to illustrate the structure of *Amphioxus* at the anterior end. The body-wall and wall of the pharynx of the left side have been cut away. The cut surfaces which remain are shown cross-hatched. We are therefore looking into the oral hood and pharynx and seeing the inside of the right hand-wall. The dorsal part of the animal is seen as a transparent object.

Labels: Light sensitive cells in nerve cord; Cut surface of body wall; Cut surface of pharyngeal wall; Synapticula; Tongue bar; Primary gill; Atrial cavity; Cut surface of body-wall; Velar tentacle; Myotomes; Nerve cord; Fin-ray boxes; Hatschek's pit; Kölliker's pit; Notochord; Wheel organ; Velum; Oral cirrus and leads into the pharynx which is lined by endoderm. By far the largest part of the gut is the pharynx, which extends for nearly half the length of the body. It is pierced by about 180 gill clefts on each side. Each developing cleft is divided into two by the down growth of a *tongue bar*. Horizontal *synapticulae* also develop. Needless to say, the pharyngeal clefts are not visible externally since the ventral part of the body in the pharyngeal region is enclosed by the atrium. The gill clefts are elongated dorsoventrally and are sloping. Thus many gill septa and tongue bars are seen in a transverse section of the animal in the pharyngeal region (see Fig. 13.8). Each is supported by an internal skeletal support which bifurcates at the base.

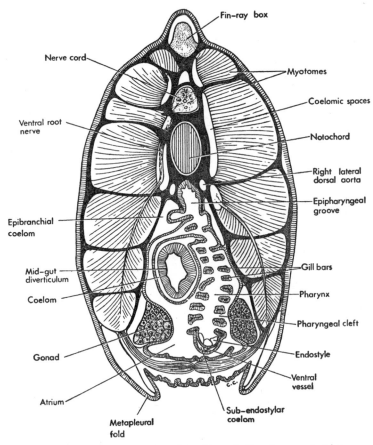

Fig. 13.8. Transverse section of *Amphioxus* in the pharyngeal region. (Partly after *Franz*.)

Arising from the top of the hoop a tongue bar divides the gill cleft into two, and like the interbranchial septa is supported by an internal skeletal rod (Fig. 13.9). Smaller dividing partitions connect the tongue bars with the interbranchial septa and lie at right angles to the length of the gill clefts. They are the synapticulae (see Fig. 13.9). The inner and side walls of the gill bars and tongue bars are covered with ciliated epithelium of endodermal origin (Fig. 13.10). Along the mid-ventral line of the pharynx lies the *endostyle* (Fig. 13.11), a tract of four groups of glandular cells alternating with groups of ciliated cells.

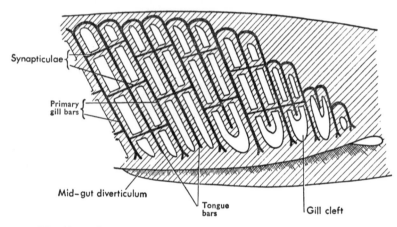

Synapticulae

Primary
gill bars

Mid-gut diverticulum

Tongue
bars

Gill cleft

Fig. 13.9. Diagram of the left side of the posterior region of the pharynx of a growing specimen of *Amphioxus* to show the formation of the gill clefts.

The grandular cells secrete mucus which is passed up the gill bars by the beating of the inner cilia. Along the mid-dorsal line of the pharynx lies the *epipharyngeal groove* in which the cilia beat towards the posterior. The endostyle and epipharyngeal groove are connected at the anterior end of the pharynx by two ciliated bands which pass on either side of the enterostome.

The cilia of the side walls of the gill clefts are those chiefly responsible for generating a current of water which enters the pharynx by the enterostome and leaves via the gill clefts, atrial cavity and atriopore (Fig. 13.12). It brings with it suspended matter including planktonic animals and plants and these are trapped by the mucus on the gill bars. These food particles are carried in the mucus to the epipharyngeal groove and thence back into the oesophagus, all by ciliary action, large and unsuitable particles having been strained off

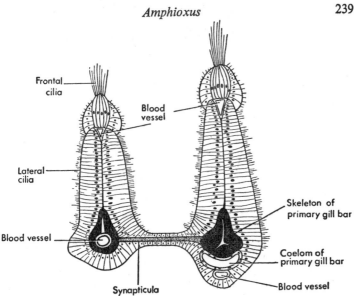

Fig. 13.10. Section across a primary gill bar (RIGHT) and a tongue bar (LEFT) of *Amphioxus*.

The endoderm is ciliated but the ectoderm is not. (After *Franz.*)

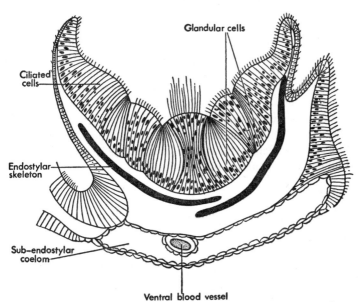

Fig. 13.11. Transverse section of the endostyle of *Amphioxus* to show the tracts of ciliated and glandular cells. (After *Franz.*)

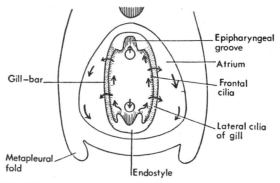

Fig. 13.12. Diagram to illustrate some of the feeding currents in the pharynx and atrium of *Amphioxus*.

The current in the epipharyngeal groove runs backwards and in the endostyle forwards. (After *Orton*.)

and rejected by the oral and velar tentacles. A very short oesophagus follows the pharynx and leads to the mid-gut, from which a large diverticulum arises and runs forwards alongside the pharynx on its right. Like the pharynx, the rest of the gut is ciliated to some extent almost all along its length and food transport is carried out by ciliary action (Fig. 13.13). In the intestine which follows the mid-gut there is a strongly ciliated region which rotates the mucus food string and, as it were, hauls it along the gut by twisting it up. The food takes about an hour to pass through the gut, during which time digestion and absorption take place. The digestive enzymes are secreted chiefly by the mid-gut diverticulum and wafted out by ciliary action into the mid-gut and intestine where absorption chiefly occurs. Digestion is largely carried out in the lumen of the gut, although some particles are ingested by phagocytes and removed by their migration from the gut lumen into the tissues of the animal.

Blood system and Respiration

The blood of *Amphioxus* contains neither cells nor respiratory pigment but is contained in definite vessels, the larger of which have muscular walls whose contraction brings about circulation of the blood, there being no definite heart. However, the arrangement of the circulatory system conforms to the general chordate plan and is represented diagrammatically in Fig. 13.14, where it will be seen that the direction of flow is forwards in the ventral or endostylar vessel, upwards through vessels in the gill bars and backwards in the paired

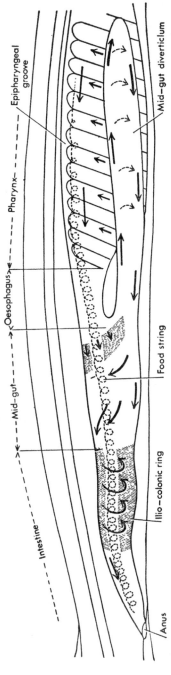

Fig. 13.13. Diagram illustrating the movement of food through the gut of *Amphioxus*. The arrows show the direction of the ciliary currents in all parts. The heavily ciliated regions of the mid-gut and intestine are cross-hatched. (After *Barrington*.)

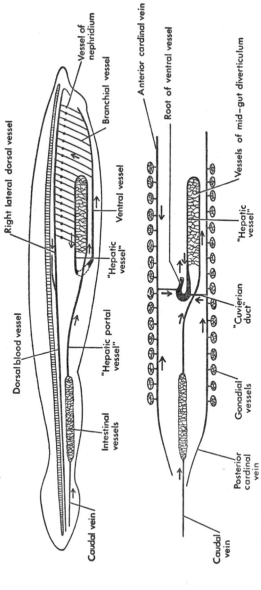

Fig. 13.14. Diagram of the main blood vessels of *Amphioxus* as seen from the right side (ABOVE) and in plan view (BELOW).

lateral aortae and the dorsal aorta formed by their union. Blood leaves the lateral aortae and the dorsal aorta by small segmental vessels and, as well, there is a small supply to the intestine. Blood is returned to the ventral vessel by factors of the venous system which include anterior and posterior cardinal veins leading, via Cuvierian ducts, into a venous sinus. There is also a portal system returning blood from the hinder part of the gut to the capillaries in the mid-gut diverticulum before it is collected from these and returned to the venous sinus, which corresponds in position in the circulatory system with the heart of higher chordates.

It is probable that the blood plays very little part in the transport of oxygen, since it has no respiratory pigment as a means of increasing its oxygen-carrying capacity above that of sea water. Also its circulation is very slow and the contractions of the main vessels infrequent and ill co-ordinated and the blood pressure low. Gaseous exchange is believed to take place through the general body surface in contact with the sea water. A region of active metabolism, the gonads, receive no arterial supply and the blood flow through the gills is contained in direct vessels rather than being spread out in a capillary network. That its main function is the transport of food substances is borne out by the copious blood supply to the gut.

THE COELOM. The coelom, lying between the splanchnic and somatic layers of mesoderm is not very extensive in the adult *Amphioxus* apart from the perivisceral coelom in which the mid-gut and intestine lie. In the pharyngeal regions the coelom is reduced by the many perforations of the walls of the pharynx and only remains as an epibranchial coelom on each side, a sub-endostylar coelom and a channel in each primary gill bar (interbranchial septum) but not in each tongue bar. The coelomic channels in the gill bars connect the epibranchial with the sub-endostylar coelom (see Fig. 13.15). There is also in each mesodermal segment a small coelomic space, the *myocoele*, and each gonad has originally a small subdivision of the coelom, the *gonocoele*, contained in it.

Excretory system

The excretory system of *Amphioxus* is very different from that of the higher chordates and somewhat resembles the flame cell system of flatworms and certain annelids since it consists of numerous nephridia of ectodermal origin. The nephridia (Fig. 13.16) lie in the epibranchial coelom on each side against the top of the gill bars. Each has a blood sinus enwrapping the tubular part from which flame

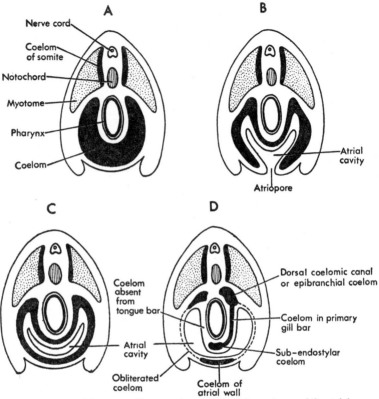

Fig. 13.15. Diagram to illustrate the relation of the coelom and the atrial cavity in *Amphioxus*.

A represents a hypothetical stage before the atrium begins to form; *B* and *C*, stages during the formation of the atrium, and *D*, the adult condition. (After *Drach*.)

cells or *solenocytes* project into the coelom. The ducts open into the atrium. There are sufficient solenocytes to provide a large surface area and it is thought that waste substances pass the wall of the intracellular tubule of each solenocyte and into its lumen when they are wafted slowly out by the beating of the flagella. There is little direct evidence to show that the nephridia are excretory but by exposing the nephridia directly to sea water containing a dye it has been shown that the dye can be transferred to the lumen of the nephridium without the intervention of the blood bathing the tubular portion. The blood did not become coloured by the uptake of dye from the sea water in which the preparation was immersed.

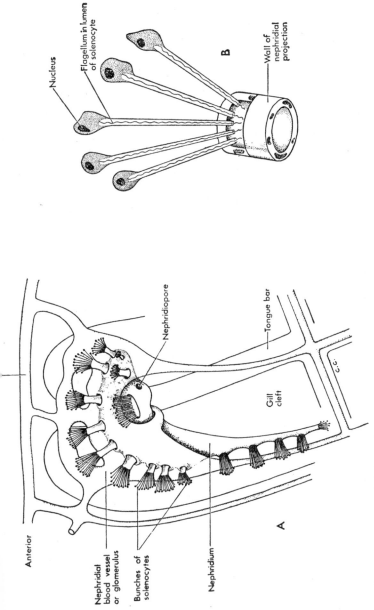

Fig. 13.16. *A* A nephridium of *Amphioxus* seen lying on the pharyngeal wall after opening the dorsal coelomic canal. At *B* is shown an enlarged view of the solenocytes opening into a part of the nephridium. (After *Franz*.)

A single large nephridium, the nephridium of Hatschek, lies to the left of the notochord and opens into the pharynx just posterior to the velum. (It should not be confused with Hatschek's pit, a ciliated depression lying in the roof of the buccal cavity within the ciliated tract forming the wheel organ.)

Nervous system

The nervous system of *Amphioxus* resembles that of the vertebrates in its general plan but differs from it in many details. It is similar in so far as the central nervous system or nerve cord lies dorsal to the notochord and the presence of its small central canal and dorsal longitudinal fissure is evidence that it has been in fact formed during development by the folding and closure of a neural plate. A small pit, Kölliker's pit, possibly containing receptor cells, marks the

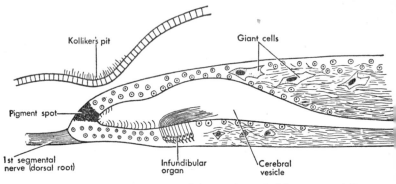

Fig. 13.17. Longitudinal section of the anterior end of the nerve cord of *Amphioxus*. (After *Franz*.)

position of closure of the anterior neuropore by which the developing central nervous system opened to the exterior (Fig. 13.17). As in the vertebrates the cell bodies of the neurons lie around the central canal, the outer part being composed of nerve fibres.

The nervous system of *Amphioxus* differs from that of the vertebrates in that it is of nearly uniform diameter throughout, having no enlarged anterior brain region. The nerves which arise in each segment consist of separate dorsal and ventral roots, the ventral roots being multiple (Fig. 13.18). In the vertebrates all the cell bodies of the neurons (with the exception of those of the autonomic system, the dorsal root ganglia and the neuro-sensory cells of the olfactory epithelium) lie *within the central nervous system*, but in *Amphioxus*, in addition to outlying nerve cells of the autonomic system, there are sensory cells (not to be confused with receptor cells) found scattered along the course of those nerves which arise from the dorsal roots, i.e. *they are not contained in dorsal root ganglia.*

The central canal enlarges at the anterior end to form a small

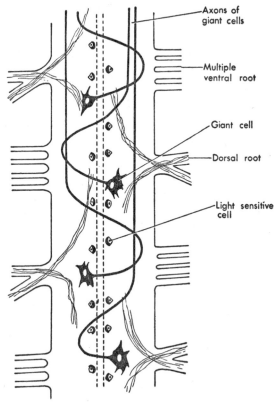

Fig. 13.18. Diagram of the nerve cord of *Amphioxus* showing the nerve roots, giant neurones and light sensitive cells. (After *Retzius.*)

cerebral vesicle whose walls contain specialized ciliated cells forming the infundibular organ and, at the extreme end, pigment cells.

The ventral nerves are exclusively motor and run directly into the adjacent muscle block. The dorsal nerves are mixed and divide into a dorsal sensory branch to the skin and a ventral mixed branch which runs to the ventral muscle of the atrial wall and to the gut (Fig. 13.19).

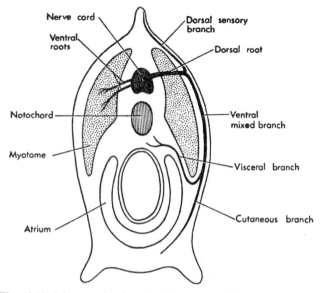

Fig. 13.19. Diagram showing the distribution of dorsal and ventral nerve roots of *Amphioxus*. (After *Prenant*.)

Among the neurons in the nerve cord are giant cells whose axons connect with a number of the ventrally placed motor cells (Fig. 13.18). It is believed that these giant cells co-ordinate the swimming movements.

The receptor system of *Amphioxus* is simple. There are receptor cells in the epidermis, especially in the anterior part and round the oral hood. These are connected with sensory cells in the dorsal nerves of the central nervous system and are believed to comprise tactile and chemosensory cells. Cells in the special epidermis lining Kölliker's pit are connected with the nerve cord and may be chemosensory too. In the nerve cord itself there are cells which are sensitive to light (Fig. 13.20). They are arranged round the central canal and are recognized by their caps of pigment which are arranged so that the direction from which the cells receive light is different at different places along the nerve cord. The one-sided perception which the animal thus has of light may lead to the spiral way in which it swims.

Reproductive organs

The sexes are separate in *Amphioxus*. The gonads are simple segmental sacs from the walls of which the germ cells are proliferated.

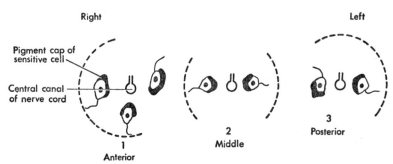

Fig. 13.20. Diagram showing the orientation of the light sensitive cells in different regions of the nerve cord of *Amphioxus*. (After *Franz*.)

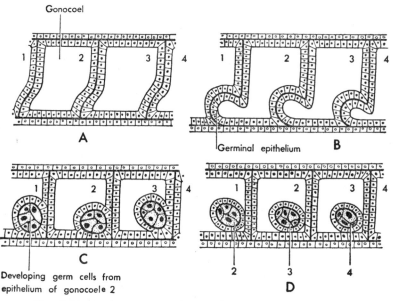

Fig. 13.21. *Amphioxus. A–D* Diagrams illustrating the origin of the germ cells from the epithelium of the segmentally arranged gonocoele cavities.

Part of each cavity becomes enclosed by the one in front of it.

Each discharges into the atrium through a pore which later closes. Although apparently simple in the adult, the formation of the gonads during development is complex (Fig. 13.21). Each is formed from a portion of the mesoderm lying near the segmented myotomal mesoderm. It becomes detached from its own segment and pushes into the somite in front. Its coelomic cavity is the gonocoele, whose lining of germinal epithelium provides the sex cells. As these grow and mature they cause the follicle containing them to bulge into the atrium. In the spring when the oocytes and sperm are ripe, they are shed into the atrium and are carried with the feeding current of water into the sea where fertilization and development takes place.

Behaviour

Almost the only responses to experimental stimuli which *Amphioxus* makes are movements of flight or escape from the stimulus. It possesses few, if any, specific reflexes but it is nevertheless capable of selecting by some process or other the type of bottom in which to settle. This can be shown by an experiment in which a number of animals is presented with a choice of different grades of sand, in one of which, the most suitable, they tend to congregate. If an animal be forced by lack of choice to live in a sand which is too fine and impermeable, it protrudes farther from the surface than it does in a coarser bottom which is more permeable to the outgoing current from the atriopore.

14. *Introduction to the Vertebrates— The Dogfish*

THE BASIC structure of the chordates has been described both in general terms and also by reference to a particular example, *Amphioxus*. The phylum Chordata contains, besides the subphyla Hemichordata, Urochordata, Cephalochordata (=Acrania) which make up the 'protochordates', the large and important subphylum Vertebrata of craniate vertebrates. They are in general more complex than the protochordates and their parts are more closely knit. Evolutionary advances have been made in many anatomical systems of the body, and although the chief ones may be listed here, the study of the dogfish will reveal more clearly the essential points of similarity and of difference between the protochordates and the vertebrates.

Although the vertebrates differ among themselves a great deal, the six main groups which comprise the living members—the lampreys, fishes, amphibians, reptiles, birds and mammals—all have certain features in common. The chief of these features are: (a) the possession of a skeleton surrounding the anterior end of the central nervous system; (b) the partial replacement of the notochord by a vertebral column; (c) the specialization of a visceral arch to form jaws at the mouth (except in the lampreys); (d) the evolution of special sense organs derived from the brain or developed in association with it; (e) the presence of a well developed blood vascular system in which the blood is circulated by the pumping of a muscular heart; (f) the elaboration of a kidney which is dependent for its functioning on a high blood pressure.

Whereas most of the protochordates are not clearly segmented in the adult form, *Amphioxus* is certainly built on a segmental plan. The vertebrates are also constructed in this way and the concept of the vertebrate as a segmented animal is one which has helped enormously towards an understanding of the anatomy of the group and the interrelationships of its members. It is perhaps not surprising that those vertebrates in which the segmental ground plan is the clearest and least modified form the lowly group of fishes, and it is

251

their study, both as adults and as embryos, which has revealed most clearly the segmental structure of the vertebrates.

Fig. 14.1 illustrates diagrammatically how the primary segmentation of the vertebrate body is found in mesodermal blocks lying on either side of the axial skeleton. These are divided from one another by connective tissue partitions. Each block during development has a small coelomic cavity communicating with the larger perivisceral coelom which is not segmented and which surrounds the gut. Each

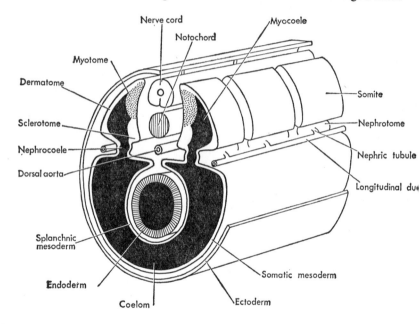

Fig. 14.1. Diagram to illustrate the segmentation of the vertebrate body.

block or *somite* has a region which gives rise to muscle (*myotome*), a more ventral region from which the adult axial skeleton is derived (the *sclerotome*) and a lateral portion giving rise to the dermis (*dermatome*). The arrangement of the nerves and blood vessels running to and from the muscles and the developing parts of the kidney are all incorporated in this segmental arrangement in a way which is clearly seen in the embryo along most of the body length and which persists in the trunk and particularly in the tail region of the adult. It is, however, altered and obscured in the head region as the development of the individual proceeds.

The Dogfish

Introduction

The common dogfish or rough hound *Scyliorhinus caniculus* belongs to the class Pisces (fishes) of the phylum Chordata, subphylum Vertebrata. (The other four chief classes of the sub-phylum are Amphibia, Reptilia, Aves (birds), and Mammalia.) The fishes are among the most primitive vertebrates because they appeared early in the course of evolution, that is, they are found as fossils in the lowest strata of sedimentary rocks and were succeeded in time by the other classes. Although the fossil record is incomplete, it looks as if at one stage in the history of the earth the only vertebrates living were fishes. Later there were animals whose fossilized remains have some characters both of fishes and amphibians and which show that the Amphibia evolved from fishes. This being so, it follows that the study of fishes ought to show most clearly the fundamentals of vertebrate structure and the basis from which the other classes have been evolved.

The fishes alive at the present time are extremely varied in size, shape and ways of life. The dogfish is chosen for study mainly for practical reasons. Its skeleton is not bony but cartilaginous, and it is therefore easy to dissect, it is not too big or too small, and it is not very popular as an article of diet. It is not very highly specialized for any particular mode of life or habitat and its structure is correspondingly close to what is thought of as that of a 'generalized fish'. Its chief disadvantage is that it is not easy to keep and to breed in captivity and therefore its early developmental stages are difficult to obtain compared with those of, for example, the trout. Its systematic position may be seen by reference to chapter 37.

External features

The dogfish is about 2 ft. long when adult, over half the length being post-anal tail. The external features which are shown in Fig. 14.2 and which should be noted are the ventral mouth connected by covered grooves to the nostrils, the openings of the olfactory organs. The eyes have no movable eyelids; the ears lack an external meatus or sound channel. Two other systems of sense organs are visible externally, the receptors known as the *ampullae of Lorenzini*, are jelly-filled tubes each opening separately on to the snout. (Their function is uncertain but they have recently been shown to be sensitive to stimulation by weak electric fields.) The *lateral line organs* lie below the surface but their position is marked by lines of pits on

The Dogfish

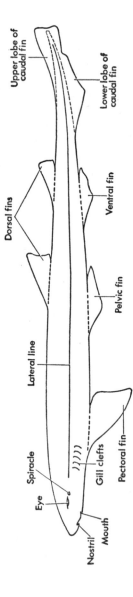

Fig. 14.2. The dogfish. Diagram to illustrate the main external features.

the side of the trunk and tail and also on the head. On the trunk and tail the lateral line is also marked by pigmentation. (For the functioning of the lateral line organs which together with the ear form the so-called *acoustico-lateralis system*, see page 296.) On each side the visceral clefts are six in number, the anterior small spiracle opening behind the eye, the succeeding five gill clefts being ventro-lateral in position. The fins comprise two unpaired dorsals, a ventral and a caudal surrounding the axis of the tail and paired pectoral and pelvic fins, the latter lying one on each side of the vent and, in the male, having their axes prolonged as 'claspers'. The body is covered completely with a shagreen of small placoid scales or denticles whose points are directed backwards. The skin is therefore smooth when stroked from fore to aft but rough and clinging when stroked in the reverse direction. This is no handicap in life because the dogfish is incapable of swimming backwards.

SKIN. The skin of the dogfish is composed of an outer epidermal layer and an inner dermis which is chiefly made up of connective tissue but which contains pigment cells or *melanophores* just below the epidermis. These cells are grouped to give the fish its spotted appearance and darker colour on the dorsal side. The epidermis has a basal growing layer, outside which there are layers of cells which are somewhat keratinized, as well as scattered mucous cells. (Keratin is a tough fibrous protein.) The chief feature of the skin is the presence of closely set *placoid scales* or dermal denticles (Fig. 14.3), each of which is a little tooth composed chiefly of dentine with a central pulp cavity and partly covered outside with a layer of enamel. Each scale is formed from an aggregation of mesodermal cells of the dermis, the *scleroblasts*, lying just below the epidermis and forming a dermal papilla (Fig. 14.4). These secrete the mineral substance of the tooth which, in both the dentine and in the enamel, is a calcium hydroxy-phosphate, *hydroxyapatite*, $Ca_{10}(PO_4)_6(OH)_2$. The differences in structure between the two regions, which do not differ in their origin in the elasmobranch fishes, lie in the amount of organic matter which each contains and in the direction of the crystal axes of the inorganic material. In the enamel there is a very high concentration of mineral substances and little of the structural protein collagen, while in the dentine there is less of the mineral and more of the organic matter. In the enamel, the crystal axes of the hydroxyapatite are at right angles to the surface of the scale, while in the dentine they are roughly parallel with the surface. The denticles are mostly single pointed on the ventral side of the animal and treble pointed on the

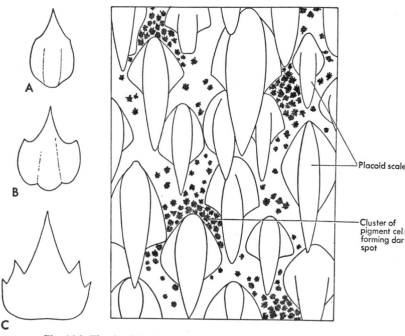

Fig. 14.3. The dogfish.

The skin in surface view. The bases of the placoid scales are set in the skin and are not visible. Outline diagrams of the shape of typical placoid scales are also shown: *A* from the ventral surface; *B* from the dorsal surface; *C* from the jaws.

dorsal. Where the skin lies over the jaws, the scales which cover it are larger and five pointed, and serve as teeth (Fig. 14.3). These are clearly skin structures and are not set in sockets in the jaw cartilages or in any way attached directly to them.

Muscles and Skeleton

Although the locomotion of the fish can be discussed apart from the skeleton and muscles (see page 258), it will be realized that the skeleton is the part of the body to which the muscles are attached and which enables the contraction of one muscle to be antagonized by another as well as providing a general framework by which the body is held together. The main increase in complexity which the dogfish shows over the acraniates is in the partial replacement of a simple notochord by a vertebral column consisting of a series of intersegmental pieces of cartilage and by the enclosure of the brain by a cartilaginous box.

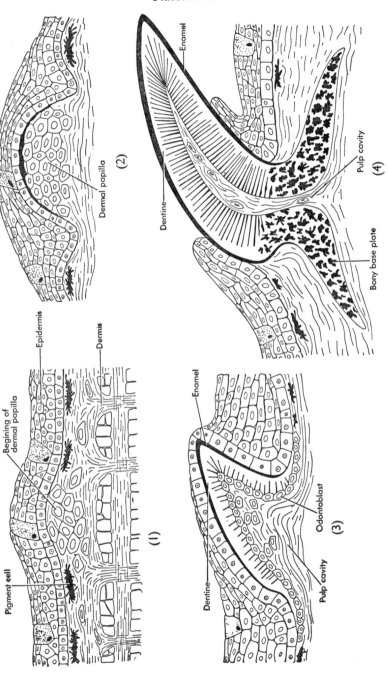

Fig. 14.4. The dogfish. (1)–(4) Diagrams illustrating the formation of a placoid scale as seen in section.

The vertebral column consists of vertebrae, each of which comprises essentially a main body or centrum, a neural arch surrounding the spinal cord and transverse processes which jut out into the horizontal septum. These parts of the vertebral column, the vertebrae are joined together by connective tissue which forms a sheath or *perichondrium* round each separate bit of cartilage and links the separate bits of cartilage together very strongly and yet flexibly. Thus, although the vertebrae are not articulated or joined together by movable joints, the whole structure is flexible up to a point, chiefly in the horizontal plane.

It will be apparent that, although one of the primary functions of a skeleton is considered to be the provision of regions of attachment

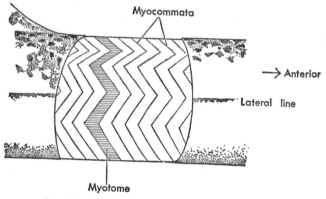

Fig. 14.5. The dogfish.
Appearance of the myotomes in surface view.

for the muscles, very few of the segmental muscles which make up the bulk of the dogfish are actually attached to the skeleton. The individual muscle fibres run between sheets of connective tissue or myocommata which divides the musculature into a series of myotomes or muscle blocks. Although these first appear in development as simple blocks of developing muscles arranged along either side of the developing vertebral column, they soon lose this simple form and in the adult fish are of complex shape. When seen from the side each myocomma traces a zig-zag line on the skin (Fig. 14.5) and each is also bent at an angle when seen from above so that each outlines a complex conical shape (Fig. 14.6) which fits into the one behind and over the one in front, thus giving the appearance of concentric rings when seen in transverse section. This complex arrangement is believed to have an advantage over the simple arrangement of myocommata across the long axis as they are at their first appearance in the embryo, in that it serves to spread out the effects of contraction of one segment over a greater length of the body than that actually occupied by a segment width, and hence to smooth the passage of a contraction wave. (In some fishes it also allows the pull exerted by a part of the muscle fibres to be aligned along a tendinous strand which is inserted into the base of the tail and serves to move it from side to side with particular vigour.)

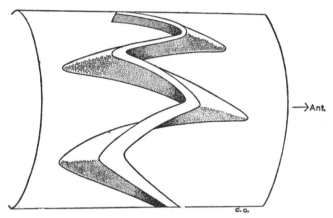

Fig. 14.6. The dogfish.

Diagram to illustrate the shape of a myotome. The myotomes anterior and posterior to it have been removed so that its shape in three dimensions is seen.

Almost all of the somatic musculature of the dogfish begins in development as segmental myotome muscle, and most of it remains as such into adult life with relatively little alteration. However, a few skeletal structures are actuated by muscles which become differentiated from the muscle blocks and which do not present the appearance of a uniform series of blocks in adult life. In this category are the fins, the eyeballs and the gill arches, the musculature of which consists of individual muscles performing particular movements and usually attached to cartilage at either end. These are best dealt with as the structures concerned are described.

But to return to the skeleton; this is intimately bound to the muscles with connective tissue which also serves to attach together the units of which the skeleton is composed. The skeleton, which in the dogfish is wholly of cartilage, is usually considered to comprise the *axial* skeleton of skull and vertebral column and the *appendicular* skeleton of the limbs and girdles in the body wall to which they are attached.

The vertebral column arises during the development of the dogfish from condensations of mesoderm cells lying against the sheath of the notochord. These come from the inner ventral side of the somite and constitute the sclerotome or segmental block of skeleton-forming tissue. From these are formed the *centrum* of each vertebra which lies in the position of the notochord, and the *neural arch*. Because the skeleton-forming tissue invades the notochordal sheath, the notochord becomes constricted midway along each vertebra but where the vertebrae abut one another the notochord is hardly constricted at all. The neural arch lies above the centrum of the vertebra and encloses the spinal cord. Each neural arch is a composite structure in *Scyliorhinus* and comprises a *vertebral neural plate* attached to the centrum and a separate *intervertebral neural plate*. A row of *neural spines*, two to each vertebral segment, roofs the spinal canal (see Fig. 14.7).

Ribs are present embedded in the horizontal septum of connective tissue that separates the epaxial from the hypaxial musculature and they are connected with short transverse processes of the vertebra. In the tail region the processes are directed ventrally to enclose a *haemal canal* in which runs the caudal artery and vein. At the hind end of the dogfish the vertebrae are duplicated so that there are two corresponding to each muscle block. This condition is known as *diplospondyly*.

The axial skeleton at the anterior end of the fish is called the *skull*. This may be defined as the skeleton of the head which in the dogfish comprises the first eight segments. There is no sharp external demarcation of the head as is provided by the neck in many higher vertebrates, but it will be seen that, nevertheless, the first eight or head segments are distinct from the succeeding trunk segments. The skull is made up of two main parts, the brain box or cranium with its attached sense capsules, and the *visceral* skeleton which is developed as a series of supporting hoops, one lying behind each visceral cleft.

The cranium arises in development at the anterior end of the notochord from paired cartilaginous plates, the *parachordals* lying one on each side of the notochord, and anterior rods, the *trabeculae* lying in front of them and soon fusing with them (Fig. 14.8). These increase in size and fuse to form a solid basis to the cranium. Meanwhile, cartilaginous capsules are being laid down around the special

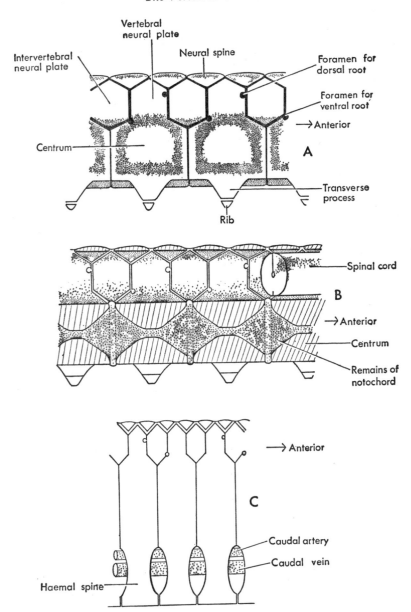

Fig. 14.7. The dogfish.

The structure of the vertebral column: *A* Side view of trunk region; *B* Sagittal section (cut surfaces of neural spines and centra crosshatched); *C* Side view of tail region.

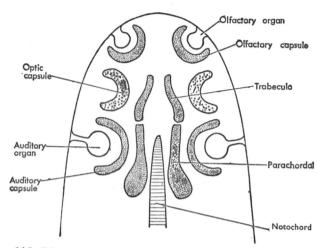

Fig. 14.8. Diagram illustrating the origin of the cranium during development.

sense organs of the head, namely the *olfactory capsule* surrounding the nose or olfactory organ and the *auditory capsule* surrounding the inner ear. These become attached to the developing skull but the capsule which develops round the eye and later goes to form the *sclerotic coat* remains separate and lies free from the cranium in a hollow at the side known as the orbit. From the basal plate, side walls grow up and partially enclose the brain, which also comes to be protected dorsally by the roof of the cranium. This, however, remains incomplete. At the hinder end of the cranium is the *foramen magnum*.

The visceral skeleton comprising the *mandibular, hyoid* and five *branchial arches* develops around the embryonic gut and is formed largely from migrating cells of the *neural crests* (see page 630). These visceral arches are considered to be serially homologous so that the arch which forms the jaws of the adult, the mandibular arch, is comparable with the succeeding arch of the spiracle or hyoid arch and in turn with the succeeding branchial arches. It is thought that a premandibular arch may have existed in ancestral forms but that the enlargement and regression of the mouth has resulted in its loss and the adoption of the function of jaws by the visceral arch corresponding to the second head segment. Some authorities consider that the trabeculae represent the pre-mandibular arch skeleton, changed in function so as to form part of the neurocranium. The resemblance between the mandibular, hyoid and branchial arches and their relation to the trabeculae can be seen most easily during the development of the embryo, a stage of which is shown in outline in Fig. 14.9.

While the typical visceral arch consists of four paired elements and an unpaired basal one, the mandibular arch is reduced to a paired upper *palatoquadrate* and a paired lower *Meckel's cartilage*. The hyoid arch consists on each side of *ceratohyal* and *hyomandibular* cartilages united by an unpaired *basihyal*. The form of the skull

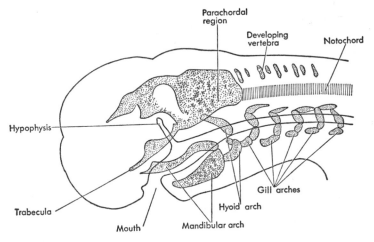

Fig. 14.9. The dogfish.

Diagram illustrating the development of the skull as seen in side view of an embryo.

of the adult dogfish is shown in Fig. 14.10, in which the relation between the visceral arch skeleton and the cranium should be particularly noted. The mandibular arch is held on to the cranium by ligaments only (the ethmopalatine and spiracular ligaments) and is not articulated directly to it. The hyoid arch, on the other hand, does articulate with the cranium, the hyomandibula abutting the auditory capsule. At its lower end the hyomandibula articulates with the mandibular arch which is thus indirectly attached to the cranium. This type of jaw suspension is known as the *hyostylic* type from the intervention of the hyomandibula as a supporting strut.

The proximal part of each of the median fins (two dorsal, one ventral, and a caudal) is supported by radial cartilaginous elements which articulate with the vertebral column and project a short way into the fin substance while the distal part of the fin is stiffened with *dermotrichia*, the so-called horny fin rays composed of the protein

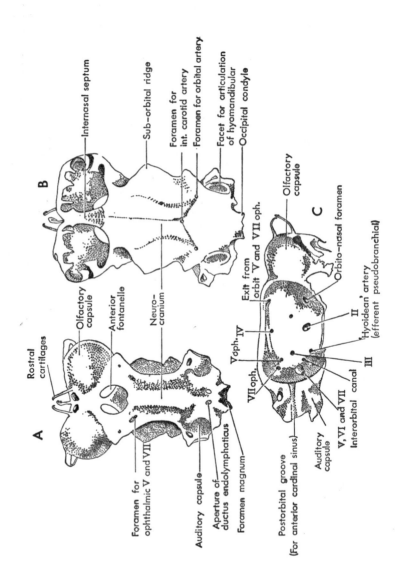

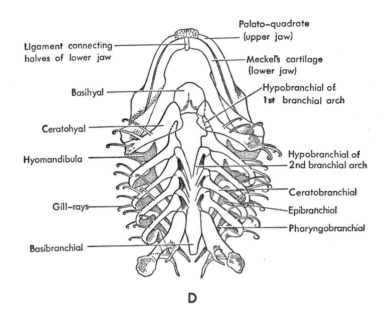

Palato-quadrate (upper jaw)

Ligament connecting halves of lower jaw

Meckel's cartilage (lower jaw)

Basihyal

Hypobranchial of 1st branchial arch

Ceratohyal

Hyomandibula

Hypobranchial of 2nd branchial arch

Gill-rays

Ceratobranchial

Epibranchial

Basibranchial

Pharyngobranchial

D

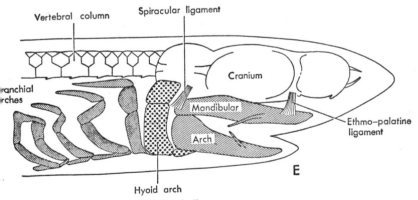

Vertebral column

Spiracular ligament

Branchial arches

Cranium

Mandibular

Arch

Ethmo-palatine ligament

Hyoid arch

E

Fig. 14.10. The dogfish. The skull.

A Dorsal view of the chondrocranium; *B* Ventral view of the chondrocranium; *C* Lateral view of the chondrocranium; *D* Ventral view of the visceral arch skeleton. (From specimens.)

E Diagram of the relation between the cranium and visceral arch skeleton seen from the side.

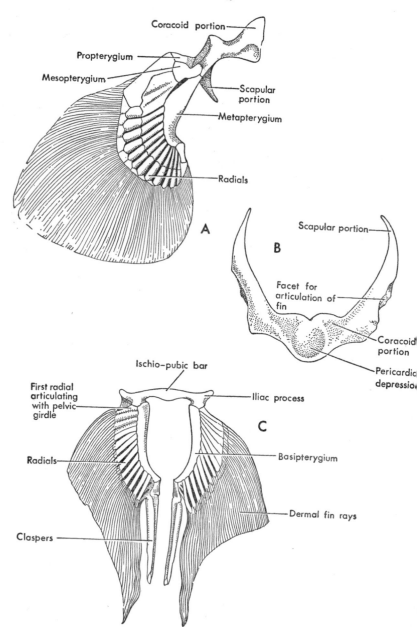

Fig. 14.11. The dogfish. The paired fins and girdles.

A Ventral view of the right pectoral fin skeleton attached to the pectoral girdle; *B* Anterior view of the pectoral girdle; *C* Ventral view of the pelvic girdle and fin skeleton of the male. (From specimens.)

elastin arising in the dermis. These are unjointed strands of stiff yet flexible material which are much more numerous than the cartilage elements which they overlie at their bases.

The appendicular skeleton is simple in the dogfish and consists of the *pectoral* girdle and fin skeleton and that of the *pelvic* fin and girdle lying just anterior to the vent (Fig. 14.11). The pectoral girdle is embedded in the lateral and ventral body wall just posterior to the gills, near to the region of the heart. This it protects and houses in a pericardial depression. Ventral coracoid and dorsal scapular portions are recognized as joining at the glenoid, the point at which the pectoral fin articulates. The skeleton of this fin has three basal elements, the *pro-*, *meso-* and *metapterygia*, which articulate with many *radials*. The pelvic girdle is a simple transverse bar of cartilage, the *ischio-pubis*, to which the *basipterygium* of the fin is attached. This articulates with many radials and in the male is prolonged into a scroll-like *clasper*. (See also p. 288.)

The gut—Feeding and Digestion

The tube through which the food passes is known as the alimentary canal or gut, which is distinguishable into different regions between mouth and anus. These regions have different functions and are connected with different organ systems of the body. Thereby the gut is correlated in its workings with the needs of the body as a whole.

The mouth of the dogfish is ventral and is supported by jaws which are the cartilages of the mandibular arch. The jaws are armed with enlarged dermal denticles. These point backwards so that any living fish or crustacean which the dogfish eats cannot easily slip out once it has been grasped by the jaws. The teeth are continually being replaced by the growth of the skin, in which they are formed, from a groove lying along the inside of the jaw (Fig. 14.12). The mouth opens into the buccal cavity, projecting from the floor of which is a hard pad formed round the basihyal cartilage. This can be raised to assist swallowing. The buccal cavity is lined with ectoderm, among the cells of which are many which secrete mucus and some which are receptors of stimuli.

The buccal cavity is not marked off sharply from the pharynx which follows it but the distinction between the region is made clear by two features. The pharynx is lined by endoderm and its walls are pierced by visceral clefts. In its walls the visceral arches develop and in conjunction with them the muscles become modified from the simple condition found in the posterior part of the body to

Fig. 14.12. The dogfish.

The formation of teeth at the jaws. The lower jaw is seen in section.
The groove in which the teeth developed is covered by a flap of skin.
(From a specimen.)

complicated muscles which constrict and open the clefts for
respiratory purposes.

Again the oesophagus is not sharply marked off from the pharynx
but is distinguished by its walls containing unstriped muscle and by
the folded mucous membrane lining. It passes without any clear
distinction into the stomach. This is a wide U-shaped tube, the first
part being known as the *cardiac* limb, and the second as the *pyloric*
limb (Fig. 14.13). The stomach is sharply marked off from the
intestine by the *pyloric sphincter*, a strong band of circular muscle.
The intestine is short and passes straight backwards but its internal
surface is increased by the presence of a *spiral valve*. This structure
consists of a projection from the wall of the intestine which runs a
helical course like that described by the steps of a spiral staircase.
It therefore forces the partially digested food in the gut to take a
long spiral route in the ileum instead of passing straight through it.

The intestine continues into a short narrow rectum carrying a
dorsal diverticulum, the *rectal gland*. The rectum opens by the anus
into a shallow *cloaca*. This cloaca which opens to the exterior by the
vent between the pelvic fins also receives the openings, in the male,
of the urinogenital sinus and in the female of the oviducts and the
urinary sinus. On either side of the cloaca there is a pore, the abdominal pore, which puts the coelom into communication with the
outside and presumably allows coelomic fluid to escape should
excess pressure be produced in the coelom.

The course and parts of the gut having been described, it remains
to mention their functions and the way in which they are carried out.
The jaws seize but do not masticate prey, which includes a variety of

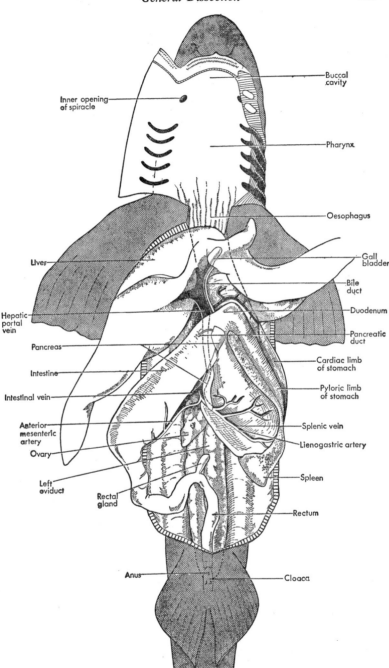

Fig. 14.13. The dogfish.
A general dissection to show the gut. (Based on *Lockyer* and *Crofts*.)

living and recently dead animals such as crabs, hermit crabs, whelks, and other molluscs and small fishes. The lower jaw is opened by the *coraco-mandibular* muscles running from Meckel's cartilage to the pectoral girdle and it is closed by the strong *adductor mandibulae* muscle which runs between Meckel's cartilage and the palato-quadrate. The buccal cavity merely receives the food and passes it on to the pharynx and thence to the oesophagus and stomach. It is despatched from the buccal cavity and pharyngeal region by the raising of the 'tongue' and the constriction of the walls, as well as by the relaxation of the oesophagus. The pharynx is important, not in nutrition but in respiration, by virtue of the gills which line the visceral clefts (see page 280).

Digestion begins in the stomach, the contents of which are acid and contain enzymes secreted from its walls. The partially digested food is eventually passed from the stomach to the duodenum past the relaxed pyloric sphincter and the digestion is completed and absorption occurs during the passage of the food through the ileum. (A fuller account of digestion in vertebrates is found in Chapter 22.) The glands associated with the digestive function of the gut are the liver and the pancreas, the liver being a large bilobed organ attached by the *falciform ligament* of connective tissue to the transverse septum at the anterior end of the perivisceral coelom. The gall bladder in which bile is collected is embedded in the liver and discharges its contents into the gut via the bile duct which opens into the duodenum. The pancreas lies between the pyloric limb of the stomach and the ileum and discharges its digestive secretion by a short pancreatic duct.

It will be apparent that along part of its length the gut is, as it were, embedded in the body and that, partly, it lies in the coelom, being suspended there by the double fold of splanchnic epithelium which, together with connective tissue, makes up the mesentery. The body cavity or coelom contains, in addition to the gut, the liver, the pancreas, the spleen (a lymph gland), gonads and heart, but in the dogfish the heart is contained in a separate part of the coelom known as the *pericardial cavity* which is cut off from the main, or perivisceral, coelom by a transverse partition of tough connective tissue, the transverse septum, formed where the Cuvierian ducts run from the cardinal sinuses into the heart (Fig. 14.14). This septum is pierced by two small openings, the *pericardio-peritoneal canals*. The pericardial cavity is lined by the *pericardium*, a connective tissue membrane in which the heart lies freely. The importance of the relatively

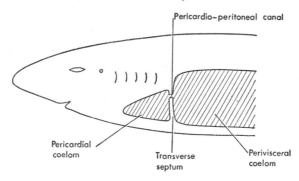

Fig. 14.14. The dogfish.
Diagram to illustrate the relation of the pericardial to the perivisceral coelom.

rigid walls of the pericardial cavity in the functioning of the heart is described below.

Blood system and Circulation

The general plan of the blood vascular system is simple and is illustrated in Fig. 14.15. A ventral vessel gives off segmental vessels which run up the visceral arches between the visceral clefts. They join a dorsal vessel or vessels from which the blood is distributed to the body. A portion of the ventral vessel becomes greatly enlarged and differentiated as the heart. The venous system eventually returns blood into the posterior chamber of the heart. The arteries are narrow vessels with strong walls in which plain muscle fibres are present, but the venous system consists to a great extent of very wide channels called *sinuses*, the walls of which have no muscle or extremely little. They have, however, connective tissue strands crossing them and serving to limit their volume and the accumulation of blood in them.

The heart is formed during development as a tube lying in a separate part of the coelom, the pericardial cavity. It grows more rapidly in size than the limits of the cavity and becomes bent into an S-shape. It also becomes differentiated into four chambers. These, in order back to front, are: *sinus venosus, atrium* or *auricle, ventricle,* and *conus arteriosus.* A diagrammatic representation of this process together with the appearance of the adult heart is shown in Fig. 14.16. The division of the contractile muscular region of the heart into chambers is necessitated by the low pressure in the venous system of the fish. In order to restore a contracted heart chamber to

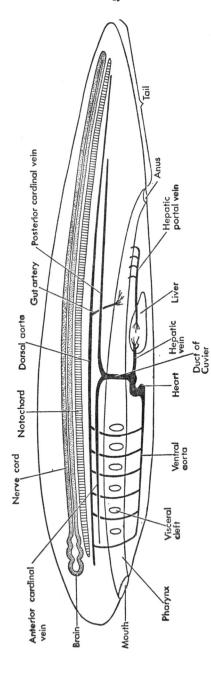

Fig. 14.15. Plan of the blood system of an ideal craniate seen from the left side.

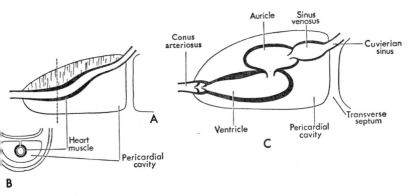

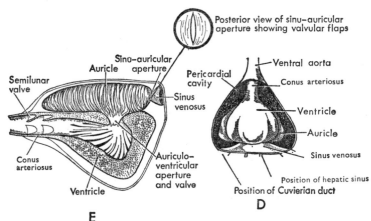

Fig. 14.16. The dogfish.

The heart: *A* diagram of an early stage in development in which the heart tube is lying in the pericardium; *B* the same in section; *C* the later stages when the tube has differentiated into the four heart chambers; *D* the heart of the dogfish seen in ventral view and *E* in sagittal section.

its relaxed state a force is required to stretch the muscle to its original size. In the dogfish the venous pressure is so small that it can only stretch a chamber with weak muscle walls but not the very muscular ventricle. However, the contraction of the sinus venosus may be strong enough to drive blood into the auricle, and that of the more muscular auricle is strong enough to drive blood into the very muscular ventricle, but another factor enters into the working of the dogfish heart because the walls of the pericardial cavity is relatively

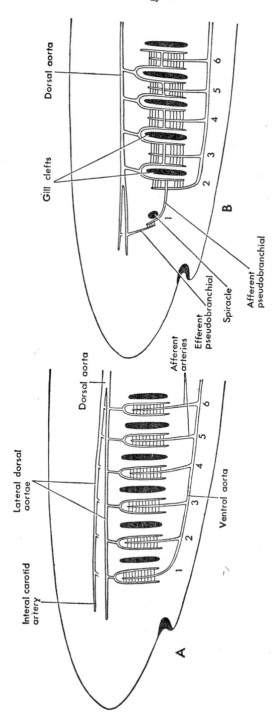

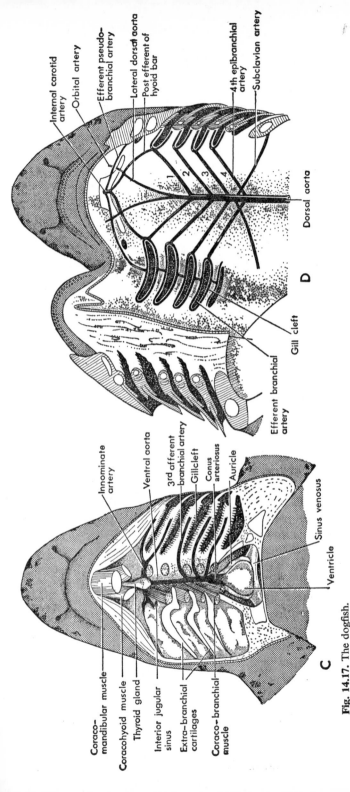

Fig. 14.17. The dogfish.

The anterior arterial system. *A* Diagram of the six aortic arches of an ideal fish. *B* The condition of the arches as seen in the dogfish. *C* The heart, ventral aorta and afferent branchial arches as seen dissected from the ventral side. *D* The efferent branchial system and arteries supplying the head, as seen in dissection. (*C* and *D* based on *Lockyer* and *Crofts*.)

Internal carotid artery

Orbital artery

Efferent pseudo-branchial artery

Lateral dorsal aorta

Post efferent of hyoid bar

4th epibranchial artery

Subclavian artery

Dorsal aorta

Gill cleft

Efferent branchial artery

D

Coraco-mandibular muscle

Coracohyoid muscle

Thyroid gland

Interior jugular sinus

Extra-branchial cartilages

Coraco-branchial muscle

Innominate artery

Ventral aorta

3rd afferent branchial artery

Gillcleft

Conus arteriosus

Auricle

Sinus venosus

Ventricle

C

rigid since it is bounded ventrally by the pectoral girdle and elsewhere is embedded in muscle surrounded by strong connective tissue. The implication of this feature is that when contraction of a heart chamber takes place and blood is driven out of the heart, fluid must enter another chamber to occupy the volume of the blood that leaves. Thus, contraction of the distended ventricle and that of the conus drives blood out of the heart and into the ventral aorta but at the same time blood enters the sinus venosus and auricle from the Cuvierian duct. The contraction of the auricle is forceful enough to distend the ventricle and since the blood is only being passed from one chamber of the heart to another, no change in the total volume contained within the pericardium is required. On the other hand, the contraction of the ventricle which follows not only drives blood into the ventral aorta but also causes a fresh inflow of venous blood into the sinus and auricle. There are valvular flaps between the sinus and auricle and between the auricle and ventricle which prevent the back flow of blood when these chambers contract. Two rows of pocket-shaped or *semilunar* valves in the conus arteriosus prevent blood flowing back into the ventricle from the ventral aorta when the force of the ventricular contraction subsides. From the ventral aorta blood is distributed to the gills, which have a considerable resistance to the passage of the blood so that its pressure falls off substantially on the efferent side. The fall, however, is not so great as might be expected because the fine vessels of the gills are not capillaries proper but somewhat larger sinusoids which offer less resistance to flow but which yet present a sufficiently large surface area for gaseous exchange.

Before it is distributed to the body by the arteries, the blood is oxygenated during its passage through the gills. Since it has to pass there through narrow vessels which offer resistance to its flow, the pressure at which it emerges from the branchial vessels is lower than that at which it left the heart. Ideally the aortic arches, from which the branchial circulation is derived, may be considered as consisting of six pairs of vessels associated with the mandibular, hyoid and four branchial arches (Fig. 14.15). These vessels consist of loops, passing from the ventral aorta to lateral dorsal aortae running one on each side of the body above the pharynx. These lateral aortae continue forwards as the *internal carotid* arteries. The next stage, illustrated in Fig. 14.17(A), can be imagined as the interruption of the simple vessel by capillaries. While the aortic arches of the dogfish bear a considerable resemblance to this scheme, they differ in several respects. Firstly, there is no direct afferent vessel of the mandibular arch, secondly the succeeding five arches are interrupted by the capillary vessels of the gills as we have seen and each is thus divided into an *afferent* and a looped, *efferent* branchial artery, thirdly the lateral dorsal aortae have fused posterior to the junction with the first efferent vessel so that the epibranchial arteries join a single dorsal aorta instead of paired lateral aortae (Fig. 14.17(B)). In Fig. 14.17 (C) and (D) the appearance of the vessels revealed by dissection is shown for comparison with the diagrammatic representation of the structures.

The mandibular arch has no complete aortic arch of its own in the adult but a branch from the first afferent loop (that of the hyoid bar) runs to the spiracle as the afferent *pseudobranchial* which breaks up into capillaries in the pseudobranch (page 280) to reunite as the efferent pseudobranchial. A branch from this forms the *orbital* artery supplying the eye region. A glance at Fig. 14.17(C) and (D) will make the arrangement in the adult elasmobranch clear and will show how it may be derived from the ideal scheme.

There is little to comment on in the rest of the arterial system (Fig. 14.18). A *subclavian* artery supplies the pectoral fin and an *iliac* artery the pelvic. There are small arteries supplying the segmental muscles with blood, and four branches from the dorsal aorta going to the viscera. These are: the *coeliac* supplying the cardiac portion of the stomach and the liver, the *anterior mesenteric* supplying the intestine and gonad, the *lienogastric* supplying the pyloric portion of the stomach and the spleen, several paired *renal* arteries running to the kidney, and the *post mesenteric* supplying the rectal gland. Since the heart contains only venous or de-oxygenated blood, it is important that there should be a supply of oxygenated blood to the heart muscle itself, especially that of the ventricles. This is provided by the *coronary* artery which originates as branches from certain efferent loops. Coronary veins return blood which has flowed through the heart muscle capillaries directly into the heart cavity.

The general return of blood to the heart is accomplished through large sinuses, the chief of which are the *anterior* and *posterior cardinal sinuses* emptying on both sides into the duct of Cuvier lying in the transverse septum (Fig. 14.19). Each Cuvierian duct, which opens into the sinus venosus, receives also the *subclavian* sinus from the pectoral girdle region, the *brachial* sinus from the pectoral fin, a *lateral abdominal* sinus from the ventral body-wall, and a *superficial lateral* sinus also. The *inferior jugular* sinus from below

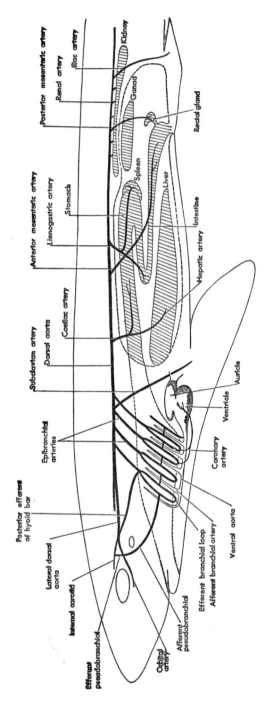

Fig. 14.18. The dogfish. Diagram of the arterial system.

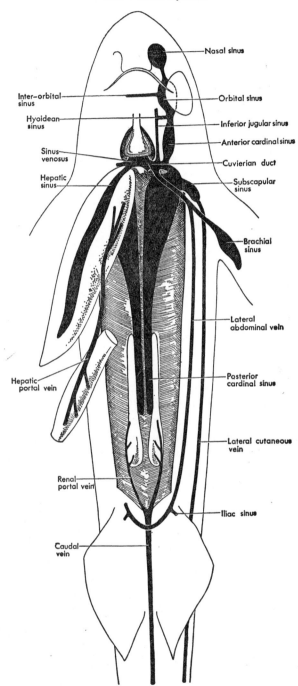

Fig. 14.19. The dogfish. Diagram of the venous system.

the pharynx joins the Cuvierian duct near the opening of the anterior cardinal sinus. The *hepatic* sinus draining the liver opens directly into the sinus venosus.

Two portal systems are present in the dogfish, the *renal portal* and the *hepatic portal*. In the renal portal system blood from the tail region is collected in the *caudal* vein which bifurcates posterior to the kidneys, each renal portal vein thus formed going to a kidney and there breaking up into capillaries. The blood thus supplied to the kidneys, together with that supplied by the renal arteries, is drained from the kidneys by the posterior cardinal sinuses. The characteristic of a portal vessel, as can be seen from this example, is that it both begins and ends in capillaries, the renal portal vein receiving blood from the capillaries of the tail muscles and breaking up again into capillaries in the kidneys.

Similarly, blood which is supplied to the gut by branches from the dorsal aorta is collected into the *hepatic portal* vein and taken to the liver, where again it flows through the capillaries of an organ on its way back to the heart via the hepatic sinus.

Gills and Respiration

Uptake of the oxygen dissolved in the sea water and release of carbon dioxide takes place through the gills, since the skin is impermeable owing to keratinization and the presence of placoid scales. The gills are richly vascular folds or laminae situated on the walls of the branchial clefts. Each cleft except the last bears a *hemibranch* on the anterior and a hemibranch on the posterior wall. The last gill cleft has a hemibranch on the anterior face only. Inside and on the anterior border of the spiracle is a rudimentary gill known as the *pseudobranch*. The structure of the gills is best understood by reference to Fig. 14.20 which shows a transverse section through a dogfish in which the gill lamellae are seen in face view as a series of folds or ridges on the surface of the gill septum: a diagram of an enlarged section of a gill cut in a horizontal plane parallel with and passing through one of the lamellae is also shown. The branchial arch skeleton lies towards the inside, while the distal part of the gills is supported by cartilaginous gill rays borne on the epi- and ceratobranchials. There are muscles running parallel with the gill rays and passing into a flap of the septum outside the respiratory folds. The contraction of these muscles appears to pull the septum inwards and thus to close the external opening of the gill pouch behind. Other

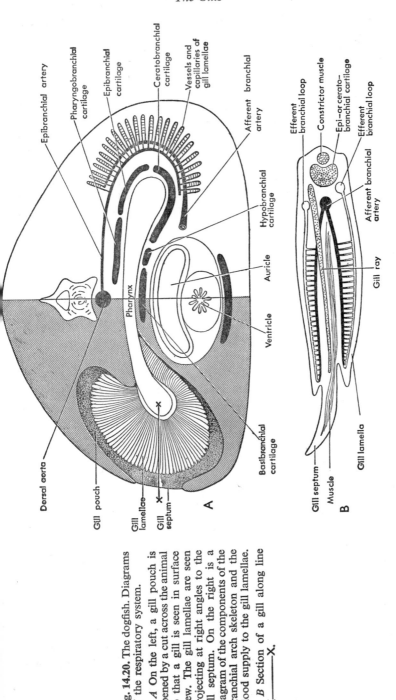

Fig. 14.20. The dogfish. Diagrams of the respiratory system.

A On the left, a gill pouch is opened by a cut across the animal so that a gill is seen in surface view. The gill lamellae are seen projecting at right angles to the gill septum. On the right is a diagram of the components of the branchial arch skeleton and the blood supply to the gill lamellae.

B Section of a gill along line X——X.

muscles seen in transverse section of the gill have the effect of con-
stricting the pharynx in the gill region.

Blood is supplied to the respiratory surface by the afferent branchial artery which gives off a branch to each lamina. After passing
through the sinusoids of the gill lamella, it is collected into vessels
joining the efferent, whence it passes into the dorsal aorta to be
distributed to the body.

Water is passed over the gills in the following way. The mouth
and spiracle are opened and the floor of the buccal cavity and
pharynx lowered. The gill clefts meanwhile are closed by the prolongations of the septa. The mouth and spiracle are now shut and
the pharynx constricted so that water is forced out through the
visceral clefts and over the respiratory lamellae. The chief muscles
which bring about the filling of the buccal cavity and pharynx by
lowering its floor are those running from the coracoid to the hyoid
and branchial arches and known respectively as the *coracohyoid* and
coracobranchials, while the emptying of the respiratory tract via the
gills is brought about by the contraction of superficial constrictor
muscles and by the intrinsic constrictor muscles of the gill pouches.

About half the oxygen which the sea water contains can be
extracted in a single passage through the gills.

Excretory and reproductive system

The main end products of protein metabolism in the dogfish are
urea (about 80%) and trimethylamine oxide [$(CH_3)_3 N=O$] which
are eliminated, and the water balance of the creature maintained, by
the kidneys. These are believed to function in the same general way
as those of other vertebrates except that urea is eliminated from the
blood stream only when it exceeds a concentration of about $2-2\frac{1}{2}\%$.
The retention of this amount of urea renders the tissues of the fish
hypertonic to the sea water in which it lives and therefore, where the
internal fluid and external environment are separated by a semi-
permeable membrane as at the gills, there is a net passage of water
into the fish. This inward stream of water is got rid of by the kidney,
a urine, hypotonic to the blood, being produced by the expenditure
of chemical energy.

It is not certain how the gonads and regulatory organs of vertebrates came to be linked during their evolution, for there are no
living animals showing clear steps in the process, but it is considered
probable that the ducts connecting the coelom to the outside (coelomoducts) which are used for the shedding of the germ cells may have

taken over the regulatory and excretory function from nephridia. Thus nephridia are present in *Amphioxus* but there are no coelomoducts present, the gonads discharging by rupture of their walls, while in the cyclostomes and fishes there are no nephridia, regulation and excretion being performed by the modified coelomoducts which constitute the kidneys.

If this is the way in which the reproductive and regulatory functions came to be linked, then the association between excretory and genital ducts is understandable. A study of their development also sheds light on their association, their adult structure and their association with the blood system.

It will be recalled that the mesoderm of the embryo consists of segmented mesoderm forming the somites and unsegmented lateral plate mesoderm. The somites are narrow where they connect with the lateral plate, and this narrow region is known as the *nephrotome* since in each segment a nephric or kidney tube grows out from it and connects with a segmental longitudinal duct. These structures will thus be seen to form outside the coelom which is enclosed between the splanchic and somatic layers of the lateral plate mesoderm. Each nephric tubule thus places the kidney portion of the coelom, or *nephrocoele*, into communication with the outside via the segmental longitudinal duct (Fig. 14.21). Such a set of tubules could develop along much of the length of the body but they appear, in fact, only

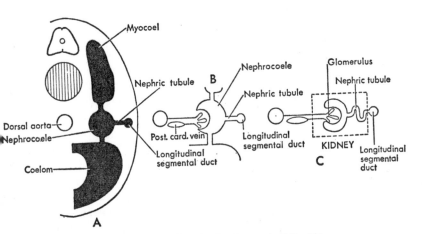

Fig. 14.21. Diagram illustrating the development of the kidney.

A Diagram of relationship of the nephrotome or kidney region of segmented mesoderm; *B* Blood supply to nephrotome; *C* Formation of kidney by separation of nephrocoele from coelom and myocoele.

in certain regions, an anterior set constituting the *pronephros* and opening into the pericardium and a posterior set constituting an *opisthonephros*.

Simple tubules connecting the coelom with the outside are clearly inadequate regulators of the internal environment and also inadequate excretory organs. Their evolution to form a compact regulatory organ, the kidney, is brought about by two main changes. Firstly, each tubule becomes associated directly with a short branch from the dorsal aorta carrying blood at fairly high pressure, and secondly, the opening of the nephrocoele into the coelom becomes restricted and eventually closed. The branch from the aorta provides a direct means of separating off an ultra-filtrate of blood which can be eliminated and the closure of the nephrocoele from the coelom provides a direct means of doing this and also necessitates, in the male, the discharge of the sex cells through the kidney duct.

The gonads do not arise segmentally in the vertebrates but from special longitudinal ridges of coelomic epithelium which come to project into the coelom. In the female, the eggs ultimately formed from them are shed into the coelom and pass out by the genital duct (*Müllerian duct*) which forms by a process of splitting off from the segmental longitudinal duct. In the male, the sperms eventually formed from the testis into which the gonad rudiment develops, are never shed into the general perivisceral coelom but pass through tubes communicating with the nephrocoele (the *vasa efferentia*) and thence into the segmental longitudinal duct.

These basic relationships are preserved throughout the members of the vertebrata but needless to say the details are often greatly modified. It is common, for example, to find vestiges of female parts in the male and vice versa, development proceeding in an indifferent way up to a certain point and then, as it were, swinging towards male or female.

To return to the urinogenital organs of the dogfish (Fig. 14.22); these show a relatively lowly stage in the elaboration of the pattern which has been described. The pronephros, that is, the anterior zone of nephric tubules, appears during development but does not persist into adult life. The opisthonephros is the functional adult kidney but even that develops unevenly, the anterior tubules having no kidney function but, in the male, contributing secretions to the seminal fluid as it is passed down the segmental longitudinal duct. The posterior part of the opisthonephros is the functional adult regulator or excretory organ or kidney proper. It extends some way behind the posterior limits of the coelom. The segmental longitudinal or *Wolffian duct* having taken over the function of conveying sperm to the exterior, urine from the kidney is passed out through newly developed collecting ducts separate from the Wolffian duct. The collecting ducts and the Wolffian duct have a common passage, the *urinogenital sinus* which opens into the cloaca at the tip of a small papilla. The vestigial anterior opening of the Müllerian ducts into the coelom can be seen in the male while the sperm sacs are believed to represent the posterior portions of the Müllerian ducts.

The terminology of the parts of the urinogenital system often appears confusing because the same structure is known by a variety of names. For example, the segmental longitudinal duct is often known by different names at different stages of development and may be termed the *archinephric duct*. The term pronephric duct may be applied to the anterior portion and the term mesonephric duct to the posterior. The term Wolffian duct is used for this urinogenital duct also. In the male its hinder end is called the *vesicula seminalis*.

In the female adult dogfish only the right ovary persists but both Müllerian ducts are functional oviducts. They have a common internal opening ventral to the oesophagus and each bears a swelling, the *shell gland*, in the anterior third. They open separately into the cloaca. The anterior part of the opisthonephros is lacking but the posterior part forms the functional kidney and is drained by the original segmental longitudinal duct.

Accessory parts of the reproductive system of the male comprise the scroll-shaped prolongations of the pelvic fin skeleton, the *claspers*, which act as intromittent organs, and the *siphon*, a muscular sac lying beneath the skin of the ventral side of the trunk which may assist in coition.

The kidneys lie above the abdominal coelom and separated from it by the peritoneum (lining of the abdominal coelom). The testes are suspended from the dorsal side of the abdomen by a double fold of the peritoneum (or mesentery) known as the *mesorchium*; the ovary is similarly suspended by a mesentery known as the *mesovarium*.

Reproduction

The reproduction of the dogfish takes place during most of the year and up to ten eggs may be laid per month by each female. Although there is only one ovary, two eggs at a time are shed into the coelom and pass by the action of tracts of cilia to the opening of the oviducts. While this is taking place, the secretion of the egg capsule has

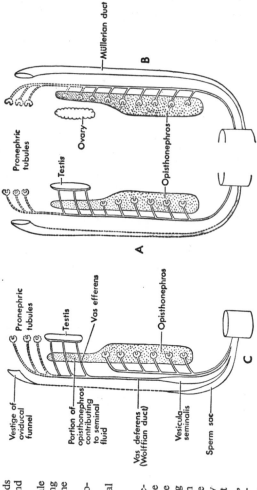

Müllerian duct

B

Pronephric
tubules

Ovary

Testis

Opisthonephros

A

Pronephric
tubules

Testis

Vas efferens

Vestige of
oviducal
funnel

Portion of
opisthonephros
contributing
to seminal
fluid

Opisthonephros

Vas deferens
(Wolffian duct)

Vesicula
seminalis

Sperm sac

C

Fig. 14.22. The dogfish. The urinogenital system.

A and *B* Diagrams of the relation between the kidney tubules, the gonads and the genital ducts of the male (A) and of the female (B).

C The condition in the adult male dogfish. (Where parts are formed during development but do not persist in the adult, they are shown dotted.)

D Dissection of the female urinogenital system.

E Dissection of the male urinogenital system.

(Based on *Lockyer* and *Crofts*.)

By comparing diagram *B* with dissection *D*, it will be seen that the female urinogenital system undergoes little change during development. Comparing *A* with *C* and *E*, it will be seen that in the male the anterior portion of the kidney does not function as an excretory organ, while the posterior excretory part has developed a separate excretory duct, the ureter, leaving the segmented longitudinal (Wolffian) duct solely reproductive in function (as the vas deferens). Vestiges of the Müllerian duct persist as an oviducal funnel and as sperm sacs.

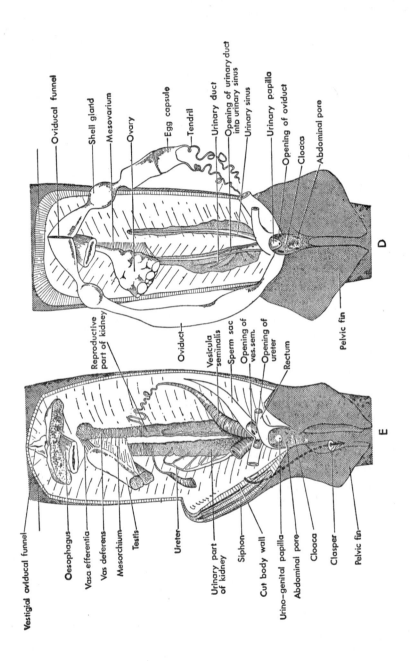

Oviducal funnel
Shell gland
Mesovarium
Ovary
Egg capsule
Tendril
Urinary duct
Opening of urinary duct into urinary sinus
Urinary sinus
Urinary papilla
Opening of oviduct
Cloaca
Abdominal pore

Pelvic fin

D

Reproductive part of kidney

Oviduct
Vesicula seminalis
Sperm sac
Opening of ves. sem.
Opening of ureter
Rectum

Vestigial oviducal funnel
Oesophagus
Vasa efferentia
Vas deferens
Mesorchium
Testis
Ureter
Urinary part of kidney
Siphon
Cut body wall
Urino-genital papilla
Abdominal pore
Cloaca
Clasper
Pelvic fin

E

begun in the shell gland. In the folds of this organ the male sperm is also stored and is ready to fertilize the egg before it is enclosed by the tough egg capsule. The sperm from the male is conveyed to the female during copulation when the pair of erected claspers is inserted into the vent of the female. The male twines round the female during this process and it is thought that water contained in the siphon may be used to flush the seminal fluid into the female. At any rate, the sperms swim up the oviduct and remain viable when stored in the folded lining of the shell gland, probably for several weeks.

The fertilized eggs are surrounded by a resistant and relatively impermeable capsule of tanned protein somewhat akin to the keratin of hair. This serves to protect the developing embryo and to retain an environment about it which contains a high concentration of urea like that which occurs in the blood of the adult. The egg capsules pass down the oviduct and are laid by the female in algal vegetation with which the long tendril-like projections on the corners of the egg case are entwined. The young fish does not hatch until about six months has passed. Little is known of the early life of the dogfish.

Nervous system and Sense organs

One of the chief features of the vertebrates is the great development and complexity of the nervous system and sense organs. This enables the animal to obtain comprehensive data from the surroundings and to behave in response to the data and to its own internal state in a highly complex manner. Nevertheless, this increasing complexity can be shown to be based on the simple tubular nervous system and cutaneous sensory nerve endings of the protochordate. The chief advances which the fish shows over *Amphioxus* are the development of a brain by the enlargement of the front end of the neural tube, the elaboration of special sense organs in conjunction with the brain, and the fusion of the dorsal sensory and ventral motor roots of the nerves arising from the spinal cord to form mixed nerves. If now the general features of the chordate nervous system and sense organs are considered, it can be seen that, apart from a few specializations, the dogfish may be taken as a good example of an animal possessing vertebrate nervous organization in a primitive form.

The central nervous system arises precociously during development as a tube, at the anterior end of which, the brain appears in the form of three vesicles (Fig. 14.23). These give rise to the fore-, mid- and hind-brain regions or the *prosencephalon*, the *mesencephalon* and the *rhombencephalon*. These parts soon become distinguishable into further subdivisions, namely the forebrain into the endbrain and between brain (*telencephalon* and *diencephalon* or *thalamencephalon*) and the hind-brain into the cerebellar region and medulla (*metencephalon* and *myelencephalon*). The telencephalon is associated with the olfactory organ, a patch of ectoderm containing neurosensory cells sending fibres inwards to the brain. The diencephalon is associated with the eye, the retina of which arises as an outgrowth from the fore-brain and is really part of it. The hind-brain is associated with the ear and lateral line organs which develop by the differentiation of regions (or *placodes*) of the ectoderm. The connection between the olfactory organ and the brain (i.e. fibres from the cells of chemical sense), as well as the connection between the eye and the brain, are thus not comparable to the nerves which connect the brain with the other receptor cells. These nerves, being aggregations of fibres from cells of the central nervous system, can be shown to be part of the same series of nerves as that to which the spinal nerves belong. (See also Fig. 14.30, p. 303.)

The five regions into which the embryonic brain can be distinguished (namely, two in the fore-brain, the mid-brain, and two in the hind-brain) rapidly alter their proportions as they develop, so that their limits are not easy to see in the adult animal. Nevertheless, the parts of the adult brain which are formed from the primary vesicles have certain general characters which make them identifiable and permit the construction of a simple idealized brain. The myelencephalon or medulla, which merges into the spinal cord, has a non-nervous roof where the connective tissue membrane covering the nervous system (the *pia mater*) becomes very vascular (see below). This region is known as the *posterior choroid plexus*. On the other hand the roof of the metencephalon becomes thickened to form the *cerebellum*. The mid-brain roof also becomes thickened as the *optic tectum* because this region becomes associated with nervous impulses originating in the eye (although it will be recalled that the eye originates as an outgrowth of the *fore-brain*). The ventral and side walls constitute the thickening known as the *crura cerebri*. The diencephalon, like the medulla, has a non-nervous roof forming the *anterior choroid plexus*. The thickening of its lateral walls forms the thalamus. From the diencephalon two outgrowths arise, a dorsal one forming the *epiphysis* or *pineal*, probably in primitive vertebrates a light perceiving eye, and a ventral hollow outgrowth,

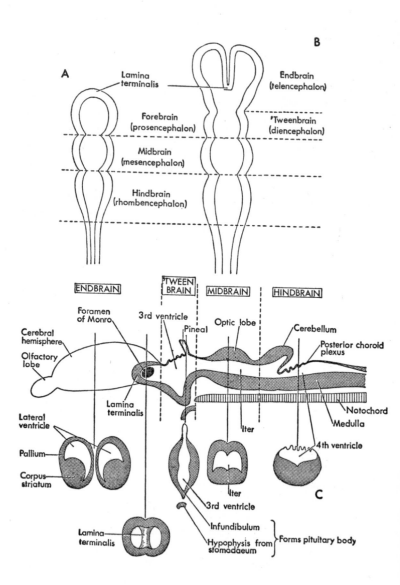

A

Lamina
terminalis

B

Endbrain
(telencephalon)

Forebrain
(prosencephalon)

'Tweenbrain
(diencephalon)

Midbrain
(mesencephalon)

Hindbrain
(rhombencephalon)

ENDBRAIN | 'TWEEN BRAIN | MIDBRAIN | HINDBRAIN

Foramen
of Monro

3rd ventricle

Pineal

Optic lobe

Cerebellum

Cerebral
hemisphere

Olfactory
lobe

Posterior choroid
plexus

Lamina
terminalis

Iter

Notochord

Medulla

Lateral
ventricle

Pallium

Corpus
striatum

Iter

4th ventricle

3rd ventricle

C

Lamina
terminalis

Infundibulum

Hypophysis from
stomodaeum

Forms pituitary body

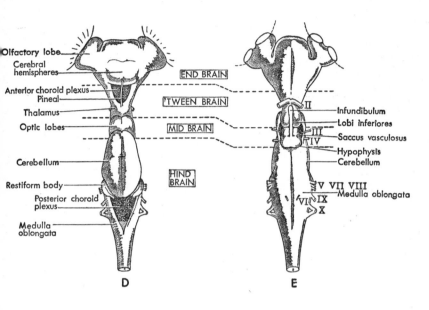

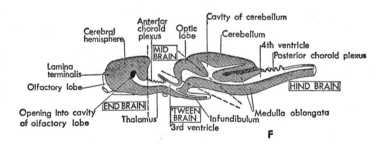

Fig. 14.23. The brain.

A and *B* Diagram of stages in the development of a vertebrate brain.

At *C* is shown a sagittal section through an ideal brain with corresponding transverse sections below.

D Dorsal view of the brain of a dogfish.

E Ventral view of the brain of a dogfish.

F Sagittal section of the brain of a dogfish.

the *infundibulum*. Together with an upgrowing pocket from the stomodaeum (the *hypophysis*—so-called because it lies below the brain) the infundibulum forms an internal secreting organ, the *pituitary body*.

The telencephalon has a small undivided medial region but is swollen into left and right *cerebral hemispheres* which project in front of the original anterior boundary of the fore-brain vesicle, the *lamina terminalis*. *Olfactory lobes* are distinguishable at the anterior end of the cerebral hemispheres and are usually closely applied to the olfactory organ. The delicate connective tissue membrane closely covering the brain and spinal cord is known as the *pia mater*, while the whole cerebro-spinal cavity is lined with a tough connective tissue layer, the *dura mater*.

The brain of the dogfish is not much more elaborate than that which has just been described but certain parts of it are better developed than others, for example the olfactory lobes of the telen-cephalon are very large, the cerebral hemispheres are small but the cerebellum is enormous and bears postero-lateral *restiform bodies*. If now Fig. 14.23(D) and (E) are examined—showing the brain as seen from above, from below and in section—the essential similarity to the idealized brain will be seen, as will also those features in which it differs.

Some other points should also be noted. The cavity of the spinal cord is continuous with that of the brain, in which it widens out to form the so-called *ventricles*, that of the medulla being known as the fourth ventricle, that of the diencephalon the third, while the *iter* or *cerebral aqueduct* in the mid-brain is the narrow passage connecting them. The cerebral hemispheres contain the two anterior lateral ventricles. The left and right halves of the brain are connected by certain definite tracts of fibres or commissures. These can be seen in section when they are cut through. The chief ones are the *anterior commissures* in the *lamina terminalis* connecting the halves of the fore-brain and the *posterior commissure* in the roof of the mid-brain. The diencephalon bears a ventrally directed infundibulum from which, together with a contribution of the hypophysis, the pituitary is derived. As well as giving rise in front to the single median pituitary body, the infundibulum bears small lateral swellings, the *lobi inferiores*. Also projecting from the floor of the diencephalon are the *sacci vasculosi* lying beside the pituitary. From the roof of the diencephalon a pineal stalk ends in a small pineal body or *epiphysis*. From the roof of the mesencephalon arise the *optic lobes*.

Sense organs

The sensory system is receptive to many different types of change in the environment. These changes constitute *stimuli* and there are sense cells very highly specialized for the reception of the various stimuli which can be perceived. In general it can be said that a vertebrate receptor cell or sense cell can respond to only one type of change or stimulus. This effective stimulus causes a nerve impulse to be initiated in the nerve fibre connecting it to the central nervous system. These impulses are interpreted by the brain according to the organ whence they come. The sense organs responding to chemical substances are the olfactory organs, which are sensitive to—that is, effectively stimulated by—very small concentrations, and the gustatory or taste buds which are, in general, less sensitive. The eye is sensitive only to electromagnetic vibrations of a certain frequency, i.e. light waves, while the ear and lateral line organs together perceive mechanical vibrations of the water via their own internal fluids. It is thought that the ampullae of Lorenzini, mucus-filled pits on the snout, may be receptive to temperature changes.

The animal is thus equipped to perceive the chemical, mechanical and electromagnetic changes in its environment and in some instances the direction from which they come. We know nothing of the 'world' in which the dogfish lives as a result of these perceptions but the relative simplicity of its brain and behaviour leads us to believe that its 'world' is in few ways similar to ours. We can only study the 'dogfish world' by the responses which the animal makes when it is given stimuli and by recording electrically the impulses carried by the nerve fibres from sense organs to the central nervous system. Thus, for example, we can say that it smells food when it moves directly towards it from a distance although the food is out of sight and stationary and at the same temperature as the water. However, when it is replete the animal no longer moves towards the food and although we do not doubt that it can still smell the food we have no assurance that, in fact, it does so. Had we conducted experiments solely with replete dogfish we might have come to the conclusion that the animal had no sense of smell!

Olfactory organs

The olfactory organs (Fig. 14.24) are large sacs with very much folded walls lined with an epithelium in which there are olfactory cells (neurosensory cells) sending nerve fibres into the olfactory lobes of the brain. The organs are housed in the thin cartilaginous nasal capsules of the skull which are incomplete ventrally where the olfactory organs open to the outside. This opening is connected to the mouth by a groove, the *oronasal groove*, which is covered by a flap of skin. From the large size of the olfactory organs and the olfactory lobes of the brain it is presumed that this sense plays a large part in the animal's life, especially in the finding of food.

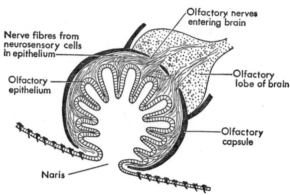

Fig. 14.24. The dogfish.

Diagram of a section through an olfactory organ to show the external opening (the naris), the olfactory epithelium, cartilaginous olfactory capsule and olfactory lobe of brain.

Sense cells which respond to the presence of chemical substances are not confined to the olfactory organs but are also found in the buccal cavity and pharynx where they are grouped together with supporting cells into separate little taste buds which are innervated by branches of the facial, glossopharyngeal and vagus nerves.

The eye

The eyes of the dogfish are housed in the orbital cavities on either side of the cranium. Each eye is attached to the walls of the orbital cavity in which it lies by three pairs of extrinsic antagonistic muscles: the *superior* and *inferior rectus* muscles which rotate the eye in the vertical plane; the *external* and *internal rectus* muscles which rotate it in the horizontal plane and the *superior* and *inferior oblique* muscles which twist it. All these movements of the eye are of limited extent but serve to direct the pupil towards specific objects in the range of vision. The coats of the eyeball are similar to those of the mammal (page 389) but the eye of the dogfish is not spherical like that of the mammal but has a flattened corneal surface (Fig. 14.25). The lens is spherical or nearly so and is attached to the ciliary body by a gelatinous membrane which is especially thick dorsally. Opposite this, on the ventral side of the lens a muscle runs from the lens to the ciliary body. By the contraction of this muscle the lens can be swung nearer the cornea (i.e. further away from the retina) and thus the image of close objects can be focused on the layer of sensitive cells. Accommodation for near vision is thus an active process of muscular contraction and the eye, when relaxed, is focused for more distant objects.

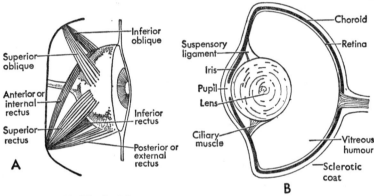

Fig. 14.25. The dogfish.

A Diagram to show the eye muscles as seen from above. *B* A vertical section of the eye.

The retina of elasmobranchs is backed by a choroid which possesses cells containing guanine crystals forming a light-reflecting surface. This can be covered by a pigment in bright light and uncovered in dim light. In dim light the pigment cells at the back of the choroid are contracted and the guanine-containing cells forming the tapetum are able to reflect the light that passes through the retina back again on to the receptor cells, thereby increasing their stimulation. In bright light the pigment cells expand, covering the reflecting guanine-containing tapetum. Light which has passed through the retina is absorbed by the pigment and is not reflected back, and halation or blurring of the image is thereby prevented. Thus the requirement for maximum light stimulation in dim conditions and the prevention of light scattering in bright conditions are both available to the fish by changes in the choroidal pigment cells.

The sensitive cells of the retina are all rods, many of which are connected to each ganglion cell. This confers sensitivity in poor light at the expense of visual acuity.

Acoustico-lateralis system

An animal is said to hear when it behaves as if it perceives a moving or vibrating object which is not in contact with it. This local mechanical disturbance is a 'sound' since the word sound must be taken to include a much wider range of stimuli than are ordinarily referred

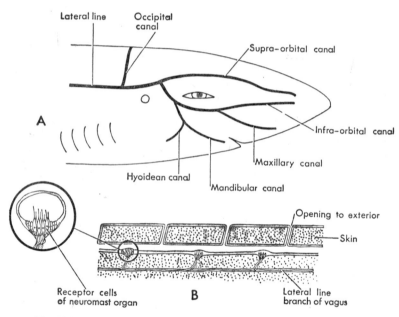

Fig. 14.26. The dogfish.

Diagram (*A*) of the distribution of lateral line canals on the head and (*B*) a longitudinal section of a lateral line with (INSET) a neuromast organ.

to as sounds for it is probable that the distinction between 'mechanical disturbance' and 'sound' (of more or less regular vibrations) is not apparent to the fish in the same way as it is to us. The ear and lateral line system must be considered together because they develop in much the same way and because the ear is innervated by a branch of the same dorsal root which supplies part of the lateral line system. Also the type of sense cell groups in the lateral lines is similar to those found in the inner ear.

Besides its sensitivity to mechanical disturbance the acoustico-lateralis system gives the animal information about its position and movement in space. This latter function is, however, confined to the ear and is not part of the function of the lateral line organs.

The lateral line runs as a mucus-filled canal below the surface all the way from the tail to just behind the spiracle. Here it connects with a system of tubes on the head which have a similar function (see Fig. 14.26). The lateral line opens to the exterior at intervals. Groups of sense cells and supporting cells occur along the lateral line tubes at intervals and are known as *neuromast organs*, the fine processes of the sense cells projecting into the mucus-filled canal. All the neuromast organs, no matter whether they lie at the tip of the snout or tail, are innervated by branches of the facial, glosso-pharyngeal or vagus nerves and hence the impulses initiated when the receptor cells are stimulated are conveyed direct to the medulla to which these nerves run. It will be noted firstly that these neuro-mast organs are not accessible to direct contact stimulation like general cutaneous sense cells but are accessible to vibrations reaching them through the water and secondly that, being innervated by cranial nerves, the impulses to which they give rise all reach the same part of the central nervous system. Further, it has been shown that they are of extreme sensitivity to mechanical vibrations, responding to much smaller mechanical disturbances than any other type of sense cell. Since the lateral line organs are all connected to the same part of the central nervous system, it seems that the intensity of stimulation falling on two points of the fish from a single source can be directly compared and hence the direction of the disturbance can be determined. This will clearly be most accurate for short distances and for long fishes (see Fig. 14.27).

This, doubtless over-simplified, explanation of the working of the lateral line system serves, however, to make clear the reason for its extent and for the type of innervation which it possesses and also to explain its great development and that of the medulla in certain deep-sea fishes, such as the scabbard fish which lives at depths where light is poor and which probably relies on its lateral line system for catching its active, living prey. The lateral line system is also believed to be of great importance in the shoaling of fishes.

The other part of the acoustico-lateralis system, the ear, is more highly differentiated but nevertheless begins as an ectodermal placode which, sinking below the surface, becomes a little vesicle

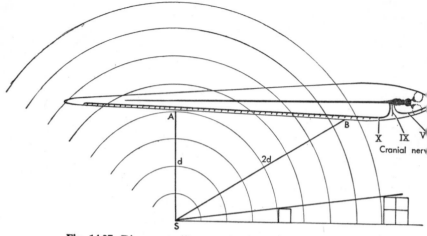

Fig. 14.27. Diagram to illustrate the functioning of the lateral line system.

The central nervous system and the innervation of the lateral line by the three cranial nerves, facial, glossopharyngeal and vagus shown in outline. A, source of sound or disturbance is shown at S, the distance SA is *d* and the distance SB, 2*d*, the intensity of the stimulus received at A is therefore four times that received at B. Only one position of S fulfils this condition. (Based on *Pumphrey*.)

and is in due course innervated by a branch of a dorsal root nerve. The simple vesicle eventually develops a complicated shape and comes to lie in a fluid-filled cavity in the cartilage of the ear capsule. The vesicle is also fluid-filled and retains its connection with the outside via the *ductus endolymphaticus*. The fluid filling the membranous labyrinth, which is formed from the embryonic otic vesicle, is known as endolymph and the fluid filling the cavity in the ear capsule is known as perilymph (Fig. 14.28).

The main body of the membranous labyrinth is known as the *utriculus* from which a lobe, the *sacculus*, projects downwards. Three semicircular canals, each bearing a swelling or ampulla, arise from the utriculus, one in each plane of space. Sense cells are confined to definite spots or *maculae* in the utriculus and sacculus and to the three ampullae of the semicircular canals, where they are known as *cristae*. There is one macula in the utriculus, one in the sacculus, and one in the *lagena*, a small outgrowth of the sacculus. Records of the impulses in the nerves coming from the maculae show that the function of this part of the labyrinth appears to be to

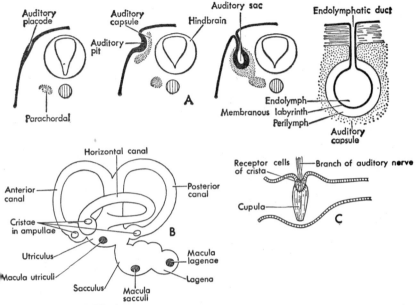

Fig. 14.28. The inner ear.

A Diagram to illustrate the formation of the ear of vertebrates during development. *B* The structure of the membranous labyrinth. *C* The structure of a crista. (*B* after *Lowenstein*.)

supply information about the orientation in space of the animal. These impulses vary in frequency according to the position of the animal, the receptor cells being stimulated when their fine hair-like processes are deformed by the touch of the calcareous grains (or otoliths) which are present in the endolymph.

On the other hand, the semicircular canals have the function of detecting turning or angular acceleration. The hairs on the receptor cells of the crista are ensheathed in a gelatinous cap or *cupola* which fits fairly closely into the ampulla and moves with the movement of fluid in the canal after the fashion of a swing door in a draughty passage. Movement of the animal in the plane of the canal causes a swirl of the fluid along that canal (but not, of course, in the others) deflecting the cupola and stimulating the receptor cells of the crista. Even when the animal is at rest a few nerve impulses per second are originated by the receptor cells of the cristae but when the cupola is deflected and the cells thus stimulated, the rate of discharge of nerve impulses is increased or diminished according to the direction of movement.

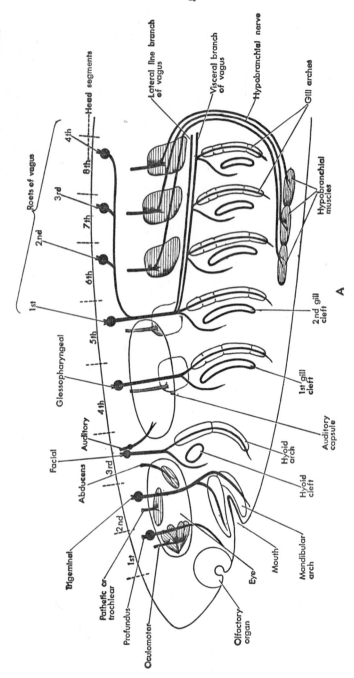

A

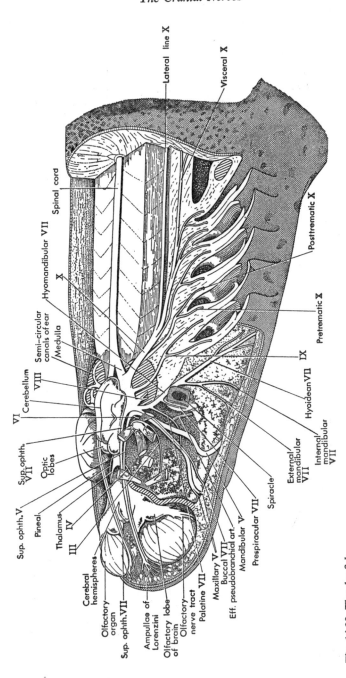

Fig. 14.29. The dogfish.

A Diagram to illustrate the segmental origin of the cranial nerves. Ventral roots and dorsal roots with ganglia are shown separately. The myotome derivatives are shown cross-hatched and visceral arch and cranial structures in outline.

B The brain and cranial nerves as seen in dissection, dorso-lateral view. (Redrawn from *Lockyer* and *Crofts*.)

General cutaneous sensitivity

Little is known about the sensitivity of the free nerve endings in the skin or to what, in particular, they respond.

Proprioceptors

There are proprioceptor end organs in the muscles of the dogfish because impulses have been detected in the sensory nerves which increase in frequency when the muscles are stretched. These end organs have recently been identified histologically as have the proprioceptors of mammals.

Spinal and cranial nerves

It will be recalled that, in *Amphioxus*, dorsal mixed nerves and ventral motor nerves arise from the spinal cord in each segment but that in the vertebrates those arising from the spinal cord join one another and form a single mixed nerve containing both afferent (or sensory) and efferent (or motor) fibres. In *Amphioxus* there are some sensory nerve cell bodies scattered along the course of the dorsal root nerves but in the vertebrates they are all gathered into the dorsal root ganglia. The only exception to this is the neurosensory cells which line the olfactory epithelium and which send nerve fibres into the olfactory lobes of the brain (see Fig. 14.30).

In the region of the brain the nerve roots remain separate, forming the so-called cranial nerves. Apart from the oculomotor and pathetic all come from the medulla, which is the part of the brain most nearly like the spinal cord and may be described as the segmental part of the brain.

It has already been seen that the segmented mesoderm of the head region comprises eight somites and it is the nerves corresponding to these that are the cranial nerves.

The table on p. 304 gives also the dorsal root (mainly sensory) and the ventral root (motor) nerves corresponding to the segment and the adult muscle derived from its embryonic somite. However, the nerves of the head region had been described in many different species of vertebrates long before the segmental structure of the head was recognized and they were known to be of relatively constant appearance in diverse animals. They had been numbered as a series from the anterior to the posterior of the brain and had taken their names from those given to them by the early human anatomists. The olfactory nerves and the optic nerve were also included in the series but, as is now clear, these are not comparable structurally with the others which are part of a segmental series. Also the auditory

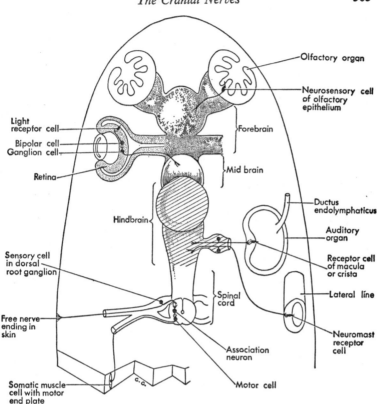

Olfactory organ

Neurosensory cell of olfactory epithelium

Forebrain

Light receptor cell

Bipolar cell
Ganglion cell

Retina

Mid brain

Ductus endolymphaticus

Auditory organ

Hindbrain

Receptor cell of macula or crista

Sensory cell in dorsal root ganglion

Lateral line

Spinal cord

Free nerve ending in skin

Neuromast receptor cell

Somatic muscle cell with motor end plate

Association neuron

Motor cell

Fig. 14.30. Diagram to illustrate the differences in relationship and in innervation between the nose, the eye, the acoustico-lateralis system and the segmental arrangement of the spinal cord region.

nerve was listed separately and is now known to be a branch from the dorsal root of the third somite. The table therefore includes the anatomical names and numbers in the series which is usually written with Roman numerals. This double system of naming is, at first sight, a little confusing and although the anatomical system denoted by Roman numerals came first in time, it is clearly inferior in that it does not explain or simplify the arrangement of the cranial nerves by comparison with the spinal nerves and it is not based on a study of their development. The dorsal and ventral roots of the cranial nerves and their relation to other segmental structures of the head is shown diagrammatically in Fig. 14.29A which should be compared with a drawing of the nerves as seen when dissected in Fig. 14.29B.

SYNOPSIS OF HEAD SEGMENTATION IN THE DOGFISH

Segment	Myotome derivative	Ventral root	Dorsal root	Sensory distribution	Anatomical Name and Number
1 Premandibular	Internal, superior and inferior rectus and inferior oblique eye muscles	+			Olfactory I Optic II Oculomotor III
			+	Skin of snout (joined with trigeminal in *Scyliorhinus*)	Profundus
2 Mandibular	Superior oblique eye muscle	+	+	Skin of snout, upper and lower jaw (also certain motor fibres)	Trochlear IV Trigeminal V
3 Hyoid	External rectus eye muscle	+	+	Lateral line of snout. Sensory and motor fibres for hyoid arch. Membranous labyrinth	Abducens VI Facial VII Auditory VIII
4 First branchial	None	−	+	1st gill cleft sensory and motor	— Glossopharyngeal IX
5 Second branchial	None	−		}	—
6 Third branchial	} Branchial muscles	+	+	2nd–5th gill clefts, lateral line and viscera. Sensory and motor fibres.	Vagus X
7 Fourth branchial		+	+		Hypobranchial nerve Vagus X
8 Fifth branchial		+	+	}	Hypobranchial nerve Vagus X

It remains to describe the course of the cranial nerves and the structures which they connect with the brain and the purpose which these connexions serve.

The dorsal root of the first segment is the profundus nerve. This is small and variable in the dogfish *Scyliorhinus* (although it is present in the spiny dogfish *Squalus*) and runs close to the superficial ophthalmic branch of the trigeminal after leaving the eyeball.

The ventral root of the first segment is the oculomotor nerve which is purely motor, conveying impulses which activate four of the eye muscles, the inferior oblique, and the superior, inferior and internal rectus muscles.

The dorsal root of the second somite, the trigeminal, has three main branches, an ophthalmic, a maxillary and a mandibular. All branches are connected with the skin sense organs while maxillary and mandibular branches also contain motor fibres which innervate the jaw muscles.

The ventral root of the second segment is the trochlear or pathetic nerve which is purely motor and innervates the superior oblique eye muscle.

The dorsal root of the third somite, the facial, has many branches. These are an ophthalmic branch which connects with the neuromast sense cells of the lateral line organs (supra-orbital canal) and with the ampullae of Lorenzini, and a buccal branch connecting with infra-orbital lateral line organs and ampullae of Lorenzini. The palatine branch to the palate connects with taste buds in the roof of the buccal cavity. The hyomandibular branch before passing behind the spiracle gives off a small pre-spiracular nerve and then after passing the spiracle divides into a mandibular branch which supplies lateral line organs on the lower jaw and a hyoidean branch which is motor and supplies some of the visceral arch muscles.

The auditory nerve also arises as part of the dorsal root of the third segment.

The ventral root, the abducens, supplies the external rectus eye muscle and is motor only.

The ventral root of the fourth segment is missing.

The glossopharyngeal is the dorsal root of the fourth segment and is a mixed nerve with sensory fibres supplying the anterior part of the lateral line system as well as motor fibres going to the muscles of the gills.

The vagus nerve is composed of fibres from the dorsal roots of the fifth, sixth, seventh and eighth segments, and like the glossopharyngeal is a mixed nerve supplying the gills, lateral line and having branches also to the heart and gut.

The ventral root of the fifth segment is missing, while the sixth, seventh and eighth somites contribute to the hypobranchial plexus of nerves supplying the ventral branchial musculature derived from buds originating from segments six, seven and eight and some posterior ones.

The connexions between the brain and organs of special sense, as well as the arrangement of neurons in a spinal nerve, are shown in Fig. 14.30. If the olfactory organ with its neurosensory cells, the eye as an outgrowth of the brain and the acoustico-lateralis system with the corresponding sensory cells in a dorsal root ganglion be compared with the arrangement in a segmental nerve of the spinal cord, it will be seen that only the innervation of the acoustico-lateralis system is of the segmental type.

AUTONOMIC NERVOUS SYSTEM. The autonomic system of the dogfish consists of a series of ganglia lying above the posterior cardinal sinus and associated with suprarenal bodies which correspond with the medullary portion of the mammalian adrenal and are believed to secrete adrenalin. (The cortical portion of the adrenal is represented in the dogfish by the separate interrenal bodies found in the kidney region.) These ganglia are connected to the central nervous system by *rami communicantes* which come off from spinal nerve roots. Fine nerves leave the ganglia to join the viscera (Fig. 14.31). The autonomic ganglia contain the motor cells characteristic of the autonomic nervous system which innervate smooth muscle of the gut and blood vessels. These motor cells are stimulated by internuncial neurons having their cell bodies in the spinal cord and whence their fibres run in the rami communicantes. There appears to be no clear division of the autonomic nervous system into the sympathetic and parasympathetic systems characteristic of mammals.

Locomotion

Swimming movements start very early in the life of the animal, while it is still an embryo no more than 3 mm. long, and these movements, which are automatic at first, gradually come to be controlled by the central nervous system so that they are related to the needs and the environment of the fish. Nevertheless the range of movements which the dogfish can carry out is small, and bending from side to side persists throughout life as the main locomotory

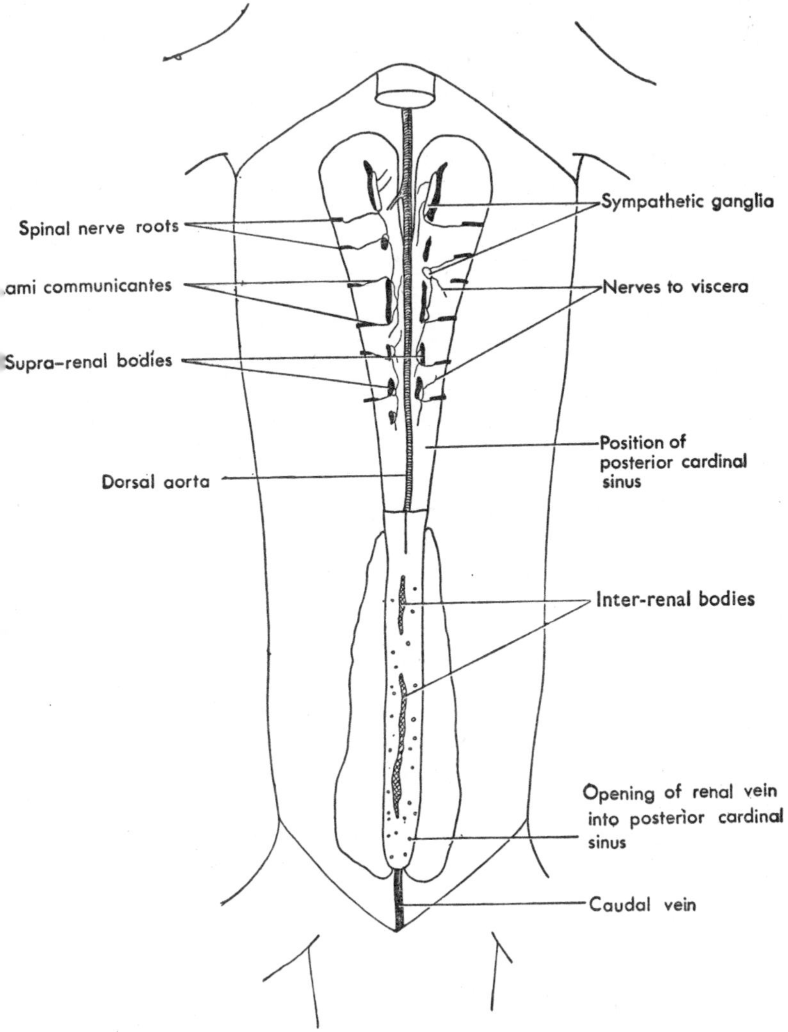

Fig. 14.31. The dogfish.

The autonomic nervous system and associated glands. The dorsal wall of the posterior cardinal sinus has been removed except between the kidneys where only the ventral wall has been removed to show the interrenal bodies. (Based on various authors.)

movement. Contraction of the muscles of one side begins at the head
end and passes down the body to the tail. A contraction on the
opposite side begins about half a second after the first and follows it
and is succeeded by a contraction on the original side, and so on.
The body is thus bent into waves which are moving backwards down
the body and which move the tip of the tail from side to side (Fig.
14.32). Some of the force which moves the animal forwards comes
from the reaction to the thrust of the sides of the animal as they are
moved obliquely backwards in the water and some comes from the

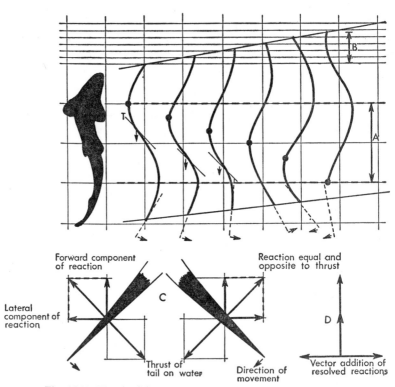

Fig. 14.32. The dogfish.

The successive postures taken up by a swimming dogfish are represented as lines. Dots mark the backward passage of a wave of muscular
contraction. Distance along the body travelled by the wave=*A*.
Distance moved forwards by fish=*B*. The backward thrust exerted
on the water by the passage of the swimming wave is illustrated by the
tangent T and its direction of movement by an arrow. Arrows also
indicate the direction of movement of the tail; at *C* the thrust of the
tail on the water and the reaction to it is analysed and the net forward
reaction shown at *D*. (Based on *Gray*.)

reaction to the sideways moving tail. It can be seen that the thrust exerted on the water by the tail can be resolved by the principle of the parallelogram of forces into a sideways and a backward component. It is the reaction to the backward component which drives the fish through the water, the sideways components cancelling one another out as the tail moves first left and then right.

In a similar way it can be shown that the *heterocercal* tail of the dogfish (i.e. one with a larger lower, or *hypochordal*, lobe than upper, or *epichordal* lobe) tends to rise in the water as it is moved

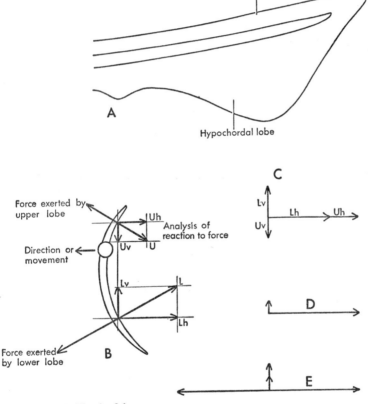

Fig. 14.33. The dogfish.

The action of the heterocercal tail: *A* shows the large hypochordal or lower lobe and the small epichordal or upper lobe; *B* the position of the tail taken up during movement to the left, end view; *C* vector addition of reactions to movement to the left; *D* resultant forces; *E* resultant of reactions to movements to right and to left.

from side to side by the lateral flextures of the swimming movements. The reaction to the larger, more flexible, lower lobe has an upwards component which more than balances the reaction to the small, less flexible, upper lobe and hence as the tail is moved from side to side the fish moves forwards through the water and the tail tends to rise and the nose to sink (Fig. 14.33). This is offset by the action of the pectoral fins which are forward of the centre of gravity and which are set at a small angle of attack to the longitudinal axis so that, as they pass through the water, they exert an upwards thrust. This is adjusted to counterbalance the effects of the heterocercal tail and the small weight of the fish in water (Fig. 14.34).

The pelvic fins do not play a very great part in the control of direction but the unpaired dorsal and ventral fins contribute to the animal's stability about its longitudinal axis and help to prevent rolling. They also contribute to its stability about its vertical axis where they diminish yawing from side to side.

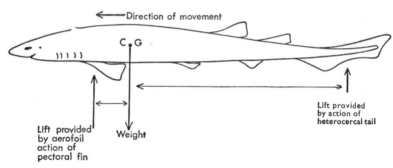

Fig. 14.34. The dogfish.

Diagram illustrating how the weight acting at the centre of gravity is counterbalanced by lifts generated by the pectoral fin and the tail. These forces are generated only during swimming so that the dogfish sinks when forward movement stops.

15. *The Frog*

The evolution of land vertebrates

IT WILL be apparent that changes affecting almost all parts of the body were necessary during the course of evolution of land living animals from their aquatic ancestors. A list of such changes can be set out in a simple form and a little reflection will show how the frog demonstrates them.

(a) SUPPORT. The weight of a body in water is less than its weight in air by the weight of the water which it displaces (Archimedes' principle); consequently aquatic animals need supporting structures of but little strength since their specific gravity is usually near to that of water and their 'weight' low. Land animals, especially large ones, need very much stronger support.

(b) MOVEMENT. The movement of fishes is chiefly effected by sinuous body movements which pass down the body and end in the movement of the tail from side to side. Movements of this type are effective for forward propulsion on land only if rigid points of resistance are available and if the body can glide over the ground. Such a type of movement is obviously of limited usefulness for movement on land where friction must be avoided. This can be done by limbs which are strong enough to lift the body off the ground and which can move independently. However, it is worth noting that even limbs which are struts, fixed horizontally at right angles to the body, are of advantage in translating sinuous body movements into forwards progression provided that they can slip forwards over the ground more easily than they can slip backwards.

(c) RESPIRATION. The air is a richer source of oxygen than is water at ordinary temperatures and it is especially richer than is the water of the tropics where higher temperatures diminish the solubility of gases. Any effective respiratory surface must be permeable to gases and hence to other small molecules such as water. It will therefore be moist and oxygen will be able to dissolve and inwards diffusion can occur. The exposure of a surface also leads to evaporation, to loss

311

of water from the underlying tissues and hence to changes of osmotic concentration and ultimately to desiccation. This risk in its turn can be lessened by sinking the respiratory surface into the body and diminishing its exposure to changes of air. The necessity for a large respiratory surface is therefore in conflict with the need to diminish water loss in a land animal.

(d) WATER. The better protected any land animal becomes against water loss the more it can become independent of the need to take in fresh supplies. Diminished water loss may be brought about by the presence of an impervious outer skin but some water loss from the kidney is necessary for the elimination of waste products of metabolism and, in 'warm-blooded' animals, *controlled* loss of water by evaporation of the secretion of the sweat glands is essential for the maintenance of a constant temperature.

(e) SENSE ORGANS. The organs for the reception of stimuli in aquatic animals are adapted for use in water which is an almost incompressible medium of specific gravity 1, refractive index 1·33, high sound conductivity and capable of carrying a great variety and a high concentration of molecules of chemosensory importance. In air the water-adapted eye would be short-sighted, the ear insufficiently stimulated by sound waves and therefore insensitive, the nose inadequately bombarded by stimulating molecules and the sensory processes of the lateral line receptor cells damaged by exposure to dry air. General cutaneous sensitivity would, moreover, be impaired by the presence of a tough impervious cuticle or the horny outer layer of the epidermis.

(f) REPRODUCTION. Eggs which are laid in the sea or in fresh water are deposited in a medium where fertilization can take place and where drying is not a danger, but terrestrial animals must resort to one of three possibilities: returning to the water to breed; the laying of fertilized eggs with impervious shells and a high water content; internal fertilization and viviparity. As is well known, the frog returns to water during the breeding season.

If the differences between the necessary adaptations of aquatic and terrestrial animals are borne in mind, it will be seen from what follows that the frog is partly adapted to life on land but yet is not freed from dependence on water. It is placed in the vertebrate class Amphibia, comprising animals distinguished by such anatomical features as the possession of a naked, scaleless skin, double occipital condyles, two auricles and one ventricle, but which are commonly recognized as being at home both on land and in the water.

The first amphibia evolved from fish-like ancestors in the late Devonian period nearly 300 million years ago and although they were rather like present-day newts in shape, they were very much bigger, bonier and clumsier, and differed in many ways as well. The frog is therefore far removed from the primitive amphibia and is an animal highly specialized for leaping on land, swimming in the water and for feeding on insects. The common frog, *Rana temporaria*, lives in damp places—marshes, ponds, ditches, the banks of streams—but is becoming rarer as these are drained and the water table falls and the demands for the creature increase with the extension of biological education. It is too familiar to need a detailed description of its external features, which may be seen in Fig. 15.1.

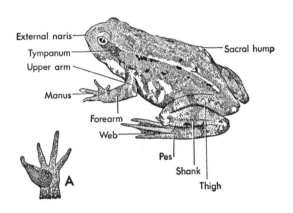

Fig. 15.1. The frog. External features.

A Underside of the left hand of male frog at the breeding season showing thickened pad of rough skin.

Locomotion

The frog swims in water by powerful backwards thrusts of its hind limbs with the toes divergent and the web between them stretched. The forelimbs usually take no part in swimming and are clasped to the ventral side of the body but when the animal is paddling around quietly the right and left forelimb may be moved alternately in a sequence like that used when crawling on land. Then the animal moves its limbs forwards in the order left fore, right hind, right fore, left hind, but it is a method which it seldom employs. In open places it leaps using its long hind legs to lift it off the ground and its fore-limbs to alight on. These are bowed out at the elbow joint and act as shock absorbers but are not capable of making long fore and after movements as would be required for walking. The hind limbs are very long, with the result that the sole of the foot can remain on the ground to transmit the thrust which the leg generates on extension while the body is being accelerated and thrown into the air (Fig. 15.2). The hind limbs have not always time to return to their fully flexed position during the leap and this action may be completed at leisure after alighting.

Fig. 15.2. The frog jumping, showing the changes in position of the parts of the skeleton.

Skin

The skin of the frog is strikingly different from that of the dogfish, being smooth, moist and slimy, and fitting loosely on the body. It is coloured by pigment confined in cells. Like the skins of all verte-brates, it is composed of an epidermal layer and a dermis. The epidermis is somewhat keratinized where it lies at the surface but is secretory where it is invaginated to form spherical mucous glands. The dermis is made of connective tissue and also contains blood vessels, muscle fibres and nerve fibres (Fig. 15.3). The pigment cells present in the dermis are of three types: (a) lipophores, which contain a fatty, yellow pigment; (b) guanophores, which contain reflecting crystals of guanine (see page 529); and (c) melanophores, which con-tain the black pigment melanin. The greenish colour of the frog is therefore due to the action of the three kinds of pigment cells on the light which falls on the skin and is reflected by it (Fig. 15.4). The guanophores reflect chiefly blue-green light by an interference effect and from this reflected light the bluer wavelengths are removed when it passes through the more superficial lipophores. Thus the pre-dominant tone is green. The melanophores reflect very little light of

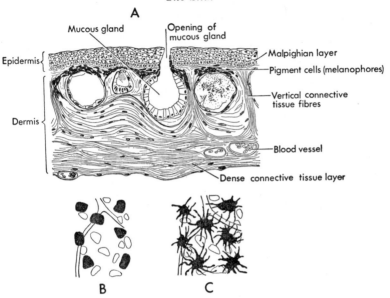

Fig. 15.3. The frog.

A Section of the skin. *B* Surface view of the skin showing melano-phores contracted, skin light in colour. *C* Melanophores expanded, skin dark in colour. (The outlines of other types of pigmented cells are also shown.)

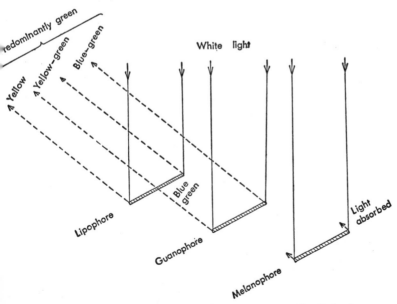

Fig. 15.4. Diagram to illustrate the action of pigmented cells in the frog's skin. (For explanation see text.)

any colour. The colour of the haemoglobin of the blood seen through the walls of the capillaries in parts of the body also affects the general hue. The distribution of the pigment cells is not uniform but more melanophores occur here and there, forming darker patches.

The frog has the power of slow colour change in response to atmospheric conditions and to the colour of its background. In dry, light and hot conditions it becomes lighter, and in dark, damp, cool conditions it becomes darker. The eye has a prominent role in the mechanism of colour change by the part which it plays in the perception of the colour of the surroundings. The size of the pigment cells is controlled by a hormone secreted by the pituitary gland into the bloodstream. This causes expansion of the melanophores in an amoeboid fashion, enlargement of the area covered by pigment, and consequent darkening of the skin. Injection of adrenalin causes contraction of the pigment cells and lightening of the colour, but it is not certain that this substance forms part of the mechanism of colour control in the natural state.

Skeleton

The skeleton of the frog (Fig. 15.5) is very different from its fish-like ancestors and from that of the present-day dogfish and is adapted to two methods of locomotion, jumping and swimming, by limb structure and movement. The skeleton is to a large extent built of bone, and although this living connective tissue, strengthened by the deposition of calcium salts, is different in its detailed structure from mammalian bone described on page 451, its origin and main features are the same. Bones originate during the development of the animal, partly by the replacement of cartilaginous precursors (*cartilage bones*) and partly by direct ossification (*membrane bones*).

THE VERTEBRAL COLUMN. This consists of only nine vertebrae and a tapering posterior prolongation, the *urostyle*. The basal and inter elements which appear during development soon become united and indistinguishable and it is believed that a vertebra is made up mainly of the basal elements whose growth around the notochord obliterates it. An adult vertebra then comes to consist of a centrum, neural arch and transverse processes, and, in the frog, is devoid of ribs. Articulations between vertebrae, additional to those between the centra, are provided by the *zygapophyses* which limit the amount each vertebra can move on the next and hence contribute to the degree of rigidity which is required to support the body while at the same time allowing for a certain amount of flexibility. The differences

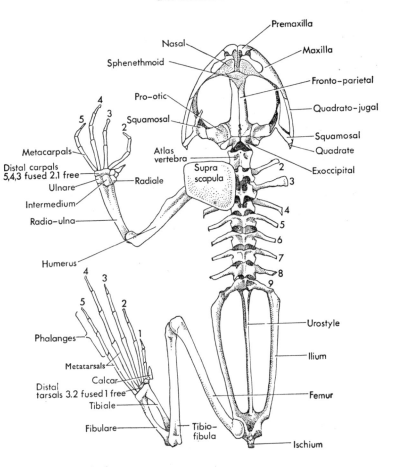

Fig. 15.5. The frog.

The skeleton seen from the dorsal side. Limbs of the right side omitted.

in shape between the nine vertebrae which make up the short vertebral column are shown in Figs. 15.5 and 15.6.

LIMBS. The five-fingered forelimb and the five-toed hind limb are regarded as the prototypes from which the tetrapod appendages have evolved. By comparison of the limbs of many animals, both living and fossil, the skeleton is considered as being made up essentially of the bones which are represented diagrammatically below (Fig. 15.7). The ideal plan of the *pentadactyl* limb is thus basically the same in

A

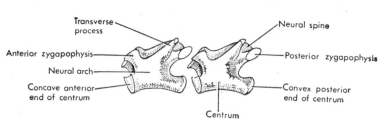

C

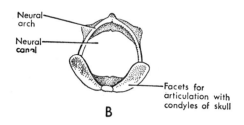

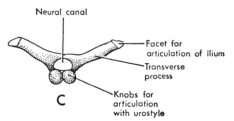

Fig. 15.6. The frog.

Vertebrae: *A* vertebrae numbers 5 and 6 seen from the left side, slightly separated; *B* the first or atlas vertebra, anterior view; *C* the ninth vertebra, posterior view.

both hind and forelimbs, although some joints are flexed differently in each. This ideal plan is rarely found in present-day animals, which diverge from it more or less widely as they are adapted to particular modes of life. There is some loss of bones and the fusion of others in the frog, as will readily be seen by comparing the ideal plan with a drawing of the fore- and hind-limb skeletons (Fig. 15.5).

In the forelimb the *radius* and *ulna* elements have become fused to form a *radio-ulna*. The proximal row of *carpals* is intact but the *centrale* is absent and the third, fourth and fifth distal carpals fused. The first digit is represented only by a *metacarpal* which does not

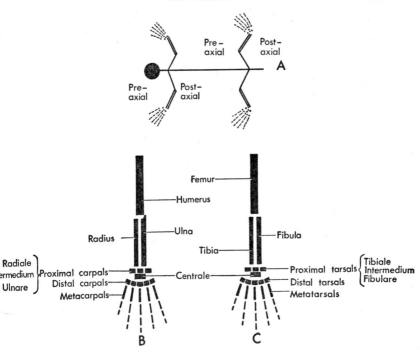

Fig. 15.7. Diagram to illustrate the composition of the pentadactyl limb skeleton.

A illustrates relation of limbs to axial skeleton and direction of bending of joints; *B* fore limb skeleton; *C* hind limb skeleton.

project free from the 'palm' of the 'hand', so the frog appears to have only four 'fingers'.

In the hind limb the thigh, shank, ankle and foot are all elongated. The *femur* articulates distally with a *tibio-fibula* (cf. radio-ulna) and this in turn with the proximal *tarsals*, the *tibiale* and the *fibulare*. The *intermedium* is missing, as are the centrale and distal tarsals 4 and 5. Distal tarsals 2 and 3 are fused and number 1 bears a spur of two small bones forming a 'prehallux' or extra digit. Like the first metacarpal of the forelimb, this does not project separately from the intact limb.

The pectoral girdle with which the forelimb articulates is embedded in the muscles of the body-wall and is not attached to the vertebral column (Fig. 15.8). It consists of the suprascapula and the bony *scapula* and *coracoid* arising as ossifications of the embryonic girdle of cartilage (cf. dogfish scapula and coracoid portions) together with a slender *clavicle* which arises as a membrane bone. The two halves of the girdle are joined by cartilaginous regions termed *precoracoid* and *epicoracoid*. (These regions are so called because recognizable separate ossifications may be formed in them in other animals, although they do not occur in the frog.) Separate median cartilages and bones are joined to the girdle and constitute the *sternum*.

The pelvic girdle consists on each side of three parts, the anterior and very long *ilia* articulating with the sacral vertebrae, the posterior ischia and the ventral cartilaginous *pubes* (Fig. 15.9). All three take part in the formation of the *acetabulum*, the socket for the articulation of the femur. The shape of the girdle and its backward extension

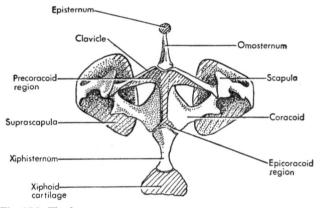

Fig. 15.8. The frog.
Pectoral girdle, ventral view. (Bone—white or stippled, cartilage—cross shaded.)

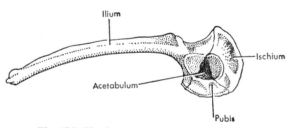

Fig. 15.9. The frog.
Pelvic girdle seen from the left side.

can be regarded as adaptations to accommodate the long hind legs and to form an extra joint to provide flexibility when jumping and alighting. The 'springiness' which exists between the girdle and the backbone, which is due to their being connected by sheets of muscle, can readily be seen and felt by examining the skinned animal.

THE SKULL. Like that of the dogfish, the skull of the frog arises from paired cartilaginous plates, the parachordals and anterior prolongations, the trabeculae, to which are added the olfactory and auditory capsules. It differs from the skull of the dogfish in that some of the cartilage is replaced by bone and some extra bones are added. These latter are all that remain of the complete superficial bony

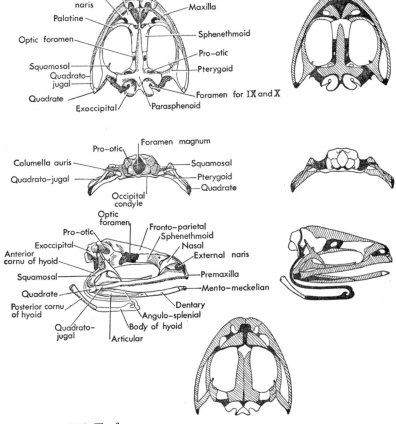

Fig. 15.10. The frog.

The skull seen in ventral, posterior and lateral views – on the left. The corresponding diagrams on the right and the one below indicate persistent cartilage (*black*), cartilage bone (*white*) and membrane bone (*shaded*).

armour with which the earliest amphibia were endowed but which, in the modern amphibia, are very greatly reduced. Such bones arise during the development of the individual, not by the replacement of cartilage by bone but from concentrations of mesoderm cells which form connective tissue membranes in which the bone is laid down directly. These two types of bone, cartilage bone and membrane bone, are distinguishable only by their origins and not by their histological structure.

Not only is the developing skull made up of the cranium and sense capsules, but also the visceral arches are present in the tadpole. The branchial arches bear first of all the external gills and later the internal gills, but at metamorphosis all the visceral arches undergo great changes of form and function which makes them almost unrecognizable as visceral arches in the adult. The mandibular arch becomes ossified and partly incorporated in the cranium, the hyoid arch possibly gives rise to the columella of the ear and certainly to part of the 'hyoid', while the branchial arches, of which there are four recognizable in the larva, contribute to the 'hyoid' and form cartilaginous supports of the glottis (see pages 324 and 327).

From the drawings of the frog's skull (Figs. 15.5 and 15.10) and the accompanying diagrams, in which persistent cartilage, cartilage bones and membrane bones are differently shaded, it will be seen that in the brain case or cranium there are only three centres of ossification developed. These give rise to the anterior, unpaired *spenethmoid*, and to the paired *exoccipitals* bearing condyles for the articulation of the vertebral column. A centre in each auditory capsule forms a *pro-otic* bone. There is no centre of ossification in the olfactory capsule. The upper part of the mandibular arch ossifies in the *palatine* and *pterygoid* positions but the *quadrate* region, with which the lower jaw articulates, remains cartilaginous. The lower part of the mandibular arch (Meckel's cartilage) ossifies only as the small *mento-meckelian* bones near the symphysis of the left and right halves.

The membrane bones are conspicuous and include the *frontoparietals* which roof over the top of the cranium and the single large *parasphenoid* which forms its floor. The olfactory capsules are covered above by the *nasals* and below by the *vomers*. The arcade of membrane bones which replaces the mandibular arch as the functional upper jaw consists of the *premaxillae*, the *maxillae* and the *quadratojugal* which articulates with the posterior end of the mandibular arch in the form of the persistently cartilaginous quadrate. The palatine and pterygoid, which we have just seen have an origin in cartilage, also receive some of their substance in the adult from direct ossification and are hence bones of mixed origin. The *squamosal* forms an additional structure connecting the point of articulation of upper and lower jaws with the auditory capsule. Each half of the lower jaw also receives additional ossifications and becomes ensheathed with a large *dentary* outside and an *angulosplenial* inside.

Parts of the cranium and visceral arches do not ossify but remain cartilaginous. These include the sides of the brain case, the olfactory

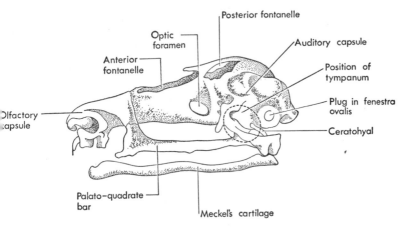

Fig. 15.11. The frog.

The skull of a recently-metamorphosed animal with the bones removed. (Based on *Gaupp*.)

capsules and parts of the auditory capsules. They are not always clearly distinguishable in the shrivelled state which cartilage takes on when dried and in which it is often seen. An idea of the extent of the cartilaginous cranium of a recently metamorphosed frog with the bones removed can be obtained from Fig. 15.11.

The hyoid arch is mainly cartilaginous and is recognized from its position and appearance during development. In the adult it forms part of the 'hyoid', in particular the anterior cornu, but there is doubt about whether the hyomandibula can be regarded as wholly homologous with the columella of the ear. Since the mandibular arch has become joined to the skull and functionally replaced as a jaw by the outer cascades of membrane bones, it no longer articulates with the hyoid arch although this retains its ancient relation to the cranium in that the anterior cornu of the hyoid abuts the auditory capsule. The other visceral arches, as has been seen, form a cartilaginous branchial basket in the tadpole but at metamorphosis degenerate, being in part incorporated in the 'hyoid' while the posterior two arches form the *cricoid* and *artyenoid* cartilages of the larynx (Fig. 15.12). The 'hyoid' plate and cornua still retain their ancestral position and serve for the attachment of muscles, among which there are those running to the pectoral girdle which by their contraction

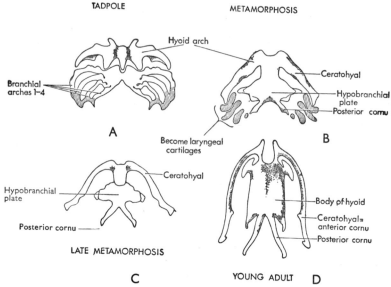

Fig. 15.12. The frog.

Branchial arches of a tadpole (*A*) and their changes at metamorphosis (*B* and *C*). *D* The 'hyoid' of a recently-metamorphosed animal. (Based on *de Beer*.)

serve to depress the floor of the buccal cavity and to enlarge its cavity. These are opposed by muscles, running transversely across the floor of the buccal cavity, whose contraction diminishes its volume. These muscles are used in opposition to one another in the respiratory movements of the frog in which the buccal cavity is used both for direct respiratory exchange through its own walls and as a force pump in the filling of the lungs.

TEETH. The lower jaw lacks teeth but small conical teeth occur on the premaxillae, maxillae and vomers. Each tooth is not set in a socket but joined to the bone by its own bone-like base. The bulk of the tooth is made of dentine which contains a central pulp cavity open at the side and the crown is covered with enamel (Fig. 15.13). They are replaced by the growth of new teeth when worn out or lost.

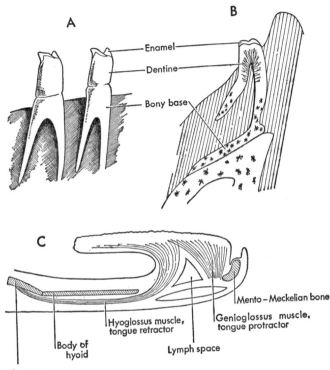

Fig. 15.13. The frog.

    A Teeth on the maxilla of a prepared skull seen from inside.
    B Section of upper jaw showing maxilla and lip.
    C Diagram of a longitudinal section of the frog's tongue and hyoid showing the arrangement of muscles.

The gut, feeding and digestion

The alimentary canal begins at the mouth, which is bounded by the wide jaws. The buccal cavity is wide and shallow and is lined with ciliated columnar epithelium whose ciliary beat is towards the pharynx. The anterior end of the tongue is attached to the inner border of the lower jaw and the free hind end can be flicked out and retracted suddenly (Fig. 15.13). As it is projected the tongue wipes against the secretion of mucous glands in the roof of the buccal cavity and becomes sticky, thus enabling it to catch insects which form the main food of the adult frog. These are swallowed by raising the floor of the buccal cavity and depressing the eyes which causes

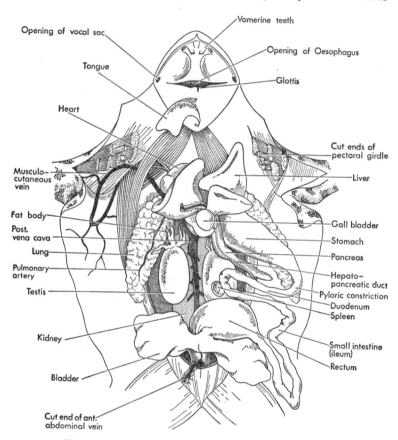

Fig. 15.14. The frog. General dissection to show the viscera.

the orbits to bulge inwards, thereby helping to push the food towards the pharynx. The internal nares open into the buccal cavity close to the vomers. In the male, but not in the female, the *vocal sacs* open ventrally near the angles of the jaw. They are made of connective tissue with an outer layer of muscle. Air is passed into them from the lungs and is then driven back again, passing the vocal cords each time. These are folds of the lining of the larynx, the edges of which are caused to vibrate and so to emit the animal's harsh croak.

The pharynx is short and not distinctly marked but is that portion of the gut into which open the Eustachian tube (hyoid visceral cleft) and the lungs. The Eustachian tube is closed at its outer end by the tympanic membrane or eardrum which is stretched across the cartilaginous tympanic ring and lies flush with the surface. The larynx, formed at the junction of the *bronchi* leading to the lungs, opens into the pharynx by a ventral longitudinal slit, the *glottis*.

The pharynx merges with the oesophagus, which is distinguished from it by the longitudinal folds of the mucous membrane of its walls. It, in turn, merges into the stomach, which is tubular and slightly curved. Its posterior end is marked by a muscular constriction, the pyloric sphincter. The intestine follows the stomach and consists of two main parts, the small intestine and the large intestine. The small intestine is further subdivided, its first part, the duodenum, lying parallel with the stomach and its second part being the coiled ileum. The large intestine or rectum is short and wide and clearly distinguishable from the ileum. It merges with the cloaca, which begins where the bladder and urinary ducts open into it. The histological structure of gut resembles in general that of the mammal but differs in detail (see pages 467–471). Likewise the processes of digestion and absorption are essentially similar to those of the mammal which are described in Chapter 22.

Associated with the alimentary canal are the liver with its gall bladder and the pancreas. The bile duct from the liver and the pancreatic duct join to enter the gut as the hepatopancreatic duct. This opens into the duodenum a short distance from the pyloric sphincter. The spleen, a part of the lymphatic system, lies in the mesentery adjacent the intestine.

Circulatory system

The heart (Fig. 15.15) lies in the pericardial coelom which is bounded by the pericardium. This tough connective tissue membrane does not cut off the pericardial coelom from the general perivisceral coelom in the same way as does the transverse septum of the dogfish but instead the heart, within its pericardium, lies freely in the general body cavity. The relationship of the parts of the coelom is illustrated in Fig. 16.2, p. 347.

The heart resembles that of the dogfish in having only one ventricle but differs in having two auricles. The sinus venosus opens into the

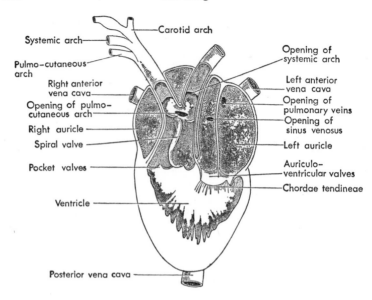

Fig. 15.15. The frog. The heart with part of the ventral side removed.

right, and the pulmonary veins into the left. The ventricle opens ventrally into the truncus arteriosus from which the aortic arches arise.

There are valves between the sinus venosus and the right auricle and between the auricle and the ventricle. The flaps of the auriculo-ventricular valves are tied down to the walls of the ventricle by connective tissue strings (*chordae tendineae*) attached to muscular projections of the ventricle wall. Three semilunar valves stand at the base of the truncus and a flap of tissue, the *spiral valve*, runs along its length, being attached to the dorsal wall but having its ventral edge free. A second row of semilunar valves occurs at the apex of the truncus.

In the heart-beat, contraction begins in the sinus venosus whose contraction drives blood into the right auricle. The auricles contract together, the blood is forced into the ventricle and this contracts and fills the truncus and aortic arches. The blood from left and right auricles (that is, from the lungs and body respectively) is mixed in the ventricle and the mixed blood simultaneously goes to the three aortic arches. Before X-ray observations were made it was thought that blood from the two auricles was largely kept separate in the ventricle by the spongy nature of its wall which prevented mixing. The different resistances to the flow of the blood in the pulmonary, systemic and carotid arteries were thought to effect the distribution of the oxygenated blood from the lungs to the head, the mixed blood to the body and the deoxygenated blood to the lungs; but this is not so. The lungs play an important part in gaseous exchange only at certain times of the year and after exertion. Oxygenation of the blood takes place freely in the skin at all times, so that the blood in the left auricle is not markedly different in oxygen content from that in the right.

The arterial system

The arterial system is shown in diagrammatic form in Fig. 15.16, where at first sight it will be seen to bear little resemblance to that of the dogfish. However, if its development in the tadpole is followed

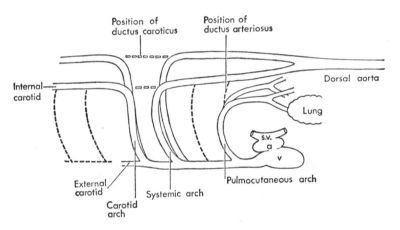

Fig. 15.16. The frog.

Diagram of the arterial arches. Only the third (carotid), fourth (systemic) and sixth (pulmo-cutaneous) are present in the adult.

and the change which takes place at metamorphosis is taken into consideration, it can be seen to be based on a set of modified *aortic arches* like those of the dogfish (see Fig. 14.17). The arches have become considerably altered with the loss of gills and the change in the method of breathing. The first two aortic arches are lost, the third gives rise to the carotid, the fourth to the systemic, the fifth is lost, and the sixth supplies the lungs and skin. At the external gill stage aortic arches 3, 4 and 5 supply the gill filaments and at the stage of internal gills numbers 3, 4, 5 and 6 bear branchiae (see also the chapter on the development of the frog, page 636).

Apart from the head region, which is supplied by the *carotid arch*, and the skin, which is supplied by a branch from the *pulmonary arch*, almost all the rest of the body is supplied by vessels which branch off from the *systemic arches* or the dorsal aorta formed by their union. Thus the *subclavian* arteries supply the arms, the *coeliaco-mesenteric* the gut, the *renal* arteries the kidneys, and the *iliac* arteries run into the legs (Fig. 15.17).

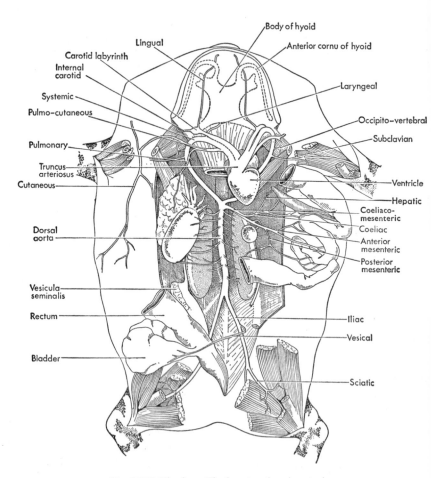

Fig. 15.17. The frog. The heart and main arteries.

Venous system (Fig. 15.18)

Entering the sinus venosus are paired *anterior venae cavae* representing the Cuvierian ducts and also the *posterior vena cava*, a new structure with no homology in the dogfish. Posterior cardinal veins are not present in the frog although present in the tadpole.

The veins which unite to form the anterior vena cava of each side are: the *external jugular* formed by the union of the *lingual* and the *mandibular*, the *innominate* formed by the *internal jugular* and the

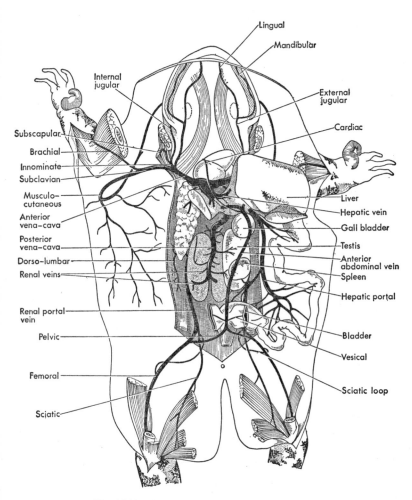

Fig. 15.18. The frog. The heart and main veins.

subscapular, and the *subclavian* vein formed by the union of the *brachial* and the large *cutaneous*. The posterior vena cava receives the *renal*, *gonadial* and *hepatic* veins. The legs are drained by the outer *femoral* and inner *sciatic* veins which unite to form the renal portal vein running to the kidney. *Pelvic* veins branching from the femorals unite to form the ventral or *anterior abdominal* vein running in the body wall and then entering the liver. Blood is returned from the gut to the liver via the hepatic portal vein and thence to the heart by the hepatic veins which join the posterior vena cava.

The pulmonary veins return blood from the lungs to the left auricle.

The chief features of interest in the frog's vascular system are thus the retention of three pairs of aortic arches to subserve the distribution of the blood to the head, body and lungs, and the functional replacement of the paired posterior cardinal veins by the unpaired posterior vena cava.

Respiration

As is well known, gaseous exchange in the frog takes place at the surface of the skin, in the buccal cavity and in the lungs. During the colder parts of the year, when metabolism is slow and the demand for oxygen small, the skin respiration provides sufficient oxygen for the animal's requirements. During the warmer months, and especially at the breeding season when metabolism is more rapid and the animals more active, skin respiration is supplemented by lung respiration which can supply an amount of oxygen about equal to that which diffuses through the skin. The amount of gaseous exchange which takes place through the skin is limited by the speed of diffusion across a given area and therefore remains nearly constant throughout the year.

Skin respiration depends for its efficiency on a number of factors. A plentiful supply of blood to the skin is needed and it can be inferred that this exists in the frog from the size and abundance of the arteries and veins of the skin and by observations of the rate and volume of the circulation of blood through small vessels in the web of the foot. The surface of the skin is permeable to oxygen and is kept moist by glandular secretion. Impervious layers such as thick keratin, bones or scales are absent from the surface of the skin. Of the skin derivatives, only keratin is present in the frog and this is confined to the outermost cells of the epidermis and is small in amount.

Gaseous exchange takes place too in the buccal cavity and depends upon the rapid change of air in this chamber brought about by the pumping action of the floor. The muscles attached to the hyoid lower the floor and air is sucked in via the nares. On raising the floor, air is driven out. By the rapid repetition of this process a supply of air is maintained, but such movements cease when the animal is immersed in water. The walls of the buccal cavity have a rich blood supply and are kept moist by mucous secretions.

Gaseous exchange also takes place in the lungs, which are elastic sacs whose walls are rich in blood vessels. The internal surface area is increased by infoldings of the walls (Fig. 15.19) which subdivide

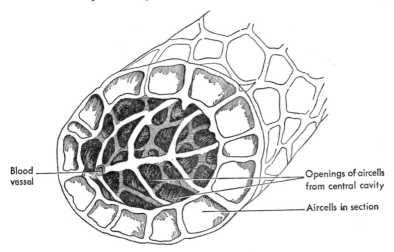

Blood vessel

Openings of aircells from central cavity

Aircells in section

Fig. 15.19. The frog.
Structure of the lung as seen by looking into the cut end of a partially inflated lung.

the cavity into many shallow air cells while leaving a central clear space (compare the structure of the mammalian lung). The lungs are inflated by air being pumped into them from the buccal cavity. For this operation the nares are closed by the upward movement of the premaxillae, which takes place when they are pressed by the mento-Meckelian bones on the shutting of the lower jaw. The glottis is opened and the floor of the buccal cavity is raised, which forces air into the lungs against their natural elasticity and against any small pressure which the body-wall may exert on them via the coelomic fluid. The glottis is then closed and buccal respiration resumed. Emptying the lungs occurs by opening the glottis when air is expelled by the collapse of the lungs due to their elastic recoil aided by the pressure of the body wall.

The control of pulmonary respiration by the nervous system is thought to depend on the concentration of oxygen in the blood circulating in the medulla of the brain. Oxygen deficiency brings about, by a nervous mechanism, increased pulmonary ventilation, whereas in mammals the chief respiratory control is exercised by carbon dioxide, whose concentration in the blood determines the respiratory rate. The oxygen capacity of frog's blood is lower than that of the mammal, being about 10 vol. per 100 vol. of blood.

Renal and reproductive system

Pronephric tubules are present as the working kidney of the tadpole, but these degenerate at metamorphosis and the functions of excretion and osmoregulation are performed by the set of tubules which appear secondly in kidney development and form the opisthonephros. These give rise to compact oval bodies lying in the lymph spaces above the coelom. Each is supplied with arterial blood at high pressure by the renal arteries branching off from the dorsal aorta and which run into the glomeruli. The kidneys are also supplied by the renal portal veins which bring blood from the hind limb and break up into capillaries surrounding the nephric tubules. Urine is drained from the kidney by the Wolffian duct. The mode of function of the frog's kidney is believed to be largely the same as that of the mammalian kidney which is described on page 535. Indeed, a large number of the experiments on filtration and selective reabsorption which were necessary to establish the mode of action of the vertebrate kidney have, in fact, been made on the frog or on other amphibia because the Malpighian bodies of these animals are large and lie near the surface of the kidney where they can be 'tapped' by fine pipettes, while the double blood supply enables the respective functions of the glomeruli and tubular portion to be investigated.

The reproductive organs of the male frog (Fig. 15.20) consist of paired testes from which the seminal fluid passes via numerous vasa efferentia into the kidney and thence through the Wolffian duct to the cloaca. Dilatations of the lower ends of the Wolffian ducts, the vesiculae seminales, are said to act as storage organs for the sperm. The Wolffian ducts open into the dorsal wall of the cloaca by a pair of urino-genital papillae. A fat-storage body lies attached to the anterior of the testis. The male bears a pigmented pad on what appears to be the first preaxial digit. This is, morphologically, the second, the

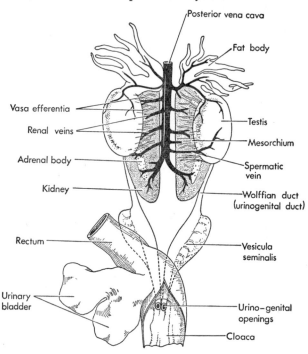

Fig. 15.20. The frog. Male urino-genital system.

pollex having disappeared except for the corresponding metacarpal which is, as has been seen, not visible as a separate digit and which is incorporated in the swelling. This pad swells and becomes rougher during the breeding season and is used for clasping the female during mating.

The reproductive organs of the female (Fig. 15.21) consist of paired ovaries and paired convoluted oviducts opening into the coelom anteriorly by oviducal funnels. The ovaries are thin-walled sacs of connective tissue from which the ripe oocytes are liberated into the coelom by the rupture of the wall. The oocytes pass into the oviducal funnels and down the oviducts to the ovisacs, thin-walled dilated parts of the oviducts. The ovisacs open into the cloaca dorsally. The eggs accumulate in the ovisacs until they are laid at the breeding season.

The kidney and kidney ducts are the same as those of the male except that the female lacks the vesiculae seminales on the Wolffian

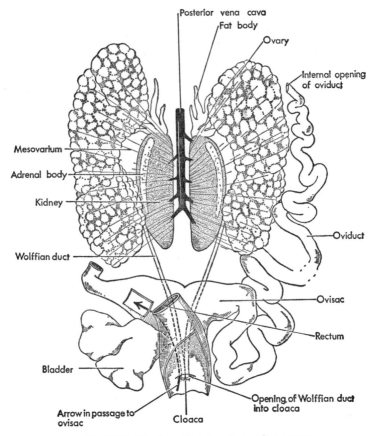

Fig. 15.21. The frog. Female urino-genital system.

ducts, which serve solely as ureters for the conveyance of urine and which open into the cloaca by a pair of urinary papillae. In both sexes the urine does not pass directly to the exterior as in the dog-fish, but is stored temporarily in the urinary bladder which is a ventral outgrowth of the floor of the cloaca projecting forwards into the abdomen. Its wall is extensible and contains unstriped muscle fibres which contract periodically to expel the urine.

REPRODUCTION. The process of reproduction of the frog takes place in the spring shortly after the animals have emerged from hibernation. Males and females congregate in ponds, the croaking of the males serving, it is said, to attract the females to the site. Mating, or *amplexus*, takes place by the male grasping the female firmly under the 'armpits' by his 'thumb' pads and sitting on her back (Fig. 15.22). The animals remain in this position for some days while the oocytes, which have accumulated in the ovisacs, are shed into the water. During their passage down the oviduct the oocytes have acquired a coat of concentrated jelly secreted by the walls of the duct. This substance is a compound known as a mucoprotein, whose

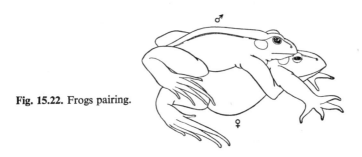

Fig. 15.22. Frogs pairing.

molecules are large and are composed approximately half of protein and half of the carbohydrates galactose, fructose and glucose linked in a way that confers on the material the power to absorb large quantities of water. A very thin layer of the concentrated muco-protein applied to the oocyte by the oviduct wall swells in water to the bulky outer layer which rapidly forms around the frogs' oocytes after laying and which serves to prevent the eggs being crowded together and possibly to protect them from infection and predators.

Seminal fluid is poured into the water by the male while the oocytes are being laid and fertilization then takes place. This leads to the development of a tadpole from the fertilized egg.

Nervous system and Sense organs

THE BRAIN of the frog (Fig. 15.23) resembles that of the dogfish in that there is no very great enlargement of any one part although it is clear from its nervous connexions that the optic region of the brain is the most important. The fore-brain consists of the cerebral hemispheres which are more elongated than are those of the dogfish and which merge into small olfactory lobes at the extreme anterior end. They are not applied closely to the olfactory organ but are connected with the olfactory epithelium by the olfactory tracts. The 'tween-brain consists of a short thalamus roofed by the anterior

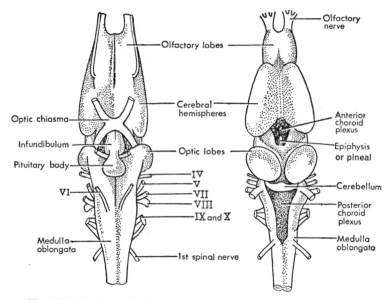

Fig. 15.23. The frog. The brain; dorsal view (RIGHT); ventral view (LEFT).

choroid plexus. From this region the pineal grows out dorsally and the infundibulum ventrally, meeting the hypophysis from the stomodaeum and giving rise to the pituitary body.

The mid-brain has two well-developed optic lobes dorsally and consists of the crura cerebri ventrally. The hind-brain is made up of the medulla roofed by the posterior choroid plexus anterior to which the cerebellum is seen as a narrow transverse ridge, very much smaller than that of the dogfish.

The part played by the brain in the life of the frog is not as clearly understood as might be expected. The cerebral hemispheres are not necessary for feeding and other activities but their removal makes the animal sluggish. The roof of the optic lobes receives fibres from more parts of the central nervous system than does any other region of the brain and hence is best enabled to act as a correlating centre. Some of the main connexions in the brain of the frog are shown diagrammatically in Fig. 29.6 (p. 573) where it can be seen that the optic lobes may be described as the dominant region. This is also shown by the arrangement of the neurons. To a great extent the nerve cells in the brain are placed round the central cavity as they are in the spinal cord, the primitive arrangement, but in the optic roof the cells are to be found in the outer layers as well as near the cavity, a type of change which will be seen in the mammals to be correlated with the great development in complexity of the brain.

The special sense organs of the frog include the eye, the ear, and the olfactory organ, whose neuro-sensory cells send their fibres along the olfactory tract to the brain. There are cutaneous nerves of tactile and chemical sensitivity distributed in the skin. Lateral line organs are missing in the adult, although present in the tadpole. Taste buds are present in the tongue and palate.

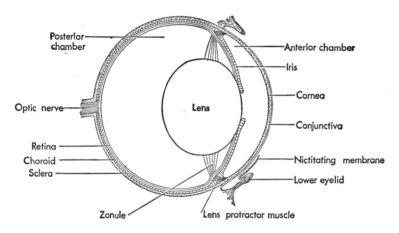

Fig. 15.24. The frog. Vertical section through the eye.

THE EYE of the frog (Fig. 15.24) is nearly spherical and contains a thick lens. An image is formed on the retina by refraction at both the corneal surface and by the lens when the frog is in the air, but accommodation to seeing very near objects (and presumably to sight in water where the effect of corneal refraction is lost) is brought about by moving the lens away from the retina. This is done by the contraction of a muscle, termed the *lens protractor*, running forwards from the lens attachment to the wall of the eyeball. The amount of light entering the eye is determined by the iris, a diaphragm whose aperture is controlled by circular and radial muscles. The eye is provided with tear glands which keep the surface of the cornea moist, and also with a windscreen wiper in the form of a fold of the lower eyelid (the *nictitating membrane*) to keep it clean and to spread the tear fluid. The extrinsic muscles are similar to those of the dogfish.

THE EAR of the frog (Fig. 15.25) consists not only of the inner ear but also of the middle ear. This comprises the upper part of the Eustachian tube (the hyoid cleft) and the structures with which it is associated for the reception and transmission of sound waves. The Eustachian tube is closed at its external end by the tympanic membrane or ear drum which is stretched across a ring of cartilage. The *columella auris* is attached inside to the centre of the tympanic membrane and is a rod of bone and cartilage which connects the ear

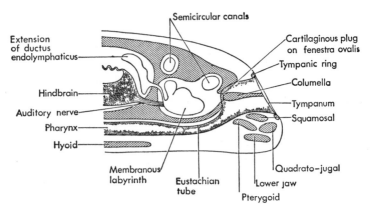

Fig. 15.25. The frog. Diagram to show the structure of the ear as seen in a transverse section of the head.

drum with the perilymph of the inner ear. This it does by its attachment to a plug which fits into the *fenestra ovalis*, a membranous region of the auditory capsule adjacent the middle ear. The plug is free to move so that vibrations of the air bring about movement of the tympanum which is transmitted through the columella to the perilymph. This in turn causes vibrations in the endolymph of the membranous labyrinth and brings about the stimulation of the receptor cells.

The structure and functions of the membranous labyrinth of the frog are essentially similar to those of the dogfish, the semicircular canals being concerned with angular movements in the three planes of space, the utriculus with position and the sacculus and small lagena probably with the reception of sounds of low frequency. The membranous labyrinth of the frog differs from that of the dogfish in that the ductus endolymphaticus does not open to the exterior but enters the cranial cavity where it forms a thin-walled sac. Projections of this sac pass backward alongside the spinal cord within the neural arches of the vertebrae but emerge between the vertebrae forming the calcareous pads which are a conspicuous feature of the ventral aspect of the vertebral column. The functions of these structures are unknown.

THE OLFACTORY ORGAN is relatively small and appears to be of little

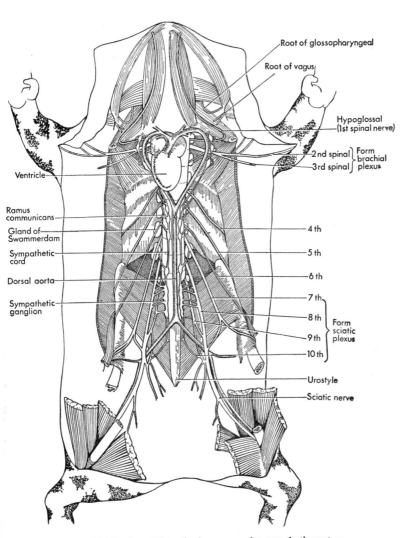

Fig. 15.26. The frog. The spinal nerves and sympathetic system.

importance in the life of the frog, since the animals seem little affected by smells.

SPINAL AND CRANIAL NERVES. The spinal nerves (Fig. 15.26) of each side number ten in the frog in accordance with the short vertebral column. They are distributed as follows. The 1st (hypoglossal) supplies the ventral part of the pharynx and buccal cavity, the 2nd and 3rd join for a short distance to form the brachial plexus and supply the arm, the 4th, 5th and 6th supply the muscles and skin of

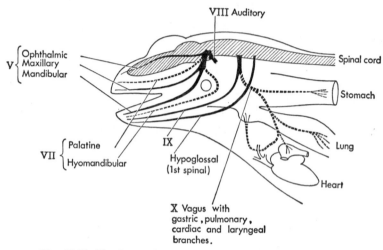

Fig. 15.27. The frog. Diagram to illustrate the distribution of the cranial nerves.

the trunk, and the remaining four (7th, 8th, 9th and 10th) form a plexus from which several small nerves and a main sciatic nerve arise and innervate the leg.

THE AUTONOMIC NERVOUS SYSTEM is well defined and consists of ten ganglia connected by a longitudinal commissure. Each ganglion receives a ramus communicans arising from a spinal nerve soon after it leaves the vertebral column. Each longitudinal sympathetic nerve cord runs alongside the systemic arch and dorsal aorta and is continued anteriorly into the skull where it has a connexion with the vagus ganglion and ends in the Gasserian ganglion of the trigeminal (V) cranial nerve. The 4th to the 10th pairs of sympathetic ganglia are connected to each other by small connectives and from each ganglion of the chain small nerves arise which run to the viscera and blood vessels. On each side, the connectives between the 1st and 2nd sympathetic ganglia embrace the subclavian artery forming the so-called *annulus of Vieussens*.

THE CRANIAL NERVES (Fig. 15.27) are similar in general to those of the dogfish but somewhat simpler owing to the absence of lateral-line organs. There is no dorsal root of the mandibular segment, namely the profundus nerve. The trigeminal (V) has ophthalmic, maxillary and mandibular branches. As well as supplying the external rectus muscle the abducens (VI) innervates a rectractor muscle which pulls in the eyeball. The facial nerve (VII) has only a palatine and hyoidean branch. The glossopharyngeal (IX) supplies the tongue, and the vagus (X) the heart, lungs, gut and larynx. The short spinal cord ends in a fine thread (*filum terminale*) running in the cavity of the urostyle.

Muscles

Correlated with the land habit, the musculature shows a marked departure from the segmental arrangement seen in the dogfish. The limbs are activated by pairs of antagonistic muscles attached to the bones of the limbs and to the girdles and the body wall, while the respiratory movements of the floor of the buccal cavity are produced by the transverse *mylohyoid* muscle, the *sternohyoid* muscles and others connected to the hyoid plate, lower jaw and the pectoral girdle. These, too, with others attached to the skull and lower jaw open and close the mouth. In the region of the abdomen, the body wall consists of a thin muscular sheet composed of several muscles enclosing and suspending the viscera and attached dorsally to the vertebral column.

The skin is loosely and sparsely attached to the underlying muscles of the whole body by thin sheets of connective tissue and separated from them by spaces filled with lymph, a watery exudate from the blood (see p. 372). Two pairs of pulsating lymph hearts return lymph to the general blood stream. One pair is situated anteriorly beneath the scapulae and open into the subscapular veins while the other pair lie posteriorly, adjacent to the end of the urostyle, and discharge lymph into the femoral veins.

16. *The Rabbit*

Introduction to the Mammalia

WHEN the structure and working of the mammals have been described it will readily be seen why they are regarded as the 'highest' vertebrates. They possess a greater independence of the environment than the 'lower' groups and this is due to their greater complexity of structure and function and, in particular, to the greater size and elaboration of their central nervous systems. They do not possess better sight than that of many birds; they are not protected by armour like many reptiles; they cannot breathe both dissolved and gaseous oxygen like the Amphibia, but the mammals have been able to survive in a greater variety of environmental conditions than the members of any other class of vertebrates. They have adapted the basic mammalian pattern of form and function more widely than has been possible with any other type of basic vertebrate construction. Thus mammals have become suited to life in the sea from the poles to the tropics, to a wide range of conditions on land and in the soil, and some have become adapted for sustained flight. No other group of animals has accomplished these feats, and although it is not possible to say why it has come about in the relatively short geological time during which mammals have been in existence, it is possible to enumerate those features of mammalian structure and function which have enabled this spectacular success to be achieved.

The chief features of mammals which have brought about their success are physiological and are connected with the maintenance of a steady internal state. Thus their body temperature is relatively constant, they possess a large volume of blood circulating at high pressure which is effective in the maintenance of a good oxygen supply to the tissues and helps to ensure uniformity of chemical composition of the tissue fluid bathing the cells of the various organs. Such an accurate adjustment of chemical and physical conditions is controlled by a highly developed central nervous system. These physiological features are difficult to use as diagnostic characters for the definition of a group of animals but they are associated in the mammal with certain structural characters by which the class may be

344

defined. These characters are:

(1) the possession of milk glands at which the young are suckled by the female;

(2) the possession of hair;

(3) the presence of the left aortic arch only;

(4) the reduction of the lower jaw to the paired dentary alone;

(5) the possession of a muscular *diaphragm* separating the thoracic from the abdominal cavity;

(6) viviparous reproduction involving an *allantoic placenta.*

All these characters are possessed by all mammals with very few exceptions: the pouched mammals or marsupials have no allantoic placenta, and the spiny ant-eater (*Tachyglossus*) and duck-billed platypus of Australasia lay eggs.

Other characteristics of mammals include the possession of a false palate, two sets of teeth, ear ossicles, *epiphyses* to the bones, external ears (*pinnae*) and sweat and sebaceous glands.

The types of mammal which are commonly used for study are the rabbit, the rat and the guinea-pig. The rabbit will be described here except that the skull of the dog will replace that of the rabbit for detailed treatment.

The rabbit

EXTERNAL FEATURES. The external appearance of the rabbit is shown in Fig. 16.1 in which the general body form and hairy coat are

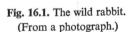

Fig. 16.1. The wild rabbit. (From a photograph.)

depicted. Its head is separated from the trunk by the neck. The tail is small. The forelimbs are short and the hindlimbs are long and disposed in a crouching position when the animal is at rest or eating. The five digits of the forelimb and the four digits of the hindlimb end in claws.

The most conspicuous features of the head are the two external ears or pinnae which are held upright when the animal is on the alert but are laid back when it is frightened or running. The eyes are large, lateral and prominent, and have a field of view of 360°; in fact the fields of view of the left and right eye overlap by about 30° in front and 9° behind. There are upper and lower eyelids bearing eyelashes and a third eyelid which can be passed across the cornea. The external nares or nostrils are at the tip of the snout and are surrounded by a small moist bare area of skin, the *rhinarium*. Large tactile hairs or *vibrissae* are borne on the lips and near the eyes. The mouth is bounded by the lips; the large upper lip is cleft in front and the halves can be retracted to bare the incisor teeth.

At the hind end the anus opens just beneath the tail. The ducts of the paired *perineal scent glands* open on either side of the anus. The urinogenital aperture of the female, the *vulva*, lies in front of the anus and houses the small *clitoris*. The urinogenital duct of the male opens at the end of the *penis* beside which the *scrotal sacs* contain the testes of the adult.

Four or five pairs of mammary glands lie beneath the skin of the thorax and belly of the female and open by teats.

GENERAL ANATOMY. The separation of the head from the trunk by the neck results in greater mobility of the head and enables the special sense organs to be directed to or aimed at any place to which the animal's attention is drawn. This mobility is chiefly of advantage to the animal in the avoidance of its natural enemies such as birds of prey.

The trunk is divided into an anterior thorax which is separated from the abdomen by the midriff or diaphragm. The thorax contains the heart and lungs enclosed by a region of the body-wall supported by bony ribs but the abdomen has a soft muscular wall which supports the viscera by its *tonus* or state of continuous slight contraction. The body cavity contained in the thorax is thus separate from the abdominal coelom, and is further divided into two parts. The pericardial cavity is very reduced since the pericardial membrane closely invests the heart. The two pleural cavities, one on each side of the heart, are separated by the *mediastinum* in the mid-line where their walls are apposed except where the heart lies between them enclosed in the pericardium. The relationship between the divisions of the coelome in the mammal and those of the fish and amphibia are illustrated in Fig. 16.2.

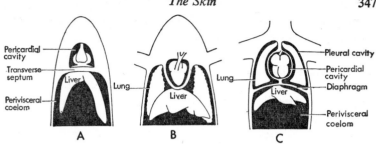

Fig. 16.2. Diagram to illustrate the divisions of the coelom in a fish (*A*), an amphibian (*B*) and a Mammal (*C*).

SKIN. Rabbits possess to a marked degree the mammalian character of a hairy skin. The epidermis, from which alone the hairs are derived, dips down into the dermis to form hair follicles and at the base of these the Malpighian layer of dividing cells is especially active. As the daughter cells become pushed upwards to form the hair shaft they become keratinized and die, so that the hairs protruding from the follicles are dead structures each with a central medulla containing air cavities and scaly walls which cause them to felt together when compressed. (For this reason rabbit fur is in demand for the manufacture of felt hats.) Not only do the cells forming the hair become keratinized but those on the outside of the general epidermis likewise undergo a transformation of their granular contents into the stable and impermeable protein keratin.

In the skin of most mammals the hair follicles are associated with sebaceous glands, likewise epidermal structures, which provide a fatty secretion by the breakdown of some of the cells. This helps to make the hairs water-repellant and to keep them from felting together. Many mammals spend a considerable time on their toilet and some have special modifications such as comb-like teeth or a rough tongue by means of which the fur is cleaned and kept free from parasites. The rabbit is not known to spend time when outside its burrow attending to its fur, apart from occasionally scratching it with its claws, and it is not known whether any toilet operations are performed when the animal is underground.

Sweat or sudorific glands are present in the skin of many mammals, although in those with thick fur they are usually restricted to the undersides of the paws and like areas. Each sweat gland is a tubular inpushing of the Malpighian layer, the deepest part of which forms a coiled tubular gland whose secretion seeps on to the surface of the skin.

The dermis is composed chiefly of areolar connective tissue and, in the deeper layers, of adipose tissue where much of the body fat is stored. Blood vessels are found in the dermis, especially at the bases of the hair follicles and around the sweat glands. Nerve fibres traverse the dermis to end freely among the cells of the epidermis, around the bases of special hairs or in receptor organs such as *Pacinian corpuscles*. Plain muscle fibres occur and, in particular, each hair is equipped with a slip of unstriped muscle originating at its base and inserted below the Malpighian layer. The contraction of this muscle, the *arrector pili*, increases the angle at which the hair lies and thus increases the thickness of the insulating layer of still air retained by the furry coat.

The chief histological features and functions of the skin of the mammal are more fully described on p. 441.

The mammary glands are epidermal structures and are present in the form of groups of compound alveolar glands each opening by a pore on a small, bare, raised area, the nipple. From their development and mode of secretion they are regarded as modified sweat glands. In an active alveolus the secretory cells composing the wall are large. The free ends break down to form the milk which is expressed by the contraction of the surrounding *plain* muscle. The base of the cell remains and grows again to begin another cycle of activity. Different alveoli of the same mammary gland are active at different times so that milk is continually produced during the period of lactation which follows the birth of the young.

The claws of mammals are formed from dense local thickenings of the keratinous outer layer and are therefore epidermal structures also.

The skeleton

Like the skeletons of the dogfish and frog, that of the rabbit is made up of axial and appendicular portions. The skull is large and strongly built and the vertebral column is distinguished into different regions each with its own adaptations to the role which it plays in holding the body together and enabling its muscular movements to be made. The limbs of the appendicular skeleton are built on the pentadactyl plan while the girdles by which they are attached to the trunk are strong and simple structures. The skeleton is made chiefly of bone, apart from the articular surfaces and a few other sites where flexibility is required. Each of the long bones and vertebrae which articulate with one another by perfect joints (or *diarthroses*) develops from three centres of bone formation and can be seen, even in the adult, to consist of a shaft or diaphysis united with an epiphysis at each end (see also page 452 on bone formation). This type of bone growth is found only in the mammals.

In the skull of the rabbit it is not easy to see all the sutures between the component bones and the dentition is so highly specialized that a larger and better skull for study is that of the dog, which will be described here instead of that of *Oryctolagus*. A figure of the skull of a rabbit (Fig. 16.16) is given on p. 363.

The skull of the dog

The skull of the dog possesses a number of anatomical features of interest and comparison with those of amphibians and fishes. The chief of these are listed below.

(1) The cranial cavity is of large size.
(2) Membrane bones are incorporated in the brain case.
(3) The auditory capsules are displaced to a ventral position.
(4) A hard palate, separating respiratory passage from buccal cavity, is formed.
(5) The paired dentary alone constitutes the lower jaw and articulates with the squamosal on each side.
(6) The hyomandibular, quadrate and articular are transformed into the sound transmission mechanism of the middle ear.
(7) The teeth are large and set in sockets in the jaws.

A diagram representing some of these points is given in Fig. 16.3, in which the cartilage and membrane bones are differently shaded. Views of the skull from different aspects are shown in Figs. 16.4–6.

It will be seen that the floor of the brain case is ossified as basioccipital, basisphenoid and presphenoid elements (cartilage bones) and that each corresponds in position to other elements forming the sides and floor of the braincase to form a series of rings. The basioccipital thus articulates with exoccipitals (cartilage bones) and these with a supraoccipital (cartilage bone), while the basisphenoid is aligned with the alisphenoids (cartilage bones) and the parietals (membrane bones). The presphenoid corresponds in position to the orbitosphenoids (cartilage bones) and the frontals (membrane bones). The ethmoid, forming the anterior wall of the braincase, is ossified as the cribriform plate pierced by many small foramina for the passage of nerves from the olfactory organs to the brain while there is also a median ethmoid ossification known as the mesethmoid which separates the left- and right-hand nasal chambers.

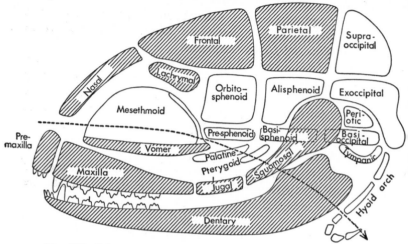

Fig. 16.3. Diagram to illustrate the arrangement of bones in the mammalian skull.

Cartilage bones, white; membrane bones, shaded. The arrow indicates the respiratory or air passage.

The nasal 'capsules' are protected above by the paired nasals while the vomer forms their floor although this bone no longer forms part of the palate. Inside the nasal chambers there are three pairs of thin scroll-shaped bones, the turbinals, formed from outgrowths of the maxillae, nasals and ethmoid.

The auditory capsule ossifies from a number of centres but these soon unite to form a single petrosal bone which houses the inner ear and fuses also with the squamosal. It is not visible from outside.

The skull is autostylic and the ossifications which develop in the old mandibular arch (the palato-pterygo-quadrate) are very different in form and function from those seen in the Amphibia. The palatine forms the posterior part of the palate and articulates with the maxilla and pterygoid. This is a small bone lying below the basisphenoid. The quadrate ossification at the posterior end is quite detached from the palatine and pterygoid and forms the incus of the auditory ossicles. It preserves its articulation in this position with the articular ossification of the lower jaw and also with the hyoid arch in the form of the stapes which is homologous with the hyomandibula of lower forms.

Of the lower jaw portion of the mandibular arch, only the articular remains, transformed into the auditory ossicle called the malleus.

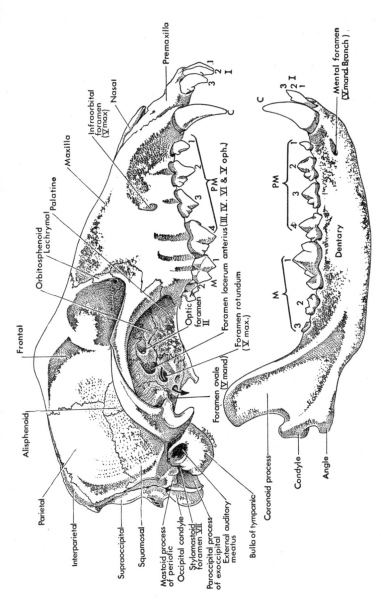

Fig. 16.4. The skull of a dog seen from the side. (From a specimen.)

Premaxilla

Nasal

Infraorbital foramen ($\underline{V}$ max.)

Maxilla

Palatine

Lachrymal

Orbitosphenoid

Frontal

Alisphenoid

Parietal

Interparietal

Supraoccipital

Squamosal

Mastoid process of periotic

Occipital condyle

Stylomastoid foramen $\underline{VII}$

Paroccipital process of exoccipital

External auditory meatus

Bulla of tympanic

Coronoid process

Foramen ovale ($\underline{V}$ mand.)

Foramen rotundum ($\underline{V}$ max.)

Foramen lacerum anterius ($\underline{III}$, $\underline{IV}$, $\underline{VI}$ & $\underline{V}$ oph.)

Optic foramen $\underline{II}$

PM

M

C

I

Condyle

Angle

Dentary

PM

M

C

I

Mental foramen ($\underline{V}$ mand. Branch)

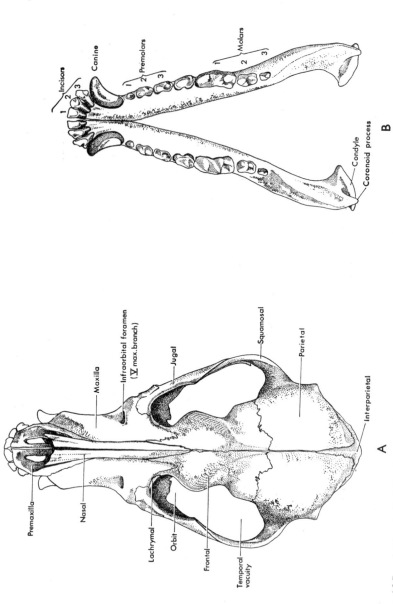

Fig. 16.5. *A* The skull of the dog seen from above. *B* The lower jaw skeleton of the dog seen from above. (From specimens.)

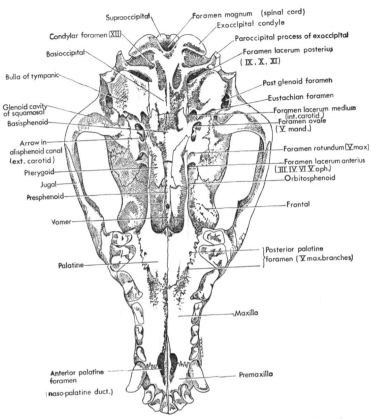

Fig. 16.6. The skull of the dog in palatal view. (From a specimen.)

The functional jaws are, of course, those membrane bones known as the premaxilla and maxilla in the upper jaw and the dentary in the lower jaw. The premaxilla and maxilla both extend on to the facial region and also possess shelves forming the hard palate, those of the maxillae uniting posteriorly with the palatines. A pair of foramina between the premaxillae and maxillae are known as the nasopalatine foramina and house the vestiges of nasopalatine canals and *Jacobson's organs*, olfactory sacs which are large and functional in reptiles but which have almost disappeared in the mammals. The hard palate formed from shelves of the premaxilla, maxilla and palatines thus separates the buccal cavity from the respiratory passage, the internal nares no longer opening into the anterior part of the buccal cavity but almost into the pharynx.

One further feature of the mammalian skull remains to be mentioned. The orbit is protected on the outside by the *zygomatic arch* which is a continuation of the upper jaw arcade formed from a process of the maxilla, the jugal and a process from the squamosal. The large space which this encloses is filled partly by the eye and partly by adductor muscles which originate on the side wall of the cranium and are inserted into the dentary. These, on contraction, close the jaws. The dentary, which has an articular process working in the glenoid of the squamosal, also has a dorsal coronoid process for the insertion of the adductor muscles just mentioned.

Of the erstwhile branchial arch skeleton little remains. The hyoid arch apart from the hyomandibula gives rise to a bony plate embedded in the base of the tongue and connected by small bones to a styloid process of the periotic. From succeeding arches are derived the cartilages of the larynx comprising a dorsal cricoid, ventral thyroid and lateral arytenoid cartilages. The epiglottis can be moved to close the opening of the glottis into the pharynx during the swallowing of food.

The main differences between the dog's skull and that of the rabbit lies in the dentition, the details of which can be seen in Fig. 16.16. The incisor teeth have enamel on the front surface only, and with use the softer dentine wears away more quickly than the enamel causing the ends of the incisors to become chisel-shaped for biting and gnawing. The incisors have persistently growing roots to compensate for the wearing away of these teeth at their ends.

The vertebral column

The vertebrae which make up the vertebral column differ considerably in shape and size with the different positions which they occupy along its length. Some of the forces acting on the vertebral column of a four-legged animal are shown diagrammatically in Fig. 16.7 where

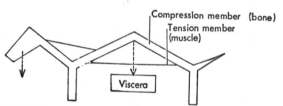

Fig. 16.7. Diagram to illustrate the mechanics of the skeleton of a four-legged animal.

it can be seen that the column may be likened to a girder supported at two points and carrying the weight of the viscera suspended from a position between them while the head load is carried on a canti-lever. It will be seen that the vertebral column acts as a compression member just as did its evolutionary forerunner the notochord. The

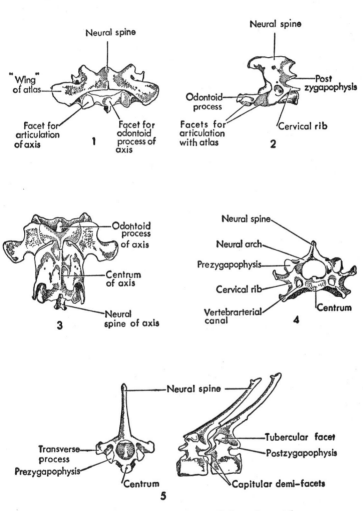

Fig. 16.8. The rabbit. Cervical and thoracic vertebrae.

1 Atlas vertebra (from above). 2 Axis vertebra (side view). 3 Atlas and axis vertebra (from below). 4 A cervical vertebra (end view). 5 Thoracic vertebrae—end view (LEFT); side view (RIGHT). (From specimens.)

tension members of the girder construction are the muscles by whose tension the vertebral column is kept in its right place. This is clearly seen by comparing a living and recently dead animal. The bones and connective tissues have not had time to change their mechanical properties but the muscles are no longer in a state of steady moderate contraction (or tonus) and the body is quite slack and incapable of standing by itself, the action of the muscles being to provide the forces which support the body.

The vertebrae comprise seven cervical or neck vertebrae, twelve thoracic or chest vertebrae, seven lumbar or trunk vertebrae, three or four sacrals and a number of caudals.

The cervical vertebrae, which are distinguished by the possession of the remains of cervical ribs fused to the transverse processes and centra, are therefore composite structures. A small foramen, the *vertebrarterial canal*, is left between the cervical rib and the vertebra proper. The first vertebra, the atlas, bears two large facets for the articulation of the occipital condyles of the skull and permits free nodding movements of the head. It lacks a well developed centrum. The axis vertebra articulates with the atlas by a peg jutting forwards into the position which should be occupied by the centrum of the atlas. This *odontoid peg* is believed to be derived from the centrum of the atlas. The articulation between atlas and axis is such that lateral movements of the head-plus-atlas can easily be made but nodding movements cannot. (The joints between the head and vertebral column may thus be likened to the 'universal joint' in the transmission system of a car.)

The thoracic vertebrae are distinguished from all others by articulating with ribs, the head (or *capitulum*) of which fits into a socket in the intervertebral position, half being hollowed out in one and half in the succeeding vertebra. The other articulating facet of each rib, the *tuberculum*, articulates with the transverse process of the vertebra. The neural spines of the thoracic vertebrae are large and point backwards.

The lumbar vertebrae are large and possess downwardly directed transverse processes. The neural spines are large also and additional surface for muscular attachment is provided by the anterior metapophyses and posterior anapophyses. Ventral median hypapophyses occur on the first two or three vertebrae.

Of the so-called sacral vertebrae only the first articulates with the ilia of the pelvic girdle but the succeeding two or three vertebrae are fused to the first sacral and are similar to it in form and may

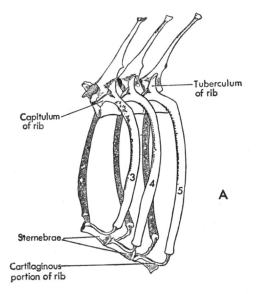

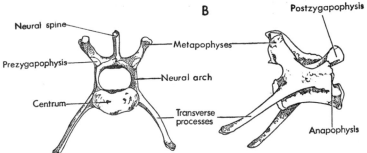

Fig. 16.9. The rabbit.
  A Three thoracic vertebrae, ribs and sternebrae. *B* Lumbar vertebra.
(From specimens.)

also be termed sacral vertebrae. The structure consisting of three or four vertebrae is known as the *sacrum*.

The anterior caudal vertebrae each possess a centrum and neural arch but the most posterior ones consist of a centrum only.

The sternum consists of six sternebrae with the xiphisternum and xiphoid cartilage at the rear.

Limb girdles

The shoulder girdle is of simple construction consisting of a triangular plate of bone, tipped with cartilage on the dorsal side and with a

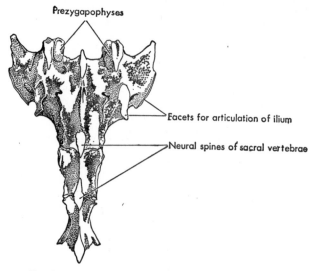

Prezygapophyses

Facets for articulation of ilium

Neural spines of sacral vertebrae

Fig. 16.10. The rabbit. Sacral vertebrae. (From a specimen.)

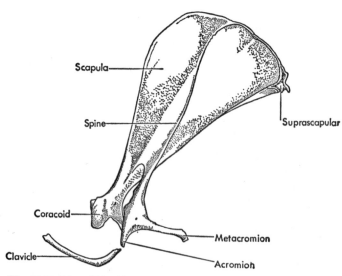

Scapula

Spine

Suprascapular

Coracoid

Metacromion

Clavicle

Acromion

Fig. 16.11. The rabbit. Left portion of the pectoral girdle seen from the left side. (From a specimen.)

ridge or spine running along its length. It is formed in development from scapular and coracoid ossifications and bears a hollow or *glenoid* to take the head of the humerus. Both scapula and the small coracoid take part in the formation of the glenoid. A slender

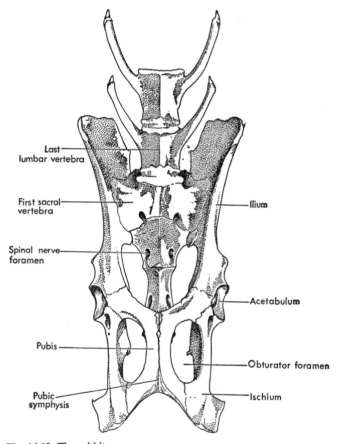

Fig. 16.12. The rabbit.

Pelvic girdle, sacral and lumbar vertebrae in ventral view. (From a specimen.)

clavicle runs from the acromium process of the spine to the anterior part of the sternum. The shoulder girdle, apart from the connexion between the clavicle and the sternum, is not otherwise attached to the rest of the skeleton but is embedded in the musculature.

The pelvic girdle comprises two halves (each called an *innominate* bone) joined together by the *symphysis* of the pubes. (A symphysis is a joint between two bones, the two ends of which are covered by a thin layer of cartilage and which are joined together by fibrous connective tissue. It has, therefore, limited flexibility.) The pubis, ilium and ischium on each side take part in the formation of a deep cup, the acetabulum, into which the head of the femur fits. A small additional ossification, the *cotyloid* bone, is also present.

The forelimb skeleton

The form of the bones in the forelimb is shown in Fig. 16.13, where the following points of construction may be noted. The humerus has a rounded head allowing considerable rotation. The distal end is pulley-like and forms a hinge joint with the radius and ulna. Although these are separate bones they are so shaped that little rotatory movement of the distal end (pronation and supination) is possible. The wrist or carpal region comprises eight bones, only one fewer than that of the ideal pentadactyl limb arrangement. This difference is due not to the loss of any element but to the fusion of the 4th and 5th distal carpals. There are five metacarpals. There are three phalanges in each digit except the first which has only two. Little movement between each of the joints of the wrist is permitted by the shape of the bones but the sum of the movements provides sufficient flexibility.

The hindlimb skeleton

As can be seen from the figures, the femur has the head set at an angle to the shaft to fit into the ventro-laterally directed acetabulum. The distal end forms a hinge joint with the tibiofibula. To carry the extensor tendon over the knee, a small bone (the *patella* or knee-cap) is present in the tendon. Such a bone is called a *sesamoid* bone and, in this instance, the patella slides in a groove, the patella groove, in the head of the femur. The fibula is slender and fused to the larger tibia distally. The tarsal or ankle region contains only six separate bones (see Fig. 16.4). Only four metatarsals and four digits are present, number one being absent. The second metatarsal articulates with two distal tarsals. Three phalanges are present on each digit. As in the forelimb, the distal phalanx of each digit is shaped to fit inside and to support a claw.

The muscular system

A comprehensive study of the muscular system of the mammal would require a long and detailed chapter to itself, but one or two of its

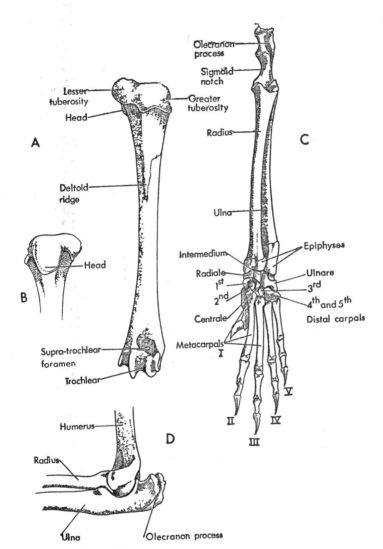

Fig. 16.13. The rabbit.

Forelimb skeleton: *A* left humerus, anterior view; *B* left humerus, posterior view of head; *C* distal joints of left forelimb; *D* right or inside view of left elbow joint. (From specimens.)

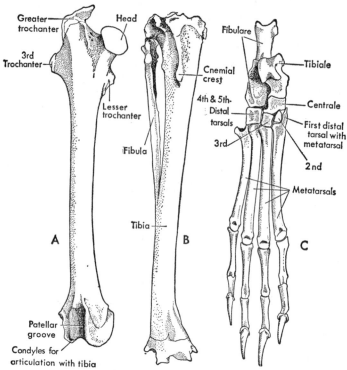

Fig. 16.14. The rabbit.

Hindlimb skeleton: *A* right femur, anterior view; *B* right tibio-fibula, anterior view; *C* right pes (or foot). (From specimens.)

chief features of interest can be mentioned. Little remains of the segmental arrangement of the fish myotomes although some of the muscles knitting together the units of the vertebral column are segmental in arrangement. They are arranged almost all around the vertebral column which can thus be bent up and down in a vertical plane and also from side to side. The muscles of the limbs and girdles are complex but movement at joints between the bones depends throughout on the action of antagonistic muscles. The bones at a joint are held together in the first place by a more or less continuous sheath of connective tissue enclosing a capsule, the *synovial capsule*, filled with a viscous fluid, the synovial fluid which lubricates the moving surfaces of the bones. These are covered with a thin layer of hyaline cartilage. In its simplest form a pair of muscles is arranged, one to flex and one to straighten the joint. The muscle has its *origin*

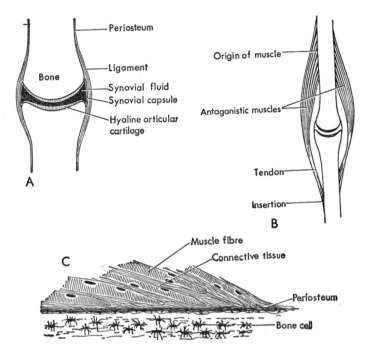

Fig. 16.15. Diagrams illustrating the structure of a joint.

A Section showing synovial capsule. *B* Origin and insertion of antagonistic muscles. *C* Attachment of a muscle to a bone by connective tissue fibres at its origin.

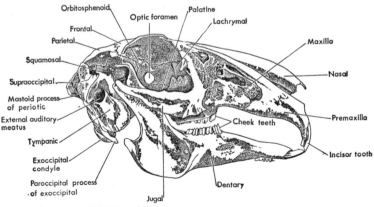

Fig. 16.16. The rabbit.

The skull seen from the right side. (From a specimen.)

on a relatively large area of bone where the connective tissue fibres of the periosteum are continuous with those which are interspersed between the muscle fibres and its tendon is *inserted* on to the other bones. The tendon is likewise composed of collagen fibres, parallel and closely packed, and, again, continuous with those of the peri-osteum. No joint is actuated by so few muscles as a single pair but a number are arranged around the bones, particularly where the form of articulation between the bones is a ball and socket like that of the hip joint.

The alimentary canal

The gut of the rabbit is divisible into the customary parts, buccal cavity, pharynx, oesophagus, stomach, small intestine, large intestine or colon and rectum with the caecum forming a large cul-de-sac at the junction of the small intestine and colon. For details of the histology of the mammalian gut the section on histology should be consulted (page 467), for details of digestion, the appropriate physio-logical chapter (page 484). There, the process of digestion in man is described because it is better understood than that of the rabbit. The main features that need to be mentioned here are those which are considered as adapting the animal to its mode of life.

The muscular lips are cleft, which enables the incisor teeth to be exposed for gnawing. The cheeks can either be sucked into the diastema between the incisor and molar teeth so that the pieces cut off by the teeth fall aside and are not taken into the buccal cavity or the cheeks can remain in the normal position so that food accumulates in the buccal cavity. The lower jaw can be switched to a forward position, so engaging the front edge of the lower incisors with the back edge of the upper incisors, or to a backward position where the molar teeth are engaged. In the forward position (shown in Fig. 16.16) the molars do not meet and in the posterior position the incisors do not meet. The molar teeth grind up the food material into quite small pieces and it is then swallowed when mixed with saliva from the four pairs of salivary glands.[1]

The posterior nares open into the posterior region of the buccal cavity, the hard palate being continued backwards a short distance by a sheet of soft tissue. The pharynx is not clearly defined but the Eustachian tubes open into the pharynx and the glottis, giving access to the trachea, also opens into the pharynx.

---

[1] These are: the *parotids* in front of the ears: the *infraorbitals* beneath the eyes: the *submaxillaries* inside the rear angles of the jaws: the *sublinguals* beneath the tongue. All have ducts opening into the buccal cavity.

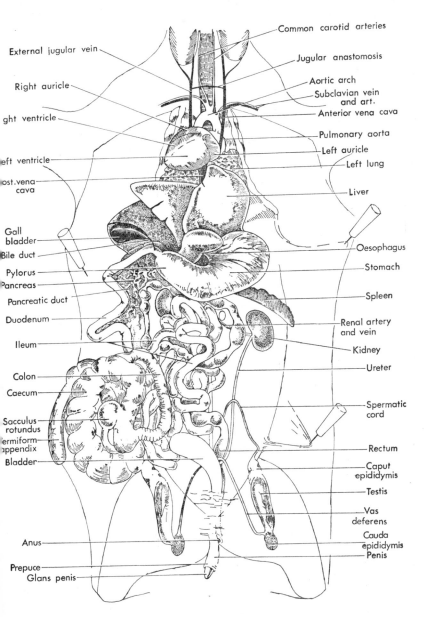

Fig. 16.17. The rabbit.

General dissection to show the main organs of the thorax and abdomen. (From a specimen.)

The stomach lies just behind the diaphragm and is bean-shaped, the oesophagus opening at the position of the hilum and the duodenum opening from the pyloric or right-hand end. For some time after a meal the pyloric sphincter is closed but later opens rhythmically. The duodenum, into which the ducts of the liver and pancreas open and which is distinguished by the possession of *Brunner's glands* in its wall, is succeeded by the rest of the small intestine known as the ileum and this opens into a rounded swelling, the *sacculus rotundus* situated near the junction of the *caecum* and the colon. The caecum is large and fairly thin-walled and ends in the *vermiform appendix*. The progress of the food along this organ is slow. It passes up one side and down the other, giving time for the digestion of cellulose by the bacteria present. The colon, or large intestine, is sacculated and absorbs water from the food, transforming it eventually into the hard pellets of the dry faeces or the soft, mucus-coated material which is eaten again. The faeces accumulate in the rectum until they are discharged at the anus.

Blood system

The mammal is distinguished by the presence of a complete double circulation and a persistent left systemic arch. The homologies between the arteries and the aortic arches of fishes and amphibia can most easily be appreciated by reference to Fig. 16.18, and the general

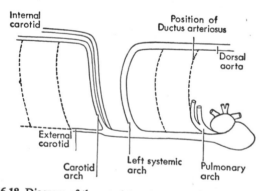

Fig. 16.18. Diagram of the arterial arches of a mammal.

Only the third (carotid), the fourth left (systemic) and sixth (pulmonary) are present in the adult.

plan of the circulation is shown in Figs. 16.19 and 16.20. The main features which require amplification are the structure of the heart and the structure and functioning of the capillaries.

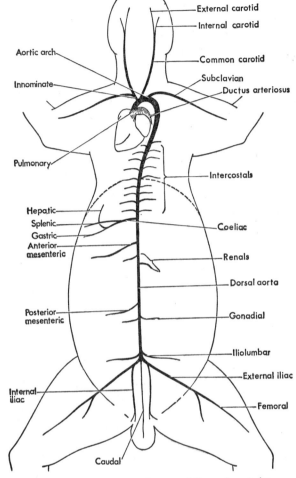

Fig. 16.19. The rabbit. Diagram of the main arteries.

The heart is of course derived in the embryo by the folding of a tube into an S-shape which, as in the frog, results in the auricles being anterior to the ventricles. The adult heart consists of four chambers, two auricles and two ventricles, the embryonic sinus venosus having been incorporated in the wall of the right auricle where, as the *sinu-auricular node*, contraction is still initiated in each beat. The two main arteries likewise arise directly from the ventricles so that the mammalian heart is a more compact organ than that of the amphibian or the fish.

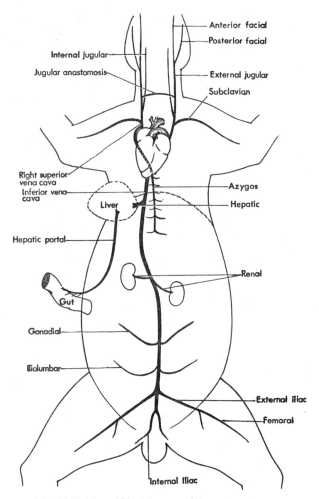

Fig. 16.20. The rabbit. Diagram of the main veins.

The left and right auricles are sufficiently thin-walled to be distended by the low pressure of the blood in the veins but yet are muscular enough to expel their contents into the thick-walled ventricles and to distend them. The ventricles are both very muscular but the left has a thicker wall than the right which is necessitated by the greater resistance of the body or systemic circulation through which it propels the blood. The right ventricle drives blood only through the lungs, and although, of course, it propels the same

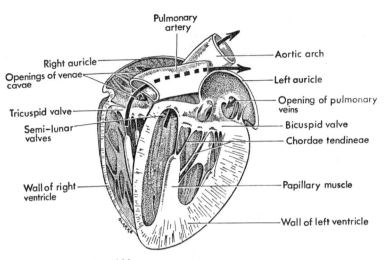

Fig. 16.21. The rabbit.
    The heart of the rabbit dissected to show the main features. It is seen
with parts of the ventral side cut away. Arrows in the right auricle indicate openings of two of the venae cavae, the third being hidden by the
pulmonary artery. The large arrows indicate the course of the blood
from the right auricle to the pulmonary artery, whose root has been cut
away to show the tricuspid valve, and the passage from the left ventricle
to the aortic arch. (From a specimen.)

quantity of blood in unit time, the distance travelled by the blood
before it reaches the capillaries is very short since the lungs and
heart are adjacent each other.

    Blood returned from the body enters the right auricle through
three separate openings of the venae cavae while that returned from
the lungs enters the left auricle through the openings of the two pulmonary veins. The auricles are separated from the ventricles by
valves which are sheets of tough connective tissue stretched across the
auriculo-ventricular openings. That between the left auricle and
ventricle consists of two flaps and is known as the *bicuspid* or *mitral*
valve, while that between the right auricle and ventricle consists of
three flaps and is known as the *tricuspid* valve. The free edges of the
flaps are attached by connective tissue strands, the tendinous cords
(chordae tendineae) to nipple-shaped muscular projections of the
walls of the ventricles. The valves can thus fold inwards towards the
walls of the ventricles but they cannot fold towards the auricles
because they are held by the chordae tendineae and the papillary
muscles. They therefore offer little hindrance to the passage of blood

from the auricle to the ventricles but when the ventricles contract they occlude the auriculo-ventricular opening and prevent blood passing back into the auricles. They have to be strong to withstand the force of contraction of the ventricles and are made of dense collagenous fibres. Because the cavity of the ventricle gets smaller during each contraction, the tendinous cords would not remain taut and would not therefore hold the valves shut were it not for the contraction of the papillary muscles to which they are attached. These, of course, contract with the rest of the heart muscle and so shorten the strings which hold the free edges of the valves. Three semilunar valves are present at the bases of the systemic and pulmonary aortae and prevent the back-flow of blood from the arteries.

During the phase of relaxation of the heart, blood flows into the auricles from the great veins and also passes into the ventricles through the open mitral and tricuspid valves. Contraction of the auricles takes place and drives their contents into the ventricles also. These then contract, the contraction beginning with the fibres that surround the auriculo-ventricular opening and which therefore constrict the bases of the valves. Pressure rises in the ventricles until it exceeds the pressure in the arteries when blood can pass the semilunar valves. As soon as the pressure in the ventricles falls below that in the arteries, the flow of blood from the heart ceases and the semilunar valves close, preventing back flow of blood. During the relaxation of the heart muscle the organ fills again with blood and the cycle is repeated. This takes place in the rabbit about 200 times a minute and in man about 70 when at rest.

The distribution of the blood to the body is done by the arteries, the walls of which are composed of several layers. They are lined by a pavement epithelium (p. 440) whose cells have crinkly edges. Since this layer is an inner or lining layer it is known as the endothelium. Outside this lies a layer of elastic connective tissue and smooth muscle fibres arranged circularly. In large arteries of which the diameter does not vary very greatly, the elastic connective tissue predominates but in small arteries or arterioles the muscle layer predominates. The elastic and muscle layer is known as the *tunica media*. Outside this there is a *tunica adventitia* composed largely of collagenous connective tissue whose fibres, which are somewhat crumpled, allow the artery to increase in diameter up to a maximum size. The plain muscle fibres are innervated by the sympathetic nervous system and their contraction is used to regulate the flow of blood in different parts of the body, and at different times. For example, the amount flowing through a muscle which is being vigorously used may be 700 times greater than the blood flow at rest.

The smallest arterioles are distinguishable from true capillaries by the presence of muscle fibres in their walls. Capillaries have only the endothelial wall, with a very thin layer of fine connective tissue fibres. They probably do not alter in size like the arterioles and variations in the amount of blood flowing through them are brought

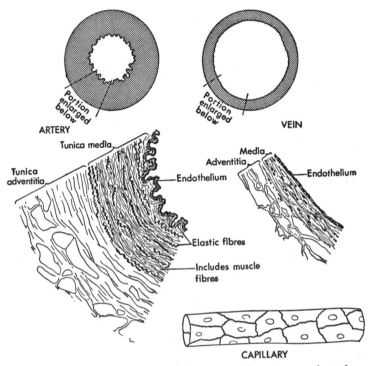

Fig. 16.22 .Diagrams to illustrate the structure of an artery, a vein, and a capillary.

about by constriction of the arterioles supplying them. The capillaries, by virtue of their small diameter, have a large surface to volume ratio and by virtue of their thin wall present little hindrance to the exchange by diffusion of chemical substances between the blood and the surrounding cells.

The capillaries join to form tiny veins or venules which in turn unite to form large veins. These have the endothelial lining characteristic of the whole blood system and a thinner tunica media and tunica adventitia composed chiefly of collagen fibres and with only a very few muscle fibres in the larger veins. Valves in the form of forward-pointing flaps occur all along the course of the veins and direct the blood flow towards the heart. The blood flow is further assisted by movements of the body muscles which compress the thin-walled veins and redistribute their contents.

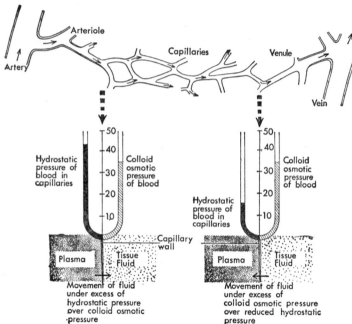

Fig. 16.23. Diagram illustrating the formation of tissue fluid at the arterial end of the capillaries and its uptake at the venous end.

(Note that the manometer merely indicates the values of the hydrostatic pressure and the colloid osmotic pressure of the blood plasma at the arterial and venous ends of the capillaries. The balance of the pressures determines the movement of fluid across the capillary wall pictured below.)

The excess of fluid formed over fluid absorbed is drained off as lymph in separate channels. (See text.)

In addition to the blood vascular system, a network of fine vessels containing *lymph* is present in the body, especially in the gut wall. The fluid collects into one main channel in the chest, the *thoracic duct*, which empties the lymph into the left innominate vein. Lymph resembles blood plasma in composition but has only about 2·5% protein instead of 7% and takes its origin from the tissue fluids. It is thought that the walls of capillaries are permeable to all but large molecules and that slow ultra-filtration of the plasma occurs into the inter-cellular spaces of the tissues. The blood pressure in the capillaries at the arterial end exceeds the colloid osmotic pressure of the blood and a transudate from the blood seeps into the tissue spaces. At the venous end of the capillaries the hydrostatic pressure of the blood has fallen below the colloid osmotic pressure of the proteins and hence fluid is taken up again. It is thought that in this way there is a continual renewal and absorption of the tissue fluid. Not all the fluid is returned in this way, however. Some enters the thin endothelial lining of the minute lymph channels and is drained into larger ducts and eventually returned to the blood. It is thought that in this way the lymphatic system acts as a sort of overflow arrangement for the return of excess tissue fluid. It is produced in greater quantities in the intestinal wall than elsewhere in the body and it is of importance in the absorption of fat, some of which is absorbed from the gut and passed direct into the special lymphatics of the villi known as the *lacteals* (p. 470).

The large lymphatic vessels have valves on their walls similar to those of the veins and lymph glands, or better, lymph nodes, also situated on the lymphatic vessels. These consist of a meshwork of connective tissue fibres enclosed in a capsule producing and containing abundance of lymphocytes, one of the types of white cells found in the blood.

The role which is played by the tissue fluid is of great importance in the transport to or from the cell of oxygen, carbon dioxide, food-stuffs, and other chemical substances. It acts as a middleman between the blood and the cell and is not contained within any cell-lined duct but bathes the outside of each cell. Lymph, on the other hand, is contained in the lymphatic vessels but is otherwise not very different in composition from tissue fluid. The blood, the tissue fluid and the lymph are thus seen as complementary in their function and are all in a state of flux, the blood circulating along a set path, the tissue fluid being produced and reabsorbed locally and the lymph draining off the excess tissue fluid and returning it to the blood stream.

Respiration

Gaseous exchange takes place in the rabbit almost entirely in the lungs, which are contained in the closed thoracic cavity and connected to the external air via the *trachea* (windpipe) at the top of which is the *larynx* with a slit-like opening, the *glottis*, in the floor of

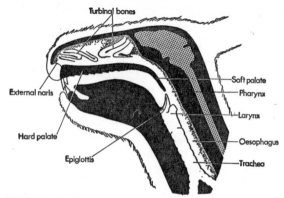

Fig. 16.24. The rabbit. Diagram of a vertical section of the head to show the respiratory passages.

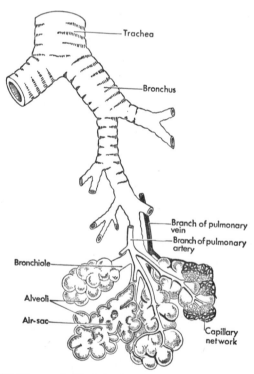

Fig. 16.25. Diagram to illustrate the structure of the mammalian lung.

the pharynx. The trachea branches at its base into two *bronchi,* one of which enters each lung. The lungs are spongy, vascular structures, each connected with a pulmonary artery, a pulmonary vein and an air pipe, the *bronchus.* This divides into smaller tubes in the substance of the lung and eventually from these bronchioles branches arise which lead into blindly ending sacs, the air sacs. These have, in turn, tiny sacculations or *alveoli* in their walls. The walls of the trachea and larger bronchi contain cartilaginous rings but these are absent from the bronchioles. Their walls and those of the alveoli are of connective tissue which is rich in elastic fibres. Some plain muscle occurs in the walls of the bronchioles. The lining of the air ways is of simple or ciliated epithelium and is very thin in the alveoli where it consists of pavement epithelium. A very rich capillary blood supply lies just underneath the alveolar lining. The great complexity and subdivision of the air spaces of the lungs provides a very large surface over which gaseous exchange occurs in a compact organ. The lungs are covered by a connective tissue membrane which is similar to that lining the thoracic cavity. These membranes are together known as the *pleura* or pleural membranes. The membrane covering the lungs and that lining the thorax are almost in contact with one another in life, being separated only by a thin layer of pleural fluid which lubricates the movements occurring between the lung pleura and the thoracic pleura during respiratory movements. Between the pleura lining the left and right thoracic cavities there is a space, the *mediastinum,* in which the heart lies enclosed in its pericardium. The cavity of the thorax is cut off from the perivisceral coelom by the diaphragm. This is a sheet of tough connective tissue in which there is also a muscle layer with the fibres arranged radially around the outer part, the centre being devoid of muscles. The wall of the thorax is supported by the ribs which are embedded in it. Two main sets of muscles actuate them, the internal and external intercostals.

When the thoracic cavity is enlarged, it enlarges the lungs at the same time because they are in contact with the wall except for a film of pleural fluid. Air therefore streams into the lungs under atmospheric pressure via the nose or mouth and air passages leading to them.

On inspiration, the thoracic cavity increases in length and diameter. Increase in length is brought about chiefly by the flattening of the diaphragm which is due to the contraction of the radial muscles. It is clear that muscle fibres which take a curved course when relaxed will, on contraction, tend to approximate to the chord which is a shorter distance than the length of the arc. The contraction of such muscles in the diaphragm thus flattens it. The increase in diameter is brought about by the movement of the ribs. These are placed at an acute angle to the vertebral column with which they articulate and on inspiration swing forwards so that both the angle and the distance between the sternum and the vertebral column increase and the volume of the chest cavity is enlarged. Forward movement of the ribs is brought about chiefly by the contraction of the external intercostal muscles which run obliquely from rib to rib in the manner shown in Fig. 16.26C. From this geometrical abstraction, in which the external intercostals are represented by the line A–B, it can be understood that when the distance A–B is reduced both ribs are moved forwards. Since the ribs increase in size from anterior to posterior when rib Z occupies the previous position of rib Y the diameter of the thorax is increased. This movement is brought about during respiration by the contraction of the external intercostal muscles which are the chief ones used in inspiration. When very deep inspiration occurs, other muscles are brought into play as well as the external intercostals. Expiration is brought about by a return to the relaxed position. The diaphragm becomes more curved from the pressure of the viscera and the relaxation of its intrinsic muscles. The costal cartilages connecting the ends of the ribs to the sternum return, by their elasticity, to their natural resting position. This return to the expiratory position is also aided by contraction of the internal intercostal muscles which run from rib to rib more or less at right-angles to the external intercostals. The shortening of these muscles has an antagonistic action to that of the external intercostals and tends to diminish the angle which the ribs make with the vertebral column. Finally, the elastic recoil of the lungs also helps in expiration.

Excretory system

The kidney is the excretory organ of the mammal and acts by extracting and eliminating soluble waste products from the blood flowing through it, thus helping to keep the composition of the blood constant. It differs from the kidney of the frog and the fish in being a *metanephros*, which implies that although kidney tubules arise from the nephrotomes of the embryo, they develop from a posterior region which soon loses all trace of segmental structure and becomes a compact body with a separate duct of its own, the ureter, for conveying urine to the bladder. The unit of kidney functioning is the

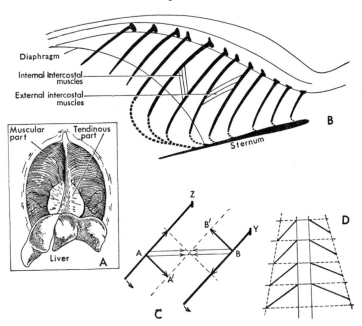

Fig. 16.26. The rabbit. Diagram to illustrate the mechanics of gaseous exchange.

A Posterior view of the diaphragm *in situ* with the liver displaced posteriorly.

B Side view of the arrangement of the ribs, diaphragm, and intercostal muscles.

C Diagram of the forces acting on two adjacent ribs produced by the contraction of the external intercostal muscles A—B. The resultant component at right angles to the posterior rib (A—A′) acts at a greater distance (Z—A) from the fulcrum Z than the resultant of the same force (B—B′) acting on the anterior rib Y. Rib Z is therefore moved forwards. Other external intercostal muscles act on the same or the other ribs.

D Diagram to illustrate the enlargement of the thoracic cavity produced by the forward movement of the ribs. The diagram represents the vertebral column and ribs seen from above. The greater area enclosed by the dotted lines on the right of the diagram is easily seen.

nephric tubule or *nephron* and the kidney consists of very many of these held together in a thin connective tissue capsule. The organ is shaped like a bean and lies outside the coelom covered with the peritoneum and frequently embedded in fat. In the rabbit, the paired kidneys lie one on either side in the anterior region of the abdomen, attached to the dorsal wall, the right one lying nearer to the head than the left (Fig. 16.17). Each kidney receives a rich blood supply from a renal artery which branches off the dorsal aorta directly and it is drained by a renal vein which joins the posterior vena cava. The blood vessels and the ureter join the organ at the *hilum*.

When seen sliced horizontally, the outer layer or *cortex* is distinguishable by its lighter colour from the inner region or *medulla*. The medulla is formed into pyramids on the concave side and these project into a space, the *pelvis*, from which urine is drained by the ureter. The blood vessels pursue a course together along the line of junction of the cortex and medulla, the arteries giving off branches to the cortex to supply the glomeruli and the veins receiving venules from the region of the kidney tubules.

Each nephric tubule (Fig. 26.2) starts as a Malpighian body in the cortex. This consists of a very thin-walled expansion known as Bowman's capsule with an inpushing of the wall containing a glomerulus or knot of blood capillaries. (Bowman's capsule, which is a part of the tubule epithelium, together with the glomerulus of blood vessels which it contains, make up a Malpighian body.) The tubule leading from Bowman's capsule becomes convoluted soon after leaving it and is then known as the proximal convoluted tubule. It loops down into the medulla, forming the loop of Henle, and then forms a second or distal bunch of convolutions before joining one of the large collecting ducts which open into the pelvis. Its walls consist of a single layer of cubical cells with an inner brush-like border (see Fig. 18.1).

Each glomerulus receives blood at fairly high pressure from an arteriole of relatively large diameter so that ultra-filtration through the thin walls of the capillaries and the thin epithelium of Bowman's capsule takes place readily. The efferent arteriole formed by the junction of the glomerular vessels is of smaller diameter than the afferent arteriole, which implies that either it acts to restrict the flow of blood through the glomerulus and thus to ensure that the arterial pressure acts on the thin-walled glomerular vessels or that some part of the blood entering the glomerulus is lost down the kidney tubule so that less flows out of the glomerulus than flows in. The efferent arteriole then runs to the tubule and there breaks up into capillaries investing the wall of the tubule. From these capillaries the blood is collected by a venule which ultimately leads into the renal vein.

The working of the kidney to eliminate waste products, to conserve necessary ones and to help to maintain a constant composition of the blood is described on pp. 535–538.

The ureter from the kidney leads into the bladder where the urine is stored. From there it passes out along a thick-walled muscular duct, the *urethra*, which opens at the end of the penis in the male and into the vestibule of the female (Fig. 16.37).

Nervous system and sense organs

Although the mammalian brain and sense organs are made on the same plan as those of other vertebrates, they are nevertheless more complex and can be said to have reached a 'higher stage of evolution'. This suggests that the minimal stimuli to which the sense organs can respond are smaller than those which can be perceived by others, or that perception is more precise, or that the range of stimuli is greater. It has already been noted that the internal environment and, in particular, the bodily temperature is kept more nearly uniform in mammals than in other vertebrates. There is no doubt that this greater stability in bodily maintenance is due chiefly to the increased effectiveness of the central nervous system and sense organs. A great deal of study has been devoted to them, especially to those of man, and their structure and functioning are accordingly better understood than they are in the lower vertebrates, partly also because the powers of perception which the sense organs confer can be studied subjectively in man and not only, as in other animals, by the interpretation of their actions.

Spinal cord

Like that of most vertebrates, the spinal cord of the mammal consists of a thick-walled tube with a very small lumen. Two deep longitudinal fissures are present in the wall in the vertical plane. The dorsal fissure penetrates nearly to the ventral canal. The ventral fissure is usually somewhat shallower but wider and in it lie the blood vessels supplying the spinal cord. The nerve cells lie in a roughly H-shaped central area and being more translucent than the cut ends of nerve fibres this region looks grey in colour. The so-called 'grey matter' which they form is distinguishable from the 'white matter' surrounding it, for that consists mainly of nerve fibres.

Each spinal nerve arises from the spinal cord by a dorsal and ventral root, the dorsal root bearing a ganglion containing the cell bodies of the sensory cells. The two roots join within the vertebral canal and the single nerve thus formed leaves the vertebral column between the neural arches of successive vertebrae. Just outside the vertebral column a small dorsal branch leaves the main trunk and

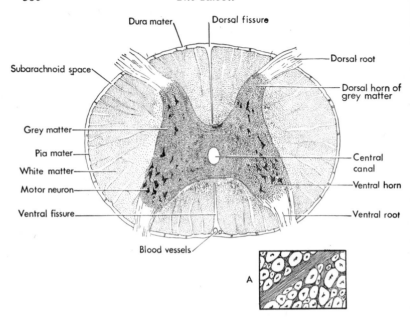

Fig. 16.27. Transverse section of a mammalian spinal cord to show the arrangement of cell bodies and fibres.

At *A* the appearance of a small part of the white matter (fibres) is shown. In life the central axons would not be shrunken as they appear in the fixed and stained preparation. (From a specimen.)

supplies the skin and muscles of the back. The main trunk supplies the ventral and lateral parts of the body. In the regions of the fore- and hind-limbs the spinal nerves supplying them form plexuses.

Brain

Much the same parts can be recognized in the brain of the mammal as can be seen in the brains of many lower forms, with the exception that only in the mammals is the end-brain or telencephalon so greatly developed. In the frog, for example, the telencephalon consists of the two cerebral hemispheres which project forwards from the lamina terminalis and which can be seen in section to have walls of nearly uniform thickness. The nerve cells lie mostly towards the inside rather than the outside. Three regions of the wall of each cerebral hemisphere are recognized, a median *archipallium*, a lateral *palaeopallium* and a ventral region known as the *corpus striatum* (or *basal nucleus*).

Stages in the evolution of the forebrain intermediate between the state of the amphibian and that of the mammal are seen in reptiles where the beginnings of a fourth region of the cerebral hemispheres can be recognized. This region, the *neopallium*, lies between the archipallium and the palaeopallium. The development of the mammalian cerebral hemispheres is chiefly due to the enormous expansion of this region. The archipallium is pushed towards the middle

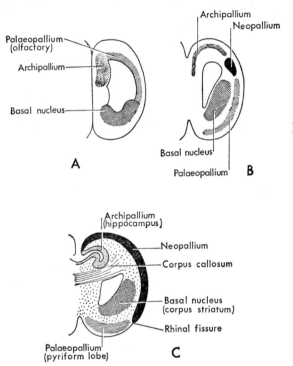

Fig. 16.28. Diagram illustrating the evolution of the forebrain as seen in transverse sections of the cerebrum of *A* an amphibian, *B* a reptile, *C* a mammal. (Based on *Romer*.)

and is known as the *hippocampus*. The palaeopallium is pushed ventrally and is known as the *pyriform lobe*.

Fig. 16.28 is a diagram illustrating the changes in the relative sizes and positions of the parts of the fore-brain, as seen in transverse section, from its condition in the amphibian to that in the mammal. It will be readily understood that, as well as the changes which have just been described, there are others which affect the connexions between the sense organs and the brain and those between the various parts of the brain. The chief change is that all the sense organs come to have nervous connexions with the neopallium of the cerebral hemispheres (i.e., the cerebral cortex) and that the cortex is also connected with the motor nerve centres of the rest of the brain and spinal cord. A brain with a well-developed cerebral cortex has thus a much greater facility for correlating the information arriving as nerve impulses from the sense organs because these impulses from all the sense organs arrive in the same structure or correlation centre. The connexions with motor neurons which are also present ensure that the appropriate motor response is made to the sum of the external sensory information, proprioceptor information and, possibly, also the stored memories of past experiences.

If the figures of the rabbit's brain are now examined, it will be seen that the brain stem is similar to that of the lower animals which have already been studied but that the telencephalon is very much larger and the cerebellum, too, is greater in size and complexity.

The medulla oblongata is a little wider than the spinal cord and its cavity, the fourth ventricle, is roofed by the posterior choroid plexus. All the segmental cranial nerves except the third (oculomotor) and fourth (pathetic) arise from the medulla. The cerebellum is well developed and consists of a median lobe or *vermis*, paired lateral lobes and the ventrolateral *flocculi*. Cut in sagittal section it shows a tree-like pattern of white and grey matter, the *arbor vitae*. Left and right halves of the cerebellum are connected by a transverse band of fibres which forms a ridge on the ventral surface of the hind-brain, the *pons Varolii*.

The mid-brain floor is formed by the crura cerebri which are thick tracts of fibres running between the fore- and mid-brains. The roof is formed by the optic lobes which are divided into four and hence known as the *corpora quadrigemina*. The cavity of the mid-brain is known as the iter or the aqueduct of Sylvius.

From the roof of the diencephalon arises the pineal stalk which ends in the pineal body. The rest of the roof of the diencephalon is non-nervous and forms the anterior choroid plexus. The infundibulum projects from the floor of the diencephalon and ends in the pituitary body which has a component derived from the stomodaeum (the hypophysis).

The telencephalon is by far the most conspicuous part of the brain, especially as seen from the dorsal surface. The paired olfactory lobes lie ventral to and in front of the cerebral hemispheres which are

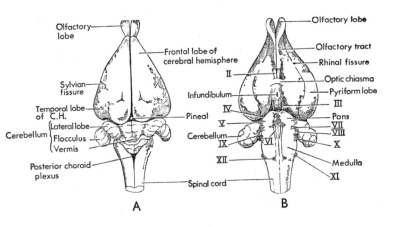

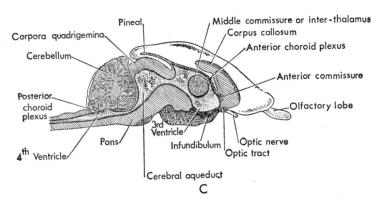

Fig. 16.29. The rabbit.

The brain as seen in (*A*) dorsal and (*B*) ventral view and (*C*) sagittal section. Cut surfaces are shaded and transverse fibre tracts are denoted by cross-hatching. (From specimens.)

smooth pear-shaped masses extending back to touch the cerebellum. In many mammals they are much convoluted or fissured but in the rabbit they are almost smooth except for a *rhinal* fissure which marks off the olfactory tracts and pyriform lobe (=palaeopallium) from the neopallium. There is also a small Sylvian fissure separating an anterior from a posterior or temporal region of each cerebral hemisphere.

The great expansion of the neopallium has affected the positions of the other components of the telencephalon which are recognized in the amphibian and it has also greatly altered the shape of the lateral ventricles. As has been seen, the palaeopallium has been pushed into a ventromedian position as the pyriform lobe, the archipallium has been pushed into a dorso-median position as the hippocampus while each basal nucleus or corpus striatum occupies an internal position below the floor of the lateral ventricle.

In the cerebral hemispheres the lateral ventricles open into the third ventricle in the thalamencephalon by the narrow *foramina of Munro* but they expand inside each cerebral hemisphere into a main body, anterior and posterior cornua, and a descending cornu which passes outwards and then downwards and inwards following the contours of the hemisphere

There are a number of transverse tracts of fibres, or commissures, connecting the right and left halves of the brain. One of these, the pons Varolii, has already been mentioned. The posterior commissure connects the right and left anterior corpora quadrigemina of the mid-brain; the soft commissure (=massa intermedia=middle commissure) is a mass containing neurons and not solely a fibrous commissure occupying a large part of the ventricle of the diencephalon. The anterior commissure connects the left and right corpora striata (=basal nuclei). By far the largest commissure is the *corpus callosum* which connects the right and left halves of the neopallium and lies above the lateral ventricles. Seen in longitudinal section it bends sharply forwards at its posterior end to join the body of the *fornix*. This structure consists of a strand of longitudinal fibres which divide anteriorly into a band on each side, the so-called pillars of the fornix running ventrally to the diencephalon while the posterior pillars run posteriorly adjacent the hippocampus.

Cranial nerves

The cranial nerves of the rabbit are essentially the same as those of other vertebrates but with the inclusion of two additional pairs, the *spinal accessory* (XI) and the *hypoglossal* (XII) which are post-occipital elements in the lower vertebrates. The oculomotor (III), pathetic (IV) and abducens (VI) supply the eye muscles; the tri-geminal (V) is a large nerve with ophthalmic, maxillary and mandibular branches but the facial (VII) is relatively small and lacks ophthalmic, buccal and lateral line branches. The auditory (VIII) is a branch of the dorsal root of the third segment as is usual. The glossopharyngeal (IX) goes to the tongue region. The vagus is large and from its ganglion arise the following branches; a main trunk to various viscera, an anterior laryngeal branch and a separate branch to the heart known, from its action, as the *cardiac depressor* branch. In addition, the larynx is innervated by another branch which leaves the main trunk near the systemic aorta, loops round the ductus arteriosus on the left or the subclavian artery on the right and runs back alongside the trachea. It is known as the *recurrent laryngeal* branch of the vagus and its course results from the evolution of a neck in the mammal and the elongation of the carotids, together with the relatively posterior position of the heart and arterial arches. The spinal accessory nerve arises just posterior to the vagus from a

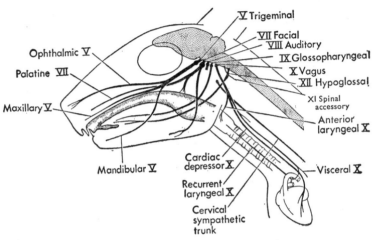

Fig. 16.30. The rabbit. Diagram of the cranial nerves.

number of roots and supplies muscles in the neck and pharynx and larynx. The hypoglossal (XII) also arises from several roots and supplies the tongue and also has a small branch to the larynx.

The autonomic nervous system

The sympathetic division of the autonomic nervous system of the mammals is not conspicuous but is nevertheless well developed and important in the life of the animal. There are anterior and posterior pairs of cervical ganglia, twelve pairs of thoracic ganglia, an unpaired coeliac ganglion and twelve pairs of abdominal ganglia. They are connected together by longitudinal sympathetic connectives. The ganglia receive nerve fibres which pass out from the central nervous system with the thoracic and lumbar nerves. These fibres synapse in the sympathetic ganglion with motor neurons whose fibres pass in

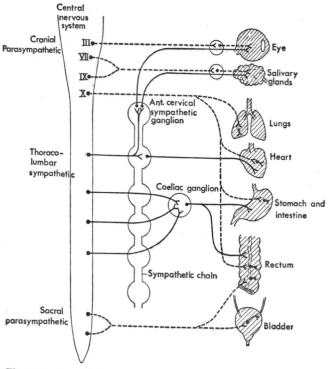

Fig. 16.31. Simplified diagram to illustrate the connexions of the autonomic nervous system of a mammal.

(Parasympathetic fibres denoted by broken lines.)

fine post-ganglionic nerves to plain muscle of the viscera and blood vessels innervated.

The parasympathetic division of the autonomic system has three points of origin from the central nervous system. Some fibres accompany the oculomotor nerve to the eye but the chief parasympathetic nerve is the vagus which supplies the heart, lungs, gut and other viscera as well as the muscles of the arteriolar walls. Some parasympathetic nerve fibres also leave the central nervous system with spinal nerves of the sacral region. The parasympathetic ganglia are situated on the organs supplied and the post-ganglionic fibres running from the motor neurons of the ganglion are therefore short.

Sense organs

Mammals possess well-developed sense organs and powers of perception beyond the scope of most other vertebrates, the sight of some birds excepted. The eye and the ear which receive physical stimuli are supplemented by sensory nerve endings in the skin which respond to changes of temperature and to touch. Sense cells stimulated by chemical stimuli provide the senses of taste and smell. Proprioceptor organs in the muscles, tendons and joints supply information to the central nervous system about the position of limbs and thus enable the co-ordination of antagonistic muscles to be effected.

Cutaneous sense

Free nerve endings of sensory nerves (whose cell bodies lie in the dorsal root ganglion) occur just below the epidermis. In addition sensory nerves frequently end in special receptor organs embedded in the dermis. It is not clearly known which of the types of receptor corpuscle correspond to particular sensations experienced, e.g. warmth, cold and touch.

Taste

Taste, or the perception of chemical stimuli, is the function of the taste buds which are found on the tongue. The receptor cells which are spindle-shaped and each end in a fine process are in contact with

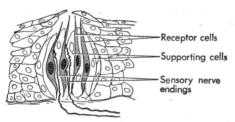

Fig. 16.32. Section of a taste bud of a mammal. (From a specimen.)

nerve endings of sensory cells. The cranial nerves which transmit these nerve fibres are the glossopharyngeal (IXth) and a branch of the facial (VIIth). The relation between the brain and the receptors for taste and smell are thus quite different.

Smell

The receptor cells for olfaction give rise directly to olfactory nerve fibres which enter the brain. There they make connexion with special ganglion cells of the olfactory lobe. Each of these ganglion cells receives fibres from several olfactory receptor cells. It is believed that this provides a way of adding together a number of stimuli which enables very feeble stimuli to be perceived. It is indeed well known that the sense of smell in many mammals is very acute. The area of the epithelium in which the olfactory receptor cells occur is large by being spread out over the scroll-like nasal turbinal bones which are present in the olfactory chamber. It is kept moist by the secretion of many mucous glands and has a rich blood supply.

Sight

The eye which is most often described in text-books is the human eye because it is best known. The eyes of mammals are much alike in general features but there are differences between those of species ranging from the vestigial eye of the mole to the large eyes of primates and carnivores and there are differences in the details of construction from one species to the next which are closely connected with their ways of life.

The human eye is shown in horizontal section in Fig. 16.33, when its likeness to a camera will be apparent. The points of resemblance and difference may be listed, when it will be seen that the similarities are many and the differences few. In each there is a lens (cornea + crystalline lens of eye) which forms an inverted image on the sensitive screen (film of camera, retina of eye). The eye can be opened or shut by the lids and the camera by its shutter. The amount of light entering the camera is regulated by the diaphragm, that entering the eye by the iris. The interior of a camera is painted black to avoid internal reflections which might blur the image. The interior of the eye is pigmented. Finally, the camera can be focused by moving the lens to take pictures of near and distant objects and the eye can accommodate or focus also, although not in the same way. It is perhaps not too fanciful to compare the necessity for development of a film to reveal the image with the necessity for the image formed on the retina to be 'interpreted' by the brain. The chief point of difference is that the sensitive screen, the retina of the eye, is not flat or plane like the film in the camera but is spheroidal. This enables the eye to have a wide angle of vision and at the same time largely to avoid the effects of spherical aberration. Another important point of difference is that the camera requires only a short exposure of the film to affect it while the eye is capable of receiving continuous stimulation by light over a long period of time.

The details of construction of the eye and the way in which it functions may now be determined, when it will be seen how each

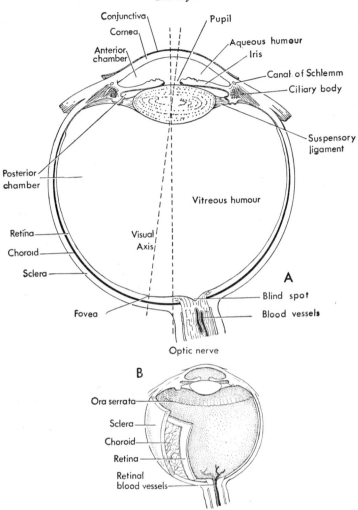

Fig. 16.33.
A Horizontal section of a human eye. *B* The interior view of the lower part of the eye after removal of part of the upper sclera.

feature is adapted to its particular role in the perception of visual objects.

The outer coat, the *sclera* or *sclerotic coat*, is of tough fibrous connective tissue in which the fibre bundles run in many directions. The cornea is made of essentially the same tissue but remains transparent instead of becoming opaque as does the sclera during its development. The skin covers the front of the eye too, of course, and is known as the *conjunctiva*. Where this skin covers the transparent cornea the dermis is missing and the epidermis is thin, little cornified and transparent also. It is richly supplied with free sensory nerve endings, the stimulation of which gives rise to the sensation of pain.

The choroid coat lines the posterior portion of the eyeball and lies next the sclera and is lined in turn with the retina which extends over the whole extent of the choroid even up to the edge of the pupil. Only the posterior part of the retina is sensitive to light, the front portion being merely a thin epithelial covering to the choroid and its derivatives. The choroid is vascular and pigmented over much of its area. Near the junction of the cornea and sclera it enlarges to form the *ciliary body*. This includes the ciliary muscles (radial and circumferential fibres) and the ciliary processes which are vascular folds projecting into the posterior chamber and by which the aqueous humour is secreted. The iris is a continuation of the ciliary body and contains circular muscles for closing the pupil and radial fibres for opening it. The retinal layer of the iris is pigmented with fine particles of a brown pigment causing it to appear blue by a light scattering effect. In eyes of other shades, particularly in brown eyes, pigment is also present in the connective tissue (choroid) of the iris itself.

The crystalline lens is a thick bi-convex structure lying just posterior to the iris, which it causes to bulge slightly forwards, and in front of the vitreous humour which partly supports it. It is made of a transparent homogeneous lens capsule within which are concentrically arranged layers of transparent fibres chiefly derived from a layer of epithelium which underlies the lens capsule over the anterior half. At the edges of the lens the fibres are produced by the division of the epithelial cells at a great rate during development and very much more slowly after the lens has reached its adult size. The lens is attached to the ciliary body by radially arranged fibres which are inserted into the capsule. These constitute the *suspensory ligaments* or the *zonule of Zinn* and serve not only to hold the lens in place but also to hold it in tension as a result of the hydrostatic pressure which exists within the sclera and keeps this turgid.

The retina, as will be seen in the section on embryology, is formed from a double-walled vesicle which grows out from the fore-brain. The outer wall becomes pigmented and is non-nervous while the inner wall forms the layer of receptor and nerve cells which constitute the sensitive screen of the eye. A number of layers can be made out in a vertical section of the retina. Working from inside the eye they are arranged in order as follows: (a) nerve fibre layer; (b) ganglion cell layer; (c) layer of fibres connecting ganglion cells with bi-polar cells; (d) bi-polar cell layer; (e) layer of fibres connecting bi-polar cells with rods and cones; (f) basal parts of rods and cones with nuclei; (g) limiting membrane of the retina through which the rods and cones project; (h) receptor layer of rods and cones. All these constitute the original inner layer of the retina which is applied to the original outer layer of the optic cup. This outer layer forms the layer of pigment cells to which the tips of the receptor rods and cones are closely applied. From the appearance of the retina as seen in section, the connexions between the cells described have been elucidated and are shown in Fig. 16.34. It will be seen that the rods and cones are connected with the bi-polar and ganglion cells in various ways, some of which are illustrated. From the ganglion cells nerve fibres run in the 'optic nerve' to the brain.

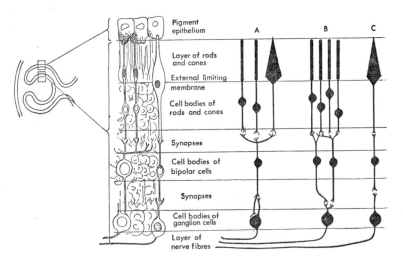

Fig. 16.34. Diagram illustrating the structure of the retina.

On the left, the embryonic optic vesicle is shown and the parts of the retina to which it gives rise are indicated.

At *A, B* and *C* three possible arrangements for the connexion of the receptor rods and cones are indicated. *A* shows two rods and one cone connected to one bipolar cell and this in turn to a ganglion cell whose axon runs into the brain. *B* shows four rods connected to two bipolar cells and theses to one ganglion cell. This arrangement is found at the periphery of the human retina and caters for vision in dim light. *C* shows a single cone connected to a single bipolar and ganglion cell. Such an arrangement is found in the *fovea centralis* and provides high resolving power and good colour vision.

The rods and cones are not arranged uniformly over the retina and they are not responsive in quite the same way to light stimulation. It is generally believed that the cones are responsible for colour vision and for vision in bright light while the rods are responsible for the perception of light of low intensity. Rods are scattered over the retina except at the *fovea*, a point on the retina where it is cut by the optical axis of the eye, but they are more plentiful towards the periphery. Cones, on the other hand, are relatively more numerous nearer to the optical axis and are present exclusively at the fovea. Moreover, each cone there is connected with a bi-polar cell (instead of several being connected with a single bi-polar cell) so that the fovea is a region of specially acute vision and greatest colour discrimination.

At the point where the 'optic nerve' joins the eye and where the fibres converge to make their exits from the retina, there are no receptor elements and there is accordingly a blind spot.

Accommodation to enable near or distant objects to be sharply focused on the retina is carried out by the alteration of the curvature of the lens and hence its converging power, and not, as in the camera, by moving the lens further away from or nearer to the sensitive surface. In the normal eye there is always a positive hydrostatic pressure due partly to the action of the extrinsic eye muscles and partly to the secretion of aqueous humour which serves to keep the sclera turgid, the suspensory ligament taut, the lens capsule under tension and the lens in a slightly flattened condition. In this state the eye is focused for distant objects. Near objects are accommodated by the contraction of both the radial and circumferential muscle fibres of the ciliary body, which has the effect of slightly reducing the circumference of the ciliary body from which the suspensory fibres arise. This in turn slightly slackens the fibres of the suspensory ligament so that the lens is allowed to take up its natural, more convex form. Greater convexity confers on it greater converging power, which enables it to bring to a focus on the retina light rays from near objects which are not parallel but diverging. This method of accommodation is different from that possessed by the dogfish and by the frog, in both of which the lens is moved bodily with respect to the retina. As in the other vertebrates, the eye is moved in its socket by extrinsic muscles similar to those of the dogfish (p. 294).

Hearing

The formation of the inner ear from the auditory placode during development has already been described (page 297) and a diagrammatic representation of the membranous labyrinth of a fish is shown in Fig. 14.28, page 299. The inner ear of the mammal is similar in many respects but differs chiefly by the addition of an outgrowth from the sacculus forming the spirally coiled *cochlea* which is the organ of sound reception. Also the inner ear is associated with various structures adapted for the reception of sound waves and their transmission to the receptor cells. The membranous labyrinth of the mammal can be represented diagrammatically as in Fig. 16.35 but the actual structure is somewhat more complex. In lateral view its appearance is shown in Fig. 16.35, but it must be remembered that it is totally enclosed in a cavity in the bony otic capsule which more or less conforms to it in shape and which is lined with the normal connective tissue membrane covering a bone, namely the periosteum. The space between the periosteum and the membranous labyrinth is filled with perilymph in which the membranous labyrinth is suspended by strands of loose connective tissue. In the cochlea the relation between the membranous labyrinth and perilymphatic chambers is somewhat different from this in that the coiled perilymphatic duct is divided into two by a shelf on which the cochlear duct of the membranous labyrinth lies. Since this shelf does not extend quite all the way to the apex of the helix the upper and lower perilymphatic ducts communicate by a small opening called the *helicotrema*. These upper and lower perilymphatic cavities are known respectively as the *scala vestibuli* and the *scala tympani*, and they are separated by the *spiral lamina*. The cochlear duct lying between them is often known as the *scala media*. The spiral lamina is composed of the linings of the scala vestibuli, scala tympani and scala media between which lies the *basilar membrane*. This has a fibrous structure. The lining of the scala media (cochlear duct) is specialized where it rests on the basilar membrane forming the *organ of Corti*. This includes in its structure inner and outer pillar cells, supporting cells and the hair cells which are the receptor cells and which are supplied with sensory fibres of the auditory nerve. Fine projections from the hair cells are embedded in a gelatinous *tectorial membrane* also formed from the lining of the cochlear duct.

It is believed that the semicircular canals which have the receptor cristae in their ampullae function in much the same way as they do in the fish and supply information to the central nervous system about *changes* of orientation in space. The sacculus and utriculus possess somewhat similar receptors known as maculae and are believed to supply information about the position in space. Neither of these

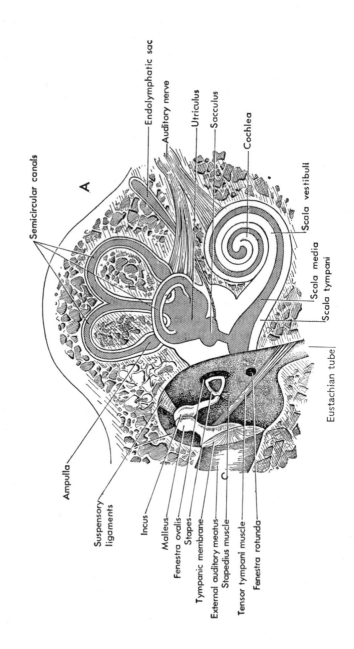

Semicircular canals

A

Endolymphatic sac

Auditory nerve

Utriculus

Sacculus

Cochlea

Scala vestibuli

Scala media

Scala tympani

Eustachian tube

Ampulla

Suspensory ligaments

Incus

Malleus

Fenestra ovalis

Stapes

Tympanic membrane

External auditory meatus

Stapedius muscle

Tensor tympani muscle

Fenestra rotunda

C

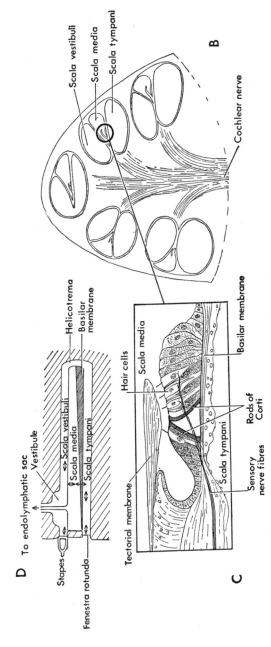

Fig. 16.35. Diagrams illustrating the structure of the mammalian ear.
A Section showing the external auditory meatus, middle ear and inner ear. *B* Section of the cochlea. *C* Enlarged section of the organ of Corti. *D* Diagram of the transmission of vibrations (sound waves) from the fenestra ovalis through the cochlea to the fenestra rotunda. (Based on various authors.)

parts of the ear needs any special connexion with the exterior but for the reception of the vibrations of the air which constitute sound waves a mechanism is necessary which can transmit the vibrations collected in air into the receptor organ which functions in a liquid. Such a mechanism is provided by the ear drum or tympanic membrane, a sheet of connective tissue and skin stretched across the hyoidean visceral cleft and connected with the inner ear by three small bones, the *malleus* (homologous with the articular), the *incus* (=quadrate) and the *stapes* (=hyomandibula). The stapes fits into a small membrane-covered hole in the otic capsule, the *fenestra ovalis*. Here the perilymphatic cavity comes to the surface, as it were, so that vibrations of the stapes directly affect the perilymph. Since liquids are incompressible, another point of 'give' in the rigid bony cavity is required (otherwise the stapes could not vibrate) and this is provided by another point at which the perilymph is separated from outside by a membrane only, namely that covering the *fenestra rotunda*. In man the area of the fenestra ovalis is much less than that of the tympanic membrane and the lever system of the ear ossicles is such as to reduce movement of the stapes compared with the movement of the tympanum. The result of these features is that the amplitude of vibration of the stapes is about a third of that of the tympanum but the pressure changes are some twenty times greater than those received by the tympanum. Vibrations collected by the pinna (or external ear) are funnelled on to the tympanum and are transmitted into the perilymph via the ear ossicles and the fenestra ovalis. This and the fenestra rotunda are so disposed that the path followed by the vibrations sets in motion the fluid in the scala vestibuli which in turn affects the spiral lamina, the fluid in the scala tympani and the connective tissue covering the fenestra rotunda. There is no doubt that the vibrations of the hair cells which rest on the basilar membrane of the spiral lamina initiate impulses in the auditory nerve but it is not certain how notes of different frequency are perceived. The length of the fibres in the basilar membrane and therefore its natural frequency of vibration varies in different parts of the helix, being longest near the tip of the spiral and shortest at the base. It is probable that different parts of the basilar membrane are responsible for the reception of different frequencies but such a simple explanation will not suffice fully to explain all the observed facts of frequency discrimination.

Reproductive system

MALE. Each testis consists of an aggregation of seminiferous tubules lined with germinal epithelium and held together by a connective tissue coat. Each testis lies in a scrotal sac after the onset of sexual maturity, having descended into it at puberty. The spermatic artery, vein and nerve forming together the spermatic cord, pass down the

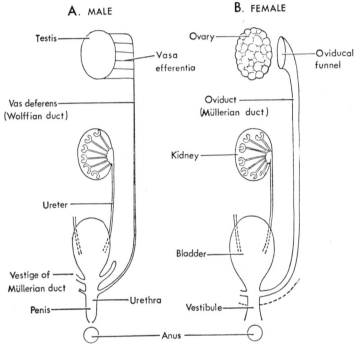

Fig. 16.36. Diagrams of the male and female urinogenital systems of the mammal.

inguinal canal to the testis which thus lies outside the general visceral coelom. At the end opposite to the position of the spermatic cord lies the *gubernaculum*, a connective tissue ligament which shortens and draws the testis into the scrotal sac.

The spermatozoa formed in the tubules pass by way of vasa efferentia into a long coiled duct, the *epididymis*, which forms a ridge on the outside of the testis. The epididymis leads into a vas deferens which is muscular and joins the urethra in the region where it passes through the *prostate gland*. Just distal to the openings of the vasa deferentia a blind sac, the *uterus masculinus*, opens dorsally into the urethra. The urethra traverses the penis to open at the tip. The penis in the normal state is small and the tip or *glans* is withdrawn into the prepuce. Erection occurs during sexual excitement and is necessary before insertion into the vagina of the female can occur. Erection is brought about by filling three strands of spongy tissue with blood. These are the ventral *corpus spongiosa* surrounding the urethra and the two dorsal *corpora cavernosa*.

The functions of the testis are the production of spermatozoids

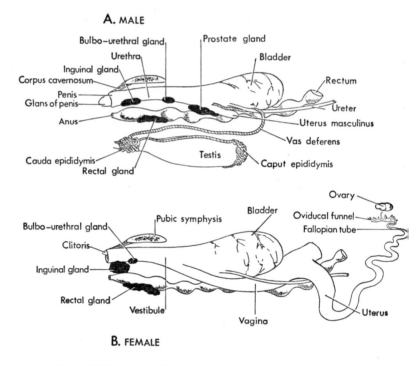

A. MALE

Bulbo–urethral gland
Urethra
Prostate gland
Bladder
Inguinal gland
Corpus cavernosum
Penis
Glans of penis
Anus
Rectum
Ureter
Uterus masculinus
Vas deferens
Cauda epididymis
Rectal gland
Testis
Caput epididymis

Ovary
Bladder
Pubic symphysis
Oviducal funnel
Fallopian tube
Bulbo–urethral gland
Clitoris
Inguinal gland
Rectal gland
Vestibule
Vagina
Uterus

B. FEMALE

Fig. 16.37. The rabbit. The male and female reproductive systems as seen from the side. (Based on *Borradaile*.)

and the secretion of a hormone by the interstitial cells (see pages 594 and 606). The function of the prostate is thought to be the secretion of a substance into the seminal fluid which activates the spermatozoa. Two additional pairs of glands lie alongside the urethra, Cowper's glands of unknown function and the perineal glands to the secretion of which the animal's characteristic smell is due.

The epididymis is regarded as being derived from mesonephros and the vas deferens is its duct, the Wolffian duct. The only trace of the female or Müllerian duct in the male is the uterus masculinus.

FEMALE. The female reproductive system of the mammal is simple in structure and consists of paired ovaries lying adjacent the openings of the reproductive tract, the upper coiled parts of which are known as the *Fallopian tubes*. Each widens into a horn of the uterus which in turn opens into a median vagina. This is a short wide duct merging into the vestibule which is distinguished by the opening into it of the urethra. The vestibule opens to the exterior. Lying on the anterior wall of the vestibule is a small erectile knob, the *clitoris*, which is regarded as homologous with the male penis although the urethra does not pass through it.

The functions of the ovary are to produce ova and hormones which control the development of other parts of the reproductive system, notably the lining of the uterus and vagina and the development of the mammary glands. The Fallopian tube serves to pass the ova into the uterus by ciliary action and is the site of fertilization. The uterus, which is capable of undergoing great enlargement, contains the developing young and expels them by muscular contraction at birth. The vagina serves to receive the penis of the male during copulation.

Natural history

Much of the natural history of the rabbit has been the common knowledge of country dwellers for centuries. Ever since their introduction into this country, probably by the Normans in the twelfth century, rabbits have been a mixed bane and blessing. Their constant grazing prevents the areas of uncultivated country surrounding their warrens from becoming the forest which is the natural climax of vegetation. They provide food for predatory birds and mammals such as hawks, buzzards, stoats and foxes, and are caught by man for the value of their fur and flesh by shooting, netting, snaring and trapping. On the other hand, in cultivated country they consume growing crops and pasture intended for cattle, gnaw the bark of trees in orchards and damage young forest plantations. Since the spread of the disease myxomatosis, which is usually fatal, the population of rabbits in this country has been very greatly reduced and already changes in natural vegetation and the productivity of fields have occurred, but it is too soon to say yet what the total effect of their destruction has been or whether rabbits will eventually return in great numbers.

Their burrows are dug most readily in light soil and may be extensive and with many entrances. There is no regularity in their arrangement. They serve as refuges in time of danger from predators and for the birth and suckling of the young which are born in a helpless and hairless condition. Rabbits can live above ground in dense undergrowth and even in moorland in which the soil is thin and waterlogged.

Feeding occurs chiefly at dawn and dusk and usually takes place near the warren. Defaecation is often performed on the same spot, which becomes marked by the accumulation of the hard faecal pellets produced during the day. Chiefly after the main feeding period the faeces produced are soft, mucus-coated pellets which are taken straight into the mouth as they appear at the anus. The food which is eaten thus passes through the gut twice. The process, sometimes known as refection, is believed to ensure that the maximum amount of nutriment is secured from it.

Rabbits do not normally wander far from their burrows and although on occasions have been known to find their way back when transported half a mile away, they probably range naturally over only half this distance or less.

17. A Survey of the Vertebrates

Introduction

IN THE past few chapters the detailed structure and physiology of *Amphioxus*, the dogfish, frog and rabbit have been described, but it will be realized that while these four animals are good representatives of the many and varied chordates which exist, they are only representatives and not the complete assemblage. While it is necessary to study a typical animal in detail, it is also necessary, for an understanding of the chordates as a whole, to know something of the rest, something, that is, of animals of this phylum, other than the four 'types'.

Jawless vertebrates

Amphioxus is so near to an 'ideal' chordate that it is hard to believe that it is very far from the mainstream of chordate evolution, yet it is specialized in having a very elaborate feeding mechanism and perhaps in its absence of sense organs. Being soft-bodied, it might not be expected to fossilize well (although fossil jellyfishes *are* known) and no trace of any fossil very close in structure to *Amphioxus* has yet been found (see p. 231). The next most primitive living chordates are the Agnatha (or jawless vertebrates), which include the cyclostomes such as *Petromyzon marinus* (the lamprey). This creature has a persistent notochord and its vertebrae are mere pegs of cartilage lying alongside it. The brain is small and the arrangement of its olfactory organ is different from that of the jawed vertebrates. It has no jaws but a rounded sucker at the anterior end in the middle of which the mouth opens. It has gill pouches opening out to the exterior from a special part of the pharynx but these are not used for food collection in the adult which parasitizes fish, sticking on to them with its sucker and rasping off pieces with its horny tongue. Nevertheless, in the larva the method of feeding resembles that of *Amphioxus* in that it depends on the passage of a current of water through the pharynx and the collection of detritus by the mucus secreted by the endostyle. It differs in that the amount of water is generated by muscular pumping and not by the action of cilia. Members of the

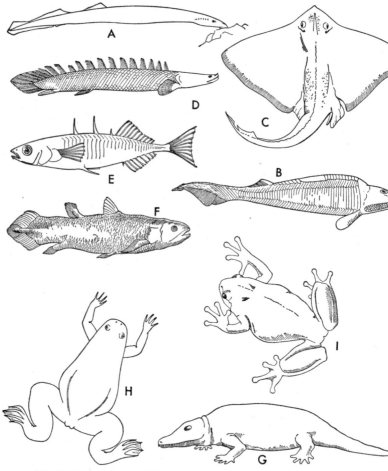

Fig. 17.1. Cyclostomes, fishes and amphibians.

A a lamprey, a present-day jawless vertebrate which can attach itself by its sucker-like mouth to living fishes while feeding and to stones at other times.

B a cephalaspid, an extinct, heavily armoured form possessing certain structural similarities to present-day lampreys.

C a skate. The spiracle lies just behind the eye but the gill slits open on the ventral side.

D Polypterus, one of the few surviving representatives of the early bony fishes. It possesses a complete bony head shield and heavy scales but its row of dorsal finlets attached to spines which can be raised and lowered is not typical of its early fossil ancestors.

E three-spined stickleback, a modern freshwater and estuarine bony fish.

Agnatha are the first vertebrates to be found as fossils but they differ very much from the present-day cyclostomes in being very heavily armoured by the deposition of calcium salts in the dermis. Nevertheless, such an animal as *Cephalaspis* resembled the lamprey in having no jaws, in having numerous gill clefts and in having a brain, internal ear and olfactory sac of a very similar type. Outwardly and in its mode of life the resemblances are slight, but it is considered that the two creatures are related and that the present-day lamprey has become highly adapted to its mode of life in parasitizing fishes.

Fishes

The first true fishes with jaws to appear in the fossil record (in the Silurian) were not like present-day cartilaginous fishes (Chondrichthyes) but were covered with heavy rhomboidal scales and differed from later fishes in that the hyoid arch was an unmodified gill arch taking no part in the jaw suspension.

These were followed in the next geological period, the Devonian, by the appearance of a large number of fish types including cartilaginous shark-like forms which resembled present-day sharks in many respects, as can be seen by comparing the drawings of *Cladoselache* and a small present-day shark such as *Squalus*. With the passage of time the cartilaginous fishes or Chondrichthyes evolved into the variety of forms which exist today. These include beside the small sharks like *Scyliorhinus* and *Squalus*, larger sharks and the flattened bottom-dwelling skates and rays. These have flattened crushing teeth and powerful jaws and live on hard-shelled molluscs and crustaceans. One of these (*Torpedo*) is notable for the powerful electric shocks which it can give from the electric organs which replace some of its musculature and are considered to be built up of modified muscle cells. Other peculiar types of cartilaginous fish

---

F Latimeria, a living tassel-finned fish discovered off Madagascar in 1940. The group of coelacanths to which it belongs, and whose fossil members it closely resembles, was previously thought to have been extinct since the Permian.

G reconstruction of an early amphibian such as *Eryops*. These creatures resemble present-day newts and salamanders in shape but were mostly much bonier, larger and clumsier.

H Xenopus, the South African clawed toad, an aquatic form which still retains lateral-line organs similar to those found in fishes.

I Hyla, a tree frog possessing adhesive pads on the tips of its digits. (From specimens or based on various authors.) (Not all to the same scale.)

include the sawfish (*Pristis*) with its elongated snout bearing a row of enlarged dermal denticles on either side. The Chondrichthyes also include the largest living fish, the basking shark (a near relation of the dogfish *Scyliorhinus*) which instead of being an active predator, as are most cartilaginous fishes, is a planktonic feeder, straining off from the water which enters its mouth by special combs on the gills the small floating organisms which abound especially in temperate waters.

Bony fishes (Osteichthyes) were also present in the fauna of the Devonian period and they, like the first jawed fishes, were heavily armoured with scales behind the head and had bones covering the cranium and jaws. The evolution of these basic species into the 20,000 present-day species, not to mention the very many additional species now extinct, is a fascinating story of adaptation to a large variety of conditions, to fresh water and to the sea, to shore life and to the depths of the ocean, to rapid swimming and even flying, and to bottom dwelling. An idea of the appearance of the early bony fishes can be gained from the surviving *Polypterus* which has many of the features of Devonian fishes preserved to the present time. The bulk of present-day bony fishes belong to the order Teleostei and they are of interest not only as constituting the most highly evolved and varied fish group but also because they are fished for food. Not only are they varied in their morphological adaptations but also in their physiology and behaviour. Many are able to live only in the sea, e.g. the cod and haddock, and many such as the carp and roach can live only in fresh water. Others such as the three-spined stickle-back and the flounder are at home in estuaries where the salinity undergoes great variation, while yet others such as the salmon pass their early life in rivers, spend a feeding period in the sea, and ascend the rivers to spawn (*anadromous* fishes). This is but one example of the seasonal migrations which many fishes undertake, often in con-nexion with their spawning habits. It had hitherto been believed that the longest of these migrations was that of the eel from European fresh waters when sexually mature to the Caribbean Sea (*catadromous* migration) where spawning takes place. Doubt has recently been cast on the belief that mature fishes migrate from Europe to the Carib-bean, although there is no doubt that the larvae pass from America to Europe with the currents and metamorphose into tiny eels on the way. It is now suggested that only American eels migrate into the Caribbean to spawn and that the stocks of both European and Ameri-can eels are all derived from these.

Fisheries

Fishing is one of the few examples left of the exploitation and use for food by man of a natural population. Catching fishes in nets has been practised since prehistoric times and the present-day methods differ only in that they are now highly mechanized and more effective in depleting the natural populations. Among the important fisheries of Great Britain are the herring fisheries using drift nets, vertical sheets of net into which the fishes swim and get stuck by their gill covers; the cod fisheries to the north, especially off the coasts of Iceland, Spitzbergen and Bear Island, and the general fisheries of

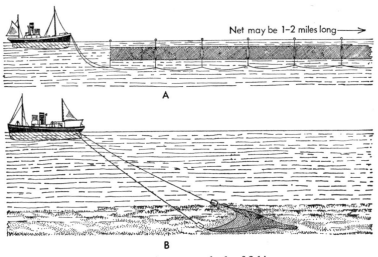

Net may be 1–2 miles long⟶

A

B

Fig. 17.2. Diagram illustrating two methods of fishing.
A Drift net fishing for herrings. The net may be up to two miles long.
B Trawling for bottom dwelling fish. (Based on *Hardy* and *Norman*.)

the North Sea for flatfish such as plaice and sole. The method used in these is the trawl; a large net bag, kept open by kite-like boards is towed slowly behind the ship and hauled up at intervals to spill the catch on deck. Other methods of fishing include seine netting in which a long net on ropes or warps is paid out as the ship steams a horseshoe-shaped course and then the two ends are winched in and the fish caught in the closing bag. A method which is coming into use at the present time is the mid-water trawl which resembles the older bottom trawl but is larger and is towed off the bottom.

The chief problem in fishing is to take only that amount of large and marketable fish which will leave a sufficient breeding population to maintain the stock of fish. Unfortunately this is not easy to accomplish for a variety of reasons. Firstly, it is difficult to design a net that catches only the big fish and lets the small ones through; secondly, it is difficult to find out what the population is and what is a safe amount of fish to remove, and lastly it is only possible to regulate a fishery if all those engaged in fishing agree and keep their agreement. Consequent upon these difficulties the history of each commercial fishery as it has been developed has always been that of good initial catches of large fish declining until the yield is no longer worth the expenditure to get it. Such fisheries have recovered if left unfished, the most immediate examples being the great improvement in catches in the North Sea following the stoppage of fishing during the two world wars. It is now becoming clear that, for the present world population and the present efficient methods of catching fish, the old adage that 'there are as good fish in the sea as ever came out of it' is no longer true, and only a self-imposed restraint on the catch removed will prevent the continued run down of the known fisheries which will eventually result in their becoming commercially valueless.

Tassel finned fishes

In addition to that group of bony fishes whose evolution resulted in the present-day teleosts and which were distinguished throughout the whole course of evolution as the ray finned fishes or Actinopterygii, another group of bony fishes with tassel-like fins called the Crossopterygii has been present. These were more numerous at times in the past than in the present day but there are still a few relics left which include the lung fishes (Dipnoi) of Australia, Africa and South America, and the coelacanth *Latimeria* of Madagascar. Not only do these fishes differ from the Actinopterygii in the construction of their fins but they have differences in the bones of their skulls, in the structure of their scales and in the possession by the lung fishes of a sac opening from the oesophagus which is filled with air and which has a blood supply from the sixth branchial arch. From the possession of these characters and from the transitional forms which are present in the fossil record, it is believed that it was from the Crossopterygii that Amphibia and ultimately the rest of the tetrapods arose early in the Carboniferous geological period.

Amphibia

From the formation of the coal measures in certain places, we may suppose the Carboniferous to have been a time of very rich vegetation growing in swampy conditions. Such would impede the movement of swimming fishes and the decaying vegetation would deplete the water of dissolved oxygen so that air breathing would be advantageous. In such conditions the earliest Amphibia probably arose, but they were vastly different from the present-day forms. Large, clumsy and heavily plated with bones on the head region, like the fishes from which they sprang, the earliest Amphibia were probably unable to do more than crawl or wriggle through the swamps in which they were partly immersed and which therefore afforded them some support as the water does a fish according to the principle of Archimedes. Gradually their limbs and air breathing improved, their bony armour was reduced, and their sense organs better adapted to life in the air instead of the water. By the end of the Carboniferous period they had given rise to animals which would be classed as reptiles and the ancient amphibians were in decline. It is not possible to trace direct descent, by means of a continuous record in the rocks, to the present-day Amphibia since fossils resembling these appear only very much later. Consequently although it is probable that our modern amphibians are derived ultimately from Carboniferous ancestors, it is not possible to trace the steps by which this process has occurred and they must be regarded as very highly specialized representatives of what was once the basic tetrapod group. In addition to the frogs and toads (Anura), the present-day amphibians include the newts and salamanders (Urodela) and the Apoda, blind, limbless, burrowing creatures which retain small scales in the skin. While the newts and salamanders are generally restricted to damp habitats, the frogs and toads range more widely, some, like *Xenopus*, the South African Clawed Toad, being wholly aquatic, some being mainly tree dwelling as is *Hyla*, while others, particularly the toads of the genus *Bufo* and others nearly related, which are of wide distribution, are mainly terrestrial. Almost all the Amphibia are obliged to return to the water to deposit their eggs but some have evolved a means of avoiding this. Some salamanders, for instance, retain their few developing eggs in the oviduct and some frogs place them in their vocal sacs or a special dorsal pouch, while the midwife toad carries them in a frothy mass around the hind legs of the male.

Reptiles

The earliest reptiles in the fossil record are distinguished from their amphibian ancestors only with difficulty but *Seymouria* from the lower Permian period is usually regarded as a reptile. Compared

Fig. 17.3. Reptiles, birds and mammals.

A Sphenodon, a lizard-like reptile retaining primitive features similar to those of its Triassic ancestors; *B* a chameleon with opposable digits, prehensile tail and long eversible tongue used for catching insects; *C* a snake; *D Stegosaurus* and *E Triceratops*, two large Mesozoic dinosaurs; *F Archaeopteryx*, a reconstruction of the earliest fossil bird; *G* a pigeon; *H* the duck-billed Platypus of Australia; *I* an opossum from South America; *J* a kangaroo from Australia. (From specimens or based on various authors.)

(Not all to the same scale.)

with its Carboniferous ancestors it has limbs and girdles much better adapted to a terrestrial life, its skull was more pointed and the orbits directed laterally instead of dorsally. There were other points of advance but it is also true that it retained some characters of the Amphibia of the period, including traces of lateral line canals, a feature normally associated with a watery habitat.

There is no doubt, however, that in the three subsequent geological periods, the Triassic, Jurassic and Cretaceous, the reptiles became the dominant vertebrate group on the land and also invaded the seas. They evolved into animals of great variety of size and habits, of which only a pale reflection remains in the reptiles present in the world today. They also gave rise to two other main lines of evolution, those leading to the birds and to the mammals, but before we trace the evolution of these we must see something of the range of reptiles in their heyday.

The features of reptiles which distinguish them from Amphibia include the possession of a single occipital condyle to the skull, the development of scales from the epidermis alone (cf. fishes), and the formation of embryonic membranes (see p. 654), but the chief advances which they have made over the Amphibia are less structural than physiological. They have, that is to say, become more nearly independent of the environment by reducing water loss through the skin, by the male internally fertilizing the eggs, and by providing the egg with a shell and the developing embryo with membranes through which it can respire and in which its excretory products can be stored so as not to interfere with development. The improvements incorporated in the physiology of reptiles and their adaptability can be illustrated by referring to a few of the species which are known either as fossils or at the present time.

The tortoises are familiar to most people but their aquatic relations are less often seen, especially the large marine turtles which may be three feet or so long. Other aquatic reptiles are also found as fossils, the ichthyosaurs being shaped like a dolphin and having long jaws with sharp pointed teeth. Plesiosaurs were also aquatic but had much longer necks and smaller heads. Both ichthyosaurs and plesiosaurs had paddle-like limbs and many were large, some plesiosaurs reaching 50 ft. in length.

Present-day reptiles can mostly be traced back to the Cretaceous period, if not further, and include the famous Tuatara of New Zealand (*Sphenodon*) which has a functional pineal eye on the dorsal surface of the head, the lizards, the snakes and the crocodiles.

Lizards vary in size from large iguanas up to 6 ft. in length to the small species common in sandy places in the south of England. Others include the burrowing desert skinks (*Scincus*), the arboreal chameleons and the limbless, viviparous slow worms (*Anguis*) which can easily be mistaken for snakes.

The snakes have probably evolved from burrowing ancestors but are now chiefly found on the ground and in trees. Some kill prey by winding the body round it and crushing it, others by their poison-fangs, while many simply rely upon their sharp backwardly directed teeth to prevent the escape of their prey which they swallow whole. It may be of large size and can be swallowed because the lower jaw is connected to the cranium by a movable quadrate and the two halves of the lower jaw are joined together by an elastic ligament instead of a firm articulation. A few snakes are found in the sea.

The crocodiles are not closely related to the other present-day reptiles and are adapted for an aquatic life by a valve which enables the mouth to be opened under water without the lungs being filled. They are the largest living reptiles.

Related to the crocodiles by their skull structure are the extinct pterodactyls, large flying reptiles which possessed wings supported mainly by the greatly elongated fourth digit. They are believed mainly to have been marine, fish-eating species. Also related to the crocodiles are the dinosaurs, two groups of reptiles which formed the dominant fauna of the Jurassic and Cretaceous periods. One group includes the biggest land animals known: *Diplodocus* was over 80 ft. long and probably weighed nearly 50 tons. Not all were as large as this but they were generally of large size as land mammals go, and it was a small dinosaur that reached only 6 ft. in length. The other group were also of large size, although none was as large as *Diplodocus*. *Stegosaurus* had a series of immense spines on its back and *Triceratops* belonged to a group which developed long heads with horns and bony extensions. Altogether the dinosaurs were a fantastic collection of animals, mostly built on a massive scale but frequently possessing relatively small heads and even smaller brains, so that it cannot be believed that, despite their size, they displayed any great advance in the complexity or refinement of their behaviour.

One small group of Permian and Jurassic reptiles, smaller than many of their contemporaries, was destined to be the basis of the next evolutionary outburst, that of the mammals. These theriodonts approached the mammalian condition in such features as the differentiation of the teeth and the size and shape of the skull, and in the condition of the limbs and girdles. In the Jurassic and Cretaceous they were replaced by primitive mammals which evolved in the Tertiary into the main lines discernible today.

Birds

Lastly, the birds arose from the reptiles but their origin is scarcely recorded in fossils until the first bird appeared on the Jurassic scene. *Archaeopteryx* is clearly a bird with feathers and wings and is un-connected by intermediate fossils with its reptilian ancestors. Yet it preserves reptilian features such as the possession of teeth, a long tapering tail supported by many vertebrae and ribs attached to the abdominal vertebrae. Nor is it connected very clearly with the next fossil birds to appear in the Cretaceous. Although the series of changes leading to modern birds is not easily traced, their evolution into many habitats is of great zoological interest since the plan on which they are organized is very different from that of the other successful group of modern animals, the mammals.

Birds have frequently been described as 'glorified reptiles' and indeed there is some truth in this because, like the reptiles, their behaviour is almost entirely of the reflex and instinctive type. This fixity of the pattern of behaviour is in contrast to that of the highest mammals which behave in ways more liable to variation and better able to adapt to changing circumstances. The type of behaviour shown by birds is almost certainly correlated with their small brain and with the predominance in the fore-brain of the floor region or *corpus striatum* rather than the dorso-lateral or pallial regions. The other part of the brain which is noticeably enlarged is the cerebellum and this is no doubt correlated with the great prowess in balance and muscular co-ordination which birds possess. On the other hand, the parts of the brain concerned with olfaction are poorly developed, as are the nasal organs.

The reptilian affinities of birds are also shown by their egg-laying habit, and by the epidermal scales covering the legs which resemble the scales of reptiles. There is little doubt that the feathers, which are keratinous epidermal structures, were evolved from scales.

Although there is no doubt of the reptilian ancestry of birds, they are nevertheless very much in advance of any present-day reptiles in many respects. They maintain a high and constant body temperature and a very high rate of metabolism which makes demands on their supplies of food and oxygen. To meet these needs they spend a large part of their life feeding, the food being stored in a crop and passed a little at a time to a muscular gizzard where it is ground up ready for digestion. The respiratory organs of birds are particularly efficient and although the lungs are of small size, air is passed through them into air sacs which are very extensive, in some birds even penetrating within the bones. Air is circulated through the lungs not by their change of size in a way similar to that of mammals, but by the enlargement of the air sacs brought about when the sternum is lowered by the rib musculature.

Not only are the feathers of birds structures remarkable for their lightness, durability and the surface area they present, but the whole of the construction of the bird's skeleton uses the minimum amount of bone consistent with the strength required for the powerful breast muscles which move the wings. Flying at considerable speeds they need highly developed and efficient sense organs for alighting or for spotting prey, and in fact the eyes of certain birds have great acuity and adaptations to enable the bird to perceive small moving objects. In most birds the eyes are situated on the sides of the head so that the animal can see nearly all around it. In hawks and owls the eyes point more nearly forwards and have overlapping fields of view, but it is unlikely that birds have the same type of binocular vision as mammals. Hearing is usually acute in birds and in some owls which hunt by night is the means of finding the prey.

Birds can carry out sequences of behaviour of great complexity and behave differently at different seasons. Thus some, such as the swallow, pair in the early summer, build nests, incubate eggs, feed young, flock in the autumn and migrate, returning the next spring to repeat the same sequence of behaviour. The ability of these small frail creatures to travel enormous distances during their migrations and to return to the same locality is astounding.

Mammals

The culmination of animal types evolved from the reptiles is in the great class of mammals. Lines of reptile evolution leading to primitive mammals are discernible from the Permian period, but the earliest creatures which are recognized as true and certain mammals are found in the Jurassic. They possessed, for example, two sets of teeth and a single bone, the dentary, in each side of the lower jaw. The brain case was large, but of the soft parts of their anatomy nothing is known except what can be inferred from the bones and their foramina. Soon after their appearance they gave rise to a large number of different lines of evolution, which led to the very diverse mammals alive today. Some of these lines of evolution can be traced in great detail, that of the horse is a well-known example, while others such as man's ancestry can only be pieced together with great difficulty. When the mammals first appeared they were smaller than the run of their reptilian contemporaries and would be thought hardly able to compete with them, yet within a short space of time, geologically speaking, the reptiles had virtually vanished and the age of mammals was in being. No doubt climatic conditions had something to do with the drastic reduction of the reptiles and the rise of the mammals, although it is hard to believe climate was the only factor responsible. There is no doubt that the great advance made by the mammals is that towards independence of the external environment and control of the internal environment of the body. This can be seen chiefly in temperature control which has enabled mammals to live in such cold conditions as the arctic seas in which the metabolism of poikilotherms (cold-blooded animals) would be reduced to a very low level. Control of the temperature of the body is done chiefly by the control of heat loss which in turn necessitates good (and variable) heat insulation. The skin and its derivatives in mammals have become waterproof integuments of great physiological importance not only in heat control but also for protection, concealment and adornment.

The other features which are of the greatest importance in the life of mammals are highly developed sense organs and nervous system. The enlarged brain case was characteristic of mammalian fossils from the first and it has continued to increase in relative size as evolution proceeded.

The teeth of mammals have played an important part in their ability to flourish on different diets, and because teeth are hard and easily fossilized they have been important also in the study of evolution.

Among the groups of mammals which are in existence at the present time, the following may be mentioned.

PROTOTHERIA OR MONOTREMATA. The Duck-billed platypus and Echidna of Australasia are primitive mammals which retain the reptilian characteristic of laying eggs but also possess the diagnostic mammalian characters of hair and milk glands. The ducts of these simply open on the ventral surface of the female and not by a teat as in the higher mammals. Their temperature is more liable to fluctuations than that of higher mammals.

METATHERIA OR MARSUPIALIA, e.g. kangaroo, opossum, koala, wombat. These are pouched mammals of which the young are born after a short gestation and kept for a time in a ventral pouch attached to a teat of a mammary gland. These animals are found chiefly in Australia which, until discovered by Western man, had no fauna of higher or Eutherian mammals.

EUTHERIA. In the highest mammals the young are born in a more advanced stage after a prolonged period of gestation during which they are nourished via a placenta which provides a means of exchange of soluble materials between the blood stream of the mother and that of the offspring. They are divided into a number of orders which are listed below together with notes on the main features of each group.

1. *Insectivora.* Eutheria with pointed cusps on the pre-molar and molar teeth, feeding mainly on insects, e.g. *Talpa* (the mole), *Erinaceus* (the hedgehog), *Sorex* (the shrew).

2. *Carnivora.* Eutheria with cutting molar teeth feeding on a flesh diet, e.g. *Canis* (the dog), *Felis* (the cat), *Phoca* (the seal).

3. *Lagomorpha and Rodentia.* Eutheria with chisel-shaped incisor teeth with permanently growing roots separated from the transversely ridged molars by a space (diastema), e.g. *Rattus* (the rat), *Mus* (the mouse), *Oryctolagus* (the rabbit).

4. *Artiodactyla.* Ungulates (hoofed animals) with so-called cloven hoofs, i.e. they walk mainly on the tips of digits III and IV which are surrounded by keratinized 'hoofs'. They are herbivores and have grinding molars with blunt cusps on ridges parallel with the jaw bones. Canines and upper incisors often absent. The caecum is small and there is often present a complicated stomach correlated with the ruminant habit 'chewing the cud', e.g. *Bos* (cattle), *Ovis* (the sheep), *Cervus* (the deer), *Sus* (the pig), the hippopotamus, the camel, the goat.

5. *Perissodactyla.* Ungulates walking mainly on the tip of digit III. Though herbivorous they do not 'chew the cud'. The molars are grinding teeth with ridges usually transverse to the jaw bone. The stomach is simple but the caecum is enlarged for bacterial digestion of cellulose, e.g. *Equus* (the horse), rhinoceros, tapir.

6. *Proboscidea.* These resemble ungulates but their 'feet' skeletons are but little different from the basic pentadactyl type. They possess an elongated 'trunk' or proboscis, with the

Fig. 17.4. Eutherian mammals.

A a monkey, *Macaca* (Primates); *B* a rat, *Rattus* (Rodentia); *C* a cheetah, *Acinonyx* (Carnivora); *D* an impala, *Aepyceros* (Artiodactyla); *E* a rhinoceros, *Rhinoceros* (Perissodactyla); *F* a sperm whale, *Physeter* (Cetacea); *G* an elephant, *Loxodonta* (Proboscidea); *H* a bat, *Rhinolophus* (Chiroptera). (Based on specimens, photographs and various authors.)

(Not all to the same scale.)

nostrils at the tip, used as a prehensile organ. Their incisors are reduced in number to two in the upper jaw and these are elongated to form the 'tusks', consisting of dentine (ivory) with an enamel cap at the tip. The molars have transverse ridges whose pattern differs in the African elephant (*Loxodonta*) from that of the Indian elephant (*Elephas*).

7. *Hyracoidea.* A small group of burrowing mammals resembling rabbits but more like the ungulates than the rodents in their general structure, e.g. *Hyrax* (the coney).

8. *Cetacea.* Marine mammals approximating to fish in their external form. Their forelimbs are paddle-like, the hind ones being absent. The tail is flattened horizontally. Hairs are largely lacking and heat insulation is achieved by means of thick layers of fat (blubber) deposited in the dermis, e.g. *Balaena* (the baleen whale) whose upper jaws are provided with plates of fused hairs ('whalebone') to act as a sieve when feeding on small Crustacea in the plankton, dolphins and porpoises, both with simple teeth.

9. *Sirenia.* Marine mammals which, unlike the Cetacea, are herbivorous; now almost extinct, e.g. *Halicore* (the sea cow).

10. *Chiroptera.* Flying mammals (bats) whose forelimbs have elongated digits to form wings, the wing surface being formed of skin stretched between the digits. The molar teeth have pointed cusps, e.g. *Pteropus* (the bat).

11. *Primates.* These include the most advanced types of mammals. The brain is highly developed and the thumb is opposable. The teeth are not highly modified, the molars having blunt cusps.

Sub-order I. Prosimii—lemurs and tarsiers, arboreal with fox-like faces.

Sub-order II. Anthropoidea—eyes facing forwards to give stereoscopic vision. (a) Platyrrhina—New World monkeys. (b) Catarrhina—Old World monkeys, e.g. *Macaca* (rhesus monkey), Great Apes, e.g. *Pan* (chimpanzee), *Pongo* (orang-utan) and *Gorilla* (gorilla) and Hominidae (e.g. *Pithecanthropus* (Java man), *Homo neanderthalensis* (Neanderthal man) and *Homo sapiens* (all living races of man)).

III. THE WORKING OF THE ANIMAL BODY

18. *The Animal Cell*

IN THE preceding chapters we have surveyed the animal kingdom and have seen, by the study of representative or typical animals, something of the variety of animal life. We have seen how animals are constructed and have looked at the ways in which they work in a mechanical sense and at the ways in which they perform those bodily activities which are known as feeding, digestion, respiration, co-ordination, reproduction and so on. Here and there we have had the opportunity to look at the structure of animals on a larger scale, as it were, so that more of their details are revealed. Just as a model of the globe shows the continents and oceans, so does glancing at an animal enable one to say whether it is a mammal with four legs and fur or a bird with two legs and feathers. But only a very general idea of a continent can be gained from a globe just as only the main features of the animal can be grasped by looking at it with the naked eye. Larger maps of the countries are needed to show the details, just as dissection into smaller parts and careful tracing and mapping of the arteries and nerves, for instance, are needed to obtain a more thorough knowledge of an animal. Even the maps in an ordinary atlas are not enough to tell you much about the roads and footpaths, so a good 'ordnance survey' map is required. This can be compared with the view of an animal which you get by cutting it into sections and looking at them with a microscope. Some of the houses on the map are marked as conventional dots but nothing can be seen about the shapes of the gardens. So, under an ordinary microscope the cells are visible and some of their contents can be made out, but one cannot be quite sure about their shapes because the light waves are about the same size as the objects and yield only a conventional picture. But when the country is surveyed the first drawings are made on a very large scale (25 inches to the mile) and all the fences and the shapes of the buildings, the ditches and the roundabouts are put in and they are put in to scale. Likewise with the aid of the electron microscope a picture can be obtained of the cell magnified almost to the stage at which some of the individual large molecules can be located and identified. Thus a good deal can be learned about the

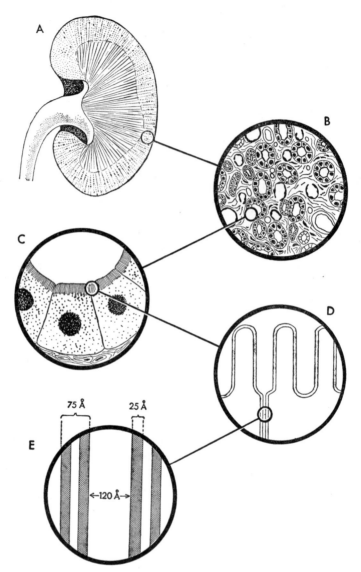

Fig. 18.1. Diagrams to illustrate degrees of magnification.

A horizontal section of a mammalian kidney; *B* portion of cortex
as seen under the low power of the light microscope; *C* renal tubule
cells as seen under the high power of the light microscope showing the
'brush borders' of the cells; *D* 'brush border' as seen in a low power
electron microscope photograph (an electron micrograph); *E* part of
same as seen in a high power electron micrograph.

structure of the cell and since that is now conceived in terms of molecules and since the movements of molecules make up what is usually called *function*, the differences between these two ways of studying living organisms, the structural and the functional, tend to disappear.

The simile can be extended a little further. Just as only a part of the world has been mapped on the 25 inch scale—the most populated and 'civilized' parts of it—so only very few cells or parts of animals have so far been examined under the electron microscope. We have therefore a very detailed picture of certain biologically important parts such as muscles, sperm and bacteria but a much less intimate knowledge about others. Historically the study of animals has proceeded from their general to their increasingly minute examination. From the accumulated knowledge the 'cell theory' was formulated during the middle of the nineteenth century. This generalization has been of the greatest importance and has led to the clear establishment of the idea that the cell is the basic unit of structure and that its workings have much in common in all living organisms. It is true that cells had been seen and recognized since the introduction of the compound microscope in the middle of the sixteenth century but it was the zoologist Schwann who first clearly stated that it is characteristic of all living things that they are composed of cells. Although there are a few exceptions to this statement, it has so nearly a universal application and has proved such a fruitful way of looking at living organisms that it, together with the idea of evolution and the idea that living things as we know them today arise only from other living things, have become the three major biological generalizations or laws.

The biologist is interested in cells because they are a constant feature of living organisms, because all the life processes are carried on in cells and by cells and because only by understanding the structure of the variety of cells which make up the animal and plant kingdom can the full range of activities of living matter be understood. In the next few chapters we shall examine the structure of cells in some detail and then study the way in which they are differentiated according to the main functions which they perform in the animal body; we shall look at the way in which they maintain themselves and the way in which they reproduce and increase in number and the method by which the characters of the whole organism (of which the cell is a part) is determined by the structure of the cell nucleus.

While no particular animal cell found in nature can be regarded as completely unspecialized and as presenting an ideal picture of what an animal cell should be, nevertheless it is possible to imagine such a cell. The concept of the generalized or ideal animal cell is useful because it is a summary of much that is known about the structure and function of cells and because an abstraction presents the essential features without the distractions which are brought in by adaptation to particular functions.

In the conventional description an animal cell is said to consist of protoplasm surrounded by a thin *cell membrane* or *plasma membrane*. The protoplasm is divisible into the *nucleus* and *cytoplasm*, the nucleus being bounded by the *nuclear membrane*. Filling the nuclear membrane is nuclear sap in which occur nucleo-proteins or chromatin material, so-called because it possesses an affinity for certain dyes. A *nucleolus*, which usually stains differently from the chromatin, is also found within the nuclear membrane. In the cytoplasm, are found various granules and vacuoles, rodlike bodies called *mitochondria*, a region distinguished by fatty globules termed the *Golgi body*, and near the nucleus a granule or granules, the *centrioles*, surrounded by a recognizable region known as the *centrosome*. This conventional description is illustrated by (Fig. 18.2).

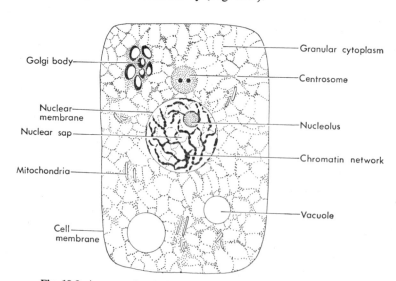

Fig. 18.2. A conventional diagram of the structure of an animal cell.

This is derived largely from stained permanent preparations but is 'idealized'. It should be compared with Figs. 18.4, 18.5 and 18.6.

There is evidence that the plasma membrane consists of lipoid or fatty material in which the molecules are arranged in two layers with their long axes at right-angles to the cell surface. (Molecules of fat spread out on water in a similar way. This spreading can be demonstrated by the well-known experiment with lycopodium powder sprinkled on the surface of water into the film of which a greasy needle is thrust.) The cell surface, when the cell is in water, has very little surface tension (not more than 1 to 3 dynes/cm. as compared

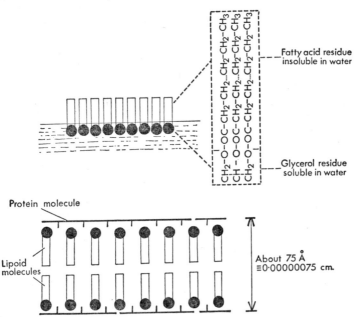

Fig. 18.3. Diagram to illustrate the arrangement of fat molecules on the surface of water (above) and their possible arrangement in the cell membrane (below).

Note that the known dimensions of these molecules agree with the thickness of the cell membrane as measured in the electron microscope (see Fig. 18.1.)

with the 70 dynes/cm. for an air-water interface), but what little strength it has is thought to be given chiefly by the protein molecules arranged to lie on the inner and outer surfaces of the fatty layer. Like the cell membrane, the nuclear membrane is thought to contain fatty material arranged in a similar way (Fig. 18.3).

Outside the nuclear membrane lies the cytoplasm, which can be described as an aqueous crystalloid and colloidal solution of a very large number of different chemical substances. In physical properties it can be shown to have a viscosity only about four times greater than that of water, yet it has a certain amount of cohesion and does not behave quite like a free-flowing or Newtonian liquid when the cell surface membrane is punctured. These properties are conferred on it by its content of large organic molecules, chiefly protein, for its content of inorganic ions is insufficient materially to affect such physical properties as the viscosity, surface tension or density of the water in which they are dissolved and which forms the greatest single constituent of the cytoplasm. It will be seen below that this conception is far too simple and the cytoplasm has a complex structure.

The chief inorganic constituents are the cations sodium, potassium, calcium and magnesium and the anions chloride, phosphate and bicarbonate, the proportions of which differ in different cells. Smaller quantities of other substances are also present. The chief organic constituents of cytoplasm are proteins of various types which can be regarded as soluble or, at least, as forming colloidal solutions. There are also present lipoids and carbohydrates. The proteins consist of long chains of amino-acid molecules which are linked together mostly by the peptide linkage —NH—CO— (see protein structure, page 480). Some are thought to be coiled to form large globular molecules with which are associated, and which bind to themselves, very many molecules of water. Others are thought of as long and thin and interlocking to some extent to give what little rigidity the protoplasm possesses. These protein molecules include enzymes which are responsible for altering the rate at which various chemical changes take place in the cell. Not all the proteins are polymer chains formed solely from amino-acids but are proteins coupled with other substances such as sugars. Of the lipoid materials present, none is soluble in water so that they are distributed as very fine droplets or films in the cell. Some are simple fats, others fats with the addition of phosphoric acid and an organic base. The carbohydrates which are found in the cell may be mono- or disaccharide sugars or polysaccharides. Some sugar molecules are linked with protein or are included in the structure of nucleic acids.

This basic knowledge of the chemical constituents which have been found and identified in recently killed cells of one sort or another does not go far to explain the way in which living cells maintain their organized state or the way in which they synthesize from the simpler substances which they receive as food the complicated molecules which they contain. It is not possible to do this at present but a hint of the way in which the cell is capable of bringing about this is given by new knowledge of the structure of the special proteins—the nucleo-proteins—which form the stainable and at the same time the most important constituent of the nucleus. Nucleo-protein, which is found mainly, but not exclusively, within the nucleus, is the material of which the chromosomes (see below) are largely composed and which appears to be associated with the synthesis of both more nucleo-protein at cell division, and ordinary cytoplasmic protein.

Not only is this role of the nucleo-protein in the normal cell so very important but the intracellular virus particles, such as those which give rise to the mosaic disease of tobacco and to influenza, are essentially of the same chemical nature and are self-synthesizing or self-perpetuating when they are contained within the living cell. Nucleo-proteins thus appear to take part in the formation of proteins from amino-acids possibly by acting as a template on which they may be fitted together.

Contained within the cytoplasm are four other types of structure which are important in the life of the cell. They are the Golgi bodies and centrosomes, the mitochondria and the *microsomes* or small cell granules. The Golgi bodies (or Golgi apparatus) form a recognizable part of the cytoplasm, particularly noticeable in secretory cells, which has a concentration of fatty or lipoid material and represents a more dense region of the cytoplasm. Frequently vacuoles which take up the vital dye neutral red can be seen in the living cell in the position occupied by the Golgi apparatus. From its prominence in secretory cells and from the change of size which it appears to undergo as the cycle of elaboration and secretion of the cell is carried on, it is thought that it provides a region where special products of the cell are collected.

Associated with the Golgi body is a small distinct region the centrosome, in which a dense darkly staining granule or granules, the centrioles, can be seen. Before cell division this divides or the two separate and form the centres of the *mitotic asters* (see below).

Mitochondria (singular, mitochondrion) are granules or filaments seen in all cells and which, in life, can move from place to place and can also undergo a wriggling motion. They have been isolated by centrifuging and have been shown to contain many different chemical substances, chief among which are lipoids and proteins. They have also been shown to respire and to possess many of the enzymes which are important in cell respiration.

Microsomes are submicroscopic particles present in the cytoplasm which contain nucleo-protein and which may act as a store of this material. The conventional picture (Fig. 18.3) should be compared with a diagram of the cell as seen in life (Fig. 18.4). Here the centrosome is invisible, the mitochondria can only occasionally be seen, the Golgi apparatus is only visible as traces in certain types of cell and, of course, none of the structure of the cytoplasmic proteins is visible because it lies beyond the resolving power of the light microscope. The nucleus appears as a fluid-filled vesicle in which parts of the chromosomes and the nucleolus can be seen. It is believed that the parts of the chromosomes which are seen in life are the genetically inert parts.

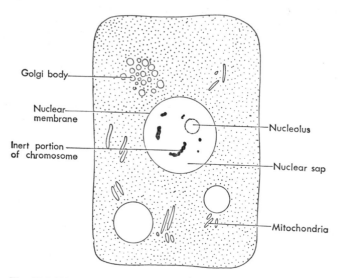

Fig. 18.4. Diagram to illustrate the structure of the cell as it may be seen in life.

In the cell which has been fixed and stained afterwards, for example by haematoxylin, the mitochondria have disappeared, as have all traces of the Golgi apparatus, but the centriole is visible. The proteins of the cytoplasm and the nucleus have been precipitated and the irregular lumps into which those of the nucleus have been thrown have stained strongly with basic dyes (Fig. 18.5). The texture, which is shown thus in the nucleus and also in the cytoplasm and which is frequently referred to as 'granular' or 'finely granular', bears little, if any, relation to the structure of the nucleus and cytoplasm during life. The picture of an animal cell which results from modern work differs from the cell as it has just been described in a

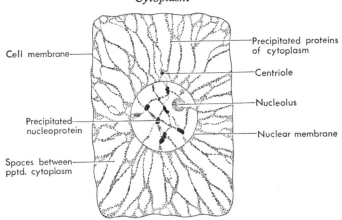

Fig. 18.5. Diagram to illustrate the structure of the cell as normally seen in fixed and stained preparations.

number of ways, and is illustrated in Fig. 18.6 which is based on the results obtained with the electron microscope and various other methods of investigation whose description is beyond the scope of this book. The results, however, are readily comprehensible.

The cell membrane dips down into the cytoplasm in places and forms a complex folded structure known as the endoplasmic reticulum, the walls of which are associated with small granules, or the microsomes (or *ribosomes*), made of a nucleic acid (RNA). It is believed that some cells can take in minute droplets in an amoeboid fashion—a process known as *pinocytosis*. This is illustrated in Fig. 18.6. The nuclear membrane can be shown to be a double structure which is perforated by small pores. A differentiated region inside the nuclear membrane can be recognized as the nucleolus but the chromosomes cannot be recognized in the non-dividing nucleus. The mitochondria consist of inner and outer layers, the outer one being smooth while the inner one is thrown into folds or ridges known as cristae which partially divide the interior of the body. The centrioles are seen to be two in number, each consisting of a short bunch of nine rod-like structures. The structure revealed by the electron microscope which has just been described and illustrated is of a more complex nature than that previously thought to exist. Nevertheless the revelation of such complex structure does help to explain how so very many complex chemical processes can all go on at the same time in such a small compartment as is the cell. For example, it can be shown that the enzyme systems which take

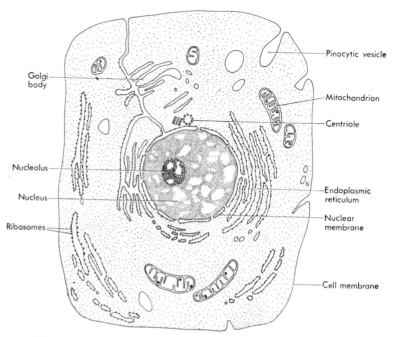

Golgi body

Nucleolus

Nucleus

Ribosomes

Pinocytic vesicle

Mitochondrion

Centriole

Endoplasmic reticulum

Nuclear membrane

Cell membrane

Fig. 18.6. Diagram illustrating details of the structure of the cell as derived from electron microscope studies.

Notice particularly the clearly defined endoplasmic reticulum and mitochondria but the absence of structures in the nucleus corresponding to chromosomes. (Based on *Brachet*.)

part in respiration are mainly located in the mitochondria, and the nucleo-proteins which are the transmitters of hereditary characters are located mainly in the nucleus.

Needless to say, the generalized animal cell which has just been discussed is not met in the animal kingdom in the form in which it has been described. All cells are specialized to some extent and are adapted in a structural way to the performance of the function or functions which, in them, is better developed than are other functions. The way in which the various types of cell are correlated with the special function which each performs will be described in the chapters on histology, where it will be seen how cells differ in the nature of the cytoplasmic inclusions, secreted matrix and other details of construction.

As we have seen, in the cell which is not dividing the nucleo-protein (or ' chromatin ' as it used to be called because of its affinity for stains) is not present in any clearly recognizable shape, but in the cell which is fixed during division the nucleo-protein has for a long time been known to appear in definite units, the *chromosomes*, which undergo a cycle of changes common to all animal and plant cells. This cycle of changes which precedes the division of the cell into two daughter cells is known as *mitosis*. Although it is a continuous process it can be divided, for convenience, into four phases which will be mentioned in the following description of the events (Fig. 18.7).

When mitosis begins the centrioles double and the chromosomes appear as long thin intertwining threads (B) which gradually shorten (C) by the coiling of the thin threads into a tight spiral (D). The phase of mitosis in which the chromosomes are long thin threads was at one time known as the ' spireme stage ' but is now usually called a part of the *prophase*. At times during the prophase it can sometimes be seen that each chromosome consists of two strands, or *chromatids*, lying side by side. Somewhere along the length of the chromosome, or pair of chromatids, is a genetically inert region or *centromere* where the separation of the two chromatids begins later in mitosis. Usually, too, an animal cell contains pairs of like or homologous chromosomes, one member of each pair derived from the paternal and the other from the maternal parent.

The chromosomes become apparent during prophase, floating in the nuclear sap within the nuclear membrane, but towards the end of prophase the nuclear membrane breaks down and the nuclear sap comes into contact with the cytoplasm when it appears to become gelated or transformed into a fibrous structure in which the fibres form a spindle-shaped body at the apices of which are the paired centrioles derived by the multiplication of the pair in the resting cell (E). The *spindle fibres*, which appear to have some elasticity and not to be a mere artifact of fixation, attach themselves to the centromeres of the chromosomes which become arranged around the equator of the spindle. This phase in mitosis constitutes *metaphase* (F).

The centromere of each chromosome then divides, and the spindle fibres by their contraction pull the chromatids of each chromosome to opposite poles of the spindle (G). This part of the mitotic cycle is usually called *anaphase*.

As the chromatids are being separated (H) the division of the cytoplasm begins at the cell wall and passes inwardly to cut the now degenerating spindle (I) in two. When the chromatids have

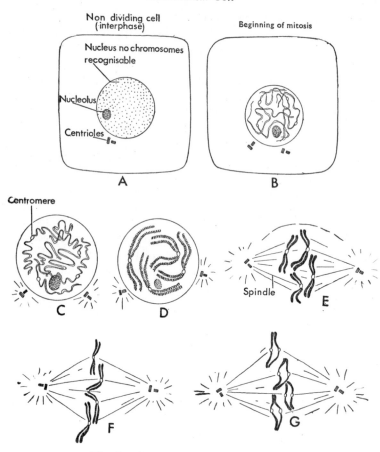

Fig. 18.7. (For caption see opposite page.)

aggregated near the remaining apices of the spindle, nuclear membranes are re-formed around them (J) and the identity of the chromatids is lost as they take up again the structure of the non-dividing nucleus (K). This is believed to involve an uncoiling of the tightly coiled spiral of nucleo-protein which constitutes the chromosome. This portion of the mitotic cycle is termed *telophase*.

Observation of the resting cell nucleus reveals very little of the complexity which appears during mitosis, when the opportunity occurs for examination of the structure of the chromosome. Then it can be seen that the chromosome is composed of zones or bands arranged lengthwise and capable of being identified as structural entities in all nuclear division of any one species of animals. Also in

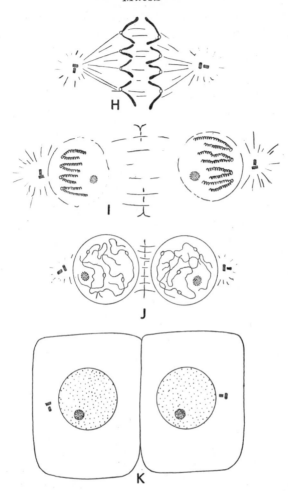

Fig. 18.7. Diagrams illustrating cell division or mitosis. (For explanation see text.)

A Interphase; *B, C, D* and *E* Prophase; *F* Metaphase; *G, H* and *I* Anaphase; *J* and *K* Telophase.

certain flies the salivary gland cell nuclei have enormously enlarged chromosomes which do not disappear as organized structures between cell divisions. So constant is the appearance of the microscopic structure of the chromosomes, and so qualitatively important do the chromosomes appear to be, that it was thought that the bands arranged in a string along the chromosome must correspond in some way to the *genes*, or character-bearing hereditary particles which the geneticist postulates. From a comparison of the arrangement of the bands and a map constructed from the frequency with which characters 'cross over' (see page 679), it is now clear that the bands of the chromosomes are, in fact, the genes of the geneticist.

They are also the specks of nucleo-protein of the cytologist but how it is possible for the nucleo-protein to act as a 'carrier' of a character which is made clear only during the development of the animal from the egg is uncertain, although suggestions have now been put forward. A great deal of work has recently been performed on the chemistry of the nucleus and on the changes which can be seen during cell division. It suggests that the chemical events are related to the visible events in roughly the following manner.

The chromosomes consist basically of a protein fibre which retains its integrity in both the dividing and the resting nucleus. In the resting nucleus it is uncoiled and has no outer sheath of attached nucleic acid molecules. During cell division the protein fibre first becomes coiled into a tight spiral after the attachment to it of molecules of nucleic acid. During anaphase and telophase it loses this layer of nucleic acid and becomes uncoiled. Accompanying these changes of the chromosomes are changes of one or more nucleoli. In the resting nucleus these contain nucleotides or nucleic acid which is transferred during prophase to the persistent protein fibre and so the nucleolus disappears. During the reconstitution of the resting nucleus the nucleic acid is transferred back to the nucleolus which reappears.

This story is a simplified version of the chemical events, one of the simplifications which has been made being the use of the term 'nucleic acid'. There are, in fact, two main types of nucleic acid which differ chiefly in the type of pentose sugar which forms part of the molecule and in one of the four organic bases present. In the type which forms the outer sheath of the chromosomes and which stains strongly with Feulgen's stain the sugar is of the type known as deoxyribose. In the type of nucleic acid which is stored in the nucleolus and also occurs in the cytoplasm the sugar is a ribose. These two sugars are denoted by the structural formulae below.

deoxyribose   ribose

In the formation of nucleo-proteins these pentose or five carbon sugars are associated with a molecule of phosphoric acid and a molecule of an organic base. This compound, of three entirely different types of molecule, is called a *nucleotide*. The two types of pentose sugar form two different nucleotides, a ribose nucleotide and a deoxyribose nucleotide. Nucleic acid is formed by the joining together of many molecules of the nucleotides, or as it is usually known, the polymerization of the nucleotides. There are thus two kinds of nucleic acid, ribose nucleic acid (or RNA for short) and deoxyribose nucleic acid (or DNA). RNA is the type of nucleic acid which is found in the nucleolus and in the cytoplasm while DNA is the type of nucleic acid which is associated with protein to form the chromosomes and is only found within the nucleus.

The organic bases which are commonly found in deoxyribose nucleic acids (DNA) are four in number—adenine, guanine, thymine and cytosine. Uracil replaces thymine in ribose nucleic acids (RNA). Their structural formulae are given below. They are joined to the sugar part of the nucleotide molecule at the opposite end, as it were, to the phosphoric acid so that when the nucleotides are linked together by the phosphoric acid groups the bases project from the chain structure so formed. The DNA molecule is now thought of as consisting of two chains of nucleotide molecules lying side by side and linked by pairs of organic bases. The whole compound structure does not lie straight but is twisted into a helical spiral (Fig. 18.8).

It was first thought that only the protein molecule of the nucleo-protein could provide sufficient variation in chemical structure to be a molecular basis for the transmission of heritable characters. It was known that the proteins of even closely related animal species, and indeed races, are slightly different from one another whereas the nucleic acids seemed to have much more in common between those derived from various organisms but it has now been shown, chiefly from work on bacteria and their parasitic viruses or *bacteriophages*, that it is probable that DNA is the active agent in the transmission of heritable characters. Moreover, the helical arrangement of the DNA molecules provides them with: (a) a built-in structural method by which they can reproduce themselves exactly, and (b) a sufficient amount of variety of their structural arrangement to account for the number of heritable characters which they are believed to transmit. This variability of the DNA molecules is believed to reside in the order along the chain in which the organic bases are arranged. With only four bases and with a chain of only 100 molecules of nucleotide

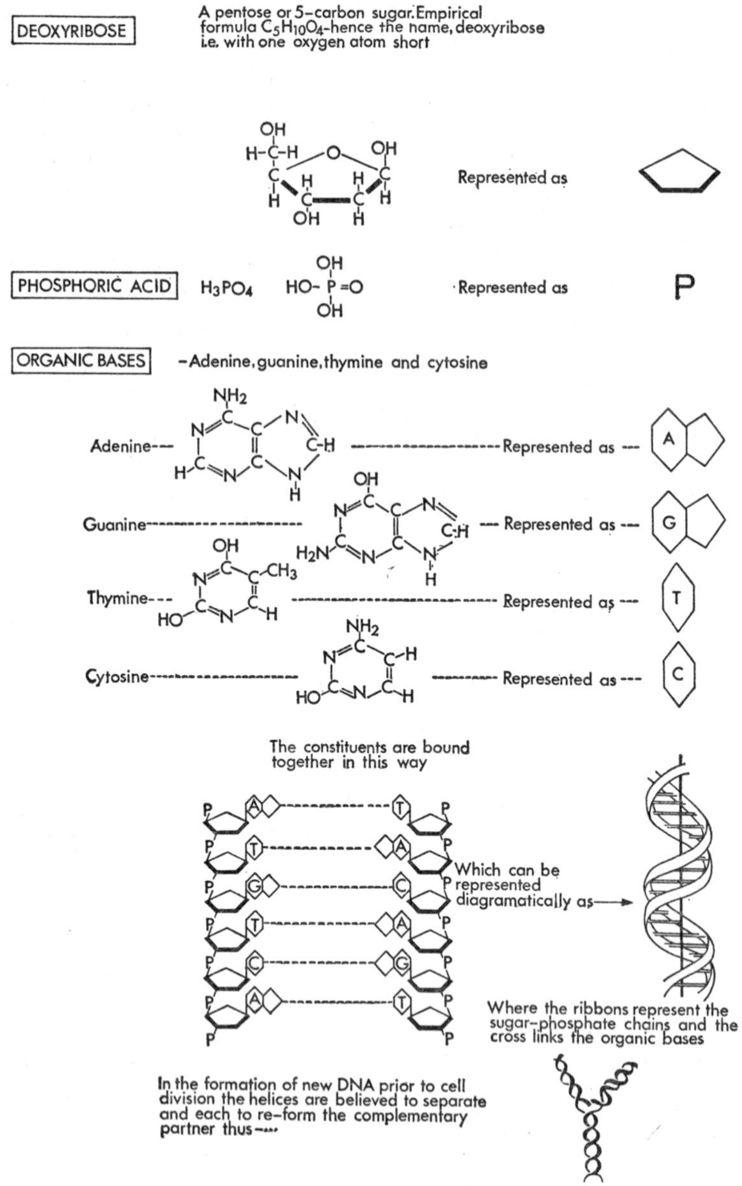

DEOXYRIBOSE A pentose or 5-carbon sugar. Empirical formula $C_5H_{10}O_4$-hence the name, deoxyribose i.e. with one oxygen atom short

Represented as

PHOSPHORIC ACID H_3PO_4 Represented as P

ORGANIC BASES -Adenine, guanine, thymine and cytosine

Adenine-- -----------Represented as --- A

Guanine---------------------- -- Represented as -- G

Thymine--- --------------------- Represented as --- T

Cytosine------------------ ------- Represented as --- C

The constituents are bound together in this way

Which can be represented diagramatically as→

Where the ribbons represent the sugar-phosphate chains and the cross links the organic bases

In the formation of new DNA prior to cell division the helices are believed to separate and each to re-form the complementary partner thus—

Fig. 18.8. Diagram illustrating the constitution of deoxyribonucleic acid (DNA).

there are 4^{100} ways in which the bases could be arranged! It is now known that DNA is among the chief agents of protein synthesis and that the sequence of organic bases in the DNA chain controls the type of protein produced as each amino-acid can only be fitted into a particular grouping of organic bases. Since enzymes are proteins and since their synthesis is determined by DNA and since, also, they are known to affect 'characters' during development, the chemical connexion between 'genes' and the characters which they represent is being elucidated. (See also pp. 663–4.)

The process of ordinary cell division or mitosis is the way in which animal cells divide unless they are destined soon to form gametes. In gametocytes (see page 611) another type of cell division occurs which differs from mitosis in that the chromosome number of the daughter cells is half that of the parent cells. This type of cell division is known as *meiosis* and takes place in the following manner (Fig. 18.9).

The chromosomes appear first in the nucleus which is about to divide as long thin strands (A). Each strand is single, and thereby differs from the chromosomes when they first appear in the mitotic nucleus where they early show a longitudinal split into chromatids. After a time the chromosomes associate in pairs (B), each pair of homologous chromosomes being made up of one derived from the paternal and one from the maternal parent. These pairs of homologous chromosomes associate so that the gene positions of one corresponds with the same gene positions of its fellow. This pairing process begins at the centromeres and the ends of the threads, or sometimes at one place or sometimes at the other, and proceeds along the length of the chromosomes like the fastening of a 'zipper' (C). Soon after this each chromosome of the associated pair divides lengthwise into two chromatids so that there are now four chromatids lying side by side (D). These become associated with one another in such a way that their original continuity along the length of the fibre is broken and during their association parts of one derived from one of the original members of the pair of chromosomes are exchanged for parts of the other (E). These points of breakage and rejoining are termed *chiasmata* (singular, chiasma) but are not shown in the simplified diagram, Fig. 18.9. The process of exchange of parts of homologous chromosomes explains the genetical behaviour of characters which are often associated or *linked* because their genes occur on one chromosome but which may become dissociated from

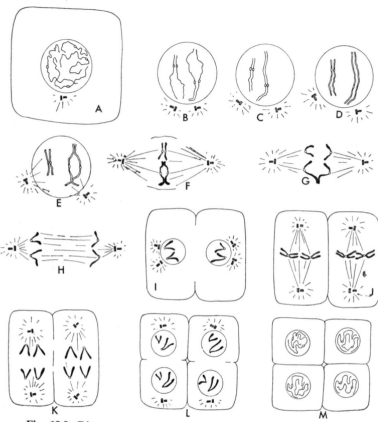

Fig. 18.9. Diagram illustrating reduction division or meiosis. (For explanation see text.)

A–E prophase; *F* metaphase; *G* and *H* first anaphase; *I* first telophase; *J* second metaphase; *K* second anaphase; *L* and *M* second telophase.

or *cross over* with one another when the chromosome continuity is broken (see page 679).

After the appearance of the chromatids and their exchange of fragments, the chromosome pairs shorten (F) and arrange themselves on the equator of a spindle in a manner comparable to that of mitosis. Their behaviour differs in that the short pairs of homologous chromosomes (or *bivalents*) are now separated so that the one *chromosome* (consisting of two side-by-side chromatids) passes towards one aster and the other *chromosome* passes to the other (G and H). At the end of the first part of the meiotic division each nucleus of the daughter cells (*primary gametocytes*) contains half the ordinary somatic number of chromosomes (I).

The second part of the meiotic division is like mitosis in that these already longitudinally divided chromosomes arrange themselves on the equator of a second spindle (J). This occurs without the resting nucleus having been reconstituted meanwhile, although a nuclear membrane may have formed temporarily. The chromatids of the chromosomes which, unlike those at mitosis, are widely separated along most of their length, are pulled apart (K) and the nuclei reconstituted as at mitosis (L). The result of this set of changes is the formation of four cells (M) each of which contains a half set of chromosomes, a condition which is spoken of as *haploid* in comparison with the ordinary somatic *diploid* condition.

The study of the changes undergone by the chromosomes during cell division and particularly during the special cell division of meiosis is one of great complexity and is of interest chiefly from the genetical point of view. Further reference to the subject will be found in the chapter on genetics (Chapter 35).

19. *The Structure of Tissues*

THE 'GENERALIZED' type of animal cell (page 422) does not occur to any extent in the body (soma) of an adult metazoan animal, though the oocyte and the cells of the early embryonic stages are of this nature. In the later stages of development of the embryo, differentiation of cell structure appears in different parts of the body and this is correlated with specialization in function, resulting in the division of labour which exists among the various parts of the body. The adult body thus becomes a composite structure made up of certain tissues and organs. *Tissues* consist of groups of cells and include in some cases material formed by the cells in which they lie embedded (e.g., cartilage), the cells of one particular tissue all being similar in structure and function but different from those of other tissues. Examples of tissues are: (1) epithelial tissue, (2) connective tissue, (3) muscular tissue, (4) nervous tissue.

Organs are those parts of the body which perform specific, though possibly complex, activities and are built up of a number of types of tissue in each case, e.g. the eye, in which are incorporated all the above examples of tissues and whose function is the formation of visual images, photo-reception and the transmission of resulting nervous impulses to the brain. The study of the cells, tissues and organs is known as *Histology*. In the following sections of this chapter, the examples will be drawn mainly from vertebrate sources.

Epithelial tissue

An epithelium is a cellular layer forming a bounding surface either externally or internally, e.g. the skin or the internal lining of the heart. Epithelia which form a lining to an internal cavity of the body not connected with the exterior are often known as *endothelia*.

Epithelia for the purposes of study may be classified according to either their structure or their function.

STRUCTURAL TYPES OF EPITHELIA

A—Simple (one cell in thickness)
B—Compound (several cells in thickness)

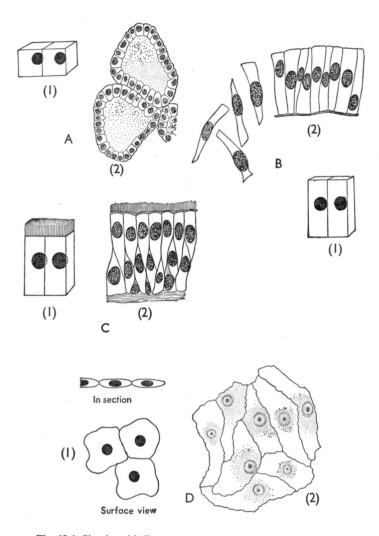

Fig. 19.1. Simple epithelia.

A (1) Cubical epithelium, (2) cubical epithelium of the vesicles of the thyroid gland.

B (1) Columnar epithelium, (2) columnar epithelium of the small intestine with a few of the cells separated.

C (1) Ciliated epithelium, (2) ciliated epithelium of the lining of the trachea.

D (1) Squamous epithelium, (2) squamous epithelium of the peritoneum of the frog.

Simple epithelia

CUBICAL EPITHELIA. The cells of these are isodiametric (i.e. cubical in shape). As are all epithelial cells, they are cemented together by a thin intercellular layer of so-called ground substance which reduces silver nitrate when exposed to light so that in a preparation treated with a 1% solution of this salt followed by rinsing in distilled water and by exposure to sunlight for 15 minutes, the cells, under the microscope, appear outlined in black. (This can be most easily seen by removing a kidney of a frog together with the peritoneum attached to its outer border and treating it as described.) Cubical epithelium is found in the vesicles of the thyroid gland (page 600), in the walls of the ducts of certain glands (e.g. the salivary glands) and forming the germinal epithelium of the ovary (page 475).

COLUMNAR EPITHELIA. The cells of these are brick-shaped with their long axes set at right-angles to the surface. The entire lining of the alimentary canal (except for the oesophagus and for those regions formed from the stomodaeum and proctodaeum, i.e. the linings of the buccal cavity and of the anus) and of its associated glands consists of this type of cell. Those of the villi of the small intestine have an outer striated border. The ectoderms of the invertebrates are also composed of columnar epithelia.

CILIATED EPITHELIA. In these, the cells are columnar but possess cilia on their outer border. They are found in the linings of the trachea and larynx and of the larger bronchial tubes in the lungs, and in the lining of the upper nasal passages and of the Fallopian tubes and vasa efferentia in the mammals. The roof of the buccal cavity of the frog and the surfaces of the gills of bivalve molluscs and of the gill bars of *Amphioxus* are other examples where this type of epithelium occurs.

SQUAMOUS (PAVEMENT) EPITHELIA. These consist of greatly flattened cells cemented together to form a single layer which under the microscope has a crazy-pavement appearance. In the vertebrates, they occur in the lining (peritoneum) of the abdominal cavities and of the heart and blood vessels. The capillary walls consist solely of pavement epithelium, as do also the walls of the alveoli of the lungs of the air-breathing vertebrates.

Compound (Stratified) epithelia

In these, there occurs an inner layer of cells known as the Malpighian layer, the cells of which constantly divide. The products of their division move outwards and eventually reach the surface where they are shed. Formed from the ectoderm of the vertebrates, these epithelia occur at the external surfaces of the body, associated with structures such as scales, feathers and claws and of nails, hair and sweat glands (in the mammals only), all of which have been formed by them. The enamel of the teeth is also the product of the cells of the Malpighian layer. The linings of the buccal cavity and of the anus, of the external ear tubes, and of the outer ends of the genital passages, are composed of compound epithelia owing to their formation as inturnings of the ectoderm.

The skin of the mammals merits special description owing to its complex nature and the variety of functions which it performs. These consist of: (1) protection of the surface of the body against 'wear and tear' by friction with external bodies, (2) reduction of loss of water by evaporation from the surfaces exposed to the drying action of the air, (3) temperature regulation, (4) excretion, (5) reception of certain sensory stimuli, e.g. touch, heat and cold, (6) protection against the injurious effects of ultra-violet light, (7) exclusion of germs.

The skin consists of two definite layers: the epidermis (the epithelium proper) formed from the ectoderm of the embryo, and the underlying dermis derived from the mesoderm. The dermis is composed of areolar connective tissue (see page 448) connecting the epidermis to underlying structures such as the muscles and in which are embedded hair follicles (hair roots) with their muscles (arrector pili muscles), sweat glands, blood vessels, nerves and fat deposits. The epidermis is divided into two main layers: the innermost layer of living and dividing cells being known as the Malpighian layer, and the outermost, which is composed of dead scales composed of a scleroprotein called *keratin*, forming the horny scarf skin (*stratum corneum*). Between these two layers are the *stratum granulosum* and the *stratum lucidum*. As the cells of the Malpighian layer divide, cells produced by their division pass outwards and on reaching the level of the stratum granulosum develop a granulated appearance due to the formation in them of drops of eleidin. After passing through the stratum lucidum the cells become the dead horny scales which on reaching the surface become detached or worn away by friction. The horny layer is thicker in those regions most subject to friction, as in the soles of the feet. The function of the horny layer is to prevent loss of water from the surface of the body, to prevent the entry of bacteria and to shield the body from abrasion, which latter function it performs by being renewed from beneath as it is worn away at the

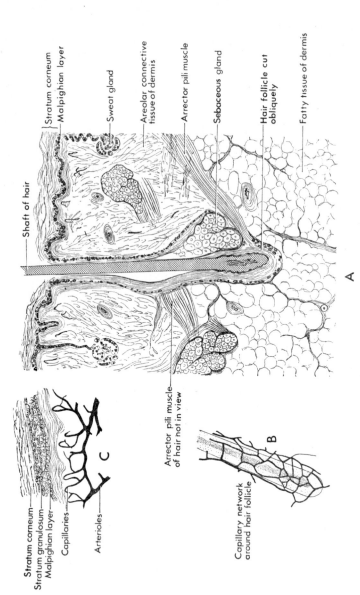

Shaft of hair

Stratum corneum
Malpighian layer

Sweat gland

Areolar connective
tissue of dermis

Arrector pili muscle

Sebaceous gland

Hair follicle cut
obliquely

Fatty tissue of dermis

A

Arrector pili muscle
of hair not in view

B

Capillary network
around hair follicle

C

Stratum corneum
Stratum granulosum
Malpighian layer
Capillaries
Arterioles

Fig. 19.2.

A Transverse section of the hairy skin of a mammal. *B* Hair follicle with surrounding capillary network. *C* Outer region of skin enlarged. (Drawn from a stained preparation.)

surface. It also protects the sensory nerve endings in the skin from excessive stimulation.

The structures associated with the epidermis are: the hairs, nails and claws, sebaceous and sweat glands.

HAIRS. These are formed in hair follicles (hair roots) which are in-turnings of the epidermis into the dermis. At the root of each follicle is a group of cells continuous with the Malpighian layer forming a sheath surrounding a papilla derived from the dermis. The division of these cells contributes to the growth of the hair. As the cell products of their division pass upwards they are converted into the keratinized elements of which the hair is composed. The papilla contains capillaries and nerve fibres and on one side the follicle is connected by a strand of unstriped muscle fibres to the underside of the Malpighian layer of the epidermis. Since the follicle is inclined to the surface, contraction of this muscle strand (the arrector pili muscle) erects the hair—an action which is best seen in a stiff-haired animal like the cat. In human beings contraction of these muscles produced by sympathetic nervous stimulation produces 'goose flesh'. The main function of the hairs is to form a heat-conserving layer above the skin. The stagnant air entangled among the hairs being a poor heat conductor. The thicker the covering of hair, the better does it serve this purpose, and the erection of the hairs when the body is becoming chilled is an additional aid. (In the animals of the cat tribe, erection of the hairs is also an expression of disturbed emotions such as fear or anger.) Many mammals grow thicker coats of hair during the colder parts of the year and shed much of the fur on the approach of summer. Also formed on one side of the hair follicle from the Malpighian layer is a sacculate gland (page 446) called a sebaceous gland whose secretion (*sebum*) forms a waxy coating to the hair which may assist the hair to resist wetting by rain.

The colouring of the hairs is often connected with camouflage, e.g. the agouti colour of the wild rabbit, the striping of the zebra and of the tiger, and the white winter coat of the stoat. Hairs there-fore may form a protection against discovery by enemies or serve to conceal a predator from its prey. Nails and claws are formed from the horny layer (stratum corneum) as are also the external coverings of the horns of ungulates (sheep, cattle, etc.).

SWEAT GLANDS. These are widely distributed in the human skin but in other mammals are often restricted to certain areas, e.g., in the dog they occur between the toes only. Sweat glands are simple tubular glands (page 446) formed by downgrowths of the Malpighian layer into the region of the dermis. Their inner ends are coiled and each is associated with blood capillaries and sympathetic nerve fibres. From the blood flowing in these, the sweat glands extract water together with salts (principally sodium chloride) and a little urea. The water containing these substances in solution is secreted and passes via the ducts to the surface of the skin where the water evaporates, absorbing latent heat of evaporation and thus cooling the body. Excessive sweating causes so much loss of sodium chloride that muscular pains result (miner's bends). Hence workers such as mine workers who sweat excessively need to drink water to which a little salt has been added. The activity of the sweat glands is under the control of temperature-regulating centres in the central nervous system. These are stimulated by changes in temperature in the blood and from them nervous impulses are transmitted to the sweat glands via the sympathetic nervous system. The amount of sweat produced is thus varied with the needs of the body at any particular time in order to assist in keeping the temperature of the body constant. *Insensible* sweating occurs when the sweat evaporates as soon as it reaches the surface but when in hot weather or as the result of much muscular exercise the amount of sweat produced is too copious for immediate evaporation to occur, then it accumulates, wetting the surface of the skin and of the hairs. Such a degree of sweating is called *sensible* sweating. Accompanying this is a reddening of the skin due to dilatation of the blood vessels in the dermis in order to produce a greater flow of blood through them with a resulting increased loss of heat brought by the blood to the skin from the deeper lying organs of the body where the heat is produced. This dilatation of the blood vessels is also the result of sympathetic nervous action originating in the temperature regulating centre in the hypothalamus of the brain. Conversely, when heat loss needs to be restricted, not only does the activity of the sweat glands become diminished but the walls of the blood vessels which contain circular, unstriped muscle fibres (page 458) constrict, thus lessening the rate of flow of blood through them and reducing heat loss.

The nerve fibres of the skin have various types of endings. A few penetrate into the Malpighian layer while others terminate in the bases of the sweat glands and of the hair follicles or end in special sense organs, e.g., the Pacinian corpuscles.

Beneath the epidermis in the Amphibia and in a number of other vertebrates, e.g., the reptile known as the chamaeleon, occurs a layer of melanophores. These are cells with branching processes containing a black pigment known as melanin. A lightening of the hue of the skin is produced by the retraction of this pigment into the central body of the cell while a darkening is produced by a spreading out of the pigment into the processes. These changes are under the control of a hormone produced by the anterior lobe of the pituitary gland (q.v.) in response to visual stimuli. Melanophores are also present in man. They are derived from neural crest tissue (see page 630) in the embryo whence they migrate in adult life and hence a wound which is covered with regenerated skin never contains melanophores and remains white while its surroundings become pigmented under the influence of sunlight.

PSEUDO-STRATIFIED EPITHELIUM. This is found lining the internal surface of the urinary bladder and has 3 or 4 cell layers. When the walls of this organ are contracted, the epithelium becomes folded, giving the appearance of a stratified epithelium.

FUNCTIONAL TYPES OF EPITHELIA

Epithelia may also be classified as: (1) protective, (2) secretory, (3) ciliated, (4) excretory, (5) respiratory, (6) sensory epithelia.

PROTECTIVE EPITHELIA. These include the skin of the mammals described above but mention may also be made of the epithelia of other types of animals. All invertebrate metazoa have a single cell-layered epithelium, the cells of which secrete a non-living external layer called the cuticle. In the Arthropoda and Mollusca this is thickened and—in the Crustacea and Mollusca—reinforced by depositions of 'lime' salts to function as the exoskeleton, while in the parasitic platyhelminths the cuticle appears to have a protective function against the digestive fluids of the host. In fish the skin is protected by scales formed from the dermis, while in the reptile the epidermis alone forms the protective covering of horny scales. These also are found covering the legs and digits of the birds. Feathers, like hairs, are epidermal structures and serve a similar purpose, namely heat conservation, as well as presenting a smooth surface over the body to reduce air friction and, in the wings and tail, to act as aerofoils.

SECRETORY (OR GLANDULAR) EPITHELIA. These epithelia contain cells which manufacture and discharge a fluid known as a secretion, having a specific function to perform such as that of digestion. Though secretory cells may occur singly and scattered among the other cells of an epithelium, as in the case of mucus-secreting cells in the epithelium of the nasal passages, they are more commonly aggregated in structures known as glands often formed as ingrowths of the epithelia into the surrounding tissues, e.g., the sweat glands of the skin of mammals. The activity of the secretory cells is frequently intermittent and the cycle of this activity is best illustrated in the case of mucus-secreting cells.

The mucus as it is produced by the cytoplasm of the cells accumulates in small droplets which coalesce eventually to form a single large drop which distends the outer part of the cell to produce a goblet-like shape. Hence these cells are often referred to as *goblet cells*. The drop of mucus is then discharged from the surface of the cell and the cycle recommences.

Glands may conveniently be classified according to their structural features as follows. (a) Simple aggregates of secretory cells. (b) Simple sacculate glands, e.g., the mucus-secreting glands of the skin of the frog. (c) Simple tubular glands, e.g., the crypts of Lieberkuhn of the small intestine. (d) Compound glands, which are of three types: (i) compound sacculate glands, e.g., the sebaceous glands of the hair follicles; (ii) compound tubular glands, e.g., the glands of the pyloric end of the stomach; (iii) compound racemose glands, e.g., the salivary glands. Compound glands consist of the secretory portions proper called alveoli (or acini) and the tubular ducts which lead the secretions to the surface of the epithelia. (Further descriptions of the glands will be found in those of the organs of which they form a part.)

CILIATED EPITHELIUM. The cells of these are columnar in shape with numerous cilia protruding from their external surfaces. The function of the cilia is to produce movement either of the whole organism or of fluids in contact with the epithelium. The free-living platyhelminths (e.g., *Planaria*) can move by means of the beating of the cilia of their epidermis. In the bivalve molluscs the lining of the mantle cavities and of the gills consists of ciliated epithelium which maintains a current of water through the interior of these animals to serve the purposes of nutrition, respiration, excretion and reproduction (see page 213). The ciliated endoderm of *Amphioxus* serves the same purpose. In vertebrates, ciliated epithelia are more restricted in extent. The peritoneum and the internal openings of the oviducts of the female dogfish are lined by ciliated epithelium whose

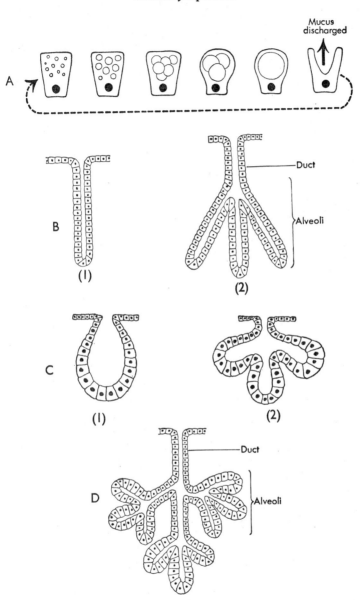

Fig. 19.3. Secretory epithelia.

A Diagram of the secretory cycle of a mucus-secreting (goblet) cell.
B Diagrams of (1) a simple tubular gland, (2) a compound tubular gland. *C* Diagrams of (1) a simple sacculate gland, (2) a compound sacculate gland. *D* Diagram of a compound racemose gland.

action directs the passage of the ova shed from the ovary towards the internal openings of the oviducts. In all vertebrates the internal openings of the oviducts are provided with ciliated epithelium for the same purpose. In the frog the roof of the buccal cavity is ciliated so that small flies trapped in mucus can be wafted back into the oesophagus. Finally, in mammals ciliated epithelium forms the linings of the larger bronchial tubes, the trachea, and the larynx. Particles of dust and bacteria entangled in mucus secreted by goblet cells in the epithelium are carried up to the glottis by the action of the cilia, whence they are usually disposed of by swallowing. Ciliated epithelia are found in the Fallopian tubes and in the epididymis.

EXCRETORY EPITHELIA. These occur in the excretory organs such as the kidneys, nephridia and sweat glands. Their cells are concerned with the removal of waste substances from the blood.

RESPIRATORY EPITHELIA. These form the layers of cells through which oxygen and carbon dioxide can diffuse. In the lungs of mammals and other air-breathing vertebrates the walls of the alveoli consist of pavement epithelium, but in the invertebrates, e.g., the earthworm, the respiratory epithelia usually consist of columnar cells.

REPRODUCTIVE EPITHELIA. These are found in the ovaries and testes (q.v.) and produce by cell division eggs and spermatozoa.

Connective tissues

While the term 'connective tissue' is primarily applied to those which bind the various organs of the body together, it is extended to include the skeletal tissues and blood, since a common basic structure is found in them all, consisting of a matrix of non-living material in which are embedded or contained cells, which (with the exception of those in the blood) have secreted the substance of which the matrix is composed. They all, too (with the exception of blood and hyaline cartilage), possess fibres running in the matrix.

Connective tissues proper

AREOLAR TISSUE This functions as a sheathing tissue, surrounding and penetrating such organs and tissues as muscles, nerves, bones and tendons, as well as forming the dermis connecting the epidermis to the underlying muscles. It also forms the external coverings of the kidneys and the liver and is also found in the mesenteries of the abdomen, in the walls of the alimentary canal, blood vessels and the trachea and its branches, and in the meninges of the brain and spinal cord. It may be described as 'true connective tissue' since without it the various parts of the body could not be held together. Its structure consists of a translucent jelly-like matrix reinforced by a network of fibres and containing various types of cells known collectively as connective tissue cells. The fibres are of two types: (1) *white fibres*, (2) *elastic or yellow fibres*. The white fibres consist of a protein called collagen, which on boiling with water swells up and produces a colloidal protein substance called gelatine, which is the main constituent of glue. These fibres are inelastic, occur in bundles which pursue a wavy course, and do not

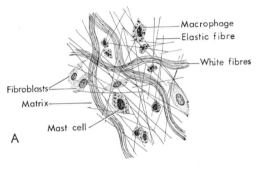

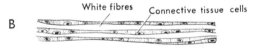

Fig. 19.4. Connective tissue.
A Diagram to show the structure of areolar connective tissue.
B Diagram to show the structure of a tendon in longitudinal section.
(After *Schafer*.)

branch. The elastic (yellow) fibres are composed of a protein called *elastin*, and, as their name implies, possess a certain amount of elasticity. They are of varying thickness and unlike the white fibres occur singly though they branch and coalesce with one another at intervals to form an irregular network. The combination of the two types of fibres enables a certain amount of stretching of this tissue to occur when a strain is imposed on it followed by a return to normal when the strain is removed (cf. the effect of pinching the skin and releasing it). This *areolar* connective tissue is well adapted to its function of binding various parts of the body together while allowing for movements of these parts relatively to one another, as for example in the bending and straightening movements of the trunk and limbs. The connective tissue cells include the fibroblasts which have secreted the materials of which the fibres are composed and are found attached to them; others are *leucocytes* from the blood, large *macrophages* (or histiocytes), and *mast cells*.

There are several types of true connective tissue, depending on the relative amounts of matrix and fibres. The dermis, for example, consists of areolar connective tissue, the fibres forming a loose network with spaces (areolae) between them filled with matrix. The coverings (periostia) of the bones and the meninges of the brain contain a great abundance of fibres and are known as *fibrous* connective tissue. *Tendons* which connect muscles to bones are composed of white fibres running parallel to one another with the fibroblasts interspersed between them and with scarcely any matrix. *Ligaments* which join bones to bones consist mainly of white fibres.

ADIPOSE TISSUE. This is a derivative of areolar tissue in which fat has been deposited in the cells, distending them to a very marked extent. It is found in the dermis of mammals in varying amounts and in the mesenteries of the abdomen and in the coverings of the heart and blood vessels. Butchers' 'suet' is produced by a heavy deposit of fat in the connective tissue around the kidneys.

Skeletal tissues

These are of two types: (1) Cartilage, (2) Bone.

CARTILAGE. The matrix consists of a tough translucent substance known as chondrin. The cells which produce the matrix lie em-

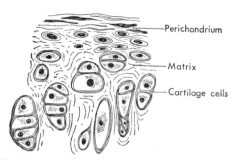

Fig. 19.5. Hyaline cartilage as seen in section. (From a prepared slide.)

bedded in it enclosed in capsules which stain more deeply than the matrix. They usually occur in small groups owing to cell division of the original cells of the embryonic cartilage. External to the cartilage is a fibrous connective tissue coat called the *perichondrium*.

This contains blood vessels supplying the cartilage cells with food and oxygen which can diffuse through the matrix to reach the cells. *Hyaline* cartilage, in which the matrix contains no fibres, is found in mammals in the articular cartilages (q.v.), the costal cartilages which join the ends of the ribs to the sternum, in the rings of cartilage of the trachea and main bronchial tubes, in the walls of the larynx, in the lower part of the nose, and in the xiphoid cartilage. In the frog it occurs in parts of the pectoral and pelvic girdles and of the skull, and forms the whole of the skeleton of the dogfish. *Fibrous* cartilage in which fibres occur in the matrix also occurs as, for example, in the pinna of the ear where elastic fibres run in the matrix in all directions, and in the epiglottis.

BONE. The matrix in bone consists approximately of 70% inorganic matter, chiefly calcium phosphate, with 30% organic

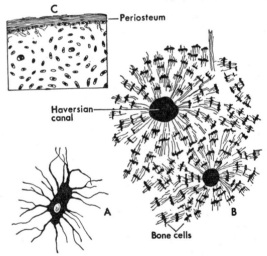

Fig. 19.6. Bone.

A Bone cell (osteocyte); *B* Haversian bone in section; *C* Section of outer region of a de-calcified bone. (From prepared slides.)

matter. The latter takes the form of interlacing collagenous fibres. The cells which have formed the matrix are called *bone corpuscles* (cells) or *osteocytes* and differ from those in cartilage in having many fine branching processes whose ends contact those of neighbouring cells. Their arrangement, too, is different. The matrix occurs in thin parallel sheets called *lamellae*, and the bone cells are sandwiched between these, each cell lying in a small cavity or *lacuna* with the processes projected through minute tubes in the matrix known as *canaliculi*. By this arrangement, food and oxygen can reach the cells from the blood vessels in the connective tissue covering of the bone—the *periosteum*—since the matrix is much less permeable than that of cartilage. Blood vessels may also run into the matrix as in compact bone (see below).

The actual arrangement of the lamellae varies. In all bones those nearest the surface run parallel to the surface but beneath these superficial lamellae two types of structure may be found: (1) compact bone in which the lamellae are arranged in what are known as Haversian systems, and (2) spongy bone. In the former the blood vessels from the periosteum run into the matrix, branching repeatedly with the branches mostly running parallel with the surface for some distance before returning to the periosteum. Around the Haversian canals, as they are called, in which the blood vessels run, the lamellae with the alternating layers of bone cells form a series of concentric rings. Any gaps between each separate group of rings (or Haversian system) are filled in by the interstitial lamellae and cells (see Fig. 19.6). In spongy (cancellated) bone the lamellae form an interlacing network, the spaces of which are filled with red marrow. This consists mainly of cells (*myelocytes*) surrounding blood vessels and is the site of the formation of new red cells. Many bones, e.g., vertebrae, ribs, the bones of the skull, and of the girdles, consist of external layers of compact bone enclosing a central region composed of spongy bone, but in the long bones of the limbs (e.g., the femur) the main shaft is composed of a hollow cylinder of compact bone. The central cavity is filled with adipose tissue known as the yellow marrow. Only at the ends of these bones does the central region consist of spongy bone.

The gross structure of a long limb bone is shown in the accompanying diagram (Fig. 19.7).

Ossification

During the early development of vertebrate animals the formation of the bones takes place in two ways: (1) many of the bones are preformed in cartilage which is later replaced by bone, (2) others are formed directly in the connective tissue of the dermis. Those bones which are preformed in cartilage are known as *cartilage bones*; those formed directly in the connective tissue are called *membrane* or *dermal bones*. The formation of the cartilage bones involves the process known as *endochrondral ossification* of the cartilage. To allow

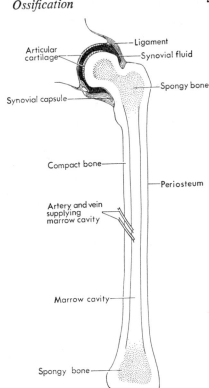

Fig. 19.7. Diagram of a long bone (e.g. a femur) as seen in L.S.

for growth of the bone, ossification commences in three places: one in the central region and the others at either end. The latter give rise to 'caps' of bone called *epiphyses* which, during the period of growth, are separated from the central ossification by cartilage which, unlike bone, is capable of growth. When, however, growth is completed the epiphyses become joined to the central region. Ossification proceeds as follows: (a) the cartilage cells become flattened and arranged in rows while calcium salts are deposited in the matrix; (b) cells known as *osteoblasts* commence to form layers of bone external to the cartilage; (c) the cartilage becomes invaded by blood vessels growing into it as extensions of those in the perichondrium (now to be known as the periosteum). Accompanying these are cells called *osteoclasts* which attack and erode the calcified cartilage. In the spaces so formed, osteoblasts produce a temporary scaffolding of bone lining the spaces; (d) the temporary bone is then removed by osteoclast cells and the osteoblasts next proceed to lay down the permanent structure of the bone.

The bones formed directly in the dermis are known as dermal or membrane bones (see pages 316 and 452).

TEETH. The structure of the teeth can be seen from the following diagram (Fig. 19.8).

The bulk of the tooth consists of *dentine* (ivory) which in chemical composition resembles bone. The *odontoblasts* (cells which have formed the dentine) lie adjacent to the pulp cavity. Their fine processes run outwards in canaliculi in the dentine. The *enamel* which

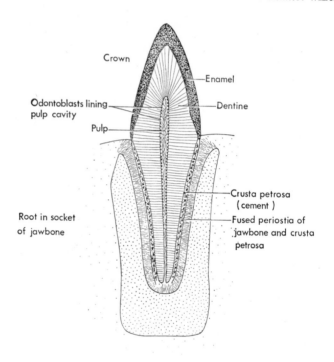

Fig. 19.8. Diagram of a vertical section of a tooth.

covers the exposed portion (crown) of the tooth is constructed of prisms set at right-angles to the surface. In addition to calcium phosphate, the enamel contains a certain proportion of calcium fluoride (CaF_2). The root of the tooth is covered by an external layer of compact bone known as the cement substance or *crusta petrosa* and is held in the socket by the interlacing fibres of the fused periostea of this bony material and of the socket of the jaw-bone in which the root lies. The pulp cavity contains connective tissue including blood vessels and nerves which enter from the aforementioned periostea via the small hole at the tip of the root.

Teeth in mammals exist in two sets: the milk or temporary teeth and the permanent teeth which later replace them. Both sets are formed from a common source. Overlying the edges of the jaw bones, the epidermis thickens and extends inwardly to form the dental germ or *lamina*. At close intervals this forms the rudiments of the teeth which are known as the *special dental germs*. These are inverted cup-like structures whose inner cells form the enamel of the developing teeth. Beneath the special dental germs vascular papillae are formed from the underlying dermis. From these develop the dentine of the crowns and roots of the teeth and the pulp cavities. The roots which develop later than the crowns grow and cause the crowns to erupt through the epidermis. The dental germs and papillae of the permanent teeth arise as lateral outgrowths of those of the temporary teeth.

Blood

This consists of a fluid called the *plasma* in which, in the vertebrates, are suspended the red and white cells of the blood. The plasma is a somewhat sticky, yellowish liquid consisting mainly of water in which are dissolved the following:

(a) mineral salts, present mainly as ions of which the chief are sodium and chloride ions (hence the salty taste of blood);

(b) soluble proteins peculiar to the blood and known as albumins and globulins. One of these is fibrinogen from which is formed the insoluble fibrin threads when the blood clots in contact with the tissues and the air following damage to the blood vessels leading to an escape of blood from them;

(c) soluble food substances, e.g., sugars and amino-acids;

(d) soluble waste products such as urea;

(e) hormones, antibodies and vitamins.

Minute droplets of fat also occur suspended in the plasma.

The red cells or *erythrocytes* of vertebrates are, with the exception of those of the mammals, oval nucleated cells in the cytoplasm of which occurs the oxygen-carrying pigment known as *haemoglobin*. In mammals the red cells are devoid of nuclei and are bi-concave discs in shape (though elliptical in the camels). Haemoglobin is a protein combined with a non-protein substance containing iron. It has the

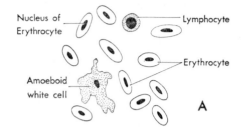

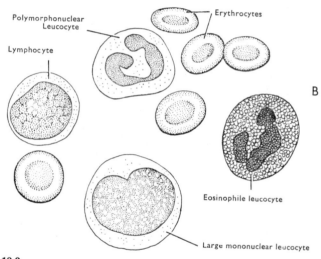

Fig. 19.9.

A Blood cells of frog; *B* Blood cells of mammal. (From prepared slides.)

peculiar property of forming a loose compound with oxygen. This compound is bright red in colour and is called *oxy-haemoglobin*. In the alveoli of the lungs, where the partial pressure of oxygen is relatively high, the haemoglobin combines readily with oxygen but where the concentration of dissolved oxygen is low in the tissue fluids (lymph) surrounding the capillaries in the tissues, the oxy-haemoglobin just as readily dissociates. In this way the red cells in the blood flowing in the capillary networks around the alveoli of the lungs absorb oxygen and transport it to the tissues, where it is released to reach the tissue cells by diffusion through the lymph.

By means of the haemoglobin much more oxygen can be carried per unit volume of blood than would be the case if the oxygen were merely in solution in the plasma. Red cells do not occur in the blood of invertebrates where the respiratory pigment, if present, is dissolved in the plasma (see blood of annelids and arthropods, pages 108 and 155).

The white cells or *leucocytes* are far less numerous than the red cells. (In man there are about five million red cells per cubic millimetre of blood but these outnumber the white by 600 to one). Some known as *phagocytes* can ingest bacteria in an amoeboid fashion; others appear to form *antibodies* and *opsonins*—the latter rendering bacteria more susceptible to ingestion and digestion by the phagocytes. In man, several types of white cells are found. About 70% consist of polymorphonuclear cells (neutrophils) with lobed nuclei and with small granules in their cytoplasm staining with both basic and acidic dyes such as methylene blue (basic) and eosin (acidic). Of the remaining percentage, the majority are lymphocytes, so named because they also occur in the lymph. These appear to be nearly all nucleus since the amount of cytoplasm is comparatively small.

In addition to the blood cells, numerous small bodies called *platelets* occur suspended in the plasma. They are thought to be concerned with clotting of the blood.

CLOTTING OF THE BLOOD. The blood while flowing in the blood vessels remains fluid but if, owing to a wound, the blood escapes and comes into contact with damaged tissues, it coagulates (or 'clots'). The purpose of this clotting is to plug the ruptured blood vessels and to prevent further escape of blood until regeneration of blood vessel walls has occurred. If a little freshly drawn blood is observed in a test tube, it will be seen to set to a jelly. Under the microscope in a drop of coagulating blood can be seen a very fine network of fibres which later contract to form a clot in which are entangled the blood cells. The yellowish fluid which is left surrounding the clot is called the *serum*. This consists of the plasma minus the soluble *fibrinogen* which had been converted to insoluble *fibrin* of which the above network is composed. The conversion of fibrinogen to fibrin is effected with the aid of an enzyme called *thrombin*. This enzyme does not actually exist in the blood circulating in the vessels but is formed from a precursor known as *prothrombin* which is prevented from giving rise to thrombin by the presence in the plasma of a substance (*antiprothrombin*—also known as *heparin*) so long as the blood is confined to the vessels. The restraining action of this antibody is neutralized by a substance called *thromboplastin*, derived from the platelets and the damaged tissues when the blood is flowing from a wound and the prothrombin in the presence of calcium ions is then able to change over into active thrombin and to produce coagulation of the fibrinogen. A condition in man known as *thrombosis* is due to the clotting of the blood within the blood vessels and the treatment consists of injecting into the patient's blood stream doses of heparin which can be extracted from the liver of other mammals. Leeches and blood-seeking flies inject an anti-coagulant into the wound they make when feeding to prevent the blood of their victim from clotting and impeding the blood flow. The blood of Crustacea clots very readily when their blood escapes from a wound—a very necessary precaution against undue loss of blood when a limb is accidentally shed during ecdysis (q.v.) or purposely to evade capture by an enemy. Persons known as hameophiliacs (or 'bleeders') on the other hand suffer from the inability of the blood to clot when a wound occurs.

Muscular tissue

Three types of muscles are found: (1) unstriped (involuntary) muscle, (2) striped (voluntary) muscle, (3) cardiac muscle.

UNSTRIPED MUSCLE consists of long, narrow, spindle-shaped cells with a central nucleus. In the cytoplasm are fine contractile threads running longitudinally. It is sometimes referred to as unstriped (or unstriated or plain) muscle. (See Fig. 19.10A.)

As its name implies, it is not under the control of the will but responds by contraction to mechanical stimuli such as stretching. It is also capable of spontaneous rhythmic action (i.e., alternately contracting and relaxing) and of remaining in a state of tonus (contraction) for long periods without fatigue. As compared with striped muscle its movements are slow and, in vertebrates, regulated by the autonomic nervous system.

In the vertebrates, unstriped muscle occurs in strands or sheets in the walls of the alimentary canal, the arteries, the bladder and the genital tract, also in the iris of the eye and in the walls of the bronchioles. The arrector pili muscles attached to the hair follicles are yet another example. Among the invertebrates it is widely distributed and its evolution can be traced from the musculo-epithelial cells of coelenterates. In these cells, only part of each cell—the 'muscle tail' —is elongated and contains contractile fibrils. In nematodes, too,

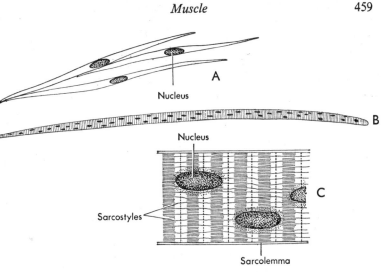

Fig. 19.10.

A Unstriped muscle fibres; *B* A striped muscle fibre; *C* Portion of a striped muscle fibre enlarged.

only part of each muscle cell contains contractile fibres but in the medusae of some coelenterates the whole of the muscle cell is elongated and converted into a contractile 'element'.

In the annelids, the whole of the muscles of the external body walls and of the gut wall are composed of unstriped muscle cells, and so, too, are the muscles of the molluscs with certain exceptions, e.g., in the scallop (*Pecten*) part of the adductor muscle consists of striped muscle fibres which produce the rapid closures of the valves of the shell used for swimming. Only in the musculature of the gut and genital organs does unstriped muscle occur in the arthropods, the muscles attached to the exoskeleton being of the striped variety.

STRIPED (VOLUNTARY) MUSCLE is called striped (or striated) muscle since it is composed of elongated fibres showing numerous transverse stripings of alternating light and dark bands. It is attached to the skeleton whose movements it produces and hence is also referred to as skeletal muscle. Each whole muscle consists of many of these fibres enclosed in an external covering of fibrous connective tissue known as the *epimysium*. Continuous with the epimysium are internal septa of connective tissue known collectively as the *perimysia* which divide up the muscle fibres into bundles or *fasciculi*. At each end of the muscle, the ends of the muscle fibres are attached to the tendons which join the periostia of the neighbouring bones. When the muscle contracts, one of these bones remains stationary while the other is caused to move, the volume of the muscle remaining unaltered during contraction so that as the muscle shortens the cross-section increases. The attachment to the stationary bone is called the *point of origin* of the muscle while that to the movable bone is known as the *point of insertion*.   (See also pp. 362–364.)

A striped muscle fibre is a composite structure. Externally it is bounded by a thin membrane—the *sarcolemma* and internally it is constructed of a large number of longitudinal contractile fibrils (the *myofibrils* or *sarcostyles*) interspersed with undifferentiated cytoplasm (*sarcoplasm*). Beneath the sarcolemma in a mammalian striped muscle fibre lie a number of scattered nuclei so that the whole muscle fibre may be regarded as a *syncytium*, i.e., a structure composed of a number of cells with no clearly defined boundaries. (The disposition of the nuclei, sarcoplasm and myofibrils varies in other groups, e.g., in the frog's muscle fibres the nuclei are scattered throughout the thickness of the fibre.)

Each myofibril is made up of a longitudinal series of disk-like elements—the *sarcomeres*. Under the ordinary microscope, the sarcomere is seen to have a central dark region known as the A band, in the centre of which is a lighter transverse stripe (Hensen's line or H zone). On either side of the A band is a clear zone (the I band). The boundary between each sarcomere is marked by a dark transverse line (*membrane of Krause* or the Z line). Two proteins, known as *actin* and *myosin*, occur in muscle fibres and studies of sections of muscle under the electron microscope have shown how these are disposed. In the A band six longitudinal myosin filaments are arranged in a regular hexagonal formation around a central one. In each of the I bands occur six thinner actin filaments, also hexagonally disposed. Their outer ends are joined to the Z lines. In relaxed muscle their inner ends project for a short distance into the space within the myosin filaments, alternating in position with them.[1] When the muscle fibre contracts, the position of the myosin filaments of the A band appear to remain unchanged but the actin filaments slide further in towards the H zone, drawing the Z lines closer together. The total effect of this action in all the sarcomeres is the shortening of the whole myofibril.

The positions of the sarcomeres of adjacent myofibrils approxi-

[1] This arrangement of the filaments is repeated many times across each sarcomere.

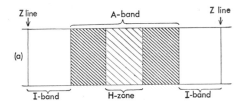

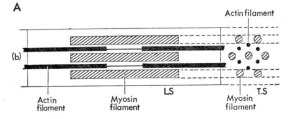

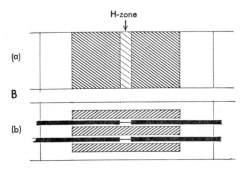

Fig. 19.11. Structural details of a portion of a sarcomere.

A (*a*) Sarcomere in relaxed state; (*b*) positions of actin and myosin filaments in a relaxed sarcomere.

B (*a*) Sarcomere in contracted state; (*b*) positions of actin and myosin filaments in a contracted sarcomere. (After *H. E. Huxley.*)

mate so that the dark A bands appear to form continuous bands across the width of the whole muscle fibre—hence the striped appearance of this type of muscle. (See Figs. 19.10 A and B and 19.11.)

At one point near the middle of each muscle fibre, a nerve fibre terminates in a branching process embedded in a plate of sarcoplasm (the *motor end plate*). (Fig. 28.4, page 553.)

Normally, striped muscle responds only to nervous impulses received via the nerve fibres supplying the muscle fibres, the impulses having originated in the central nervous system by the act of the will or, in the case of reflex actions (see Ch. 29), in the sense organs or sensory nerve endings in response to stimuli. The muscle responds to this nervous stimulation by a rapid contraction of its muscle fibres followed by a slower relaxation but usually when a muscle contracts it is in a state of *tetanus*, i.e. a series of contractions occurs so rapidly that the muscle scarcely relaxes at all between each individual contraction. This state is produced by a stream of nervous impulses continuing all the time the muscle is maintained in a state of contraction.

Striped muscle becomes fatigued when performing work but it is capable of remaining in a state of *tonus* or partial contraction for a long time. This is brought about by having only a fraction of the fibres in contraction at any one time and continually changing those which are in this state. Such tonus is responsible for the various postures assumed, e.g. an arm bent at the elbow when resting on a table.

CARDIAC MUSCLE is found in the walls of the heart. It is in the nature of a *syncytium*, i.e. it is composed of many single-celled elements united together by linked projections from the individual cells to form a single tissue.

Each cell contains longitudinal contractile fibrils with faint transverse dark stripes alternating with light ones. Its properties are intermediate between those of voluntary and involuntary muscle. Like the former it is rapid in action but it is not easily fatigued and is not under the control of the will. Its contractions and relaxations follow one another in an alternating rhythm which never ceases during the

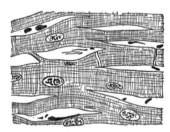

Fig. 19.12. Cardiac muscle.

whole lifetime of the animal but whose rate is governed by the autonomic nervous system to meet the immediate needs of the animal. In vertebrates the rate is slowed by the action of the vagus nerve and quickened by that of the sympathetic system. In the medulla oblongata of the brain is a collection of neurons (q.v.) known as the *cardio-inhibitory centre*. Distension of the aorta by too rapid action of the heart stimulates nerve endings in its walls to transmit nervous impulses to this centre via nerve fibres known as depressor fibres. These, in mammals, form a separate nerve (the depressor nerve) but in the frog occur within the vagus nerve. The neurons of the centre then transmit nervous impulses to the region of the sinus venosus (or sino-auricular node in mammals where the sinus venosus is absent) where the waves of contraction begin and slow down their rate. Another centre, the *cardio-accelerator centre*, also in the medulla, sends impulses via the sympathetic nerve fibres to the same region of the heart to speed up the rate of contraction in response to various stimuli (among them emotions!). Adrenalin (q.v.) also has the effect of speeding up the rate of heart beat and since the amount of this in the blood is increased when muscular action occurs, the heart beats more rapidly during periods of muscular activity. At the same time, the extent of the contractions and relaxations of the heart muscle are increased so that, in a given time, a greater volume of blood passes through the heart with a consequent increase of blood flow throughout the circulation (except in certain places such as that of the gut wall). In this way an increased supply of sugar from the liver and of oxygen from the lungs reaches the muscles while the carbon dioxide produced is more rapidly removed and carried to the lungs for excretion.

Nervous tissue

Nervous tissue consists mainly of *neurons* (or nerve cells). The basic type of neuron is found in the nerve net of hydra (page 54) and of other coelenterates. Each neuron has several projecting threads of cytoplasm whose ends form connexions known as *synapses* (singular —synapse) with those of neighbouring neurons or with the 'muscle tails' of the cells of the ectoderm and endoderm. Between the cells of the ectoderm and—to a much lesser extent—those of the endoderm are sensory cells, each provided with an external hair-like projection and a basal branching process connected with the nerve net. These cells receive stimuli and transmit nerve impulses which are propagated through the nerve net to the 'muscle tails' of the musculoepithelial cells. In triploblastic animals where a central nervous system exists, three types of neurons occur: (1) motor (or effector) neurons, (2) connector (or relaying) neurons, and (3) sensory (or receptor) neurons. The characteristic features of these neurons is shown in the accompanying diagrams of the motor and sensory neurons of a mammal (Fig. 19.13).

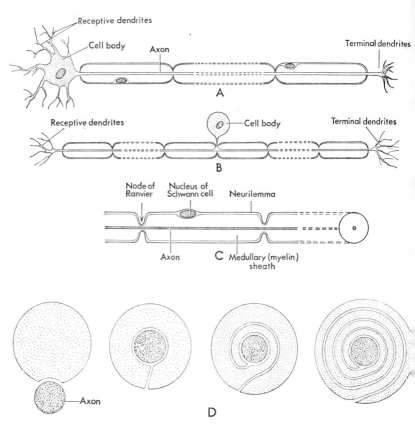

Fig. 19.13. Diagrams of neurons.

A Motor neuron; *B* Sensory neuron; *C* A portion of a medullated nerve fibre; *D* Action of a Schwann cell in forming the myelin sheath.

The central portion (cell body or *perikaryon*) of a motor neuron contains the nucleus and from it projects a number of short processes with branching ends known as *dendrites* by which nerve impulses may enter the neuron. In addition there is a longer projection called the *axon* which also terminates in a branching process. This serves as a pathway by which nervous impulses pass out of the neuron. The end of the axon forms a synapse with either a dendrite of another neurone or terminates in a muscle fibre. A connector neuron has a similar structure but its axon always connects with a dendrite of another neuron (either a connector or a motor neuron). The sensory neuron of a mammal differs in that it possesses only one receptive dendrite as well as its axon. Moreover, its cell body may be situated on a T-shaped junction of the dendrite and the axon, as in the case of those of the spinal region where the cell bodies are situated, the dorsal root ganglia of the spinal nerves. A stage in the probable evolution of this T-shaped junction is to be found in the fish where the dendrite and the axon connect separately with the cell body but are intertwined for a short distance in the proximity of the cell body. The two processes may then have become fused together.

A conspicuous feature of neurons is the presence of granules in the cytoplasm of the cell body. These are known as *Nissl's granules.* They consist of ribose nucleo-proteins and hence are probably concerned with the synthesis of the proteins of the nerve cell.

The nerves which connect the central nervous system to the various parts of the body are bundles of nerve fibres (axons and dendrites)

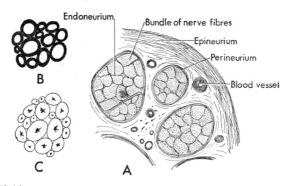

Fig. 19.14.

A T.S. of a large nerve (sciatic nerve); *B* A few nerve fibres in T.S. showing myelin sheaths stained black with osmic acid; *C* A few nerve fibres in T.S. showing axons stained with methylene blue. (From a prepared slide.)

bound together by an external coat of fibrous connective tissue known as the *epineurium.* In the larger nerves internal partitions of connective tissue (the *perineurium*) divide up the fibres into smaller bundles. The nerve fibres are usually *medullated* (or *myelinated*), i.e., each individual nerve fibre has a sheath of *myelin*—a fatty substance surrounding the fibre which is often referred to as the *axis cylinder,* and which itself consists of fine longitudinal fibrils called *neurofibrils.* The myelin sheath is not continuous but is interrupted at frequent intervals—the so-called *nodes of Ranvier.* External to this sheath is a continuous thin membrane, known as the *neurilemma,* secreted by

Schwann cells whose nuclei lie just beneath it—usually one in each internode. At the nodes the neurilemma sharply constricts the myelin sheath. Many of the nerves are 'mixed', i.e. they contain *afferent* nerve fibres conveying nervous impulses towards the central nervous system while others are *efferent* and carry nervous impulses away from it. Not all nerves contain myelinated fibres, some are composed of nonmedullated fibres. The role of the Schwann cell in the formation of the myelin sheath is shown in Fig. 19.13.

The central nervous system of vertebrates is composed of a vast number of neurons embedded in a matrix made up of so-called *neuroglia* cells each of which has numerous branching processes. It is ensheathed by connective tissue membranes called the *meninges*. The one immediately in contact with the surface of the central nervous system is the *pia mater*. Lining the wall of the protective bony cranium and neural arches of the vertebrae is a tougher membrane known as the *dura mater*. Separating these two is a space filled with the cerebro-spinal fluid which acts as a water cushion to protect the delicate nervous tissue of the central nervous system and traversing this space to form connexions between the two membranes are partitions known as the *arachnoid* membranes which also form an internal lining to the dura mater.

Internally, with the exception of the cerebral hemispheres of the brain, the central nervous system consists of a central core of grey matter surrounded by white matter. Only in the cerebral hemispheres is there an external layer of grey matter. The general disposition of the grey and white matter is seen in a transverse section of the spinal cord (Fig. 16.27). The grey matter contains cell bodies of neurons with dendrites and axons, all of them non-medullated and embedded in neuroglia, while the white matter consists only of medullated nerve fibres conducting nerve impulses mainly up and down the central nervous system.

The nature of the nerve impulses which it is the function of the neurons and their nerve fibres to conduct is partly physical and partly chemical (see Chapter 28, p. 549).

20. *The Structure of Organs*

The Alimentary canal

IN GENERAL the greater part of the alimentary canal of the coelo-mates is lined by a single layer of cells—the endoderm—except for the anterior and posterior ends—the stomodaeum and proctodaeum —which are lined by inturnings of the ectoderm. In the arthropods these extend much further in so that only the relatively short mesen-teron and its associated glands are lined by endoderm. Where the ectoderm is stratified, i.e. in all vertebrates, the linings of the stomadaeum and proctodaeum are also composed of stratified epithelium as is also the lining of the oesophagus. Unlike the strati-fied epithelium of the external skin, these linings have no keratinized layer, the cells formed by the Malpighian layer (page 441) merely becoming flattened as they approach the surface where they are rubbed off by friction with solid substances passing over them during the process of eating, swallowing and defaecation (egestion). Ex-ternal to the above linings are 'coats' of various tissues, mainly connective and muscular.

(a) THE BUCCAL CAVITY. In vertebrates the stratified epithelium lining this cavity and covering the surface of the tongue rests on a 'corium' of fibrous connective tissue. From the surface of the tongue project numerous small projections or papillae, some of which are known as circumvallate papilla, others as filiform or fungiform from their shapes. Embedded in the epithelium are groups of sensory cells—the *taste buds*—innervated by the VIIth and IXth cranial nerves (Fig. 16.32). A large number of small secretory glands producing mucus lie in the corium with their ducts opening to the surface of the epithelial lining of the buccal cavity. Their secretions, together with that of the salivary glands, keep the surface of the epithelium perpetually moist and help to lubricate the passage of food through the buccal cavity. Hence this epithelium together with its underlying connective tissue layer is often referred to as a 'mucous membrane', as are also other lining layers of the alimentary canal where mucus is produced.

467

(b) THE PHARYNX. This has a histologically similar lining (although lacking taste buds) to that of the buccal cavity except that in mammals the upper region leading into the nasal cavity is lined by ciliated columnar epithelium continuous with that of this cavity and of the Eustachian tubes (page 340). Surrounding the corium is a striped muscle coat by which the voluntary portion of the act of swallowing is effected. A number of lymph glands, of which the tonsils are conspicuous examples, occur in the corium.

(c) THE OESOPHAGUS. External to the mucous membrane, which is folded to permit of the expansion of the oesophagus during the passage of food, are a number of coats: (i) the submucous coat, (ii) the muscular coat, (iii) an external fibrous connective tissue coat. Marked off from the mucous membrane by a thin layer of muscle—the *muscularis mucosae* lies the submucous coat which consists largely of areolar tissue. In this are numerous mucus secreting glands, blood vessels, and lymphatics. The muscular coat is also in two layers; an inner one of muscle fibres arranged circularly and an outer one of longitudinally disposed fibres. Except at the upper end of the oesophagus, all the muscle fibres are unstriped but at that end the muscle fibres are striped like those of the pharynx. The function of the muscle coat is to convey the food by peristaltic waves of contraction down to the stomach.

(d) THE STOMACH AND INTESTINES. To avoid repetition it may be stated that the walls of these organs are all constructed on the same plan, i.e. in order from within outwards, the coats composing the walls are: (i) the mucous membrane (epithelium and corium), (ii) the muscularis mucosae—a thin band of unstriped muscle fibres, (iii) the submucous coat of areolar connective tissue containing blood vessels and lymphatics, (iv) the muscle coat, (v) the peritoneum—a thin bounding coat of connective tissue with an external layer of squamous epithelium (page 440).

In the *stomach* the columnar epithelium dips down into the connective tissue composing the inner region of the mucous coat at close intervals to form the gastric glands. Numerous goblet cells (page 446) lie scattered in the epithelium next to the cavity of the stomach and in the ducts of the glands. These secrete mucus. The gastric glands are simple or compound tubular glands (page 446). The inner secretory regions (*alveoli* or *acini*) consist of cells known as *peptic* or *chief cells* which secrete the enzymatic gastric juice but scattered along the course of the alveoli and applied externally are the *oxyntic*

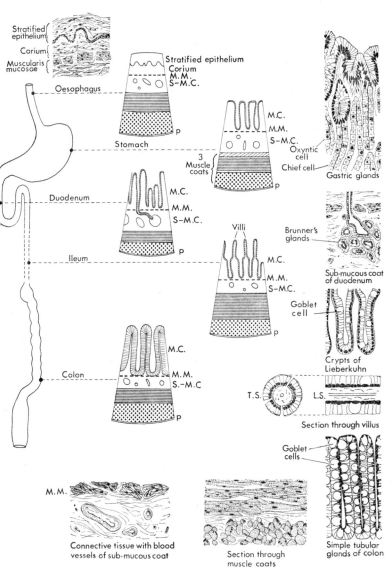

Fig. 20.1. The histology of the alimentary canal.

M.C.=mucous coat (mucous membrane); S-M.C.=sub-mucous coat; M.M.=muscularis mucosae; ////=oblique muscle coat of stomach; ≡ =circular muscle coat; ∴∴ =longitudinal muscle coat; p=peritoneum. (From prepared slides.)

cells which produce the hydrochloric acid which added to the secretion of the peptic cells gives the acid medium in which the pepsin and the rennin of the gastric juice can best operate. The muscular coat of the stomach contains, in addition to the inner layer of circular and outer layer of longitudinal unstriped muscle, a third layer of obliquely placed fibres between the circular muscle and the submucous coat.

In the small intestine the mucous membrane is thrown into circular folds and has a pile-like surface owing to the presence of innumerable finger-like projections known as *villi*. Between the bases of the villi the epithelium dips down to form the glands. At the commencement of the duodenum these are of the racemose type (page 446) projecting down into the submucous coat and known as *Brunner's glands*, but throughout the rest of the small intestine the glands are simple tubular ones, the *crypts of Lieberkuhn*. They secrete the *succus entericus* or intestinal juice. The outer borders of the columnar cells of the epithelium of the villi are striated with fine markings at right-angles to the surface. The interior of each villus consists of connective tissue, in the centre of which is a *lacteal* (lymph vessel) ending blindly near the top of the villus and connected with the lymphatics of the submucous coat. Surrounding the lacteal is a plexus of capillaries derived from the blood vessels of that coat. There are also a few unstriped muscle fibres running longitudinally whose contractions can shorten the villus to drive the lymph in the lacteal towards the lymphatics of the submucous coat. Numerous lymphocytes (page 457) are found in the connective tissue of the villi—they assist in the transport of fat re-formed from fatty acids and glycerine in the epithelial cells following absorption, to the central lacteal. The muscle coat has an inner circular and an outer longitudinal layer.

In the *colon* (*large intestine*) the mucous membrane consists mainly of very numerous simple tubular glands. There are no villi but the whole of the epithelium including that of the glands contains a large number of goblet cells whose secretion of mucus provides for the lubrication of the passage of the semi-solid faeces which are formed from the chyle by absorption of water by the walls of the colon.

The walls of the stomach and intestines are innervated by branches of the vagus and the sympathetic nerves. There are two networks (*plexus*) of neurons: (1) Auerbach's plexus situated between the circular and longitudinal muscle coats and (2) Meissner's plexus in the submucous coats. The vagus nerve fibres end in contact with the neurons of Auerbach's plexus but the sympathetic nerve fibres are

connected to the muscle cells. The function of the vagus is to stimulate the action of the muscles and of the sympathetic nerves to inhibit
the action, but movements of the muscles involved in peristalsis are
carried out by the operation of the two plexi.

Lymph glands occur along the length of the intestines in their
walls. The most prominent of these occur along the ileum and are
known as *Peyer's patches*.

The glands associated with the Alimentary canal

(1) THE SALIVARY GLANDS. These are compound racemose
glands (page 446). The cells of the alveoli secrete either mucin or the
watery solution containing the diastatic enzyme ptyalin (p. 484).

(2) THE PANCREAS. This too is a compound racemose gland, the
cells of whose alveoli secrete the pancreatic juice. Embedded in the
connective tissue binding the alveoli together are patches of cells
(*the islet cells*) which function as endocrine organs producing the
hormone *insulin* (page 605).

(3) THE LIVER. The liver of vertebrates is a lobed organ and consists of a large mass of cells derived from the embryonic endoderm
interpenetrated by blood vessels, lymphatics and branches of the
bile duct. The blood vessels are branches of the hepatic portal vein
and hepatic artery and of the hepatic veins; the first two vessels being
afferent and the last efferent. Under the microscope, a section of a
small piece of liver of a mammal shows a number of scattered *portal
canals* in each of which are seen in cross-section a branch of the
hepatic portal vein and of the hepatic artery together with a branch
of the bile duct and several lymphatics, all bound together by a thin
covering of connective tissue called *Glisson's capsule*. The Glisson's
capsules are surrounded by liver cells tunnelled by numerous spaces
called lacunae, each separated from its neighbours by a single layer
of cells. From the portal canals radiate finer branches of the hepatic
portal vein and hepatic artery which in turn give off numerous
capillaries (*sinusoids*) which run through the lacunae to enter the
branches of the hepatic vein which are interspersed in the regions
between the portal canals. The endothelium of the sinusoids lines the
lacunae and, according to some authors, becomes disrupted to form
a discontinuous layer of cells (*cells of Kupfer*), although later work
indicates that this may not be the case. Between the adjacent cells
of the walls of the lacunae are fine tubes (*bile canaliculi*) which run
to join the finer branches of the bile ducts which lead into the larger
ones in the Glisson's capsules. In the pig's liver, the liver cells are

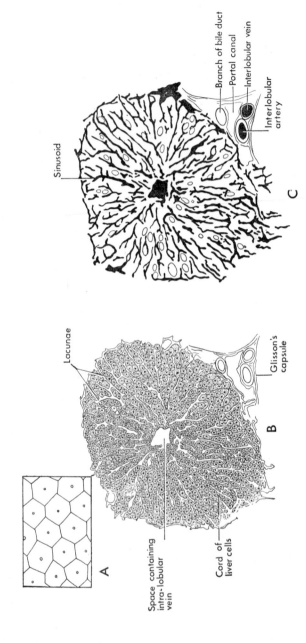

Fig. 20.2. The liver.

A Arrangement of liver lobules as seen in a transverse section of the lobules.
B A transverse section of a liver lobule showing the 'cords' of liver cells and a Glisson's capsule.
C A transverse section of a liver lobule to show the blood vessels and sinusoids (injected). (Drawn from prepared slides.)

divided into masses called *lobules*, which are polyhedral in outline as seen in a cross-section of the liver and separated by connective tissue continuous with that of the Glisson's capsules. In the centre of each lobule is a branch of the hepatic vein (the *intralobular* vein) and the liver cells appear to form 'cords' radiating from this with their intervening lacunae between them. In other mammals the lobules are not so clearly defined owing to the absence of the connective tissue septa and the pattern of arrangement of the liver cells and the lacunae alters with variations in the distribution of the blood in the various vessels. Sometimes the pattern resembles that in the pig's liver but at other times the 'cords' of the liver cells appear to radiate from the Glisson's capsule, the orientation of the liver cells and lacunae altering with changes in the blood pressure in the branches of the hepatic artery and vein. Externally the lobes of the liver are covered by a thin connective tissue coat—the *liver capsule*.

The respiratory organs of mammals

In mammals, the walls of the larynx, trachea and bronchial tubes are composed of connective tissue with an inner lining of ciliated epithelium (page 440). Embedded in the walls of the larynx are plates of cartilage derived from the visceral skeleton of the embryo and in those of the trachea and main bronchial tubes incomplete transverse rings of cartilage, whose overlapping ends are joined by strands of unstriped muscle. In the epithelium are numerous goblet cells which together with small glands of the racemose type (page 446) lying in the connective tissue of the walls secrete mucus. The mucus serves to trap dust particles and bacteria and is constantly wafted upwards by the ciliary action of the cells of the epithelium and expelled via the glottis to be disposed of by swallowing. In the walls of the finer branches of the bronchial tubes and of the bronchioles there are no rings of cartilage but in those of the bronchioles occur elastic fibres and circular unstriped muscle fibres whose prolonged contractions in certain cases produce attacks of asthma. The bronchioles terminate in thin-walled *air sacs* beset with hollow projections called the *alveoli*. The walls of the air sacs and of the alveoli are composed of a single layer of squamous (pavement) epithelium (page 440). They are invested by a close network of capillaries connected with branches of the pulmonary artery and vein which accompany the bronchial tubes (Fig. 16.25).

The kidney

The structure of the mammalian kidney has already been described on pages 378–9 while its microscopic structure is illustrated in Figs. 18.1, 20.3 and 26.2.

Except in their shapes, the kidneys of the dogfish and of the frog do not differ materially from those of the mammals. It must be emphasized, however, that those of the dogfish and frog are opistho-nephric in origin while the kidneys of the mammal are metanephric. In both, the network of the capillaries investing the bodies of the tubules receives blood not only from the glomerular capillaries but also from branches of the renal portal veins.

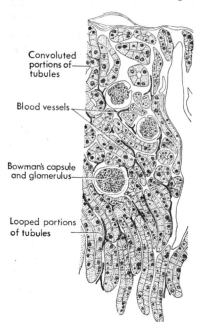

Convoluted portions of tubules

Blood vessels

Bowman's capsule and glomerulus

Looped portions of tubules

Fig. 20.3. Kidney.
T.S. of part of the cortex.
(From a prepared slide.)

The gonads

TESTIS. The testis in all vertebrates consists of many coiled *semini-ferous* tubules which are blind at their inner ends and which join the vasa efferentia (the epididymis) of the mammal. The tubules are bound together by connective tissue continuous with the outer fibrous covering of the testis (the *tunica albuginea*). Scattered among the tubules within the connective tissue are strand-like patches of cells (the *interstitial cells*) which act as endocrine organs, producing the hormones responsible for the appearance of the secondary sexual characters (page 606). The blood vessels of the testis also lie in the connective tissue between the tubules. The wall of each tubule consists of a single layer of cubical cells (the *germinal epithelium*) encased in a thin connective tissue sheath. The cells of the germinal epithelium repeatedly divide to form by mitotic divisions of their

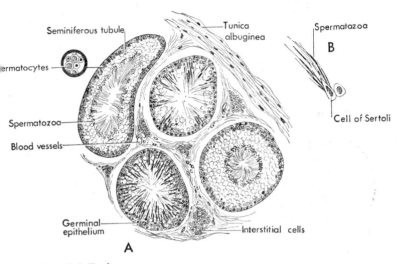

Fig. 20.4. Testis.

A T.S. of a testis of a mammal. *B* Developing spermatozoa attached to a cell of Sertoli. (From a prepared slide.)

nuclei an inner zone of cells several cells in thickness. These cells (the spermatogonia) give rise to the primary spermatocytes. These by meiotic division of their nuclei form groups of four spermatids. The spermatids become attached to certain elongated cells (the *cells of Sertoli*) of the germinal epithelium and develop into spermatozoa. In a section of an adult testis all stages in the formation of spermatozoa can be seen under the microscope.

OVARY. The ovary is a solid body whose substance (the *stroma*) consists of fibrous connective tissue containing many elongated spindle-shaped cells and blood vessels. The surface of the ovary is a continuous layer of cells (the *germinal epithelium*). Certain of the cells of this layer enlarge to form primary oocytes which sink into the stroma accompanied by envelopes of cells also derived from the germinal epithelium. Each oocyte and its investing cells is called a

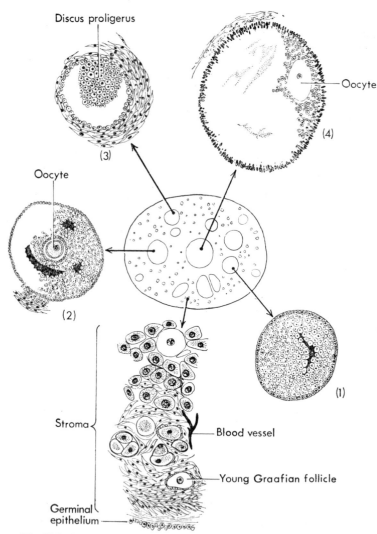

Fig. 20.5. Ovary of a mammal as seen in transverse section.
(1)–(4) stages in development of the Graafian follicles. (From a slide.)

Graafian follicle. In a section of an adult ovary many Graafian follicles can be seen in various stages of development. In the stroma there are in addition to the follicles, *interstitial cells* which like those of the testis produce the sex hormones. A mature follicle has an internal cavity filled with fluid containing the oocyte surrounded by an envelope of cells (*discus proligerus*) attached to one side of the wall of the follicle. The size of each individual follicle depends on its age and that of the oocyte which in turn is conditioned by the amount of yolk present in it. The Graafian follicles of corresponding age in a fowl are therefore much larger than those of a mammal. Eventually each mature follicle bursts to liberate the oocyte. In mammals, the cells of a follicle which has discharged its oocyte proliferate to form a solid mass (the *corpus luteum*). This soon disappears if the animal does not become pregnant. If, however, pregnancy occurs, the corpus luteum continues to increase in size during the period of the pregnancy and persists for some time after the birth of the young. It functions as a temporary endocrine organ (page 606).

21. *Nutrition*

Nutritional requirements of animals

EVERY living animal requires a supply of food for the maintenance of life and the processes connected with life, including growth and reproduction. The protoplasm forming the living substance in the animal body is in a labile state, i.e. its material substance is constantly undergoing change; new chemical substances are constantly being incorporated (*assimilated*) into it while those already forming part of its actual substance are being degraded into simple compounds which form excreta and are ejected. Accompanying this constant change is the equally constant degradation of *potential energy* at a high level to *heat* or *kinetic energy*. The energy at high level is in some unexplained way stored in the chemical substances assimilated by the protoplasm and it is these substances which we know as '*foods*'.

While animals possess certain powers of chemical synthesis such as the formation of fats from sugars, they do not possess the same powers as do plants of building up (*elaborating*) foods such as sugar and proteins from the simple inorganic substances: carbon dioxide, water and mineral salts together with the absorption of energy from an external source, i.e. the sun, and the storing of that energy at a high level in those compounds. This is because no animal possesses the power of making the unique substance known as chlorophyll by which plants are able to absorb light energy and to incorporate it in the foods made by them. Hence the dependence of animals on plants for food either directly by feeding on plants or on animals which have themselves obtained their food by eating plants. Those which feed entirely on plants are called *herbivores*, whilst those which feed on the herbivores are known as *carnivores*.

A large proportion of the food ingested by an animal is used to provide energy for movement; the remainder is used for maintaining the protoplasm, growth and reproduction as previously stated. The general process in which the stored energy of food is released is called *respiration*. This important subject is dealt with at greater length in Chapter 24 (page 502).

FOODS. There are three classes of foods: carbohydrates, fats and oils, and proteins.

Carbohydrates. These are compounds of the elements carbon, hydrogen and oxygen; the ratio of the hydrogen and oxygen atoms in the molecules being 2:1 as in water. Carbohydrates are classified as:

(1) Monosaccharides, e.g. glucose (dextrose), fructose (fruit sugar), and galactose. The general formula is $C_6H_{12}O_6$.

(2) Disaccharides, e.g cane sugar (sucrose), malt sugar (maltose) and milk sugar (lactose). The general formula for these is $C_{12}H_{22}O_{11}$.

(3) Polysaccharides, e.g. starch, cellulose and glycogen, their general formula being $(C_6H_{10}O_5)_n$.

Polysaccharides are insoluble in water though capable of forming colloidal solutions. They are not able to pass through membranes such as those lining the gut. Disaccharides form true solutions but are able to diffuse through such membranes only very slowly. Monosaccharides form true solutions and are also able to diffuse through membranes easily. Poly- and di-saccharides can be hydrolysed to monosaccharides. In animals this conversion occurs during digestion (see page 484). The condensation of monosaccharides to polysaccharides can also occur, viz. glucose can be converted into glycogen in muscle tissue and in liver cells for temporary storage.

Fats and oils. There are also compounds of the elements carbon, hydrogen and oxygen, but with the ratio of the hydrogen to the oxygen atoms in the molecules being much higher than those of carbohydrates (cf. glucose $C_6H_{12}O_6$, a carbohydrate, with tristearin, a fat of empirical formula, $C_{57}H_{110}O_6$). Fats are esters of glycerol $(C_3H_5(OH)_3)$ and certain fatty acids, the chief ones being stearic acid $(C_{17}H_{35}COOH)$, palmitic acid $(C_{15}H_{31}COOH)$ and oleic acid $(C_{17}H_{33}COOH)$. Thus:

$$CH_2-O-CO-(CH_2)_{16}-CH_3$$
$$CH-O-CO-(CH_2)_{16}-CH_3 \qquad \text{glyceryl tristearate}$$
$$CH_2-O-CO-(CH_2)_{16}-CH_3$$

$$CH_2-O-CO-(CH_2)_{14}-CH_3$$
$$CH-O-CO-(CH_2)_{14}-CH_3 \qquad \text{glyceryl tripalmitate}$$
$$CH_2-O-CO-(CH_2)_{14}-CH_3$$

$$CH_2-O-CO-(CH_2)_7-CH=CH-(CH_2)_7-CH_3$$
$$CH-O-CO-(CH_2)_7-CH=CH-(CH_2)_7-CH_3 \qquad \text{glyceryl trioleate}$$
$$CH_2-O-CO-(CH_2)_7-CH=CH-(CH_2)_7-CH_3$$

Fats are glyceryl esters which are solid or semi-solid at ordinary temperatures (*c.* 15°C), while oils are liquid at the same temperature, but in all cases the melting points are comparatively low so that in general the fats are semi-liquid in the protoplasm and storage tissues, particularly in warm-blooded animals. Fats and oils are insoluble in water but can be dispersed in a watery fluid in the form of minute droplets forming what is known as an *emulsion*. The emulsion is stabilized by the presence in the watery fluid of substances which reduce the surface tension of water. This is the function of the bile salts (page 486) in the bile of vertebrates, and since in cells fats and oils are dispersed throughout the protoplasm, presumably similar surface tension-reducing substances must be present. Fats and oils are hydrolysed to glycerol and fatty acids in the presence of water but the action is exceedingly slow unless an enzyme called a *lipase* is present. Alkalis react with fats to form glycerol and soaps. Thus:

$$C_3H_5(C_{17}H_{35}COO)_3 + 3NaOH = C_3H_5(OH)_3 + 3C_{17}H_{35}COONa$$

| (glyceryl stearate) | (caustic soda) | (glycerol) | (sodium stearate or soap) |

It was previously thought that, in the intestine, owing to the presence in the pancreatic and intestinal juices of sodium bicarbonate, part of the fat after hydrolysis formed soaps which diffused into the epithelium of the villi but the absorption of fat is now known to be more complex and to involve the organic acids in the bile (see page 486).

Fats in animal cells frequently occur in combination with other substances, notably phosphoric acid. Phospho-lipids (compounds of phosphoric acid and fats) form an important constituent of the protoplasmic membranes of bounding external and internal surfaces in cells which present a barrier to the passage of various substances into and out of the cells. Since fats are soluble in ether, the cytolysis (break up of cells) produced by the action of ether is thus readily explained.

Fats and oils form important reserve foods and are frequently stored in special regions in the bodies of animals, as for example in the connective tissue around the kidneys or in that of the dermis in mammals, in the fat bodies attached to the gonads in the frog and in the livers of fish. Carbohydrates are readily converted into fats for storage. Both they and the fats serve for energy production.

Proteins. Proteins are compounds of carbon, hydrogen, oxygen and nitrogen, together with, in certain instances, sulphur and phosphorus. Proteins consist of large molecules formed by the condensation of α-amino acids. About twenty of these amino-acids have been isolated from different proteins by the method of hydrolysis. Typical amino acids found in proteins are:

Glycine (α-amino-acetic acid) $CH_2(NH_2)COOH$
Alanine (α-amino-propionic acid) $CH_3CH(NH_2)COOH$
Phenylalanine (β-phenyl-α-amino-propionic acid) $C_6H_5CH_2CH(NH_2)COOH$
Cystine (ββ-dithio-diα-amino-propionic acid) S—CH_2—$CH(NH_2)COOH$
S—CH_2—$CH(NH_2)COOH$

Amino-acids are converted into proteins by the process of condensation with the liberation of water, producing a characteristic *peptide* linkage (-NH-CO-) between the condensing amino-acids

$$NH_2 \cdot CH_2 \cdot CO \cdot OH + H \cdot NH \cdot CH \cdot (CH_3) \cdot COOH \rightarrow$$
glycine   alanine
$$NH_2 \cdot CH_2 - CO \cdot NH - CH_2(CH_3) \cdot COOH + H_2O$$
peptide
linkage

During digestion the peptide linkages of the proteins are broken down by the addition of water, so that the constituent amino-acids are re-formed. The hydrolysis of proteins is accelerated by the proteolytic enzymes (proteases): pepsin, trypsin and erepsin (see pages 485–488).

Amino-acids are amphoteric, possessing both basic and acidic groups and, as will be noticed above, even after condensation certain of these 'survive'. Hence combinations with other acids or basic substances can occur, e.g., phosphoric acid can link up with the basic NH_2 groups not concerned in the peptide linkages.

Proteins, on account of their large molecules, do not diffuse readily and hence the necessity for their hydrolysis by digestion into diffusible amino-acids before they can be absorbed into the animal body. The constituent amino-acids can then also be built up into the particular 'pattern' of protein peculiar to the animal concerned. Since there are tens or hundreds of amino-acid residues in any protein molecule and since there are twenty or so different amino-acids, it is clear that an extremely large number of proteins may be found in living things, the proteins differing in the proportions of the various amino-acids and the order in which they are arranged.

The majority of proteins are insoluble in water, though many are soluble in salt solutions. Familiar examples of a soluble protein are gelatine and albumen, but these form not true solutions as do electrolytes, e.g., NaCl, but colloidal sols or gels.

The physical properties of protoplasm are closely allied to those of proteins, and this is not surprising since proteins 'make up' a large proportion of the protoplasm of the cells of animals. Proteins are hence essential for growth and repair of cells and tissues. Reproduction which involves the production of new cells is also dependent on an adequate supply of proteins.

Certain substances produced in the bodies of animals, such as keratin (found in the exoskeleton) are proteins, as are also the non-living matrices of connective tissue and bone. Mucus is an example of a conjugated protein (i.e., a compound of protein with a non-protein substance), being composed of protein and an amino-sugar.

Finally, it must be stressed that the foods, carbohydrates, fats and proteins do not fulfil the entire nutritional requirements of animals. Water is essential for many purposes in the body, such as transport and excretion, and mineral salts are required for blood and bone formation. In addition, small amounts of iodine (for the formation of thyroxin) and of the accessory food factors called vitamins are needed. Vitamins are so important for the proper functioning of the body that a brief account of them must be given.

Vitamins. Although there had been earlier attempts to feed animals on purified diets it was in 1912 that Hopkins found that young rats fed solely on pure maize meal failed to grow normally. However, the addition of a small amount of milk to their diet resulted in normal growth. Following this discovery, it came to be generally recognized that certain essential substances present in the normal diet of animals were required regularly in small amounts for the proper functioning of the animal body. These substances were named *vitamins* since it was at first thought that they were all amino-compounds (i.e. containing the amino group of atoms NH_2). This view is now known to be incorrect and while the name 'vitamin' is still employed, it is more correct to call them *accessory food substances*. They are individually distinguished by the addition of a capital letter to the name 'vitamin': Vitamin A, Vitamin B, etc.

In some animals certain of the vitamins are actually synthesised in their bodies (e.g. the formation of vitamin D in the skin of a mammal when exposed to ultra-violet light) or produced by the micro-organisms in their intestines, but in the majority the vitamins needed are obtained from external sources, i.e. from their diet. Lack of vitamins in the latter case leads to mal-functionings of the body known as *deficiency diseases* such as scurvy due to vitamin C, the main symptoms of which are gum disorders with loosening of the teeth and easily produced haemorrhages in the skin as the result of slight knocks. The actual roles played in the *metabolism* of an animal by the various vitamins is not yet fully understood though vitamin C (ascorbic acid) is known to be associated with the respiratory processes.

Details of the principal vitamins are given in the following table.

Vitamin	*Deficiency effects*	*Principal food sources*
A (fat soluble)	Retardation of growth. Night-blindness. Impairment of epithelial tissues with decreased resistance to infection.	Carotenes in foods such as green vegetables, carrots, milk, butter, fish-liver oils. [In the cells of the intestinal wall carotenes are converted to vitamin A]
B complex including (1) B1 Thiamine hydrochloride (2) Riboflavin (water soluble)	Polyneuritis or 'beri-beri' Dermatitis, digestive disorders, anaemia	Yeast, peas, beans, whole-meal bread. Yeast, milk, lean meat, liver, eggs, peas and green vegetables.
C Ascorbic acid (water soluble)	Scurvy	Fresh vegetables and various fruits especially oranges, lemons, tomatoes and blackcurrants. Rose 'hips'.
D Calciferol (fat soluble)	Rickets in children, i.e. malformation of bones	Fish-liver oils, butter and eggs. Formed in the skin on exposure to sunlight.
E Tocopherol	Loss of fertility in male and abortion of embryos in female.	Wheat germ oil, green vegetables, eggs and liver.

22. *Digestion and Absorption*

Since all animals, with a few exceptions (e.g. *Taenia*, which is bathed in the digesting food of its host), ingest food which is usually in a solid, insoluble form, it is necessary for such food to be changed into soluble compounds before it can enter their actual bodies. Moreover, these compounds must not only be soluble but also be capable of diffusing through animal membranes such as the ectoplasm of the cells lining the alimentary canal. Colloidal substances in the *sol* conditions, e.g., egg albumin or starch, are not able to diffuse through such membranes. A simple experiment will disclose this. A length of fresh sausage skin (part of the wall of the intestine of a pig) is inflated by blowing into one end by means of a funnel made from a drawn-out test-tube; some starch *sol* made by boiling a little starch in water, is introduced into the sausage skin which is then suspended in water in a beaker. After 24 hours the water in the beaker is tested with iodine solution. No blue colour is formed, showing that the colloidal starch is unable to pass through the sausage skin.

Before the food can enter the body it must therefore be converted into compounds of a simple crystalloid nature which are able to diffuse through membranes. The process by which this is done is called *digestion* and it is effected by the action of water on food substances producing hydrolysis. An example of this is the hydrolysis of starch to glucose.

$$(C_6H_{10}O_5)n + nH_2O \rightarrow nC_6H_{12}O_6$$

The water is not, however, able to react with the starch except in the presence of a catalyst (or *enzyme*), the enzyme in this case being a diastatic one such as *ptyalin*, in the saliva of mammals. Again a simple experiment can be used to demonstrate this and also the ability of the glucose to diffuse through an animal membrane.

For this purpose the previous experiment is repeated using starch solution mixed with a little commercial diastase powder.* After 24 hours the water in the beaker is tested for the presence of glucose by

* Commercial diastase contains maltase as well as diastase and converts starch to glucose.

484

boiling a small quantity (half a test-tube) of it with Fehling's solution. The formation of a brick-red precipitate of cuprous oxide indicates the presence of glucose. This shows that not only has the starch been digested to glucose but also that the glucose has diffused through the sausage skin.

The digestion of food requires the presence of a number of enzymes, since enzymes are mainly specific in their action and each class (and in some cases each type of food substance) requires the presence of a specific enzyme for digestion. The process of digestion of food in the vertebrates is probably best known in the case of man, in whom ingestion and digestion, and absorption of digested products, takes the following course.

After entering the mouth into the buccal cavity, the food is bitten into pieces by the incisor teeth and then ground up by means of the molar teeth, being thus reduced to a mash by admixture with the saliva. The saliva, which is secreted by the salivary glands, contains the enzyme *ptyalin* (a diastatic enzyme or *amylase*) which converts starch to maltose and has a pH of approximately 6–7 which is suitable for the action of the ptyalin. The food is then worked into a lump (or *bolus*) by the action of the tongue and pushed back into the pharynx. Here contact with the sensitive lining of the back of the pharynx sets up a reflex action which results in the bolus being gripped and pushed down the oesophagus by a wave of contraction in its muscular wall (*peristaltic action*). At the same time the larynx is drawn upwards and the glottis is closed by the epiglottis to prevent food from entering the larynx. The soft palate rises to stop food passing upwards into the nasal passages.

On reaching the entrance to the stomach the food is admitted by the relaxation of the cardia (the ring of muscle at the entrance). The food is retained in the stomach for a period during which it is mixed with the gastric fluid secreted by the gastric glands (see page 468) by gentle squeezing set up by rhythmical contractions of the stomach walls (see musculature of coats of stomach, Fig. 20.1). The gastric secretion contains mucus, hydrochloric acid (0·5 to 0·6%) and the enzymes *rennin* and *pepsin*. The starch digestion commenced in the buccal cavity continues until the acid gastric secretion penetrates the food and stops the action of the ptyalin, which cannot 'work' in an acid medium. The rennin coagulates soluble protein (*caseinogen*) in milk, converting it into insoluble *casein*. Pepsin causes the partial breakdown by hydrolysis of proteins to smaller molecules (groups of linked amino-acids) called *peptones*. This enzyme will only 'work' in an acid medium (optimum pH 1·5) and this is provided by the presence of the hydrochloric acid in the gastric juices. During gastric digestion the pyloric sphincter (a ring of muscle at the entrance to the duodenum) remains closed, but as the food becomes progressively more acid, the sphincter relaxes from time to time to allow some of the fluid contents (*chyme*) to be forced on by peristaltic action of the stomach walls into the duodenum. Eventually all the contents of the stomach are thus discharged into the duodenum.

Once in the duodenum the chyme becomes mixed with three digestive fluids: (1) the *bile*, (2) the *pancreatic fluid*, (3) the *intestinal secretion*. The bile is a greenish fluid secreted more or less continuously by the liver cells and stored till required in the gall bladder. The presence of the acid chyme in the duodenum causes the formation in the cells of its lining of a *hormone* (see page 599) which is transported to the gall bladder by the blood, causing it to contract and discharge bile through the bile duct into the duodenum. The bile contains no enzymes but instead certain so-called bile '*salts*' (sodium glycocholate and taurocholate) which, like the modern detergents, reduce the surface tension of the water in the chyme and enable any fats in the chyme to become emulsified (split into minute drops) for more effective digestion. Being alkaline, the bile helps to neutralize the acid in the chyme, this being necessary since the enzymes in the duodenum require an alkaline medium for their operation. (Bile also contains pigments which are excretory products.)

The pancreatic secretion is stimulated by another hormone (*secretin*) produced in the walls of the duodenum by the action of the acid chyme and transported by the blood stream to the pancreas. It is strongly alkaline and contains the following enzymes: (1) a lipase (a fat-hydrolysing enzyme) called *steapsin* which 'converts' fats to fatty acids and glycerol; (2) a diastatic enzyme, pancreatic amylase; (3) *trypinsogen* which is a precursor of the proteolytic (protein-hydrolysing) enzyme *trypsin* which 'converts' peptones to amino acids and is converted into the active enzyme by *enterokinase* (see below).

The intestinal secretion produced by glands (see Fig. 20.1) in the walls of the small intestine is also alkaline and contains the following enzymes: (1) *erepsin*, which, like trypsin, 'converts' peptones to amino-acids; (2) *invertase* which 'converts' cane sugar to glucose and fructose; (3) *maltase* which 'converts' maltose to glucose; (4) *lactase* which 'converts' milk sugar (lactose) to glucose and galactose. It also contains the co-enzyme (activator) *enterokinase* (see above).

The final products of digestion consist of amino-acids derived from the proteins of the food, fatty acids and glycerol from the fats and simple hexose sugars derived from starch and other more complex carbohydrates. These are capable of diffusing into the walls of the intestines. The amino-acids and sugars diffuse into the blood flowing in the capillary networks of the villi (see page 470) and are carried by the blood to the liver via the portal vein, where they are dealt with in various ways (see page 497). The fatty acids combine with the bile salts or react with the alkalis of the intestinal fluids (sodium carbonate and bicarbonate) to form soaps, before diffusing together with the glycerol into the villi. Once inside the cells of the epithelium of the latter, the fatty acids are released from combination with the bile salts or in the soaps and react with the glycerine to form fat droplets which enter the lacteals in the centre of the villi. From the lacteals the fat emulsion ultimately reaches the blood via the lymphatic system (see page 373). The bile salts return in the portal circulation to the liver for re-issue in the bile.

SUMMARY TABLE OF DIGESTION

Site	*Enzymes*	*Change produced*
In the buccal cavity (saliva)	Ptyalin	Starch→maltase
In the stomach (gastric secretion)	Rennin Pepsin	Caseinogen→casein Proteins→peptones
In the intestines A. Bile	No enzymes	Fats emulsified
B. Pancreatic secretion	(1) Trypsinogen + enterokinase→ Trypsin	Peptones→amino-acids
	(2) Amylase	Starch→maltose
	(3) Steapsin (lipase)	Fats→fatty acids + glycerol
C. Intestinal secretion	Enterokinase (see above)	—
	Erepsin	Peptones→amino-acids
	Maltase	Maltose→glucose
	Invertase	Sucrose→glucose and fructose
	Lactase	Lactose→glucose and galactose

Further experiments to show the action of certain of the digestive enzymes can be carried out as follows.

(1) To show the action of rennin on milk protein, half a test-tube of milk is warmed to a temperature of 25°C and a little junket powder is added (this contains the enzyme *rennin*). The liquid in a short while turns solid owing to the conversion of the soluble caseinogen of the milk to a gel of insoluble casein.

(2) To show the action of pepsin on a protein, milk is diluted by adding three parts of water to one part of milk by volume, then a few drops of dilute hydrochloric acid are added to half a test-tube of the diluted milk which is then well shaken to produce a finely dispersed coagulum of casein. The liquid is kept at 25°C and a saltspoonful of commercial pepsin is added and well shaken up with the milk. In time the cloudy liquid clears owing to the formation of soluble peptones. To the liquid is then added enough caustic soda solution to make it strongly alkaline and then two or three drops of copper sulphate solution. A pinkish-rose colour indicates the presence of peptones.

(3) To show the action of trypsin on proteins, a small cube of hard-boiled white of egg is placed in each of the four basins: A, B, C, D, and covered with *distilled water*. A small crystal of thymol is added to each basin to prevent bacterial action. The water in C is made alkaline by adding a pinch of sodium bicarbonate while that in D is made acid by adding two drops of dilute hydrochloric acid. Nothing is added to the water in A but a saltspoonful of trypsin powder (Benger's food will do) is added to the water in B, C, and D. In the course of several days, the white of egg in C will be seen to break up and disappear, followed more slowly by that in B. No change occurs in A and D. This shows that proteins are digested by trypsin most readily when in an alkaline medium.

Digestion in chordates other than man

Throughout the vertebrates, apart from the buccal cavity and the 'design' of the intestinal region, the general plan of the alimentary canal is the same and the process of digestion and absorption follow the same order. The most marked differences are: (i) the absence of salivary glands and of the salivary secretion in all classes of vertebrates other than mammals, and (ii) special modifications in the herbivorous mammals. These modifications are needed to deal with the large amount of cellulose present in their diet. The enzymes needed for the digestion of cellulose are called '*cellulases*' and it is doubtful if any vertebrate produces these. Herbivores therefore utilize bacteria which secrete these enzymes to assist them by digesting the cell walls of the plants eaten and so releasing the cell contents for normal digestion. Part of the sugars and fatty acids produced by the breakdown of the cellulose are probably also absorbed by the animal. The ruminants (e.g. cows, deer and camels) have a modified stomach (see Fig. 22.1), in the paunch (*rumen*) of which

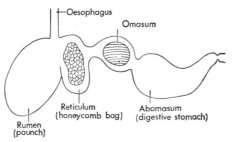

Fig. 22.1. Diagram to show the structure of the stomach of a ruminant.

the food undergoes bacterial digestion. It is then regurgitated and ground up by the molar teeth ('chewing the cud') before being swallowed for a second time. If sufficiently 'ground up', the food passes on to the true digestive stomach (*abomasum*) through the honeycomb bag (*reticulum*) and the manyplies (*omasum*). The latter probably acts as a filter so that only food which has been finely ground passes on while the honeycomb bag serves to store water, particularly in the camel. In horses and in rabbits and rodents, the stomach is of the normal type but the caecum is enlarged (see Fig. 16.17). The food on reaching the caecum first ascends it and then descends to reach the colon. In the caecum, bacterial digestion occurs while in the colon water is also absorbed (as it is in all land vertebrates) so that the faeces (undigested remains of the food plus bacteria and pigments derived from those of the bile) on reaching the rectum consist of semi-dried material. This is an important fact for the wild rabbit which seldom drinks water.

Finally, it must be mentioned that all digestive fluids contain *mucus*, whose main function is to lubricate the passage of the food through the alimentary canal. This is especially true of the saliva, which in some mammals, including the rabbit and the carnivores (e.g. dog) contains little or no ptyalin. In the dogfish and the frog a copious secretion of mucus is produced by mucus-secreting cells in the lining of the buccal cavity and the pharynx.

In *Amphioxus*, the food which consists of microscopic algae is driven into the pharynx through the enterostome by the powerful ciliary action of the cells lining the pharynx and the 'gill slits'. Cells in the endostyle secrete mucus which is wafted up the sides of the pharynx into the hyperpharyngeal groove together with the food particles entangled in it. There it is driven back by ciliary action into the mid-gut where it forms a cord and passes back through the intestine rotated by the cilia of its lining. Enzymes appear to be secreted by the cells of the lining of the hepatic diverticulum and the intestine and the digested food diffuses into the blood vessels in their walls.

Digestion in the invertebrates

IN THE PROTOZOA. Apart from the parasitic protozoa such as the Haemoflagellata (e.g. *Trypanosoma*), *Monocystis* and the malaria parasite, food is ingested into food vacuoles in the endoplasm where digestion occurs (*endocellular or intra-cellular digestion*). By the use of suitable indicators such as Neutral Red or Congo Red, it can be demonstrated that the contents of the food vacuoles are at first acid in nature and then alkaline. This is easily done by adding a very little of these dyes to a suspension of bacteria in water and, when the bacteria have absorbed the dye, adding some Paramecium and observing the food vacuoles under a microscope. This would indicate that the sequence of digestion is similar to that of higher animals. The parasitic types either absorb the predigested food of their hosts (e.g. the Haemoflagellata) or employ extracellular digestion (e.g. *Monocystis* and the malaria parasite).

IN THE COELENTERATA. Ingestion and egestion take place through a single aperture leading into the enteron (digestive cavity). Digestion is both extra- and intra-cellular. Enzymes secreted by certain glandular cells of the endoderm effect the major part of the digestion in the enteron but small particles of the food are engulfed by pseudopodial action by certain of the cells of the endoderm and digested in food vacuoles.

IN THE PLATYHELMINTHES. The free-living planarians (Turbellaria) ingest their food by means of a suctorial pharynx which can be everted (Fig. 4.2). Digestion occurs in the much-branched gut lined by endodermal cells which secrete enzymes. The extensive branching of the gut enables the products of digestion to pass readily to all parts of the animal's body, thus overcoming the handicap of the lack of a transporting system. *Fasciola* has a similar gut though the pharynx is not eversible and feeds on blood sucked in by the pharynx, but *Taenia* absorbs the digested food of its host through its surface. The flattened shape of the proglottids with their large surface-to-volume ratio facilitates the absorption of the food.

IN THE ANNELIDA. The digestive system of the earthworm (Fig. 6.4) may be taken as typical of the annelids. The food which consists of vegetable matter, i.e. humus mixed with soil or parts of leaves, is ingested by the action of the suctorial pharynx and passes by peristaltic action through the oesophagus to the crop. From here it passes into the gizzard where it is ground up into small fragments by muscular walls of the gizzard contracting and relaxing alternately with the assistance of the sand grains swallowed with the food. Digestive enzymes are secreted by the cells of the endoderm of the intestine, in the cavity of which the food is digested and then absorbed through its walls into the blood vessels in them. The longitudinal infolding of the intestinal wall on the dorsal side, known as the typhlosole, increases the absorptive area. In addition there is probably a proteolytic enzyme in the secretions of the pharyngeal lining which consists mainly of mucus to lubricate the passage of the food into the mouth.

IN THE ARTHROPODA. Digestion is extracellular as in the vertebrates. The alimentary canal of the crayfish (Fig. 8.5) is peculiar in that only a relatively short region of the gut is lined by endoderm and capable of absorbing digested food. This region is the mid-gut (mesenteron) but its small internal area is compensated for by the blind outgrowths into the haemocoele on each side forming the hepatic caeca in which both digestion and absorption occur. The food, which consists of carrion (dead fish, voles, etc.), is grasped by the chelae and pushed towards the mouth. Here it is held down by the third maxillipeds while the mandibles seize it and tear off portions which are ingested and pass through the short oesophagus into the mill-chamber of the proventriculus. In this the food is further broken down into small particles by the 'teeth' of the gastric mill (for method of operation see page 154) and acted upon by enzymes secreted by the cells lining the hepatic caeca and diffusing through the filter chamber forwardly into the mill chamber. Only the smallest particles are able to pass back through the filter chamber into the mid-gut for final digestion and absorption. The proventriculus and the hind gut are lined by ectoderm which secretes a cuticle and so do not play any part in absorbing food.

To show digestion by means of the digestive fluids of the crayfish, a live crayfish is removed from water and held securely by the carapace in an inverted position. With the rubber bulb squeezed flat, the point of a pipette is inserted between the mandibles into the mill-chamber. On releasing the pressure on the rubber bulb, the brownish fluid contents of the mill-chamber are withdrawn into the pipette. The crayfish can then be returned to the water none the worse for the operation. The fluid can be used to show the digestion of white of egg, as in Expt. 3, p. 488.

In insects, digestion and absorption also occurs mainly in the mid-gut and digestive caeca where the necessary enzymes are secreted. Enzymes do, however, diffuse through the gizzard (see Fig. 9.5) forward into the crop. Labial glands also occur and produce a salivary fluid containing a starch-digesting enzyme (amylase) which is exuded on to the food in many cases (e.g. cockroach and housefly) to soften it before ingestion. In the cockroach, the solid food is enclosed in a chitinous membrane (peritrophic membrane) secreted by the lining of the foregut before passing into the mid-gut. This membrane offers no barrier, however, to the diffusion through it of either enzymes or the products of digestion. The reason for its formation is obscure.

IN THE MOLLUSCA digestion is to a large extent intracellular. In the gastropods and bivalves the food enters the stomach in a finely divided form either because it has been rasped off by the radula in the gastropods or because it has been collected in particulate form by ciliary action. A certain amount of digestion takes place in the stomach but the process is completed by the taking up of the food particles by cells of the digestive gland. This structure is composed of tubules lined by enzyme-secreting and phagocytic cells and opens into the stomach. Food particles are transported within the tubules by ciliary action. In bivalves the gut contains many amoebocytes and these also take up the food particles and wander through the gut wall into the haemocoele. Molluscs are frequently highly adapted structurally to feeding on particulate types of food and the alimentary canal is likewise specialized by the possession of ciliary sorting mechanisms and the liberation of amylases from the so-called *crystalline style*. This is a transparent rod-like structure, secreted in a pocket of the stomach into which it projects. It is rotated by ciliary action and liberates enzymes as it is worn away. Digestion in the cephalopods, which are carnivorous animals, is chiefly extracellular.

IN THE ECHINODERMATA both intracellular and extracellular digestion occur. In the starfishes the stomach may even be extruded through the mouth and wrapped around the prey so that digestion takes place outside the animal's body. The pyloric caeca contain many phagocytic cells and it is probable that they take up small food particles and migrate through the gut wall. The details of digestion in the sea urchins, brittle stars and holothurians are not well understood but it is probable that some preliminary digestion takes place in the gut and is completed by phagocytic action.

23. *Transport and Circulation*

THE MOVEMENTS of substances into and out of the body of an animal or within it depend primarily on the random movement of their molecules or ions known as diffusion. To enter or leave the body substances have to pass through a surface which is permeable to them. This surface may be an external one such as the skin, or the lining of an internal organ, e.g. the alveolar walls of the lungs, which is in communication with the external environment by ducts or other passages, e.g. the trachea. Within the bodies of coelomate triploblastic metazoa exist internal surfaces such as the endothelium of the blood capillaries which also permit the diffusion of substances through them. In general it may be said that the surfaces through which diffusion can occur are of the nature of semi-permeable membranes permitting the diffusion through them of ions and molecules of small dimensions. Thus the relatively small molecules of the productions of digestion, e.g. hexose sugars, fatty acids and glycerine and amino-acids, can pass through the cellular lining of the intestines whereas the larger molecules or colloidal particles of di- or polysaccharides and proteins cannot. Hence the necessity for the digestion of complex foods. Excreta produced by the catabolic processes of the body must also eventually pass out of the body through a surface such as walls of the kidney tubules and these excreta also consist of relatively small molecules.

Once substances such as simple food molecules and oxygen have entered the body through a surface, they have still to travel to all parts of the body where they are needed. In Protozoa, coelenterates and Platyhelminthes the distances to be traversed are generally so small that diffusion alone—aided possibly by the circulation of the cytoplasm as in the Protozoa—is sufficient for their distribution. The same applies to the excreta in these animals which by diffusion reach the surface where they are to be eliminated, though in certain cases wandering amoebocytes may play a part. These occur, for example, in the coelomic fluid of the annelids, engulfing excreta and transporting them to the lumen of the gut for elimination in the faeces. In the large majority of the Metazoa, the rate of travel provided by

diffusion is inadequate and in consequence the transport of substances within the body must be speeded up. This is effected by the
presence of a blood vascular system composed of tubes—the blood
vessels—in which a transporting fluid—the blood—is kept in circulation by a definite pumping organ known as the heart or by contractile blood vessels performing the same function as in the annelids
and *Amphioxus*. The blood is caused to circulate through the blood
vessels by alternate contractions and dilatations of the heart or
contractile vessels, owing to the action of muscle cells in the walls of
these organs assisted by the operation of internal valves which direct
the flow of the blood in a constant direction. The general scheme (or
'layout') of a blood system which includes a heart is shown in Fig.
23.1, where it can be seen that the blood vessels are of three types:

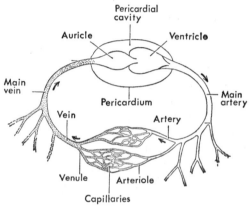

Fig. 23.1. Diagram to illustrate the general scheme of a closed blood
system.

(1) the arteries and the arterioles (smaller arteries) which convey
blood *away* from the heart; (2) the veins and venules (smaller veins)
which lead blood to the heart, and (3) the capillaries which are fine
tubes connecting the arterioles with the venules and whose walls
consist of a single layer of flattened cells.

The blood system of the Arthropoda shows a departure from this
scheme in that capillaries are lacking, the arteries conveying the
blood from the heart to a cavity (or cavities) known as the haemocoele in which lie the various organs of the body so that these organs
are actually bathed by the blood. Even the pericardial cavity is part of
the haemocoele, so that auricles are also lacking, the pericardium
acting in their stead to supply the ventricle with blood returned to

it from the rest of the haemocoele. The molluscs have a blood system resembling that of the arthropods but possessing auricles.

In blood systems where capillaries exist, the blood does not come into contact with the cells of the various organs as in the Arthropoda and the Mollusca and the blood system is said to be a 'closed' one as opposed to the 'open' ones of the Arthropoda and of the Mollusca. It is therefore necessary that substances such as oxygen and food should pass out through the walls of the capillaries in order to reach the cells of the organs and tissues. This they do, and travel to their destination—partly by diffusion and partly by the mechanical flow in a fluid called the *lymph* which penetrates through the intercellular spaces and thus comes into intimate contact with the cells of the body or at least into close proximity with them (see pages 372–3). Carbon dioxide produced by the respiration of the cells and nitrogenous excreta from them reach the blood flowing through the capillaries in the same way.

The functions of the blood include the following:

(1) Transport of various substances connected with the metabolism of the body (metabolites) from one part of the body to another, e.g. oxygen from the respiratory surfaces to the tissues digested foods from the gut to the tissues and excreta from the tissues to the excretory organs;

(2) Distribution of heat produced in the tissues by respiration thereby helping to maintain an even body temperature. To prevent overheating of the body, particularly in the warm-blooded mammals and birds, it is usually necessary that heat losses should occur through the external surfaces of the body and this loss is facilitated by the conveyance of heat to the surfaces from the tissues by the blood;

(3) Assisting in chemical co-ordination (page 599) by distributing to all parts of the body hormones produced by the endocrine organs (Chapter 32);

(4) Acting as a defence against disease-producing bacteria which may have gained entrance to the body. This defence consists of the phagocytic action of the colourless blood cells (i.e. their feeding on the bacteria in amoeboid fashion) and of the formation within the blood of antibodies;

(5) Acting as a supporting agent through the medium of the blood pressure in erectile organs, e.g. the penis of the mammals, and as an aid to locomotion in the protrusion of the foot in molluscs, e.g. *Anodon*;

(6) Maintenance of a constant internal environment favourable to the performance of the normal activities of the cells of the body.

While the plasma of the blood (page 455) serves to transport soluble substances in physical solution, the carriage of the respiratory gases (oxygen and carbon dioxide) presents a special problem owing to the low solubilities of these gases in water. The method of overcoming this problem in the case of oxygen is the employment of respiratory pigments capable of forming 'loose compounds' with oxygen, e.g. the haemoglobins of the annelids and vertebrates and the haemocyanins of the arthropods and Mollusca (see pages 157 and 209). Carbon dioxide is carried partly in solution and partly in the form of the unstable bicarbonate ion (HCO_3). (Special reference will be made to the part this ion plays in the transference of oxygen from the plasma to the red cells and vice versa (pp. 519–20).)

In addition to the exchange of metabolites between the blood circulating in the capillaries and the cells of the tissues via the lymph with their resulting effects on the composition of the blood, there are others which occur as the blood flows through certain organs such as the gut, the lungs or gills, the excretory organs. These in a mammal are summarized in Fig. 23.2 but the number of exchanges occurring between the cells of the liver and the kidneys and the blood are too numerous to be shown in a simple diagram. The liver produces more changes in the composition of the blood flowing through it than does any other organ in the body, through its functions of food storage (page 479), deamination (page 527), detoxication (conversion of toxic substances, produced by bacterial action in the intestines and absorbed into the blood stream, into non-poisonous compounds which are later excreted), secretion (page 486) and excretion (page 486). Also owing to the high rate of metabolism in this organ, it contributes to the blood a considerable amount of heat.

For details of the various blood vascular systems found in animals described in this book, reference should be made to the appropriate sections dealing with them, but in the case of the vertebrate systems it will be useful to compare them to show how mammalian circulation which is adapted to life in the air has evolved from the primitive form found in the fish.

Comparison of the blood vascular systems of the fish, frog and mammal

1. The heart of the fish has one auricle and one ventricle, and the

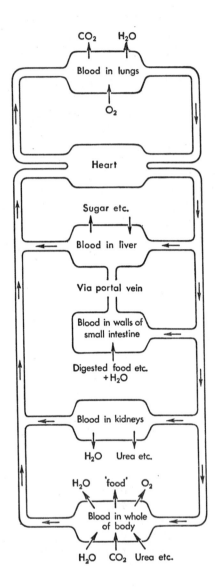

Fig. 23.2. Diagram to summarize the exchanges between the blood and the tissues.

circulation is a *single* one, i.e. the blood in making one complete circuit of the body passes through the heart once only.

In the mammal the heart is divided into two auricles and two ventricles, and the circulation is a *double* one, the blood passing twice through the heart during one complete circuit of the body.

The circulation in the frog is *incompletely* double in that only part of the blood passes twice through the heart in completing the circuit. The auricles only are double, both opening into the single ventricle.

2. The main veins of fish are shown in Fig. 14.19. There are two portal systems: the hepatic portal vein and the renal portal veins. The blood is returned from the kidneys to the heart by a pair of posterior cardinal veins and from the head to the heart by a pair of anterior cardinal veins. The anterior and posterior cardinal veins on each side enter a transversely running vessel (ductus Cuvieri) leading to the sinus venosus. Blood from the liver returns to the sinus venosus by two hepatic veins entering the sinus venosus in the centre.

The venous system of the tadpole resembles that of a fish but during metamorphosis a median posterior vena cava replaces the two posterior cardinal veins for the return of the blood from the kidneys to the sinus venosus which opens into the right auricle. The hepatic veins discharge blood into this vessel instead of opening independently into the sinus venosus as in the fish. The Cuvierian ducts become the anterior venae cavae of the adult frog. (In some Amphibia, e.g. newts and salamanders, the posterior cardinal veins persist in the adult stage in addition to the posterior vena cava.) Both hepatic and renal portal veins are found, though some of the blood returning from the hind limbs by-passes the kidneys via the anterior abdominal vein and unites with that in the hepatic portal vein. Two pulmonary veins, one from each lung, open into the left auricle; these are, of course, not present in the fish.

In the adult mammal there is no sinus venosus, the three venae cavae opening directly into the right auricle. There is only one portal vein—the hepatic portal vein, blood reaching the kidneys directly from the dorsal aorta only and not, as in the fish and the frog, by a renal portal system as well as from the dorsal aorta. The posterior vena cava extends beyond the kidneys to receive the veins from the hinder regions of the trunk and hind limbs and tail. In the embryonic stage the venous system includes posterior cardinal veins and these later become modified to form the azygos veins of the thoracic wall of the adult.

3. In order to compare the arterial systems of the fish, frog and

mammal, it is first necessary to refer to the arterial system of the bony fish since this is more nearly related to those of the frog and the mammal than is that of the dogfish. The arterial system of the bony fish resembles that of the dogfish but the dorsal aorta divides into two branches in the pharyngeal region. These two branches—the lateral dorsal aortae or suprabranchial vessels—are directly connected with the efferent branchial vessels bringing blood from the gills, whereas in the dogfish the efferent branchial vessels are connected to the median dorsal aorta by the epibranchial vessels. In the developing embryo of the lung fish, six pairs of afferent and efferent vessels are formed in succession in the visceral arches but the first two pairs, those of the mandibular and hyoid arches, have only a fleeting existence. The remaining four pairs persist in the branchial arches of the adult, each afferent branchial vessel being connected to the corresponding efferent branchial vessel by capillaries in the filaments of the gills.

At the stage when the internal gills are functioning, the tadpole of the frog possesses an arterial system similar to that of the bony fish, but at metamorphosis a number of modifications of this system occur. With the disappearance of the gills and their capillaries, the afferent and efferent vessels in each branchial arch become continuous. The anterior pair form the carotid arches, the second pair the systemic arches, the third pair degenerate while the fourth pair form the pulmocutaneous arches with their connexions with the lungs and the skin. At the same time the portions of the aortae between the carotid arches and the systemic arches known as the ducts of Botalli become reduced to fibrous bands, and the pulmocutaneous arches lose their connexions with the lateral dorsal aortae. The ventral aorta becomes the truncus arteriosus. In the adult salamanders, no portions of the arterial system are lost or degenerate, apart from the ducts of Botalli, all four arches being present and the pulmocutaneous arch retaining its connexion (the ductus arteriosus) on each side with the lateral dorsal aorta. (See also pp. 329 and 639–643.)

The mammal, even in the embryonic stage, never develops gills in the visceral clefts so that the dorsal and ventral portions of each 'aortic arch' are continuous from their first appearance. The plan and course of development are however the same as in the fish and tadpole but as development proceeds the ventricle as well as the auricle becomes divided into two and the pulmonary arch—which, however, has no cutaneous branch—becomes split off from the ventral aorta and acquires a separate opening into the right ventricle.

The ventral aorta leading from the left ventricle is connected to the dorsal aorta by one systemic arch only—the left one, the right one disappearing. The systemic arch bears the carotid and subclavian arteries derived from the carotid arches of the embryo. While the foetus is developing inside the uterus, its lungs are not functioning and the connexion between the pulmonary arch and the systemic arch—the ductus arteriosus—remains open, so that blood issuing from the heart through the pulmonary artery is largely by-passed into the systemic arch instead of flowing through the former to the lungs. Also at this stage an opening (foramen ovale) exists in the septum between the two auricles so that most of the blood which enters the right auricle passes into the left auricle instead of entering the right ventricle. When the young mammal is born, the lungs become functional and the ductus arteriosus closes up to form a fibrous band, so that all the blood issuing from the right ventricle passes to the lungs via the pulmonary artery. At the same time the foramen ovale in the septum between the auricles closes up so that the two streams of blood (oxygenated and deoxygenated) flowing through the heart are entirely separated.

24. *Respiration*

THE WORD 'respiration' can have several meanings. For instance, it is used to denote the breathing movements of mammals, to denote the uptake of oxygen from the air in the lungs and the giving out of carbon dioxide and also to denote those chemical changes going on in cells which use up the oxygen and produce the carbon dioxide. It is not practicable to confine the meaning of the word to one part only of this whole complex process but the various aspects of the respiratory activities are often known by names which serve to distinguish them from each other. Thus the chemical changes going on in the cells which are analogous to combustion are known collectively as *tissue* or *cellular respiration*. The intake of oxygen and the elimination of carbon dioxide is known as *gaseous exchange* while the breathing movements are said to bring about the *ventilation of the lungs*. By this means it is generally possible to avoid confusion although a little reflection will show that even these various divisions of the process of respiration are not sharply defined.

The comparison between respiration as a whole and the chemical process of combustion or burning began to be made in the seventeenth century, but it was not until the work of Lavoisier (1743–94) in the second half of the eighteenth century that the chemistry of combustion and respiration was put on a firm scientific basis by the use of the term oxygen for the gas which is consumed in these processes. Lavoisier's emphasis on weighing in the investigation of reactions led to the realization that the heat evolved in combustion had no weight and that matter is conserved and not destroyed during combustion (although we now know that this is not so in reactions involving the atomic nucleus). Both the idea of heat and that of conservation of matter, which were later more thoroughly worked out and formulated, had great importance for biology as well as chemistry.

It is now clear that the process of respiration as a whole is closely similar to combustion but differs from it in certain important respects. The chief points of similarity and difference between the processes are as follows:

(1) Both are oxidation reactions involving oxygen, taken over all.

(2) Both processes, respiration and combustion, result in the production, from a material such as glucose, of carbon dioxide and water with the liberation of energy.

(3) All the energy liberated in combustion is set free as heat or light while in respiration it is mostly conserved in the formation of new chemical bonds. These in turn, may be used in the performance of mechanical work, as in muscular movement, or in osmotic work involving the movement of substances against an osmotic gradient, or be absorbed in the formation of endothermic compounds such as urea.

(4) The heat liberated in combustion must be set free sufficiently rapidly to maintain a high temperature in the burning substance or the reaction stops. In respiration all the energy released, including such as appears as heat, is liberated slowly, the reactions being controlled by enzymes.

(5) At one time it appeared that the process of combustion involved simple reactions but it is now known that even an apparently straightforward reaction like the burning of carbon monoxide in oxygen takes place in a number of stages. The reactions which take place in respiration occur as an exceedingly complex series of steps.

With these features of the respiratory process in mind it will be convenient to consider firstly the way in which an animal cell can bring about the oxidation of glucose or glycogen to carbon dioxide and water, and secondly the way in which the highly specialized striped muscle cell can use the energy which these reactions set free for its contraction and the performance of work in the sense in which the word is used in physics.

In the process of cell respiration all the steps are catalysed by appropriate enzymes and some of the energy which might otherwise be set free as heat is locked up in the formation of special valency bonds in complex organic phosphates which are synthesized from materials present in the cell. The chief of these complex substances, known as *adenosine triphosphate* (ATP), is used in the cell as an intermediary for the transfer of that energy which is made available during cell respiration to other chemical reactions which require energy to be supplied before they can proceed. So far ATP is the chief substance known which can play this part and *the essential feature of the respiratory process is the synthesis of ATP*. This substance may be likened to ready money which can be used at once for making purchases. The stock of ready money can be replenished from the bank where the money is stored. Once the current account (glycogen) has been exhausted, no more ready money can be drawn to pay for purchases (e.g. muscular movement) until the deposit account (fat or glycogen stored in the liver) can be tapped.

The adenosine triphosphate (ATP) which is synthesized in respiration is of value to the cell, as has been seen, by virtue of its power of storing energy in a way which yet leaves it readily available. This property depends on the chemical structure of ATP which is written below. Although it is written in full, all that it is necessary to know for the present purpose is that it consists of a basic substance, adenine, a sugar with five carbon atoms called ribose and three phosphate radicals.

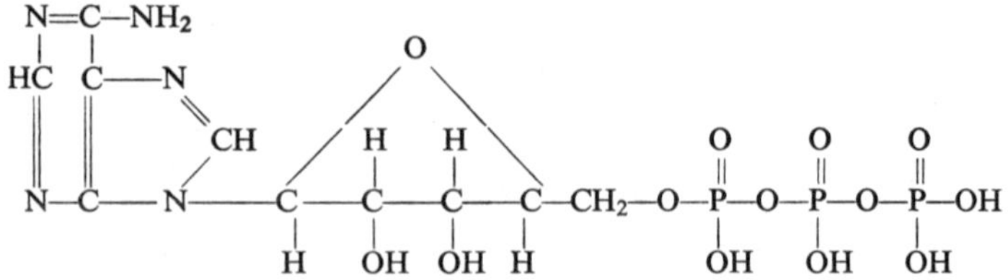

| Adenine | Ribose | Phosphate radicals |

The three phosphate radicals which are joined to the sugar are linked in different ways. When the last phosphate bond is broken by hydrolysis thus:

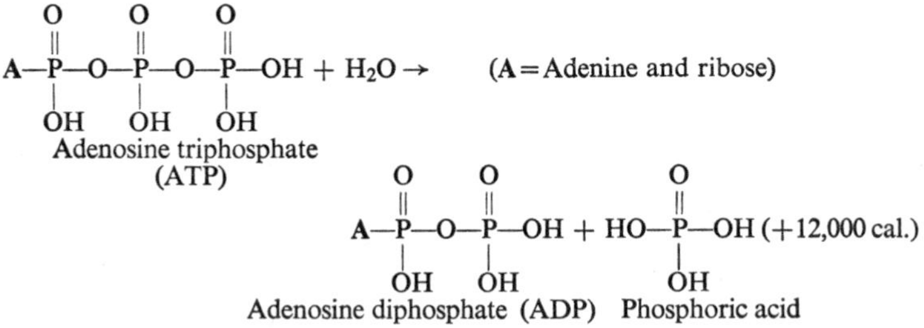

$(A = Adenine\ and\ ribose)$

Adenosine triphosphate
(ATP)

Adenosine diphosphate (ADP)   Phosphoric acid

12,000 calories per gram-molecule becomes available. When the second bond is hydrolysed in the same way, again 12,000 calories become available, but when the last phosphate radical is removed from the organic residue by hydrolysis then only about 2,000 calories per gram-molecule are liberated. The two end phosphate radicals are said to be attached by *high-energy bonds*. In the possession of these lies the importance of ATP. The energy stored in the high-energy bonds of ATP is used whenever energy is required by the cell for reactions which are energy-consuming. One of the most important of these is believed to be the reaction between the molecules of the two main types of protein found in muscle, namely myosin and actin. In the muscle fibril the long molecules of myosin and actin are so arranged that they slide along one another when the muscle contracts (see page 460). It is thought that the energy required to bring about this reaction comes from the hydrolysis of the high-energy bonds of ATP. Thus ATP serves as it were to collect the energy of respiration and to make it available for a reaction between proteins which needs energy before it proceeds and which is the basis of the contraction of muscle and hence the performance of mechanical work.

We can thus see one way in which the process of respiration is of importance in the life of the animal, and it is not a great step to appreciate that the same material, ATP, may be used in other reactions going on in the cell which need energy to be supplied to them. We must now follow the way in which the oxidation of carbohydrate takes place. This involves two main sets of chemical changes one known as glycolysis and the other as Krebs cycle or the citric acid cycle. The first is essentially a set of intramolecular changes which do not involve oxygen while the citric acid cycle brings about the final oxidation of the products of glycolysis (pyruvic acid or lactic acid) to carbon dioxide and water. *In both of these sets of chemical changes the energy which is set free can be used in the synthesis of the high-energy bonds of ATP.* This involves the incorporation of inorganic phosphate. It follows therefore that phosphate radicals are an essential part of the respiratory system of animals.

Glycolysis

The first stage in the utilization of the carbohydrate present in the cell is its conversion into an ester of glucose and phosphoric acid. The starting point is *glycogen* $(C_6H_{10}O_5)n$, a starch-like polysaccharide made of linked glucose-units. Glycogen can be represented by the structural formula:

$(C_6H_{10}O_5)n$

When hydrolysed it gives rise to glucose, thus:

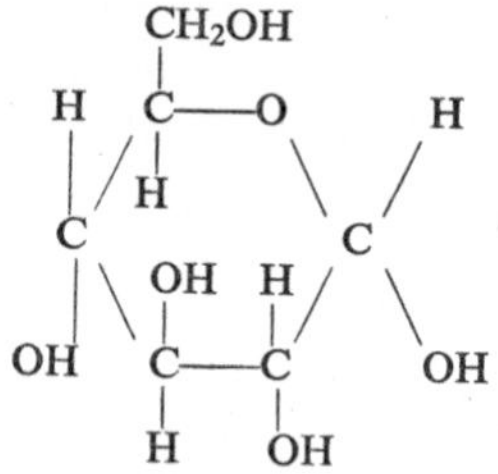

Glycogen reacts with inorganic phosphate radical to give glucose phosphate, an ester of glucose and phosphoric acid, the reaction being catalysed by the enzyme phosphorylase. The glucose phosphate is then split into two molecules of phosphoglyceraldehyde:

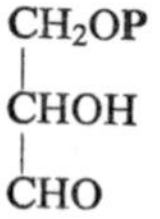

$$
\begin{array}{l}
CH_2OP \\
| \\
CHOH \\
| \\
CHO
\end{array}
\qquad
\left[\; P = \text{phosphate radicle} \quad
\begin{array}{c}
O \\
\| \\
-P-OH \\
| \\
OH
\end{array}
\; \right].
$$

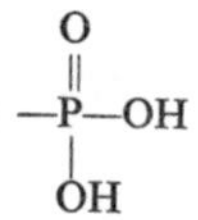

As is well known, the oxidation of an aldehyde to an acid is an exothermic reaction, e.g. acetaldehyde to acetic acid. The next step in glycolysis is then the oxidation of this aldehyde (phosphoglyceraldehyde) to an acid. If this were carried out by molecular oxygen, the energy products would be liberated as heat, but in the cell the oxidation is provided by the addition of phosphate and the removal of hydrogen which enables energy produced to be shunted into a high-energy phosphate bond. This compound then hands on its high-energy phosphate radical to ADP, thereby converting it into ATP. Thus we see how an exothermic reaction in the cell leads to the formation of the energy currency ATP. This example is one of a number of chemical sequences by which the energy of exothermic reactions is captured by the cell in a convenient form for its later use.

Further changes result in the formation of *pyruvic acid* ($CH_3-CO-COOH$) from which *lactic acid* may be formed by the addition of two hydrogen atoms ($CH_3-CH(OH)-COOH$). The whole process can be summarized by saying that *one of the 6-carbon* glucose units of which glycogen is a polymer is split into *two 3-carbon* molecules of lactic acid with a gain of three molecules of ATP formed from ADP and inorganic phosphate. This series of changes does not require the direct use of oxygen, the so-called oxidation being in part dehydrogenation, and it thus provides an anaerobic mechanism by which the chemical bond energy of foodstuffs may be transferred to ATP.

Aerobic oxidation cycle, Krebs cycle or the citric acid cycle

In addition to anaerobic glycolysis just described the oxidation of 3-carbon compounds (pyruvic acid or lactic acid) to carbon dioxide and water is brought about by a cycle of chemical changes known as the citric acid cycle or Krebs cycle in which, again, the energy liberated in the process can be transferred to the high energy bonds of the ATP formed. Pyruvic acid can combine with CO_2 to form *oxaloacetic acid* to which another molecule of pyruvic acid can join forming citric acid

$$CH_3\text{---}CO\text{---}COOH + CO_2 \rightarrow HOOC\text{---}CO\text{---}CH_2\text{---}COOH$$
Pyruvic acid   Oxaloacetic acid

$$HOOC\text{---}CO\text{---}CH_2\text{---}COOH + CH_3\text{---}CO\text{---}COOH \rightarrow$$
Oxaloacetic acid   Pyruvic acid

$$HOOC\text{---}C(OH)\text{---}CH_2\text{---}COOH \; [+CO_2]$$
$$|$$
$$CH_2COOH$$
Citric acid, a tricarboxylic acid

A series of changes then takes place in which water is involved and in which there is a *net* removal of four hydrogen atoms and three molecules of CO_2 together with the regeneration of oxaloacetic acid. The process may be represented diagrammatically as shown below. It is believed to take place chiefly in the mitochondria.

In addition to the oxidation of lactic acid, Krebs cycle brings about the synthesis of more ATP through some of the intermediate steps. Thus, like anaerobic glycolysis previously described, it also serves for the transformation of the energy liberated in the chemical reactions to be captured as high-energy phosphate bonds.

The diagram of Krebs cycle given above is very much simpler than is the series of changes which do, in fact, take place in the living cell. It illustrates, however, that carbon dioxide molecules are produced as such and that hydrogen atoms are removed. These are removed, not as free hydrogen, of course, but combined with intermediary substances which are thereby reduced. These substances are called *hydrogen acceptors*. One such hydrogen acceptor is *cytochrome* which is a pigment resembling haemoglobin in chemical structure and, like it, capable of existing in a reduced and an oxidized form. Cytochrome

Respiration

is reduced when it accepts hydrogen and this reduced form can be oxidized by molecular oxygen when catalysed by the enzyme cytochrome oxidase, water being formed from the hydrogen previously accepted.

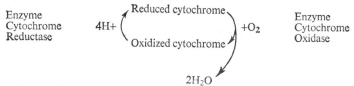

Enzyme
Cytochrome
Reductase

4H+

Reduced cytochrome

Oxidized cytochrome

+O$_2$

Enzyme
Cytochrome
Oxidase

2H$_2$O

There are also other substances which play an important part in the oxidation reactions of the cell by acting as hydrogen acceptors that are readily reoxidized. Chief among them are vitamin C (ascorbic acid), the so-called co-enzymes I and II, and the tripeptide glutathione. The only feature which they have in common is the ease with which they may be reduced and reoxidized.

Ascorbic acid

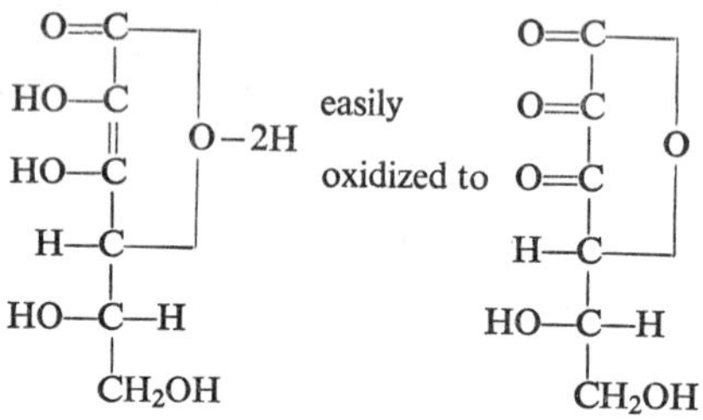

O=C—
HO—C
          O − 2H
HO—C
H—C—
HO—C—H
CH$_2$OH

easily

oxidized to

O=C—
O=C
          O
O=C
H—C—
HO—C—H
CH$_2$OH

Glutathione—3-amino-acid residues from glutamic acid, cysteine and glycine.

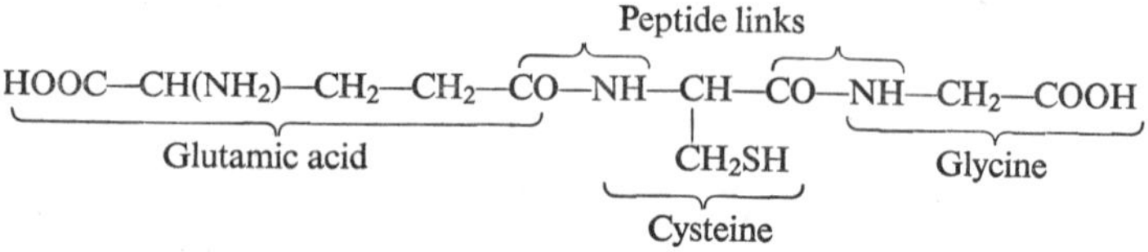

Peptide links

HOOC—CH(NH$_2$)—CH$_2$—CH$_2$—CO—NH—CH—CO—NH—CH$_2$—COOH

Glutamic acid

CH$_2$SH

Glycine

Cysteine

It can be seen from these examples—which are only a few of the processes involved in cell respiration—that the changes are complex, but that they take place in stages. A very much simplified diagram which illustrates some of the processes is given below (Fig. 24.1). In the complex reactions it will be realized that pyruvic acid occupies an important place. Its importance is further enhanced because fats and proteins can, in many instances, be converted into pyruvic acid and hence used in respiration.

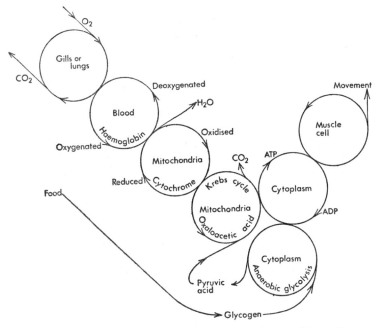

Fig. 24.1. Diagram illustrating the interrelation of some of the cycles of chemical change involved in respiration.

The supply of oxygen

Whereas there is good evidence that the essential process in respiration, namely the making of the high-energy bonds of ATP, takes place in much the same manner in all living cells, there are many different ways in which oxygen is transported from the environment in which the organism lives, to the cell in which the chemical processes occur. Moreover, although all the chemical processes of respiration take place in the aqueous medium of the cell there is a limit to the amount of oxygen which can dissolve in water and this renders it vitally necessary for the cell and organism to have means of increasing its rate of oxygen supply if metabolism is intense. A comparison of the oxygen available in the atmosphere and that which is dissolved in water shows clearly the superiority of the atmosphere as a source of oxygen and the need for oxygen-carrying devices within the bodies of the animals.

In the atmosphere oxygen is present at a partial pressure of about 160 mm. Hg since it occupies approximately 21% by volume of the mixture of gases. One litre of air, which weighs about 1·5 gm., thus contains, at ordinary room temperature (16°C or 60°F) about

$$\frac{32 \times 21 \times 273 \times 1,000}{22,400 \times 100 \times 289} = 0 \cdot 28 \text{ gm. of oxygen}$$

(Where 32=mol. wt. of oxygen; 22,400 ml.=gm. mol. vol.; 21=% of oxygen in atmosphere; 289°=Abs. temp.)

The solubility of oxygen in water is such that, when air is in equilibrium with water at room temperature, the water contains about 0·7 vol. of oxygen per 100 vol. of water or 7·0 ml. per litre measured at S.T.P. Thus 1 litre of water, saturated with oxygen at 16°C, contains 0·0095 gm. of oxygen, as can be seen from the following calculation:

22,400 ml. of oxygen at S.T.P. weigh 32 gm.
7 ml. of oxygen at 760 mm. Hg and 289°A weigh

$$\frac{32 \times 7 \times 273}{2,240 \times 289} = 0 \cdot 0095 \text{ gm.}$$

or, say, approx. 0·01 gm.

In other words, volume for volume, air is about thirty times a richer source of oxygen than water which is in equilibrium with the atmosphere. Weight for weight the atmosphere is roughly 20,000 times richer in oxygen than water saturated with the gas. These physical facts are of great significance in the respiratory processes of animals.

The supply of oxygen to the respiring cells thus depends on many factors, the chief of which are as follows:

(a) the amount of oxygen present in the respiratory medium;
(b) the rate of renewal of the respiratory medium;
(c) the rate of diffusion of the oxygen from the medium into the animal which depends, among other things, on the relative rates of diffusion of oxygen in air and in water;
(d) the rate of transport of oxygen from the respiratory surface to the respiring cell;
(e) the rate at which the oxygen is consumed by the respiring cell.

We have already seen that the amount of oxygen present in the respiratory medium is great in air and small in water and it is well to remember also that (unlike the solubility of most solids) the solubility of gases diminishes with rise in temperature. Thus arctic oceans are richer in oxygen than are tropical seas.

It is necessary now to look at the various factors listed and to see how they may be related to the types of respiratory mechanisms found in animals.

Protozoa

No adaptations are found among the members of the Protozoa which appear to be especially concerned with the renewal of the respiratory medium or the transport of oxygen. Nevertheless the motile ones, and some of those which are sedentary like *Vorticella*, renew the water which is adjacent their pellicles by movement or by the creation of currents which are essentially feeding currents. Some are sensitive to the concentration of oxygen and move to places where it suits their needs. When a culture of the colourless flagellate *Bodo* is first placed under a coverglass, the organisms are distributed at random but after a time, as the oxygen in the water is used up, they will be found to accumulate at the edge of the coverslip where atmospheric oxygen is dissolving and diffusing inwards.

Parasitic protozoa such as *Monocystis* live in sites where oxygen is probably not deficient, as a plentiful supply is needed by the developing spermatozoa of the host. The blood parasites such as *Plasmodium* and *Trypanosoma* are also well situated since they occupy a place in the oxygen-carrying tissue of their hosts. Nevertheless it is thought that parasitic protozoans may be able to rely on anaerobic respiration for their energy requirements.

Even with the small amount of oxygen dissolved in water, there is no difficulty in accounting for the supply of oxygen to protozoans by diffusion alone, for it can be calculated that only a very small gradient of oxygen concentration between the inside and the outside medium is required.

Coelenterata

The Coelenterata consists of only two cell layers and yet may attain a large size, e.g. medusae. In these forms the bulky mesogloea of the animal contains few, if any, living cells. Hence all the cells that are actively metabolizing are near the supply of oxygenated water outside the animal or are near the contents of the enteron which, in many species, is changed quite often. Hence the coelenterates can rely, as do the Protozoa, on the process of diffusion to supply the oxygen that they require.

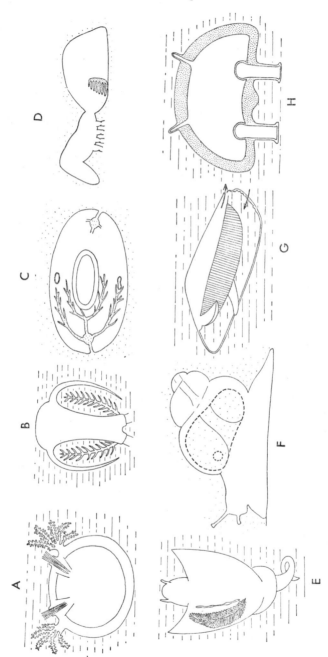

Fig. 24.2. Diagram to illustrate the variety of organs of invertebrate animals which function in the exchange of respiratory gases.

Air is shown as light stipple; water as horizontal lines. *A* the lugworm (*Arenicola*), T.S. of gill region. *B* the crayfish (*Astacus*), T.S. of cephalothorax. *C* an insect, T.S. to show tracheae. *D* a spider, L.S. to show lung book. *E* a winkle (*Littorina*) removed from shell and with mantle cavity opened to show ctenidium or gill. *F* a snail (*Helix*) – outline of air-filled mantle cavity and its opening. *G* a mussel (*Mytilus*) – with one valve of shell removed to show left ctenidium or gill. *H* a starfish (*Asterias*), T.S. of arm to show gills and tube feet.

Platyhelminthes

The Platyhelminthes are not known to have any special methods of procuring oxygen from the medium in which they live or any special means of transporting it although their metabolism is, in general, more rapid than that of the coelenterates. The free-living Turbellaria are mostly small and thin so that nowhere has oxygen a great distance to travel before reaching the respiring cell. The Trematoda e.g. *Fasciola* and the Cestoda, e.g. *Taenia*, are larger animals living in the gut or bile duct where oxygen might be expected to be deficient. There is evidence that they can respire anaerobically, breaking down glycogen (of which they contain considerable quantities) to fatty acids, although they are capable of aerobic respiration when oxygen is available. The precise chemical changes which the respiratory processes of these parasites involve is by no means established.

Annelida

With the separation of the muscular body-wall from the gut wall by a coelom which took place during the evolution of the Annelida, the evolution at the same time of a blood vascular system assisted the transport of food materials about the body and of oxygen from the surface to the tissues. The pigment which the blood contains can transport oxygen from the outside medium to the respiring tissues. Instead of the 0·7 ml. of oxygen per 100 ml. which water can dissolve, the blood of the lugworm (*Arenicola marina*) can dissolve about 7 ml. of oxygen per 100 ml. of blood and it is likely that the oxygen capacity of the blood of the earthworm is of the same order. In these annelids the oxygen-carrying pigment, haemoglobin, is in the blood plasma and not in corpuscles. Since the haemoglobin of annelids is of very large molecular size, the molecular weight being of the order of 2,000,000, it is clear that its rate of diffusion is very low and the possibility of its leaking out of the capillary walls remote. Blood is circulated by contraction of the muscular walls of the main blood vessels and picks up oxygen diffusing in through the cuticle in its passage through capillaries which lie near the outer epithelium or even between its component cells as in the earthworm.

Arthropoda

Many ways of obtaining oxygen from the environment are found in the Arthropoda. In general, Crustacea such as *Astacus* have thin-walled feathery gills through which blood is circulated and over the outer surface of which a current of water is maintained (see page 213). The blood of many species contains, not haemoglobin, but a copper-containing compound, haemocyanin, which also has an affinity for oxygen. Haemocyanin is, in general, not such an 'efficient' respiratory pigment as haemoglobin and the oxygen capacity of the blood of crustaceans such as the lobster (*Homarus*), the edible crab (*Cancer*) and the crayfish ranges from 1·5 to 3 volumes per cent, at best only about four times the oxygen capacity of water.

Insects are mainly terrestrial and breathe air which reaches very near to the actively metabolizing cells by fine tubes or tracheae, provided with spiral chitinous thickenings which keep them open along the greater part of their length (see page 180). Diffusion alone suffices to supply oxygen to many small insects and during active movement is probably aided by slight changes of size brought about by general muscular activity. In bigger insects large tracheal vessels are present which can be ventilated by special abdominal movements. The spiracles are the openings of the tracheae to the exterior and they can be opened and closed in response to increase or decrease in carbon dioxide concentration in the tracheal system. (For the method of gaseous exchange in aquatic insects see p. 194.)

The spiders have internal cavities connected to the outside by an aperture and lined with very thin cuticle. They contain many projecting leaves arranged like the leaves of a book only with small air spaces between them. From this similarity they are known as lung books.

Mollusca

Various molluscs are adapted for carrying out gaseous exchange in the sea, in fresh water and on land. Marine molluscs generally possess a gill or gills through which a good flow of blood is maintained and around which the water is constantly renewed by ciliary action, usually on the gill itself. Gastropods such as the whelk (*Buccinum*) and the winkle (*Littorina*) have a gill which functions only in gaseous exchange but the bivalves, such as the mussel (*Mytilus*) have large and complex gills, one of whose functions is to strain off the small particles and organisms which they collect for food. This entails the production of a current of water by the action of cilia which serves both for feeding and for respiration. There is no doubt that a good deal of gaseous exchange also takes place over the general body surface for this, as the name Mollusca implies, is soft and not covered with any thick hard cuticle except where it is, or can be, protected by the shell. In squids and octopodes the gills are large, well supplied with blood and contained in a chamber the contents of which are renewed by muscular action of the walls.

Gastropods living on land generally have the mantle cavity opening to the air by a small aperture and with many blood vessels on the lining. This pulmonary cavity may be ventilated by active movement and periodical opening of the aperture or pneumostome. Gastropods living in fresh water are mostly of the pulmonate type and in most, e.g. *Planorbis* and *Limnaea*, the pulmonary cavity is filled with air which necessitates a periodical return to the surface to fill it with a fresh supply.

Echinodermata

Metabolism in the echinoderms is slow and the demands which they make on the oxygen supply of the sea are small. Gaseous exchange takes place over the general body surface, especially through the tube feet and the thin-walled outgrowths of the body which form the gills. No respiratory pigment is well developed but the circulation of water and coelomic fluid in various body cavities acts as a transport agent.

Vertebrata

The vertebrates are all equipped with well-developed organs for gaseous exchange and with a respiratory pigment for the carriage of oxygen about the body. In most the special respiratory surface is needed because the rest of the body is covered with skin which is thick and impervious, being covered with a tough protein, keratin. This is augmented by scales, feathers or hair, except in the Amphibia, and hence (except in these animals) little gaseous exchange can take place through it. The respiratory pigment is needed because their bodies are of larger size than many invertebrates and their metabolism is, in general, more active and hence the demands for oxygen are greater: this is particularly true of the birds and mammals which have a constant body temperature.

The gills of fishes, both cartilaginous and bony, are thin-walled structures supplied with deoxygenated blood coming directly from the heart. Water is caused to flow over them in one direction by movements of pharyngeal structures (page 280) and gill covers and the dissolved oxygen which it contains is partly removed. In the most active fishes such as trout and salmon, about 80% of the oxygen dissolved in the incoming water is removed. Fishes which live in conditions where the water is poorly oxygenated, for example in fresh waters in the tropics, may respire by taking air into the gut or swim-bladder.

Amphibia respire partly by means of lungs and partly over the outer surface of the body and the lining of the buccal cavity. Their skin is relatively rich in blood vessels and is kept moist, partly by the habits of the animals which seek sheltered and humid places to live in and partly by the secretions of epidermal glands. An account of respiration in the frog has already been given.

Among the reptiles gaseous exchange over the body surfaces is very small in amount because the skin is thick, scaly and keratinized and in tortoises and turtles it is also covered by bony plates. Ventilation of the lungs in snakes and lizards is brought about by rib movements as no diaphragm is present but in the tortoises a compartment of the coelom containing the lungs can be enlarged and diminished by other muscular movements since the ribs are fixed.

Birds possess a very complex system of lungs and air sacs which open from them. Air can thus be passed through the lungs into the air sacs and back to the outside air via the lungs again. Although the exact course of the air is not understood there is no doubt that the bird's lungs and air sacs together make up a remarkably efficient gaseous exchange system and one which can work at a slow rate when the bird is resting and at an extremely high rate when the bird is flying.

Enough has already been said (pp. 373–6) about the general arrangement in the mammal of the lungs, chest and diaphragm to give an idea of its working, but no mention of its control by the nervous system was made. The nervous control of the respiratory movements of mammals resides in *respiratory centres* in the medulla of the brain. In normal breathing a group of neurons sends impulses to those muscles which cause inspiration and this phase then occurs. Stretch receptors in the lungs are stimulated and send back impulses as the lungs are filled and these inhibit or stop the impulses which cause inspiration. Expiration is largely a passive process of the return of the chest wall and lungs to their resting sizes. The respiratory centre is affected greatly by the chemical composition of the arterial blood which it receives and readily responds to increased carbon dioxide concentration by bringing about an increase in the depth and frequency of respiratory movements. It also responds to an increased acidity of the blood in the same way, and ventilation of the lungs is increased. The respiratory centre is not nearly so sensitive to oxygen lack as to carbon dioxide increase but there are receptors in the aortic arch and the carotid sinus which are sensitive to a diminished oxygen concentration of the blood and which can act on the respiratory centre to bring about increased ventilation, especially in times of emergency. There is no doubt, however, that the normal control of respiratory movements is largely related to the carbon dioxide concentration of the arterial blood.

The transport of oxygen from the lungs to the tissues is performed by the respiratory pigment haemoglobin which consists of a 'coloured' molecule containing iron attached to a protein, the whole being contained in non-nucleated cells. The protein is of much smaller molecular weight than that of the haemoglobins and haemocyanins of invertebrates and is about 68,000. Were it not contained in cells with walls which are impermeable to it, it could not be kept in blood vessels such as the capillaries which allow the passage through their walls of some of the plasma proteins. The structural formula of the *haem* portion of the molecule is shown below and it is important to notice that the iron is in the divalent, or ferrous state. When the

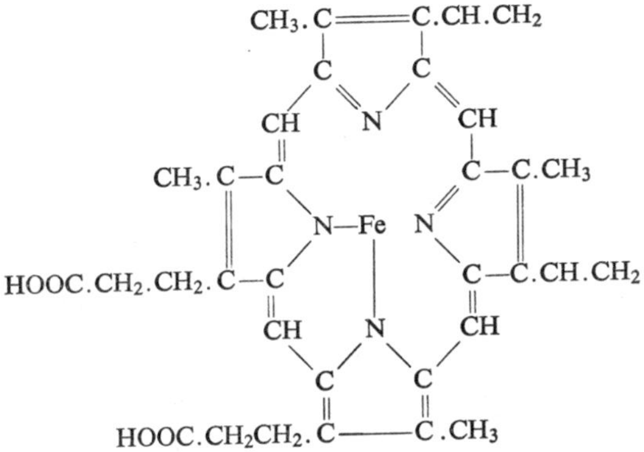

Haem

haemoglobin is converted by the uptake of oxygen into oxyhaemoglobin this occurs without the oxidation of the iron to the ferric state. This oxidation *can* be brought about by oxidizing agents but the molecule of haem is then completely altered and can no longer associate with and dissociate from molecular oxygen as can ordinary haemoglobin. The exact way in which ordinary haemoglobin can accept oxygen when the concentration of oxygen is high, and yield it up when the oxygen concentration is low, is not understood but this property is of great importance in the carriage of oxygen by the blood and is usually expressed graphically by an *oxygen dissociation curve* (Fig. 24.3). In this, the proportion of haemoglobin which is in the oxygenated state is plotted as ordinate against the oxygen pressure as abscissa. It will be seen that the graph expresses the usefulness of haemoglobin as a carrier of oxygen by showing the conditions under which haemoglobin will absorb oxygen from the air and the con-

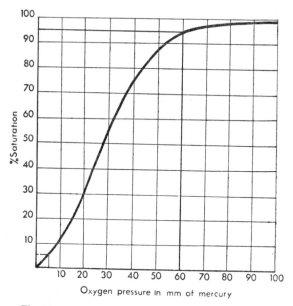

Fig. 24.3. The oxygen dissociation curve of haemoglobin.

ditions under which it will yield oxygen to the tissues. Thus, in Fig. 24.3, haemoglobin is shown to be 95% saturated with oxygen at an oxygen pressure of 60 mm. Hg, and to be 5% saturated at a pressure of 5 mm. Hg. It is found that the precise form of the oxygen dissociation curve of haemoglobin is affected by the presence or absence of carbon dioxide in the blood and it also varies somewhat in animals with different ways of life.

In general, the amount of haemoglobin in the blood of birds and mammals is such that the blood can carry, when fully saturated, between 10 and 20 volumes of oxygen per 100 volumes of blood, approximately twenty times the amount which could be carried in simple solution.

The carriage and disposal of carbon dioxide will not be dealt with at such length as that of oxygen because its elimination is much simpler for aquatic organisms on account of its greater solubility (100 vol. per 100 vol. of water). Its elimination by terrestrial forms is also easier because of its much greater rate of diffusion than that of oxygen.

The carriage of carbon dioxide by the tissue fluids and blood in vertebrates is, however, more complex than simple solution, only part of the gas being carried in this way. Of the remainder, part is combined with the basic (–NH₂) groups of proteins and by far the

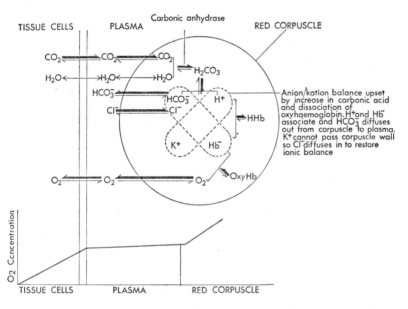

Fig. 24.4. Diagram illustrating the carriage of CO_2 by the blood. (Based on *Roughton*.)

greater part, about four-fifths, is in the form of bicarbonate ion, HCO_3^-. Carbon dioxide from respiration is liberated into the blood where it saturates the plasma and the corpuscles which have envelopes permeable to it. It combines with water both in the plasma and in the red cells to form carbonic acid. This takes place more quickly in the corpuscles owing to the presence in them, but not in the plasma, of the enzyme *carbonic anhydrase* which catalyses the reaction:

$$CO_2 + H_2O \rightleftharpoons H_2CO_3 \qquad (1)$$

This carbonic acid ionizes thus:

$$H_2CO_3 \rightleftharpoons H^+ + HCO_3^- \qquad (2)$$

In the corpuscles there are also potassium ions and these, together with hydrogen ions, are originally in equilibrium with the protein haemoglobin which behaves as a weakly acid substance, thus:

$$HHb \rightleftharpoons H^+ + Hb^- \qquad (3)$$
$$KHb \rightleftharpoons K^+ + Hb^- \qquad (4)$$

The influx of carbonic acid, which is a stronger acid, i.e. one which is more highly ionized, drives equation (3) towards the left by the increase in the number of hydrogen ions present in the corpuscles. At the same time the loss of oxygen from the haemoglobin molecule diminishes the acidity of the haemoglobin, since reduced haemoglobin is a weaker acid than oxyhaemoglobin. The removal of Hb^- leaves a surplus of the anion K^+, although this is balanced by the influx of the HCO_3^- ions. Unlike the cations such as K^+, these can freely diffuse out from the corpuscles into the plasma where the HCO_3^- concentration is much lower but in so doing would again upset the anion–cation balance and they are replaced by the inwards diffusion of chloride ions to take their place.

Thus the carbon dioxide comes to be carried largely in the plasma as bicarbonate ion which originates in the corpuscle owing to the presence of carbonic anhydrase. The uptake of CO_2 by the blood is, as has been seen, assisted by the loss of oxygen which takes place at the same time during the course of circulation.

It will be seen that when the blood reaches the lungs and carbon dioxide is free to escape into the alveoli the chemical reactions will then be impelled in the reverse direction from those just described and that this will be aided by the oxygenation of the haemoglobin. The carriage of CO_2 as bicarbonate in the plasma following its formation in the corpuscle is dependent on the movement into and out of the corpuscle not only of the CO_2 involved but also of the chloride ion as a compensating agent. This movement of Cl^- is often known as the *chloride shift*. The reactions involved are shown diagrammatically in Fig. 24.4. A useful exercise is to prepare a similar diagram showing the release of CO_2 as the blood passes through the lungs. The carriage of some CO_2 in direct combination with the basic $-NH_2$ groups of the haemoglobin is omitted.

25. *Metabolism*

IN THE last few chapters we have seen something of the minute structure of the cell, the way cells are adapted to the performance of particular functions, and the way in which some of the functions are performed by organs composed of various tissues. We have seen how food material is absorbed and have followed the fate of those absorbed molecules which are oxidized with the transfer of energy to

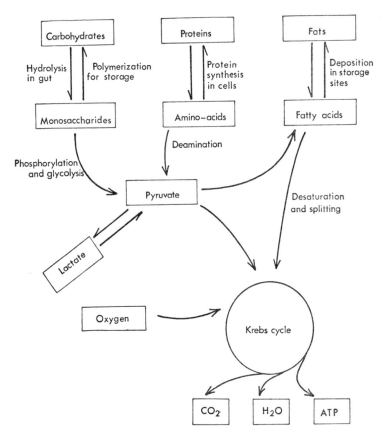

Fig. 25.1. Diagram illustrating a few of the main pathways in the metabolism of carbohydrates, proteins and fats. The complete picture is enormously more complex than is shown here.

organic phosphates (e.g. ATP) that are the currency of energy transfers. It will be the task in the present chapter to see something more of the chemical transformations which take place in the animal body and which are collectively known as metabolism, while the substances undergoing change are known as *metabolites*. Few parts of the body are composed of molecules which individually have been for long in any particular place. There is continual change taking place even in such apparently durable materials as the dentine of the teeth, but in most places the rate of change is much more rapid. The changes affect all the materials of which the body is composed—water, salts or ions, the main organic materials classified as protein, carbohydrate, and fats, as well as small amounts of accessory food factors. Each can be dealt with in turn, although it will soon be apparent that the substances are frequently closely interrelated.

Water

Water may well be said to be the basis of all life and living organisms contain as much as 96% water by weight. The jellyfish of our seas are composed of roughly 1% organic material, 3% salts and 96% water. While the jellyfish is at the extreme end of the scale, some larval insects may contain as much as 92% of water by weight. At the other end of the scale, some adult insects adapted to dry conditions contain only 46% water. Most animals lie somewhere between these two extremes, the frog being composed of about 80% water and a man of about 66%.

To a greater or lesser degree water is continually being lost by evaporation from land animals and some loss is necessary for the elimination of toxic excretory products. Water may be gained osmotically by aquatic organisms and its elimination may become a considerable metabolic involvement since the separation of water from a solution requires energy to be supplied and this can come only from the respiratory cycle.

The regulation of the osmotic concentration of animal fluids will be discussed in Chapter 27, from which it will be clear that they must all be pictured as having a stream of water continually flowing through the protoplasm, passing in through the body surface, or from the gut or made during the oxidation of foodstuffs from the hydrogen atoms which they contain. The water may pass out by evaporation over the surface of terrestrial animals or may be separated off from the body fluids and released, generally at a lower osmotic concentration. The movement of water is part of the sum of molecular changes which constitute metabolism and since it is in part derived from the oxidation of foodstuffs and since its elimination requires energy if its solute concentration is below that of the body, its changes cannot be separated from those of other substances which are metabolized. In other words, water should not be thought of merely as a general solvent in which the chemical reactions of the body take place but as a metabolite as well.

Ions

Various inorganic substances are required for the maintenance of life, as has been seen in the chapter on Nutrition. A short account of the principal ones is given below. Sodium ions are a universal constituent of protoplasm and are often about balanced by chloride ions. Sodium is usually taken in with the food and absorbed from the gut, but it has been shown that some invertebrate animals, for example the freshwater mussel *Anodon*, can absorb ions, including Na^+ from the water in which they live and in which the ions are present in a *very* much lower concentration than they are in the body of the animal. Sodium ions are not distributed uniformly throughout the body, and in the mammal, for instance, are less plentiful than potassium ions in the protoplasm of the nerve fibre and the blood corpuscle. Their inflow during the passage of a nerve impulse is reversed after the impulse by the outward pumping of ions by the expenditure of energy.

Potassium is likewise a universal constituent of protoplasm but is generally present in smaller concentrations than sodium, although there are exceptions to this, such as the protoplasm of vertebrate nerve fibres and certain insects such as honey-bee larvae and some moths.

Calcium and magnesium are very rarely absent from living organisms and in some animals, such as the molluscs and crustaceans which secrete a shell impregnated with calcium salts, are very plentiful indeed although in an insoluble state. The metabolism of calcium leading to the deposition of calcium carbonate or calcium phosphate is a common property of animals, including Protozoa, coelenterates, molluscs, crustaceans, echinoderms and chordates. In all of these, calcium salts are deposited in the tissues or externally in madreporarian corals, having been first transported to the site of deposition in soluble form. These mineral deposits form skeletons among the Protozoa, external skeletons in the proper corals and are deposited in organic matrices to form the shells of molluscs, the carapaces of Crustacea and the ossicles of echinoderms. The bones and teeth of vertebrates are well known to be largely composed of calcium phosphate and the egg-shells of birds are also strongly impregnated with calcium carbonate.

In snails it has been shown that a store of calcium in the digestive gland is used up when the shell is repaired after being broken and that the calcium is probably transported combined with an organic compound rather than in the ionic state. In crustaceans, some of the calcium salts are withdrawn from the carapace prior to moulting but most of the new calcium deposits come from the sea water after moulting in marine forms. It is said that in *Astacus* calcium salts withdrawn from the carapace are stored before moulting in the calcified thickenings on the stomach wall called the gastroliths.

Less seems to be known about the metabolism of magnesium, although it is generally present in body fluids, sometimes in greater amount than calcium. In general, calcium and magnesium ions have an effect on physiological processes such as muscular contraction, particularly the heart-beat, which is contrary to that of sodium and potassium.

There is no doubt that for metabolism to proceed normally, a particular balance of the main cations as well as a particular cation–anion balance is required. This is necessary partly for its effect on proteins, the solubility and reactivity of which are affected by the ions present in the medium. Also there is no doubt that the presence of certain ions, particularly calcium, is of great importance in determining the permeability of membranes and hence the movement of substances about the body.

Other mineral cations are necessary for the metabolism of certain substances. Thus iron is a constituent of haemoglobin and is required also for such respiratory enzymes as cytochrome as well as the 'muscle haemoglobin' or *myoglobin* which occurs as an intracellular oxygen carrier in muscle. During the degradation of the haemoglobin of effete red blood corpuscles, iron is removed and stored mainly in the liver, combined with protein, the remainder of the haem molecule being converted into bile pigment. The iron is used again in the synthesis of haemoglobin and little is excreted from the body.

Copper is required in the Mollusca and some Arthropoda for the synthesis of the blood pigment haemocyanin, but little is known about its metabolism. Zinc is required in minute quantities as it is present in the enzyme carbonic anhydrase which catalyses the decomposition of carbonic acid in the blood of vertebrates. Cobalt is a constituent of vitamin B_{12} (cobalamine).

The anions of chief importance are chloride, sulphate, carbonate, bicarbonate and phosphate, with fluoride and iodide required in small quantities. Chloride ions are by far the commonest and are present in most marine animals in about the same concentration as that in which they occur in sea water. Sulphate irons form only a small proportion of the total anions and are not present in great quantity in food. They are derived in the mammal chiefly by the oxidation of the sulphur contained in some amino-acids of the ingested proteins and are excreted in urine when produced in excess of the bodily requirements. The sulphur which is an essential constituent of various proteins such as the keratin of skin, collagen of tendon and connective tissue, and the hormone insulin is derived from sulphur combined in organic molecules taken in as foods.

Carbonate and bicarbonate must be included for the sake of completeness, but it will be realized that the amount of these ions is related to the production of carbon dioxide during respiration.

Phosphate is of great importance in metabolism and is a constituent of bone and teeth, where it is combined with calcium. Phosphate ions are essential for the metabolism of carbohydrates and occupy a unique position in providing high-energy bonds for energy transfers, as has been seen in the chapter on Respiration. It is also thought that phosphate is necessary during the metabolism of fat. The absorption of carbohydrates and fats depends on the transient formation of phosphate esters under the control of enzymes.

Fluoride is present in small amounts in human bones and teeth, and its presence in sufficient quantity in teeth is thought to help in the prevention of decay.

Iodide is required in small amounts for the manufacture of thyroid gland hormones, and can be shown to accumulate in the endostyles of tunicates, *Amphioxus*, larval lampreys and in the thyroid glands of fishes, Amphibia, reptiles, birds and mammals which are homologous with the endostyle of the lower chordates.

Organic compounds

Details of the metabolism of the foodstuffs are best-known for the mammal. It is likely that many of the details of cellular respiration are of much the same type in all animals but there is a considerable variation in other aspects of metabolism, that leading to the excretion of nitrogenous compounds having been studied in greater detail than others.

Metabolism of carbohydrates

The metabolism of carbohydrates begins with its digestion in the gut by enzymes secreted by the cells of the alimentary canal or its associated glands. The result is almost always the production of a monosaccharide sugar, glucose, fructose, galactose, etc., which is absorbed—a process which may involve the sugar molecule in temporary esterification with phosphate ion. Transferred into the blood, the sugar is conveyed to storage depots or is used. In mammals the storage is in the form of a polymer, glycogen, in the liver and muscles. The conversion is controlled by an enzyme and is also affected by a number of hormones, *insulin* from the pancreas promoting the reaction glucose → glycogen, and *adrenalin* from the adrenal acting in the reverse direction (see Chapter 32). If the sugar is to be metabolized directly, it is again converted into a phosphate ester and enters the cycle of changes which has already been discussed in the chapter on respiration. It will be recalled that one of the substances in this cycle is pyruvic acid which we shall see plays an important part in connecting the pathways by which carbohydrate, fat and proteins are metabolized and, if necessary, converted into each other.

Relatively little is known about the metabolism of carbohydrate in lower animals but in some Crustacea and molluscs as well as in some insects glycogen is stored. In insects, continuous activity such as flight rapidly reduces the amount of stored carbohydrate and in crustaceans the amount falls after moulting, possibly owing to the conversion of glucose into chitin. In the snail, carbohydate is stored during the autumn, reaches a maximum at the beginning of hibernation, and falls during the winter when the animal is not feeding.

Metabolism of fat

In the mammal fat is largely absorbed into the lymphatic system where it appears after a fatty meal. The lymph is returned to the blood via the thoracic duct opening into a factor of the anterior vena cava and the fat is eventually removed from the blood, some by its deposition in fat storage cells and some by being used directly for oxidation. In this case the fat is hydrolysed and long-chain fatty acids which are relatively stable, especially if fully saturated (i.e., there are no double bonds in the molecule), are prepared for oxidation by being desaturated, i.e. by the removal of two hydrogen atoms of adjacent carbon atoms which then become linked by a double bond. This leads the way for the breaking up of the long chain of the fatty acid into shorter units. This is a very much simplified version of a complex series of reactions which also involves linking the fat molecule with phosphoric acid and an organic base when it becomes more reactive. The splitting up of the long chain of the fatty acid molecule is believed to take place from the end bearing the carboxyl (COOH) group. Two carbon atoms are removed at a time, giving rise to a remainder and to acetic acid. This can easily be incorporated into the citric acid (Krebs) or aerobic glycolytic cycle (see page 507).

As with carbohydrate metabolism, little is known of the metabolism of fat in animals other than vertebrates and especially mammals. Many insects, however, store fat as their reserve food supply and are known to be able to make it from carbohydrate but nothing is known of the intermediate stages in its synthesis or in its breakdown.

Metabolism of protein

Whereas in the mammals, at least, the various carbohydrates used are more or less interconvertible and the fat requirements not highly specific, the protein requirements are determined by the need for a variety of amino-acids which cannot be synthesized from simpler molecules. If these amino-acids were present in the food in the correct proportions for the animal's needs, the intake of protein need not exceed the demand for the amino-acids it contains. The proportions of the amino-acids in the food are not necessarily those required by the animal and more protein must be eaten, digested and absorbed than would otherwise be necessary. Since there is no store for amino-acids, those taken in which are in excess of the requirements for the building up of the animal's own particular proteins and other nitrogenous compounds are used in other ways. The first step in their utilization is the removal of the amino or $-NH_2$ group, a process known as *deamination*. This takes place chiefly in the liver by an oxidative process and results in the production of ammonia which is rapidly converted into urea. The reactions can be summarized by the equations

$$2\,R\text{---}CH(NH_2)\text{---}COOH + O_2 \rightarrow 2\,R\text{---}CO\text{---}COOH + 2NH_3$$

$$2NH_3 + CO_2 + H_2O \rightarrow CO\diagup^{O-NH_4}_{\diagdown O-NH_4} + O_2 \rightarrow CO\diagup^{NH_2}_{\diagdown NH_2} + 2H_2O$$

Needless to say the process is far more complicated than is indicated by these equations and takes place in steps controlled by enzymes. The formation of urea involves the linking of the ammonia with a carrier molecule, another amino-acid, ornithine.

It will be seen that a protein such as alanine $CH_3CH(NH_2)COOH$ after deamination becomes CH_3—CO—$COOH$ or pyruvic acid, and this can readily be incorporated into the citric acid cycle. Other amino acids when deaminated may have more complex residues but they consist of C, H and O (with a few exceptions) and are fairly easily transformed into simpler molecules which can be oxidized.

Those amino-acids circulating in the blood which are required for the synthesis of the proteins peculiar to the animal are removed by the cells and linked together in a specific order. This process probably takes place chiefly in the microsomes of the cell which are rich in RNA but how the process results in a specific pattern or order of amino-acids in the protein molecule is not completely understood.

Nitrogenous waste material results from the deamination of protein absorbed in excess of bodily requirements and also to a smaller extent from the deamination of protein or amino-acids which have once formed part of the body and which have been replaced. Thus if no protein is eaten, nitrogenous waste material continues to be excreted, derived chiefly from the degradation of tissue proteins.

In addition to the synthesis from amino-acids of soluble proteins such as serum albumin, insoluble structural proteins are also made. In the mammals, the keratin of the skin, hair and claws is lost by friction with the surroundings and in birds the keratinous feathers are lost at the moult. Amphibia and reptiles slough their skins periodically with the loss of keratin.

The interrelationship of the main pathways of the metabolism of proteins, carbohydrates and fats can best be shown by a diagram. It will be seen that pyruvate is a substance of great importance as providing a link between the changes which carbohydrate, fat and some amino acid molecules may undergo. It will also be apparent why the diets of various men and other vertebrates can be so different yet sustain life. The Eskimos eat little but proteins and fat, the Gauchos of South America little but proteins, while many African and Far Eastern people consume a diet consisting largely of carbohydrate, often, in fact, lacking sufficient protein to provide enough of the essential amino-acids.

Metabolism of nucleic acids

The nucleus contains nucleic acid united to protein. It is believed that the metabolism of the protein fraction follows the normal pathways. The nucleic acid, however, contains in addition to sugar and phosphate groups, organic bases of which guanine is an example.

$$
\begin{array}{c}
\text{HN—CO} \\
|\quad\ | \\
\text{NH}_2\text{—C}\quad\text{C—NH} \\
\|\quad\ \|\quad\ \diagdown\text{CH} \\
\text{N—C—N}
\end{array}
$$

This undergoes breakdown which results in the formation in man of uric acid

$$
\begin{array}{c}
\text{HN—CO} \\
|\quad\ | \\
\text{OC}\quad\text{C—NH} \\
|\quad\ \|\quad\ \diagdown\text{CO} \\
\text{HN—C—NH}
\end{array}
$$

which is further oxidized in most species of animals to allantoin

$$
\begin{array}{c}
\text{H}_2\text{N} \\
| \\
\text{CO}\quad\text{CO—NH} \\
|\quad\quad\ |\quad\ \diagdown\text{CO} \\
\text{HN——CH—NH}
\end{array}
$$

Uric acid is excreted in the urine, being sufficiently soluble for the elimination of normal amounts. Guanine and similar substances can be synthesized in the body but some may be absorbed from the gut since nucleoproteins of the food can be split up by specific enzymes first into protein and nucleic acid and this in turn can be broken down to units each containing a molecule of sugar, base and phosphoric acid, and these can further be split into their components.

Vitamins

There are certain substances which cannot be made by the body even although, as we have seen, the major classes of organic compounds involved can be built up into more complex compounds and degraded into simpler ones via which they can also be converted into each other. All those processes are controlled, usually in stages, by complex systems of enzymes which in their turn have to be synthesized. The picture of metabolism is therefore one of unbelievable complexity yet based upon a small number of different elements, carbon, hydrogen, oxygen and nitrogen being the commonest. It is perhaps not surprising that there are a few materials which have to be supplied ready made, and it is perhaps not surprising that they are different for different animals and that they are mainly in the nature of adjuncts or catalysts for other reactions. An account of these vitamins has already been given (p. 482).

Only a very brief outline has been given here of the chemical changes, the sum of which constitutes the metabolism of the body. It will be appreciated that some of these processes go on in all cells of the body (e.g. respiration), while others are often confined to the cells of a particular organ, e.g. the synthesis of serum albumin by the liver. The complexity of the processes needs no more emphasis, but it is worth considering how such complexity can be contained within the small dimensions of the cell. Recent studies made with the electron microscope have revealed that the cell protoplasm has a highly complex structure and have provided some physical basis to which the main activities of the cells could be attached. Examples of this are the synthesis of proteins by the microsomes and the respiratory activity of the mitochrondria. Further refinements may be expected to make the correlation between function and structure still clearer and that if it were ever possible to study function by studying the position and movements of atoms, then the study of form would have become the study of function.

26. *Excretion*

THE TERM excretion is used in everyday life in an inexact way but in biology it is generally taken to mean the elimination from the body of some part which is now waste but which has passed through a bounding surface and has been part of the substance of the body. Thus the faeces are not usually regarded as excretory matter since they are chiefly the undigested remains of the food and bacteria. The term excretion is often taken as synonymous with *nitrogenous excretion*, the waste products of protein and nucleoprotein metabolism being the most important substances involved, but carbon dioxide formed during respiration is also a waste material and its elimination is sometimes designated *carbonaceous excretion*. However, for the present the term excretion will not include the elimination of carbon dioxide but will be confined to the ridding of the body of materials which cannot be any further metabolized and which are chiefly the end products of nitrogen metabolism but which may include also a few other substances in small quantities.

We have already seen in the chapter on metabolism that in mammals most of the waste nitrogen comes from the elimination of amino acids taken in in excess of the bodily requirements. This is termed *exogenous* nitrogen while that which comes from the breakdown of substances which have been incorporated into the body is known as *endogenous*. This distinction has been shown to be an artificial one; by feeding compounds containing radioactive nitrogen, the replacement by freshly absorbed amino-acids of those in the existing body proteins is shown to be continuously taking place. Moreover, there appears to be no difference in the pathways by which endogenously and exogenously produced amino-acids are dealt with.

Nitrogenous end products

It is well known that the main nitrogenous waste of most mammals is urea, but this is not true of much of the animal kingdom. Ammonia is the substance which is produced by the deamination of amino-acids and although this is a highly toxic substance it is also soluble and readily diffusible and can be eliminated rapidly enough by aquatic animals whose rate of metabolism is not high and whose body surfaces are permeable. The main nitrogenous excretory product in Protozoa, Coelenterata, aquatic annelids, molluscs and crustaceans, as well as many fishes, is ammonia. In protozoans the ammonia is believed to be lost by diffusion over the body surface for it has been shown that its concentration in the fluid from the contractile vacuole is not significantly higher than in the water outside. In coelenterates much the same is true, as it is in polychaete worms such as *Nereis* and *Arenicola*. The leech, too, excretes chiefly ammonia but both the common earthworm (*Lumbricus*) and the Indian earthworm *Pheretima* excrete an appreciable fraction of their nitrogen as urea.

Crustaceans such as *Carcinus* (crab) and *Astacus* excrete chiefly ammonia, as do the echinoderms and both the freshwater and marine molluscs including such creatures as whelks, mussels and cuttlefish. The terrestrial gastropods such as snails and slugs which are not fully bathed in water excrete little ammonia but much uric acid. The same is true of insects which convert their waste nitrogen into uric acid; this being very sparingly soluble, and water being in short supply, the urine forms a paste rather than a solution.

Although most of the invertebrates excrete chiefly ammonia where water is plentiful, other substances are found in small quantities in the water in which they have lived or in their excretory fluids. These include urea, uric acid and also some amino-acids. These last should perhaps be looked upon as having escaped from the body rather than as having been excreted and their loss as being the result of having bounding surfaces which must of necessity be permeable to dissolved oxygen, carbon dioxide and ammonia.

The fishes have a plentiful supply of water around them but for those living in the sea, as we have seen in the chapter on osmoregulation, the water is not readily available since sea water has a higher osmotic concentration than the internal environment of the fish. It is not surprising, then, to find that freshwater fishes, which excrete plentiful dilute urine, pass out their waste nitrogen largely as ammonia, while marine teleosts change a good deal of their nitrogenous waste into trimethylamine oxide. This substance, which has

$$CH_3$$
$$CH_3 \!\!-\!\! N \!\!=\!\! O$$
$$CH_3$$

the formula shown is less toxic than ammonia. They also excrete some urea so that the end products of their nitrogen metabolism include some ammonia, some urea and some trimethylamine oxide. The elasmobranch fishes such as *Scyliorhinus* also excrete some trimethylamine oxide but most of their nitrogenous end products are converted into urea which, as has been seen (p. 282), raises the osmotic potential of their blood above that of sea water and thus serves an apparently useful purpose.

Amphibia generally have permeable skins and are forced to live in conditions where there is a moderate supply of water. Their end product is mainly urea although some ammonia occurs too.

The reptiles and the birds, on the other hand, possess impermeable skins and mostly live in terrestrial habitats. They have little surplus water and their structure and functioning is adapted to conserve what there is. The relatively insoluble and non-toxic uric acid is the chief nitrogenous end product. This applies especially to the desert-dwelling reptiles such as lizards and to the birds, whereas aquatic reptiles such as alligators and turtles may excrete a proportion of their waste nitrogen in the forms of ammonia and urea. It is an interesting observation that during the development of the bird while it is enclosed in the egg, the chief excretory product is ammonia up to about the fifth day, then urea until about the ninth, and thereafter uric acid which is stored in the allantois.

The chief nitrogenous end product of the mammal is urea. Small amounts of ammonia are present, as is uric acid derived from nucleic acid metabolism.

It will readily be seen from the above examples that where water is plentiful, ammonia, the first formed nitrogenous product, is excreted directly but that where water is less plentiful it is converted into urea. This substance is very soluble and little toxic. When water is very scarce, however, urea is not the main excretory product but is replaced by uric acid or urates. These substances are typical of excretion in birds, reptiles and insects. Very little is known of the synthesis of uric acid from the ammonia first formed by deamination, either in vertebrates or in insects, nor is the method of excretion in the kidney tubule of birds and reptiles or the Malpighian tubules of insects completely understood. In insects it is now thought that the uric acid is passed into the lumen of the tubule in the manner which is outlined below.

In the upper part of the tube, water and potassium hydrogen urate are passed into the lumen. Together with CO_2 these substances can be looked upon as recombining to give potassium bicarbonate and uric acid. As water is absorbed from the lower part of the tube the uric acid is precipitated, since it is relatively insoluble and its concentration soon rises to saturation. The potassium bicarbonate is also reabsorbed and, outside the tubule, neutralizes uric acid to produce potassium hydrogen urate which enters the upper part of the tubule. The process is illustrated diagrammatically below (Fig. 26.1).

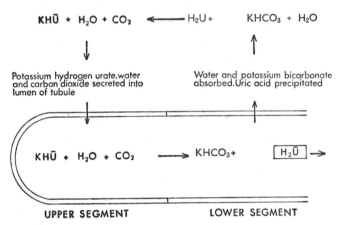

Fig. 26.1. Diagram to illustrate the formation and excretion of uric acid in the Malpighian tubule of an insect. (Based on *Wigglesworth.*)

Excretory mechanisms

We have seen that many aquatic organisms lose their excretory products through any permeable parts of the body wall and that in Protozoa, coelenterates and echinoderms no special excretory organs are present. In Crustacea and Mollusca ducts leading from the coelom to the outside are present and there is evidence that these are excretory in function. Thus the urine flowing from the 'green gland' of *Astacus* can be collected by inserting a small pipette into its opening. On analysis the fluid collected can be shown to contain some nitrogen, mostly as ammonia but also as amino-acid, urea and even a little as protein. It is believed that the means of urine formation is by the secretory activity of the cells, although the hydrostatic pressure of the blood has been shown to exceed that of the blood colloids so that ultra-filtration (see section on kidney) may also play a part. In the molluscs a similar duct occurs and this, as has been seen in the section on *Anodon*, produces urine by a process of ultra-filtration and secretion.

While the details of excretory processes in invertebrates are not always well understood, the method of excretion in the vertebrate has been extensively studied and it is generally agreed that the process takes place approximately as described in outline below. Each excretory tubule of the kidney consists of a blind termination (Bowman's capsule) in the cortex of the organ in which a knot of blood capillaries (the glomerulus) is placed (Fig. 26.2). This knot is

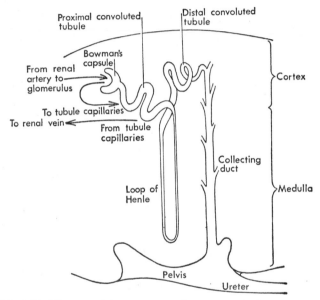

Fig. 26.2. Diagram of the structure and arrangement of an excretory tubule of the mammalian kidney.

supplied directly by a small arteriole branching off from the renal artery. The hydrostatic pressure of the blood in the glomerulus is therefore relatively high. The walls of the blood vessels and the thin cellular wall of the kidney tubule in this region are permeable to most of the constituents of the blood except the proteins and hence a solution is driven through into the lumen of the Bowman's capsule because the hydrostatic pressure of the blood exceeds the osmotic pressure of the blood proteins to which the walls are impermeable. A diagrammatic representation is given in Fig. 26.3. (It will be re-called that the osmotic pressure of a solution is related to the *number* of solute molecules. For a given percentage concentration of a substance the larger the molecules the fewer in number there will be. (Molecules of protein are very large.)

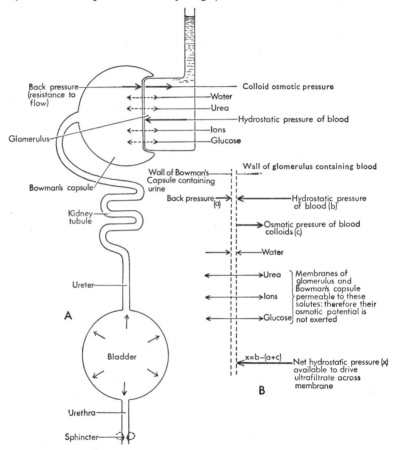

Fig. 26.3. Diagram illustrating the formation of urine in the vertebrate kidney tubule.

The so-called ultra-filtrate of blood which passes from the glomerulus into the kidney tubule passes down the tubule driven by the continued passage of ultra-filtrate from the blood. During its passage down the tubule various constituents are reabsorbed and others may be added (Fig. 26.4). Most of the water is taken back, as is all of the glucose, most of the ions and a little of the urea. The site of reabsorption of the main constituents of the ultra-filtrate is somewhat different in the mammal and the amphibian, no doubt

partly related to the differences in kidney structure, the frog lacking
the long thin portion of Henle's loop. In the frog, most of the
glucose and a third of the salts and water are absorbed in the proximal convoluted tubule and the remaining two-thirds in the distal
convoluted tubule. In the mammal, all the glucose and most of the
salts are absorbed in the proximal convoluted tubule together with
some water. The loop of Henle and the distal convoluted tubule are
responsible for the absorption of the rest of the water. The resulting
fluid which leaves the kidney for storage in the bladder is hypertonic
to the blood and has, as its main osmotically active constituent, the
waste product urea but it contains also some ions and creatinine.

The concentrations of the chief substances found in plasma and
in urine are set out below. The third column of the table indicates the
number of times which the substances have been increased in concentration.

	Plasma %	*Urine* %	*Increase*
Water	90–93	95	—
Protein	7–9	—	—
Glucose	0·1	—	—
Urea	0·03	2	60 ×
Na^+	0·32	0·35	1 ×
NH_4^+	0·0001	0·04	400 ×

That the glomerular filtrate is, in fact, blood plasma without the
protein has been shown by taking samples from amphibian kidneys
directly with micro-pipettes. The rate of glomerular filtration has
also been measured and again it has been shown to be sufficient to
account for the amount of excretory matter in the urine. Further-
more, samples of the fluid have been withdrawn at various points
along the tubules, again by micro-pipettes, and it has been shown
that, passing from the glomerulus, the concentration of glucose falls
while that of urea rises.

The picture that has just been given is that derived from experiments on amphibians and reptiles, but there is no doubt that in other

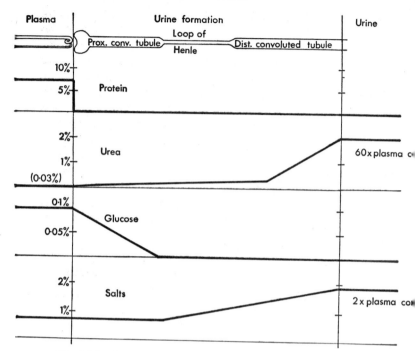

Fig. 26.4. Diagram illustrating the changes in composition during the formation of urine from blood plasma.

vertebrates the mechanism is somewhat different. For example, it is known that the dogfish kidney is capable of retaining urea within the body and it is believed that this is due to the presence of a urea-absorbing segment of the kidney tubule. On the other hand, there are teleost fishes from which the glomeruli are absent so that the whole of the urine must be produced by secretion across the tubule wall. Such fishes do not excrete very great quantities of urine and, as with other teleosts, much nitrogenous wastes and excess salts leave the body via the gills. In birds and many reptiles the main nitrogenous excretory product is uric acid and it is believed that this is mainly passed into the urine by secretion from the walls of the tubule.

27. Osmotic Regulation

Origin of osmotic pressure

The molecules of both the solvent and the solute of a solution are in continual motion. This results in their being distributed evenly throughout the solution after a lapse of time, however they may have been distributed in the first instance. The process of diffusion of the solute (and of the solvent too) is a result of the random movement of the molecules and a process of extreme importance in biology because of the part it plays in the transfer of many substances over small distances. The random movement of molecules in conjunction with a semi-permeable membrane also gives rise to the development of osmotic pressure. A semi-permeable membrane is one which allows the passage through it of molecules of solvent but not of solute.

If a pure solvent is separated from a solution by a semi-permeable membrane, solvent molecules pass through the membrane in both directions at a rate proportional to the number of molecules hitting the membrane. Because there are more solvent molecules per unit volume in the pure solvent than in the solution (since some of the space in the solution is occupied by the solute molecules, assuming an 'ideal' solution), more solvent will pass from the pure solvent to the solution than will pass in the reverse direction. If a sufficient hydrostatic pressure be exerted on the solution, as by connecting it to a vertical column of solution in a tube, and if the membranes be strong enough to sustain the pressure, then the number of molecules passing from solution to solvent can be increased and, at a certain value of hydrostatic pressure corresponding to a certain concentration of solute, can be made to equal the number of molecules passing in the direction of solvent to solution. The pressure which can thus be set up in a solution and which is revealed when it is separated from solvent by a semi-permeable membrane is known as the osmotic pressure of the solution. It can also be said that the property of being able to set up an osmotic pressure in these circumstances is known as the *osmotic potential* of the solution. This concept is of particular use in zoology when the osmotic pressure of a solution may not be actually developed but where its osmotic potential has frequently to be taken into account. A solution is said to be *isotonic* with another if it has the same osmotic potential and to be *hypertonic* and *hypotonic* if it is of higher or lower osmotic potential respectively.

The osmotic potential or *tonicity* of a solution can be measured directly by balancing the osmotic pressure developed at a semipermeable membrane against a hydrostatic pressure. It is difficult to do this easily and accurately in practice so indirect methods are generally used. Other physical properties are proportional to the osmotic potential and are more easily measured. For instance, the depression of the freezing point of a solution below that of the pure solvent is directly proportional to its osmotic potential and can be measured with considerable accuracy. It is the property most commonly employed in biological work to indicate the tonicity of a solution.

The tonicity or osmotic potential of a solution depends on the concentration of solute particles and is proportional to the molar concentration of the solute. A solution which contains the grammolecular weight of an unionized substance dissolved in 22·4 litres (the gram-molecular volume of a gas) has an osmotic potential of 1 atmosphere at 0°C. This 180 gm. of glucose (of molecular weight 180) dissolved in 22·4 lit. has an osmotic potential of 1 atmosphere at 0°C or 180 gm. dissolved in 1 lit. has an osmotic potential of 22·4 atmospheres. It will also be readily appreciated that a 1% solution of urea of mol. wt. 60 has a greater osmotic potential than a 1% solution of sucrose (mol. wt. 342) since the urea solution has a greater molecular concentration. It will clearly have a *very much* greater osmotic potential than a 1% solution of haemoglobin of molecular weight 68,000.

Permeability of membranes

It will be apparent that the boundaries between the cells of organisms (including the cell walls and outer plasma membranes of plant cells) and the boundaries between the organism and the environment need to be permeable, not only to solvent (water) molecules but also to other inorganic and organic ions and molecules for the purpose of food intake and translocation, respiration and excretion. This means that they cannot be semi-permeable in the strict sense. It is also apparent that some selection must be exercised over the types of molecules which enter and leave the body or the cell although this selection need not necessarily be exercised at the surface membrane.

Exactly how this is done by the cell is not understood but it is known that some of the properties of the cell membrane are dependent upon its being made of orientated fatty or lipoid molecules held together by protein.

It is also apparent that the bounding epithelium of an animal must not form a complete barrier between it and the outside world (for this would prevent all the exchanges which are necessary for the maintenance of life). It follows that there must be some regions where it is permeable to some extent, however much it may be protected elsewhere by impermeable material such as calcareous scales or epidermal keratin. If the boundary membrane of an aquatic organism possesses the properties of a semi-permeable membrane to some extent and if it has a higher concentration of solutes inside than is present in the environment, some net ingress of solvent (*endosmosis*) takes place. It is perhaps easiest to visualize this in small and transparent animals.

Protozoa

Although the inward passage of water across the body surface cannot, in the nature of things, be made visible, the water which accumulates in the body of protozoans such as amoeba and *Paramecium* can be seen to be removed and discharged to the outside by the continuous working of the contractile vacuole. If this is prevented, as by poisoning the animal with cyanide or depriving it of oxygen, amoeba soon loses its ability to get rid of superfluous water but does not at first lose its tendency to take in water, so it swells before it finally disintegrates. Conversely, if an amoeba which lives in fresh water is transferred to sea water or even to brackish water, it is no longer osmotically superior to its environment so water no longer enters through the surface and the contracile vacuole no longer fills and discharges. Instead, the whole animal may lose water and shrink if its environment is a sufficiently concentrated solution. Indeed, protozoans which normally live in the sea do not possess contractile vacuoles but some marine amoebae may develop them when transferred to fresh water. Parasitic Protozoa such as *Monocystis* and *Plasmodium* are believed to possess an internal osmotic concentration of such a value that they are more or less in equilibrium with their hosts' tissues or cell fluid, for they do not possess contractile vacuoles.

It will be appreciated that in the protozoans, as in all other animals, the maintenance within the cell of an osmotic potential

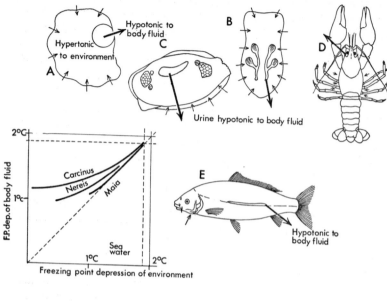

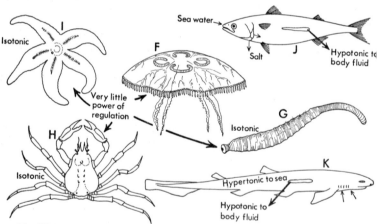

Fig. 27.1. Diagram illustrating osmotic relations of various animals.

Freshwater: A protozoa, B platyhelminths, C molluscs, D crustacea, E fishes.

Marine: F coelenterates, G annelids, H crustacea, I echinoderms, J bony fishes, K elasmobranchs.

The inset graph illustrates the relationship of the internal and external tonicity of three species as measured by the depression of the freezing point. Their internal osmotic concentration shows different figures of dependence on that of their environment. (Based on various authors.)

greater than that of the environment almost always involves the uptake of a certain amount of water and that the elimination of this water, against a gradient of osmotic potential, requires the expenditure of energy. This energy is provided by cell respiration (Ch. 24) but it is not known how the respiratory reactions are coupled to the separation of water molecules from a solution so that water may be expelled by the contractile vacuoles.

Coelenterata and Platyhelminthes

Both freshwater and marine animals are included in the phylum Coelenterata and none of them has any obvious means of regulating its internal osmotic concentration. The marine forms such as *Obelia*, jellyfishes and sea anemones are believed to be approximately isotonic with the sea although differing slightly in the proportion of the various ions present. It is not known how fresh water coelenterates such as hydra manage to keep an osmotic concentration higher than that of their environment and yet have no obvious means of eliminating water. This suggests that the permeability of the cell membrane to water is very low, in spite of its delicate appearance.

The Platyhelminthes in general have a system of flame cells and excretory ducts which probably also act as osmoregulatory organs and pass some excess water to the outside. Like the parasitic Protozoa, the parasitic forms probably differ little from their habitat in osmotic potential and are also protected by a thick cuticle. One species of small marine turbellarian (*Gunda ulvae*) has been studied in connexion with its powers of resistance to dilution of the sea water in which it lives and it has been shown to withstand immersion in fresh water for some time if calcium ions are present. The animal swells to some extent and its endoderm cells become vacuolated with the water which it stores but its normal condition is regained soon after the animal is returned to sea water.

Annelida

The annelid worms, which include the marine polychaetes and the freshwater and terrestrial oligochaetes, show little power of osmoregulation except in a few species such as the polychaete *Nereis diversicolor* which can live in estuaries where the salinity of the water constantly fluctuates. The earthworm is restricted to habitats where at least its immediate surroundings are of high humidity, and it can equally well live for some time immersed in water. It avoids desiccating conditions and can be looked upon normally as being in a similar osmotic relation to its environment as is a freshwater animal. It excretes through the nephridia a urine of lower osmotic concentration than its coelomic fluid from which the urine is principally derived. It thereby rids itself of the excess water which enters the tissues through the gut and skin.

Arthropoda

The Arthropoda include animals which are adapted to many different types of habitat from the purely marine to estuarine and from freshwater to an aerial environment. In general, marine forms such as the spider crab, *Maia*, have an internal osmotic concentration which is the same as that outside and any dilution of the medium in which they live is closely followed by the dilution of their body fluids to the same level. In consequence they are not very tolerant of the dilution of their surrounding sea water and do not naturally live where such changes occur. On the other hand, the Shore Crab, *Carcinus*, can tolerate a range of salinities from pure sea water to nearly fresh water and, although its internal osmotic concentration does not remain constant, it varies much less than that of *Maia* when the outside medium is diluted. The tonicity of the body fluids of freshwater forms such as *Astacus* is greater than that of the water outside so that there is a continuous net inward passage of water through the permeable regions of the body such as the gills. The excess water is eliminated by the 'green' or antennary glands which have been shown to produce urine with a very low salt content. The green gland is richly permeated with haemocoelic spaces and it has been considered that the main agency in the formation of the urine is an ultra-filtration of the blood in much the same way as occurs in the vertebrate kidney. However, it is not certain that this is so because the walls which separate the blood spaces from the interior of the nephridial tube are made up of cells resembling those in other animals which are known to be secretory, and it is perhaps more likely that the chief process in the formation of urine is a secretory one.

There are many terrestrial animals found among the Arthropoda, ranging from crustaceans like tropical robber crabs which can live for short periods on the land, and wood-lice which are fully terrestrial but confined to humid places, to the insect pests of grain and timber which not only live in dry places but eat nothing but very dry food as well. The chief features of these animals which enable them to reduce their water loss to extremely small amounts is the protection of much of the body surface by a chitinous cuticle to which an almost impervious waxy layer is added in the insects. The insects excrete chiefly uric acid as their nitrogenous waste material and this is only slightly soluble and hence scarcely toxic. It is voided in the solid form, and not as a solution, and therefore requires hardly any water for its carriage. Insects such as flour beetles and furniture (wood) beetles depend for much of their water on that which is liberated from carbohydrate respiration. It will be recalled that the oxidation of glucose results in the production of water and carbon dioxide according to the overall equation $C_6H_{12}O_6 + CO_2 \rightarrow 6CO_2 + 6H_2O$ and although in most animals this *metabolic water* is an insignificant fraction of their total water turnover, it forms the most important source of water for many insects which live in extremely dry habitats. Even although most of the external surface of the body is protected by a waxy cuticle which renders it impervious, certain pathways for gaseous exchange must be left. In the insects there are the tracheae which are fine tubes forming a system of branching ducts taking air to all parts of the body. Since their walls are supported by spiral chitinous thickenings they do not change their diameter greatly with the movements of the insect's body and hence only the larger portions of them are ventilated by the bulk passage inwards and outwards of air from the outside. The greater part of the tracheal system relies on diffusion to bring about the exchange of gases. The greater part of the permeable region of the insect is thus in contact with still air and with air which is enclosed in the tracheal system: hence the amount of water lost during respiration is very small.

Mollusca

Among the molluscs, as among the Arthropoda, there are forms which are adapted to types of habitat which differ greatly in their osmotic conditions. In the sea are found gastropods such as the whelks (*Buccinum*), sea hares (*Aplysia*) and ormers (*Haliotis*) which have little or no power of regulating their internal osmotic potential and are normally of the same tonicity as the sea water outside. Even the bivalve *Mytilus*, the common mussel, which is found in estuarine conditions, is incapable of maintaining an osmotic potential in its tissues which differs greatly from that of outside. Its metabolism seems, however, to be well adapted to working at different tonicities. Other molluscs, particularly those which occur on the shore and which are exposed to the air twice daily when the tide is out, seem to rely chiefly on their behaviour to protect themselves against the desiccating conditions to which they are exposed but to which their submerged relatives are not subjected. Thus, at low water, winkles and topshells are to be found between the fronds of seaweeds, cockles buried in the sand and mussels with their valves closed. In other words, they avoid exposing the permeable, soft parts of their bodies to the atmosphere and are elsewhere protected by their shells. A few molluscs, such as the tiny snail *Hydrobia*, are at home in estuaries and seem not to be affected by the daily fluctuations in the salinity of the water.

Molluscs are plentiful in fresh water, the pond snails and the fresh-water mussels being well-known members of the fauna of lakes and streams. They maintain an internal osmotic concentration which is low compared with that of marine molluscs but which is well above the very small concentration of salts in the water which they inhabit. Moreover they are capable of living in distilled water for some time although they gradually lose salts by excretion in the urine. They can take up salts from solutions as dilute as $0 \cdot 1$ mM* or, say, one sodium ion in 10,000,000 molecules of water! From these facts it would appear that the body wall is not very permeable to water, otherwise the output of urine which would be required to prevent waterlogging would soon wash out the animal's salt content. Like-wise the body wall appears to be well-nigh impermeable to salts in an outward direction but permeable in an inward direction because the animals are known to take up salts from extremely dilute solutions.

Many gastropod molluscs are adapted to life on land but, unlike the arthropods, they are not—except when they have retreated into their shells—covered with an impervious cuticle. They are in general confined to relatively humid conditions and tend to be nocturnal in their habits and to be more active in rainy than in dry weather. They excrete or store much more of their waste nitrogen in the form of uric acid that do aquatic gastropods and are believed to produce relatively little urine. Their respiration, although not confined to the pulmonary chamber, mostly takes place over its walls. The chief respiratory surface is thus, as in insects, not directly exposed to the air but has access to it only via a small opening.

Vertebrata

The osmoregulation of the vertebrates is in general better understood than is that of the invertebrates. Control over the internal salt concentration is exercised chiefly by the kidney but factors such as the

---

* A millimolar (mM) solution contains one-thousandth of a gram-molecule per litre of solution.

permeability of the outer surfaces of the body are also of great importance in the maintenance of a steady internal state.

Freshwater fishes are hypertonic to the water in which they live, and take up water chiefly through the gills because the rest of the body is protected by scales. They possess opisthonephric kidneys with glomeruli and secrete a plentiful urine which is hypotonic to the blood. They are thus in much the same relation to their environment as are the freshwater protozoans. Marine bony fishes, on the other hand, have an osmotic potential of their blood which is lower than that of the sea and they are therefore in danger of the osmotic withdrawal of water should their regulatory mechanism fail. This mechanism involves drinking water, absorbing both the salt and water into the blood and excreting the excess salt by the agency of special chloride secretory cells on the gills. The amount of urine produced is small and it is relatively concentrated. Moreover, it is known to be produced in some teleosts solely by a secretory process because the kidney tubules lack the glomeruli which are necessary for the normal method involving ultra-filtration. Marine elasmobranch fishes are in a very curious position relative to the osmotic potential of their environment. They maintain a concentration of about 2% of urea in their blood and tissues in addition to a salt content of about 1%. The combined osmotic potential of these two components is greater than that of the sea and thus the animals, unlike the marine teleosts, are osmotically superior to their environment. They are thus in no danger of desiccation but their permeable surfaces permit a small net gain of bodily water to occur. This is eliminated as urine which is hypotonic to the blood.

Whilst they are in the fresh water which is indispensable to them, the amphibia are osmotically similar to the freshwater teleost fishes. On land they are restricted to damp situations and have few adaptations to enable them to withstand desiccation. The skin, however, is probably of importance in regulating the inward passage of water and its permeability may be under nervous or hormonal control. How far this can operate in the reverse direction, that is, to diminish evaporation, is not known.

Both the reptiles and the birds are adapted for the conservation of water. Their main nitrogenous waste product is uric acid which is excreted as a semi-solid paste. The covering of scales or feather helps to diminish cutaneous water loss, but the water loss of birds accompanying respiratory gas exchange, particularly during flight when metabolism is intense, remains fairly high.

Mammals are found in the sea, on land and in the air, but in all these habitats the essential features of their osmoregulatory mechanism is the same. They all have an almost impervious skin, and many are further protected by a hairy coat. On the other hand, they have skin glands which can secrete fluid on to the surface and thereby play an important part in temperature regulation. They are all dependent on supplies of moist food or drinking water and they all excrete a hypertonic urine in which the chief nitrogenous waste product is urea. This has the advantage that, although it is soluble and has to be carried out of the body in solution, it is non-toxic and is also *very* soluble and hence relatively little water need be expended to rid the body of a large amount of waste nitrogen. The exact water content of the blood and tissues is maintained with considerable accuracy in most mammals by the action of the kidney, the workings of which are dealt with in the chapter on excretion.

Water loss during respiratory exchange is reduced as far as possible by the construction of the lungs. The air-sacs, where the greatest part of gaseous exchange occurs and whose walls are thin and permeable to gases, do not lie in the pathway of the tidal air and are hence protected from direct contact with a continually changing atmosphere. It will be recalled that a similar arrangement is found in insects where exchange of gases in the tracheae depends largely on the process of diffusion.

28. *The Conduction of the Nervous Impulse*

A GREAT deal has been taken for granted in previous chapters where the transmission of an impulse along a nerve and its effect on another neuron or a muscle have been considered. Up to the seventeenth century muscles were thought to change in size—to swell up—when they 'contracted' as a result of a fluid passing into them from the nerves. Swammerdam (1637–80) showed that they changed only in shape and not in size and this discovery paved the way towards an understanding of the part played by the nervous system in initiating muscular contraction, although it was not until nearly a hundred years later that Galvani, in 1791, showed that stimulation by an electric current of a frog's nerve attached to its muscle caused the muscle to contract. Fifty years later du Bois-Reymond demonstrated that when an impulse passes along a nerve (as shown by a contraction of the attached muscle) there is always a momentary electrical disturbance set up in the nerve. This occurs however the nerve has been stimulated, whether by electrical, mechanical or chemical means. During the last hundred years very many experiments have been made to try to discover exactly how a nervous impulse is transmitted along the axon of a nerve cell.

It will be remembered that every nerve fibre is a prolongation of a nerve cell and that the protoplasm is continuous with that of the cell body but isolated from that of the adjacent fibres by a sheath of fatty material, the myelin sheath. A motor neuron, with its cell body in the spinal cord and ending in a muscle of the foot may therefore include an uninterrupted thread of protoplasm a metre long. It seems to us, however, that no sooner have we thought of moving a toe than the action is made, so it is clear that the transmission of a message by the nervous system is rapid.

There are several features of the nervous impulse that we can list as needing an explanation. They are (a) that the impulse is always accompanied by a momentary electrical disturbance, (b) that the impulse passes quickly along the nerve and (c) that an impulse can cause an effector to act, e.g. a muscle to contract.

Many of the experiments which have been done on the transmission of the nervous impulse have been made on a preparation consisting of a frog's sciatic nerve and the 'calf' muscle (gastrocnemius). If two electrodes are placed on the nerve, connected to a sensitive galvanometer and the nerve stimulated by pinching, the galvanometer registers a deflection as the impulse passes the electrodes. That an impulse has passed and been the cause of the galvanometer deflection is shown by the contraction of the muscle. By suitable instruments and with electrodes placed at different points along the nerve the speed of the impulse can be measured. It is found to have a finite velocity. Hence there is no doubt that the nervous impulse is not simply a tiny electrical current flowing along a conductor (the nerve axon), for that would occur with very great speed and would affect the whole length of the nerve fibre at once.

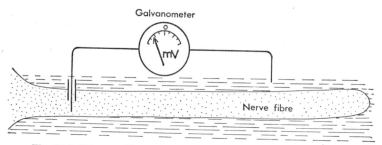

Fig. 28.1. Diagram illustrating the existence of a potential difference between the inside and outside of a nerve fibre.

The tiny electrical disturbance which passes along a nerve fibre is not the impulse itself although it marks its passage. It has been shown that, in the resting nerve, there is a potential difference between the axon inside the myelin sheath and the outside of the sheath of about 90 mV (0·09 volts) and that this is connected with the existence of differences in the concentrations of potassium ions (K^+) and sodium ions (Na^+) inside and out (Fig. 28.1). The K^+ concentration inside is very much higher than it is outside and the Na^+ concentration is lower inside. The electrical insulating property (expressed as the dielectric constant) of the myelin sheath is high in the resting nerve but has been shown to fall in the region of the impulse.

These observations put together make it look as if the nervous impulse is a transient decrease in the insulating property of the axon sheath which allows a tiny current to flow from inside to outside with the movement of ions across the membrane. In the resting state the membrane is said to be polarized and to become temporarily depolarized during the passage of the impulse. At the point along the nerve where the impulse is passing and depolarization is occurring the potential difference between the outside and the inside of the membrane therefore falls (Figs. 28.2 and 28.3). It is believed that any stimulus which starts the progression of an impulse causes a momentary increase in the permeability of the membrane to sodium ions which can therefore enter. (They are present in much greater concentration outside than inside so when the membrane becomes permeable to them their distribution tends to become equalized.) In so doing they reduce the potential difference which exists between the inside $(-)$ and the outside $(+)$ to zero and even to becoming positive inside and negative outside. The conductivity of the membrane which occurs at the point where the impulse begins moves along the membrane since the very passage across of the Na^+, as it were, renders the adjacent portions conducting.

After the inwards passage of sodium has taken place the permeability of the membrane to sodium diminishes and the permeability to potassium increases so that this cation moves in the opposite direction and changes back to their resting state the charges on either side of the membrane. Although these changes of ionic charges can provide the energy required for the propagation of the nervous impulse the energy stored as ionic concentration differences would rapidly be used up were the difference not maintained by an active, energy-consuming metabolic process. This is believed to be the active extrusion of sodium ions from the nerve fibre.

This very much over-simplified version of a complex process is nevertheless in accord with many items of experimental evidence. For example, if the concentration of K^+ outside the nerve fibre is raised to a value equal to that inside, conduction of the nervous impulse is abolished. If the nerve is placed in a Na^+ free solution conduction soon stops and if a nerve is deprived of oxygen so that the respiratory processes cannot take place its power to conduct is soon abolished also.

Other features of the nervous impulse remain to be mentioned. It would be expected from the method of propagation of the impulse outlined above that the impulse would pass in both directions along a nerve fibre from a point of artificial stimulation. This does, in fact, occur. If the stimulus to the nerve is strong enough to start an impulse at all that impulse travels along the length of the fibre with constant

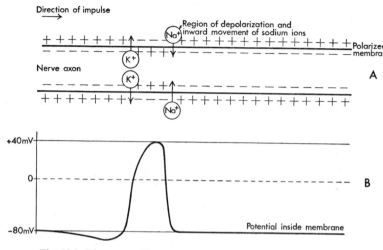

Fig. 28.2. Diagram to illustrate the passage of a nerve impulse along a nerve.

The upper diagram (*A*) represents the distribution of charges before (RIGHT), during and after (LEFT) the passage of an impulse, which is imagined as moving from left to right. Below (*B*) is a corresponding graph of the potential inside the nerve fibre which is imagined to be caught at *an instant of time*. It will be seen that the inside of the nerve is negative to the outside before and after the passage of the impulse, but positive during it.

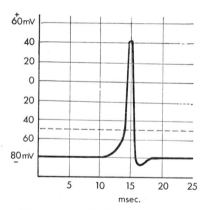

Fig. 28.3. Graph of the potential inside a nerve fibre during the passage of a nerve impulse.

This is the normal record obtained by an electrical pick-up and amplifying system. Compare with Fig. 28.2.

intensity. In other words, energy for the process of propagation comes from the nerve fibre and not from the stimulus. Such a response to a stimulus where the stimulus is either strong enough or not strong enough and to which a response either does take place or does not take place is said to be an all-or-none response. Lastly, after the nervous impulse has passed there is a short period of time during which the nerve is not able to respond to another stimulus. This interval is known as the refractory period. The transmission of the effect of the nervous impulse to the muscle will be dealt with in the next paragraph.

Neuromuscular and synaptic transmission

The transmission of the effects of the nervous impulse to the muscle which the nerve supplies takes place via the motor end-plate. This

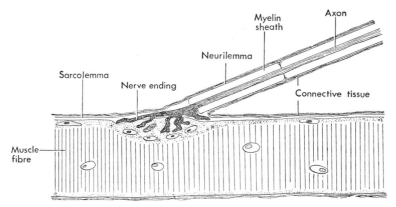

Fig. 28.4. Diagram of a motor end-plate of a nerve lying on a muscle fibre.

The sarcolemma of the muscle fibre and the neurilemma of the nerve fibre are continuous, allowing contact between the membranes bounding the protoplasm of the axon and that of the muscle fibre. (Based on *Gutmann* and *Young.*)

is a distinct region of granular cytoplasm lying just inside the sarcolemma of the muscle fibre and containing numerous nuclei. The nerve axon ends outside the sarcolemma opposite the region of granular cytoplasm in a number of irregular branches. The very thin connective tissue sheath investing the muscle fibre is continuous with a similar sheath around the nerve fibre. (See Fig. 28.4.)

The arrival of a nervous impulse at the motor end-plate causes the muscle fibre to contract. It is known that this contraction is accompanied, as is the transmission of an impulse along a nerve, by a momentary electrical disturbance of the otherwise polarized membrane of the muscle cell. This electrical manifestation may not be the cause or trigger which initiates muscular contraction but it certainly accompanies it and it is thought to be started by the depolarization of the muscle cell membrane in the region of the end-plate by a substance (*acetyl choline*) released at the motor end-plate region. This substance is quaternary ammonium base and exists in solution in an ionized form. It is thought that the muscle cell membrane is permeable to acetyl choline ions and their passage across it may initiate depolarization. Although the account just given is not established with certainty for striated muscle there is little doubt that the autonomic motor nerves act by releasing chemical substances at their terminations for it can be shown that salt solution perfusing a heart whose vagus nerve (parasympathetic) is strongly stimulated can cause another heart to slow down when the same fluid is transferred to it. The substance which acts in this way and which is liberated when the vagus nerve is stimulated is acetyl choline.

When certain of the so-called sympathetic nerves of the autonomic nervous system are stimulated they produce an effect like that produced by the hormone adrenalin and it is known that a substance closely allied to adrenalin is liberated at the nerve endings. The sympathetic nerve supply to the heart is such a nerve and its stimulation produces acceleration of the heart-beat just as does injection of adrenalin into the blood stream.

The transmission of a nervous impulse from one neuron to another is not so well understood but it is now clear that there is no protoplasmic continuity between one nerve cell and the next. Each neuron is connected to others by some form of synapse, often involving the close apposition of many fine branches from each neuron. It seems likely that chemical transmission from one neuron to another takes place and acetyl choline has been shown to affect the passage of impulses through certain autonomic ganglia where it is known that synapses between association and motor cells occur.

29. Perception, Co-ordination and Response

WE ARE all aware that we live in a changing world, but only when we stop to think for a minute about the nature and extent of the changes do we realize how extremely inconstant is the environment which we perceive. From second to second we have a slightly different view; sounds pleasant and unpleasant come and go; we step out of doors into the cold dry air and back to the warmth and high humidity of a house. And so it is in the lives of all animals, whether or not they respond to the changes or appear to us to respond to the changes which assail them.

Any change in the environment or the position of the animal in relation to its environment which can be perceived by an organism is called a *stimulus*. Only if a change can be perceived can it be called a stimulus. Thus there are 'wireless waves' in the air, varying in intensity, at all hours of the day but we cannot perceive them. If we work in a constantly noisy room we become accustomed to the sound and only perceive the environment to be noisy when there is a change of sound. So the two essential features of a stimulus are that it is a change in the environment and that it is a change that can be perceived or appreciated.

Although the world which we perceive by means of the stimuli impinging upon us appears of extreme complexity, it is possible to separate the stimuli into five main types. These are: changes in temperature, in light wavelength and intensity, in the effect of gravity, in mechanical movements and vibrations, and in the concentration of chemical substances. Although we have organs for the reception of these stimuli and although in general they appear to us to be clearly separate in type from one another, the same is not true for all animals. Although we are aware of the perception of various stimuli by ourselves, we cannot be sure that the same powers of perception are possessed by other animals because we have only indirect evidence to go upon. We can say that many have stimulus-perceiving organs constructed in the same way as our own, and we can say that

555

they appear to us to behave as if they perceived the stimuli which we perceived, but how far their perception of them does, in fact, resemble ours it is clearly impossible to find out. An example may help to make this clear. A small piece of meat placed in a dish with some planarians is soon fed upon by the animals until they are replete. Whether they encounter the meat accidentally in their wanderings or move towards it as a result of perceiving chemical substances diffusing from it is beside the point for the present purpose, which is simply to show that they do act, by feeding on the meat, in such a way as to make it appear that they have perceived it. However, had the experimenter used only animals which had just been fed and which were 'not interested' in food they would probably not have settled on the meat and it would have been possible to conclude from the experiment, wrongly as it happens, that the planarians were unable to perceive the meat.

Protozoa

Not all of the five types of stimulus mentioned above can be perceived by all organisms but it is possible in many to find and identify definite organs for the perception of one type of stimulus. It will be easily seen that this degree of complexity cannot be expected in the Protozoa where the body is non-cellular. The perception of stimuli by the Protozoa is difficult to investigate but there is no doubt that many of them do respond to a variety of stimuli and that their protoplasm has a general sensitivity to changes in the environment.

As has already been seen, amoeba reacts to strong light and to mechanical vibrations by withdrawing pseudopodia and rounding itself up. It does not appear to be sensitive to the direction in which gravity acts or to temperature except in so far as its metabolism is increased in rate by increase in temperature up to maximum value, above which it falls off again. No organelles have been recognized in amoeba by which any of the stimuli could be perceived. Similarly *Paramecium* has no receptor organelles but it can perceive contact or proximity to an object as evidenced by its avoiding reaction which can also be given in response to change in the chemical composition of its environment as when it enters a region of acidity.

The parasitic Protozoa are apparently very insensitive to changes in their environment so far as can easily be seen by their bodily movements. There is no doubt that they are capable of perceiving changes in their environment, for it is extremely difficult to explain their behaviour otherwise than by assuming that they have some perception of the environment. Thus the sporozoites of *Plasmodium* injected into the blood of man by the mosquito do not remain in the blood but enter the cells of the liver. All particles of blood will at some time pass through the liver capillaries so there is no difficulty in understanding how the sporozoites can be filtered off, but it is difficult to understand how they are enabled to enter liver cells and not to enter other cells unless they can perceive some difference between the liver and other tissues through which they pass. The only other explanation would be that they are taken up by the cells of the liver and that it is the mammal which perceives the parasites. Since, however, they are found in ordinary liver cells and not in phagocytic cells, this seems unlikely.

The free-living flagellate *Euglena* possesses a spot of pigment which is believed to be concerned with the perception of light. The evidence for this is that the animal does orientate itself with respect to the direction of light in such a way that the shielding of a sensitive spot at the base of the flagellum by the pigment spot in the cytoplasm would account for the observed behaviour by producing a change in direction of movement. Also flagellates such as *Euglena* which possess a pigment spot respond to the direction of light, whereas those without a pigment spot are sensitive only to the general light intensity.

That some form of conduction through the protoplasm of a protozoan occurs is clear, because, for example, *Paramecium* halts at an obstacle and by altering the direction of beat of the cilia backs away and starts in a different direction. This could only happen if more than half of the cilia altered their direction, i.e. if the effect of stimulation of the anterior end were passed along the body. Fine threads in the ectoplasm connecting the basal granules of the cilia are believed to carry out this function of co-ordination of the ciliary beat, and although they have not been proved to co-ordinate cilia in *Paramecium*, a similar system of fibres has been shown to co-ordinate the movements of cilia in other ciliates since cutting the fibres destroyed co-ordination.

The responses made by protozoans to stimuli are limited because the means by which they can be made is limited. Nevertheless they do respond in a way which may be related to the stimuli which they receive. Thus *Paramecium* swims upwards in the absence of other stimuli and is thus believed to be reacting to the force of gravity. If, however, it encounters an obstacle this behaviour is altered and the avoiding reacting ensues. In an electric field (which is, one would suppose, an unnatural type of stimulus) it swims towards the cathode.

When bacteria are plentiful it may anchor itself by its trichocysts and continue to maintain a feeding current by the action of cilia. When *Paramecium* meets a suitable conjugation partner it settles and adheres to it. All these actions appear to be related to the stimuli which the environment is providing for the animal and they depend for their execution on the processes of perception, conduction and response.

Metazoa, Coelenterata

With the evolution of the Metazoa and the increase in the size and complexity of the body which occurred some cells became set aside for the function of perception and others for response. As cells

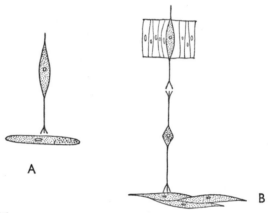

Fig. 29.1.

At *A* is shown the simplest possible connexion between a receptor or sense cell and an effector such as a muscle fibre.

At *B* is shown the usual arrangement with a neuron or neurons coming between the receptor (or sense cell) and the effector.

became specialized for these functions so it became necessary for the powers of conduction which we have seen in the Protozoa to be a general property of their protoplasm to become more highly developed so that rapid conduction over greater distances could occur. The cells which specialize in perception were known as sense cells, those which specialize in conduction as nerve cells or neurons and those which respond as effectors. The simplest possible arrangement of these three types of cell which one can imagine is the connexion of one sense cell to one effector by one neuron. This would not be very much more advantageous to the animal than having the processes of perception and response combined in the same cell, and although we may imagine a simple stage like the one just mentioned, there is no doubt that the evolution of connexions between the neurons was not long in appearing. As soon as the neurons became connected to one another the stimulus received by one sense cell could result in the transmission of a message to all the neurons and hence to all the effector cells. Moreover, if the same stimulus were received by more than one sense cell one can imagine that the effect on the neurons and effectors would be augmented. Examples of animals possessing a system of sense cells, neurons and effector cells of this stage of complexity are found in the phylum Coelenterata. The spindle-shaped sense cells of the ectoderm have already been described and so have the nerve cells which are connected to them and to the muscle tails of the musculo-epithelial cells. It is readily seen how the stimulation of a single tentacle by a *Daphnia* for example brings about the contraction of that tentacle followed by the contraction of the others and the opening of the mouth. The tentacles and the mouth do not act entirely independently of one another but their actions are coordinated to a certain extent. The type of arrangement of neurons which occurs in hydra and in other coelenterates is often known as a nerve net. It has a number of properties which result from the arrangement of the neurons. For example, conduction of the message takes place in all directions from the point of stimulation, and because the message has to pass some sort of barrier at the synapse as it is transmitted from one nerve cell to another it gradually becomes weaker as it gets farther away from the point of origin.

Not all coelenterates have a uniform network of neurons over the whole of their bodies. In the sea anemones, for example, there are pathways running from the tentacles to the longitudinal muscles which conduct more quickly than is possible in other directions because there are fewer but larger neurons and hence, as it were, smaller resistance and fewer hindrances. As a result of this, when the tentacles are stimulated the muscles which cause them to be withdrawn are brought into action first and are followed by others which cover up the oral end completely.

Although hydra has no sense organs but only sensory or receptor cells scattered among the other cells of the epithelia, some coelenterates have definite organs in which there is a concentration of receptor cells and also other structures which aid in their functioning. For example, some medusae have eyes in each of which there is a lens-like structure backed by a cluster of sensory cells and pigment cells. Other medusae such as *Obelia* possess eight statocysts (see page 50) set around the margin of the bell into each of which sensory cells project where they may be stimulated by statoliths. These bodies are somewhat denser than the fluid inside the statocyst and hence they tend to lag behind when any movement is made by the medusa or to fall to the bottom if the medusa is stationary, thus stimulating by contact the receptor cells lining the cavity. There has been no clear demonstration that the statocysts do function in the perception of the animal's position in space but their structure strongly suggests that they do so.

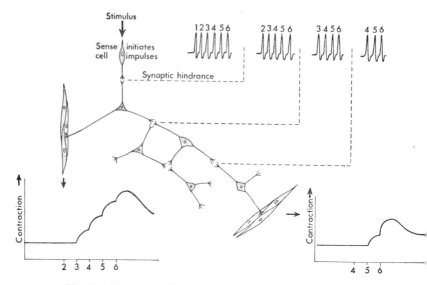

Fig. 29.2. Diagram to illustrate the events in the receptor-transmitter-effector system of a sea anemone.

A sense cell is shown connected to a portion of the network of neurons and this in turn is connected to two groups of muscle fibres. The nerve impulses passing at various points are shown, as recorded electrically, at the top of the diagrams. The responses made by the two groups of muscle fibres as recorded graphically are shown at left and right.

In the sea anemones no sense organs of the kinds found in medusae are present but the nervous system has been the subject of many experiments. It is a nerve net and conducts impulses in all directions. Nevertheless in certain regions most of the neurons run in a particular direction (up and down in the mesenteries) so that there is, for instance, rapid conduction of impulses from the tentacles to the longitudinal muscles. A strong stimulus can thus quickly bring about retraction of the tentacles. An anemone makes no response to a single electric shock but the second and third and subsequent shocks call forth increasing response. This type of response is said to involve *facilitation*, the first stimulus making it possible for subsequent stimuli to be transmitted. The importance of this in an animal possessing a nerve net is that a single stimulus does not bring about a complete contraction of all the muscles at once but the response is graded according to the number of stimuli received. It would clearly be very disadvantageous for an anemone to shut up every time it was touched lightly on one tentacle. Instead, just the tentacle may be withdrawn and only after repeated touching does the whole animal contract.

Platyhelminthes

Among the Platyhelminthes only of the Turbellaria is much known about the powers of perception, co-ordination and response. They have a diffuse nervous system lying below the epidermis, similar to that of the coelenterates but in addition there are nerve cords which are aggregations of nerve cells and fibres forming the rudiments of a central nervous system and, at the anterior end, there is a pair of cerebral ganglia containing many neurons and with which the nerve cords connect. The nervous system co-ordinates the muscles during locomotion, as can be shown by cutting one of the nerve cords when the muscular waves of the two sides get out of step. Cells in the nervous system, especially the anterior ganglia, are connected with receptor cells at the surface of the body. These are most numerous at the anterior end and in addition to undifferentiated receptor cells there are, in many turbellarians, two or more eyes, each of which consists of receptor cells connected to the central part of the nervous system, surrounded by pigment cells which limit the directions from which the light may strike the sensitive cells. Planarians therefore may be sensitive, not only to the general light intensity but also to its direction. In general they move more rapidly in bright light than in dim and they change their direction more frequently too. This automatically results in their accumulation in dark places for which they appear to have a 'preference'.

Annelida

Although the planarians may be said to have the rudiments of a central nervous system it is not until we come to the annelids that a well-defined central nervous system is present. This has the familiar form of a pair of cerebral ganglia above the gut linked by connectives to a double ventral nerve cord running the length of the body. There is probably no sub-epidermal plexus of nerve cells, the neurons—apart from those concerned with the gut—being either receptor cells in the epidermis or motor and association neurons situated in the central nervous system.

The essential way in which the neurons of the earthworm are arranged is shown in Fig. 6.7E. It will be seen that a sensory cell is connected to an association cell and this is connected to a motor neuron, an arrangement which constitutes the simplest form of a *reflex arc*. Stimulation of the receptor cells results in an impulse being passed to the association neuron which in turn stimulates the motor neuron. The association cell might be thought to be unnecessary or to be a hindrance, but it is important because it is connected not only with one receptor and one motor cell but also with other receptor and motor neurons. It is believed that one of the principal ways in which the central nervous system of the earthworm works is by the action of reflexes and chains of reflexes. In locomotion the shortening of the longitudinal muscles of one segment stretches the one behind and stimulates receptor cells. These send impulses to the central nervous system which stimulate association neurons and these in turn, motor neurons. The motor neurons send impulses to the muscles which then contract. This very simple arrangement is not quite that which is found in the real animal, as can be demonstrated by severing the muscles of an earthworm and leaving the two portions connected only by the nerve cord. The pull of the contracting muscle could not, in such a preparation, be transmitted from one segment to the next but it can be seen that such a cut does not interrupt the backwards passage of a contraction of the longitudinal muscles, showing that the connexions of at least some of the association neurons extend over more than one segment.

In addition to this reflex mechanism by which a wave of contraction of the longitudinal muscles is propagated relatively slowly there are three special sets of neurons which together make up the so-called giant fibres. These lie in the dorsal part of the nerve cord along its whole length. In each segment the middle, and largest, giant fibre is connected to two pairs of giant cells and each lateral giant fibre to one pair of giant cells. An oblique partition occurs between each length of giant fibre corresponding to a segment. Experiments show that the middle fibre normally conducts posteriorly and the lateral ones anteriorly. In each segment the giant fibres are connected to motor neurons. Their use is to bring into action all the longitudinal muscles almost simultaneously and so to cause the animal to withdraw quickly from a stimulus. The rate of conduction in the giant fibres may be 1,800 times as rapid as the conduction along the nerve cord which involves the ordinary nerve cells and their synaptic connexions.

In the earthworm the cerebral ganglia and subpharyngeal ganglia do not dominate the workings of the central nervous system and probably serve mainly to receive impulses coming from receptor cells in the prostomium and peristomial regions. They may also have an effect on the excitability of the nervous system as a whole, for worms which have had their cerebral ganglia removed are more sensitive than normal.

In other annelids the arrangement of neurons is basically similar to that of the earthworm but there are differences in the connexions which give rise to different reflex patterns of muscular contraction and movement. Thus the polychaete *Nereis* does not move by peristalsis-like contractions but by lateral flexures. The polychaetes, too, usually have better developed sense organs than earthworms and, as has been seen, *Nereis diversicolor* has four simple eyes on the prostomium, each connected to the cerebral ganglia by a short nerve tract. Each eye consists of a pigmented cup lined with receptor cells and containing a central lens-like structure and probably serves to perceive a change in intensity of illumination rather than to produce an image of the environment.

Very little is known about the receptor mechanism of polychaetes in general except that receptor cells are found in the epidermis interspersed among epithelial cells and are particularly numerous on the palps and cirri.

Arthropoda

The nervous system of the Arthropoda is built on the same plan as that of the annelids but shows great advance over it. The chief differences are:

(a) great development of the ganglia, particularly the cerebral and suboesophageal;
(b) the reduction in number of the ganglia corresponding to the reduction in number of the body segments;
(c) the extension of one neuron over several segments.

Coupled with these changes goes a very great improvement in sense organs and very great increase in complexity of behaviour, especially in the insects.

The compound eye of arthropods has already been described (p. 161) but it is worth recalling what are its chief features.

(i) It is made up of many separate units or ommatidia (up to 28,000 in dragonflies).

(ii) The image which the animal perceives is probably built up from the many small parts of the whole picture perceived by the separate units which are usually isolated from one another by pigment.

(iii) The eye is satisfactory at perceiving the movement of objects even although discrimination between objects which lie close together is poor. Resolving power clearly increases and definition improves with increasing numbers of ommatidia.

Some organs of arthropods which receive other types of stimuli are also well-defined structures. Examples of these are the statocysts of decapod crustacea such as *Astacus*, prawns and mysids, and the hearing organs of insects. In addition to these there are nerve endings in various parts, particularly the antennae which have been shown to be sensitive to chemical substances and even to the water content of the air.

The arthropod is thus provided with much more information and with much more accurate information about the outside world than is the annelid, and hence it is necessary that the complexity of the nervous system should be greater so that:

(a) the movements of which the limbs are capable should be fully utilized;

(b) the possibilities of varying the response accurately according to variations of the stimuli should be great.

In addition to direct responses to the environment, the more complex nervous system of the arthropod has the possibility that complex sequences or 'patterns' of behaviour can be somehow 'built-in' to the nervous system and evoked for use at a particular time in the animal's life. Thus a female of the solitary wasp *Ammophila* stings a caterpillar until it is immobile but not dead and then carries or drags it back to a burrow which she had previously constructed. She places it in the burrow and lays an egg on it, crawls out and closes the burrow with a small stone. It is unlikely that the wasp looks ahead as we understand the words. That it does not act in a way which is guided by its past experiences is shown by the fact that the animal behaves on the first occasion that it performs the sequence of actions in the same way as it does after many repetitions. Such behaviour is called instinctive.

Instinctive behaviour has evolved in the insects possibly to its highest level in the animal kingdom, as is shown by the life cycles of the varied members of colonies of social insects such as the termites and the bees. It might be said that behaviour as complex as they show could only be controlled by a nervous system of the size that these small animals possess if it were fairly rigid and hence could depend on fixed connexions between a relatively small number of neurons. Insects may be contrasted in this respect to mammals, whose behaviour is more variable and adaptable, resulting from their endowment with a central nervous system of large size and great complexity.

Even in the central nervous system of those insects which perform very complex behaviour patterns, the cerebral ganglia do not dominate every activity. In general they contain few motor cells and the animal can walk and fly without the cerebral ganglia. The sub-oesophageal ganglia contain some motor neurons which innervate the mouthparts and they too can be removed—the animal can be decapitated—without interference with walking or flying. The cerebral ganglia contain chiefly association neurons and constitute the region where the reflex behaviour of the body is controlled in response to the stimuli received by the dominant sense organs of the head. Although simpler muscular patterns are not affected and even such activities as copulation and oviposition may be unimpaired, the complex forms of behaviour are eliminated after removal of the cerebral ganglia especially if they require light stimuli to set them off.

Mollusca

The form of the nervous system in molluscs is very different from that of the annelids and arthropods, and much less is known about the connexions of the neurons. The basic arrangement is considered to consist of paired cerebral, pleural, pedal and visceral ganglia situated near the parts which they innervate and united by connectives, but this arrangement can be very much modified as it is in the snail, where the ganglia are grouped close together around the oesophagus. The ganglia are even more concentrated in squids and octopodes where a veritable brain is formed from the ganglia which lie adjacent one another surrounding the anterior part of the gut. Experimental work on the behaviour of the lower molluscs is not easy to assess but it can be said that, in general, the ganglia control the movements of the parts of the body in which they are situated, e.g. the pedal ganglion controls the movements of the foot. In the octopus, however, the various regions of the 'brain' have been shown to be clearly related to the parts which they innervate. Thus the cerebral ganglia co-ordinate feeding movements and probably swimming as a whole; the pedal ganglia innervate the tentacles and funnel, and the visceral ganglia the mantle cavity. Large optic ganglia lie adjacent the eyes and are connected to the brain by the optic tracts. Eyes are found in the cephalopod molluscs which are among the most highly developed sense organs present in invertebrates. Many molluscs, such as snails, winkles and scallops, have simple eyes comparable with those of annelids, but octopodes, squids and cuttlefish possess eyes in which there is a well-developed lens, a retina and powers of accommodation comparable in efficiency with that found in vertebrates. The octopus, being a large and active invertebrate equipped with well-developed sense organs, has been used for experimental work on the powers of learning and perception which it possesses, and the relation between learning and brain structure.

Echinodermata

The nervous system of the echinoderms shows some of the features of that of the Coelenterata in that there is a diffuse nervous system lying below the epidermis which controls movements of spines, etc., but the movements of the tube feet are co-ordinated by radial nerve strands running along the arms of the starfish. The receptor organs of echinoderms are very poorly developed.

Vertebrata

It is commonplace to say that it is among the vertebrates and particularly among the mammals that the structure and functional complexity of the nervous system reaches its maximum. The dorsal tubular nervous system in which most of the cell bodies are situated is found in *Amphioxus*, but while this animal has the basic chordate arrangement it has no well-developed sense organs such as vertebrates possess and it has no anterior expansion of the nerve cord forming a brain. Its nervous system, while showing the primitive separation of dorsal and ventral roots of the segmental nerves, is thus not representative of the chordates as a whole and the dogfish and frog provide better examples. The structure of the sense organs and

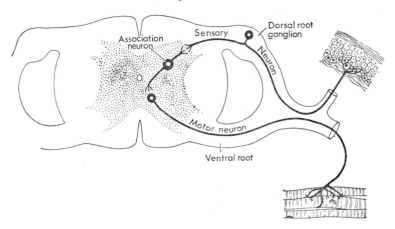

Fig. 29.3. Diagram to illustrate the basic arrangement of neurons in the spinal cord of a vertebrate.

brains of the dogfish and frog have been described, but the way in which the component neurons are connected has only been briefly mentioned. The basic arrangement is most easily understood by considering the arrangement in a trunk segment. The sensory neuron cell bodies are situated in the ganglion of the dorsal root of the spinal nerve. A nerve fibre from each neuron extends in one direction from the skin and in the other direction into the spinal cord. Impulses resulting from stimulation of the free nerve endings in the skin pass along that portion of the nerve fibre known as the *dendron* towards the cell and then away from the cell body along the *axon* of the neuron into the cord. Here the nerve endings are connected with association neurons and these in turn with motor neurons. These possess short dendrons but long axons which run out from the spinal cord via the ventral roots of the nerves to the muscles which they can bring into action. The cell bodies of the motor and association neurons are thus situated in the spinal cord and the cell bodies of the sensory neurons in the dorsal root ganglia. Those cell bodies which are found in the cord are typically arranged around the central canal, in an H-shape as seen in transverse section. Because they contain less of the myelin or fatty sheath material than do the nerve fibre tracts, they are more translucent and constitute the grey matter of the spinal cord. The white matter, which is largely composed of longitudinally running fibres, is thus found outside the grey matter. The motor neuron cell-bodies are situated mainly in the ventral horn of grey matter.

The neurons which we have seen so far are concerned with the perception of the outside world and the response of the animal's body musculature and are hence known as somatic sensory and somatic motor components of the nervous system. There is another functional division which is concerned with the regulation of the gut and blood vessels by the action of plain muscles and which is known as the viscero-sensory and viscero-motor system. This consists of sensory cells which, like the somatic sensory cells, have their cell bodies in the dorsal root ganglia but whose free nerve endings lie in the gut

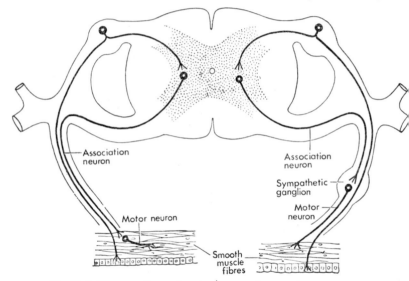

Fig. 29.4. Diagram illustrating the nerve pathways of the autonomic nervous system—sympathetic on the right, parasympathetic on the left.

wall. The association neurons in the cord with which they are connected send their axons to motor cells (viscero-motor cells) which are situated, not in the ventral horn of grey matter, in the spinal cord, but in ganglia lying outside the central nervous system. These ganglia are known as the autonomic ganglia and they are thus distinguished by containing the cell bodies of viscero-motor neurons. The fibres from these viscero-motor neurons run to the plain muscles of the gut and also to that of the blood vessels but in this case they are generally bound up with and distributed with the segmental somatic nerves instead of taking an independent course. The arrangement of the neurons in this manner is shown in Fig. 29.4.

The functional division of the neurons of vertebrates into somatic sensory, somatic motor, viscero-sensory and viscero-motor corresponds in general to the way in which the visibly distinct nerve are arranged. Thus the spinal nerves comprise somatic sensory fibres which conduct impulses from the skin sense organs (exteroceptors) and from the sense organs in the muscles (proprioceptors), together with the somatic motor nerves which innervate the somatic, striped muscles. The division of the nervous system which comprises the visceral system is more difficult to see as a separate entity but autonomic ganglia are found in various parts of the body, connected on the one hand with the central nervous system and on the other hand with the organs which they innervate. The motor portion of the autonomic nervous system has two functional subdivisions, the so-called sympathetic and parasympathetic systems. These differ in their action on the muscles and also in their anatomy. We have already seen that the viscero-sensory fibres come from the gut and from the blood vessels and pass via the dorsal root ganglion where their cell bodies are situated. The association neurons are long and send fibres to the motor cells which are situated in the autonomic ganglia. Those going to the sympathetic ganglia travel via a small visceral branch of the segmental nerve known as the ramus communicans. In the sympathetic ganglion the association fibres link up with motor neurons which send the so-called postganglionic fibres to the gut. These are non-myelinated. Some postganglionic fibres also travel to the muscular walls of blood vessels via the spinal nerves. The postganglionic, motor fibres may thus be long and the preganglionic, association fibres short. The action of the sympathetic division of the autonomic nervous system resembles that of adrenalin and causes an increase in heart rate, contraction of arterioles and slowing of digestive processes.

The parasympathetic portion of the autonomic nervous system differs from the sympathetic in that its action resembles the action of the drug acetyl choline and causes a slowing of the heart rate, relaxation of the arterioles and a hastening of digestive processes. Anatomically it differs from the sympathetic in that the preganglionic or association neurons send long fibres to the parasympathetic ganglia which are situated on the organs concerned. The postganglionic motor fibres are thus very short. The chief parasympathetic fibres run in the vagus nerve, branches of which accompany the gut.

There is some variation of the exact distribution of the autonomic nervous system in members of different classes of vertebrates and the

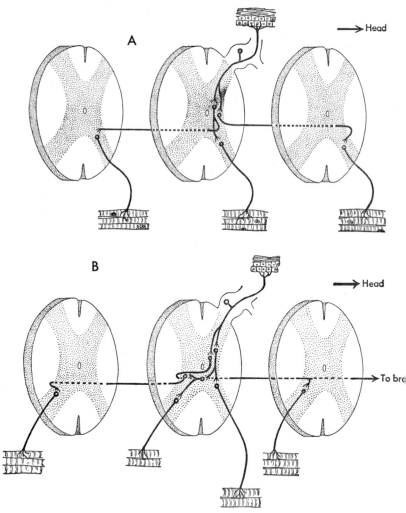

Fig. 29.5. Diagrams to illustrate some possible connexions between a sensory cell and motor cells in the spinal cord.

In *A*, those connexions shown are: (1) to the same segment (CENTRE); (2) to the segment posterior on the same side (LEFT); (3) to the segment anterior on the same side (RIGHT).

In *B*, those shown are connexions: (1) to the same segment of the same side and of the opposite side (CENTRE); (2) to the opposite side of the segment posterior (LEFT); (3) to the opposite side of the segment anterior as well as to the brain (RIGHT).

description given above is necessarily generalized and does not apply equally to the dogfish, frog and mammal but gives a picture of the essential anatomy of the vertebrate autonomic nervous system and its central connexions.

The functional divisions of the nervous system can now be examined in relation to the cranial nerves. It will be recalled that these may be regarded as persistently separate dorsal and ventral roots. In the dogfish the ventral roots corresponding to the first three somites are called respectively the oculomotor (III), the trochlear (IV) and the abducens (VI) and are made up of somatic motor nerve fibres only. The corresponding dorsal root of the first segment, viz. the profundus (accompanying the trigeminal) possesses somatic sensory fibres only. The trigeminal (V) possesses these and some viscero-motor fibres to the jaw muscles, while the facial (VII) and its branch the auditory (VIII) (forming together the dorsal root of the third segment) possess not only somatic sensory fibres but also viscero-sensory and viscero-motor as well. The same applies to the glossopharyngeal (dorsal root of 4th segment) and to the vagus (X) (dorsal roots of 5th, 6th, 7th and 8th segment). The vagus, as we have seen, includes those viscero-motor fibres which are typically part of the parasympathetic division of the autonomic system.

It will be seen, therefore, that while the ventral motor roots remain 'pure' the dorsal sensory root may contain both sensory and motor fibres of the visceral division and somatic sensory fibres but are devoid of any somatic motor component. These facts are tabulated on p. 572.

We have seen the essential way in which the three types of neuron found in the nervous system, sensory, association and motor, are connected, but so far we have looked only at their connexions in any one segment. Needless to say, the segments of the vertebrate are interconnected just as are the segments of the annelids and arthropods. There are very many association neurons in vertebrates whose fibres connect the sensory and motor cells with others up and down the cord and in the brain. In fact the very great complexity of the vertebrate nervous system is largely due to the vast number of association neurons which enable all movements to be carried out in relation not only to external stimuli but also to the internal state, past experiences and the sum total of sensory information which the animal has at that moment. Some of the many types of interconnexion are illustrated in Fig. 29.5 where one sensory neuron is shown connected by association cells to motor neurons on (a) the same side

CRANIAL NERVE COMPONENTS

Nerve	Name	Components
1	Olfactory	Special neurosensory cells
2	Optic	Special nerve tract
3	Oculomotor	Somatic motor
4	Trochlear	Somatic motor
5	Trigeminal	
	Superficial ophthalmic	Somatic sensory
	Maxillary	Somatic sensory
	Mandibular	Somatic sensory
		Viscero-motor
	(Profundus	Somatic sensory)
6	Abducens	Somatic motor
7	Facial	
	Superficial ophthalmic	Somatic sensory
	Buccal	Somatic sensory
	Palatine	Viscero-sensory
	Hyomandibular	Somatic sensory
		Viscero-sensory
		Viscero-motor
8	Auditory	Somatic sensory
9	Glossopharyngeal	Somatic sensory
		Viscero-sensory
		Viscero-motor
10	Vagus	Somatic sensory
		Viscero-sensory
		Viscero-motor

of the cord, (b) the opposite side of the cord, (c) segments above and below, and (d) association neurons whose fibres run to the brain. It does not need much imagination to understand how complex the interconnexions in the central nervous system can be when many thousands of neurons are involved.

In spite of this a general plan of the connecting fibres can be made out, and, just as we have seen that sensory neurons are found in the dorsal root ganglia and motor neurons in the ventral horn of grey matter, so we can see that the main tracts of association fibres running towards the brain from the spinal cord are situated in the dorsal column of white matter and the main descending tracts running from the brain to the motor cells are in the lateral tracts.

The main connexions between the various parts of the brain and between the brain and spinal cord are more difficult to follow but in general it can be said that the brain of the dogfish is little more than a glorified spinal cord to which have been added centres where the fibres coming from the sense organs terminate. Thus the fibres from

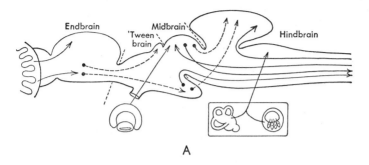

A

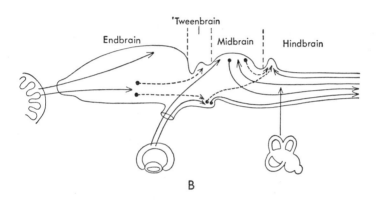

B

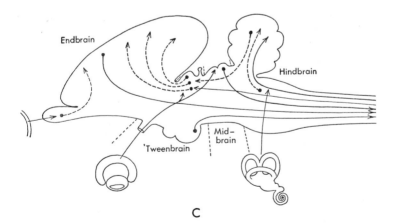

C

Fig. 29.6. Diagram to illustrate some of the nervous connexions in the brains of *A* the dogfish; *B* the frog; *C* the rabbit.

the neuro-sensory cells of the olfactory organs pass via the olfactory lobes to the cerebral hemispheres and fibres from the relay cells of the retina pass via the optic tracts (=optic nerve II) to the optic lobes of the mid-brain. The region of the brain which has more connexions than other regions can be seen in the diagram above to be the roof of the optic lobes (optic tectum of the mid-brain) while the cerebral hemispheres are little more than relay centres for olfactory impulses. Although the brain plays an important part in the life of the animal, especially by receiving information from the special sense organs, many of the ordinary body movements can be performed by a dog-fish whose spinal cord has been cut just behind the brain. Such an animal swims continuously and can respond to touch. It seems that the brain acts in normal life by modifying or inhibiting the swimming rhythm which is otherwise continuously active.

Much the same state of affairs is seen in the brain of the frog and although the cerebral hemispheres are relatively larger than those of the dogfish they do not seem to play a very much greater part in many everyday activities. The most important correlation centre is still the optic tectum.

The picture is very different in the mammals, for here the neo-pallium (see page 381) which forms the bulk of the cerebral hemi-spheres has connexions not only with the olfactory organs but also with almost all parts of the brain via association neurons and with the sensory and motor tracts of the spinal cord. Cutting the spinal cord just behind the brain upsets the activities of the animal in a much more profound way than it does in the dogfish, and even cutting the connexions of the cerebral hemispheres with the rest of the brain produces drastic effects on various activities. It is known that cells controlling motor neurons innervating almost all parts of the body are arranged in a fixed pattern over the surface of the cerebral hemispheres of the human brain and areas are also set aside for sensory endings, so it is not surprising that, since co-ordination and control have been concentrated in the cerebral hemispheres, their removal has devastating effects. Even so there are still regions of the human cerebrum (the frontal lobes) that can be surgically removed without markedly upsetting the behaviour.

This short account of the connexions of the neurons in the central nervous system gives point to the comparison of the brains of dogfish, frog and mammal as representative stages in the evolution of the brain. The dogfish brain, as we have already seen, differs little from the 'generalized' vertebrate brain, consisting of the three primary divisions into fore-, mid- and hind-brains. No part is excessively developed although it can be said that the cerebellum is relatively large and the olfactory lobes are conspicuous. Other fishes, such as the pike which hunts by sight, have much larger optic lobes, and fishes such as the carp, which depends on taste, have relatively large medullas.

The brain of the frog shows some advance over that of the dogfish in possessing a relatively large telencephalon but functionally it is little better off. However, it is possible to recognize in the structure of the frog's cerebral hemispheres the arrangement of neurons from which the evolution of the mammalian cerebrum has occurred. In a transverse section of the cerebral hemispheres the cell bodies of the neurons can be seen mainly to occupy their primitive position near the central cavity (cf. spinal cord). The ventro-lateral region is known as the striatal area; the median dorsal area is called the archipallium. In between them is an area called the palaeopallium. No trace of the new region to be evolved in the mammals is yet present but it is fore-shadowed in the reptiles by the appearance of a small new area lying between the archipallium and the palaeopallium. In the reptiles also the striatal area has moved to occupy a more central position near the floor of the lateral ventricle. In lower mammals these changes have gone much further and the whole dorsal surface of the telencephalon is occupied by the neopallium. The median archipallium has been crumpled up in a median position while the palaeopallium has been pushed ventrally. Finally, in higher mammals the neopallium has expanded still more and has become convoluted. This has the effect of providing a much larger surface area and of being able to accommodate more neurons which in the new cerebral cortex occupy a peripheral instead of a central position near the ventricle as they do in the fish and the frog. Very little can be seen of the old pallial regions from the outside, the archipallium being completely hidden as the hippocampus and the palaeopallium represented by the so-called pyriform lobe on the ventral surface. The whole organization of the brain has been transformed from being virtually an enlarged region of the spinal cord associated with the eyes and nose to being an immensely complex mechanism into which sensory information is continuously being poured, in which memories may be stored and from which the appropriate motor messages are sent out.

As yet we have only the most hazy idea of how such a mechanism works, but there is reason to believe that the basis of all nervous activity is the same in the sense that it involves conduction of a nerve impulse by a neuron. It is thought that the type of impulse is the same in all nerves, whether sensory, association or motor, and that it takes place in a way that has already been described. It is also believed that there is no continuity between the protoplasm of one neuron and that of another and that some chemical means is present which serves to transfer a nervous impulse from one neuron to another or from a nerve ending to a muscle. If the type of nervous impulse is the same in all nerves, it is difficult, at first sight, to understand how different sensations are perceived, since the impulses which the sense organs send to the brain must all be of the same type, no matter from which sense organ they come. The probable explanation of this must lie in the connexions which the receptor cells make with the central association neurons. It is known, however, that the intensity of stimulation is indicated by the frequency and not the intensity of the impulses which are passed. To pursue this matter further is beyond the scope of this book, and the next chapters will therefore deal with the physiology of the sense organs and aspects of behaviour of the vertebrates which have not yet been dealt with.

30. *The Senses of Vertebrates*

Introduction

IN THE chapter on perception, co-ordination and response we have seen how various animals are influenced by the environment and how they respond to changes in it. In Chapter 28 an account was given of the way in which the neurons are believed to function individually. The task which the present chapter undertakes is to state briefly the ways in which the sense organs of vertebrates function in the reception of the stimuli to which they are adapted. The traditional five senses—seeing, hearing, smelling, tasting and feeling—are not biologically comparable with one another when the structure and nervous connexions of the sense organs are examined carefully, nor is that list of the senses a complete and clear one because animals possess a means of perceiving their orientation in space and the speed at which their orientation may change. Fishes have a system of lateral-line organs of which man has no equivalent and of which the function is hard to interpret and harder still to imagine. We know from our own experience that the senses of tasting and smelling are easily confused although anatomically separate, but for an aquatic animal the distinction between their functions seems to be even harder to make. Accordingly it is more satisfactory to consider the working of the sense organs of vertebrates if their anatomical relationships are borne in mind.

The eye develops as an outgrowth of the fore-brain and the original hollow vesicle becomes cup-shaped. Cells of the inner layer become differentiated into receptor cells with their sensitive ends pointing away from the direction whence the light comes. This 'inverted retina' is explained as being due to the original derivation of the central nervous system from a dorsal sensitive region of ectoderm which evolved into a tubular shape and from which the eyes evolved as lateral outgrowths (see Fig. 30.1). However, by whatever steps the vertebrate eye has evolved it is clear that it is anatomically a part of the brain and, as has already been seen, it is not comparable with a sense organ such as a skin touch receptor which is supplied with a sensory branch of a segmental nerve. The eye contains not only

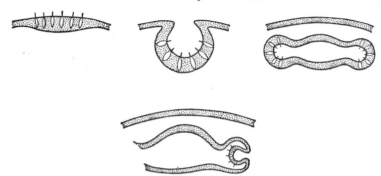

Fig. 30.1. Diagram illustrating possible stages in the evolution from a dorsal sensory area of a tubular nervous system, of which the eye is an outgrowth. This would account for the inversion of the retina.

receptor cells but also various grades of association neurons, some of which have connexions with the brain via the optic tract (= optic nerve II).

The olfactory organ presents a somewhat different picture. The receptor cells are essentially neuro-sensory cells, i.e. receptor cells+nerve cells, in that their outer ends are receptive and their inner ends are drawn out into nerve fibres which run directly into the olfactory lobe of the brain. These neuro-sensory cells are believed to be a type of sensory cell which was evolved very early in the evolution of vertebrates and this argument is used to suggest that the olfactory sense is of very ancient origin.

All the other sense organs are innervated by the series of sensory, dorsal root nerves which include certain cranial nerves and the dorsal roots of the spinal nerves with which they are serially homologous. The largest sense organ of this type is the inner ear, which develops from an ectodermal thickening or placode firstly into a small rounded vesicle and then into a complex structure embedded in a corresponding cavity in the auditory capsule of the skull. It is regarded as homologous with the lateral line organs, which develop in the same way and have similar receptor cells and are innervated by another branch from the dorsal root of the same segment and other homologous nerves.

The inner ear is far from simple and in the various classes of vertebrates is able to respond to sound, to the direction of gravity, and to the angular change of velocity of an animal in three planes. These movements may be referred to as pitching, rolling and yawing.

As has been seen in the chapter on the dogfish, although the lateral line system of receptor organs extends the entire length of the body, it is innervated from the VIIth, IXth and Xth cranial nerves only. It is believed to be an extremely sensitive detector of close-range disturbances in the water and hence may be of importance in detecting obstacles, enemies and prey, and in the shoaling behaviour of fishes.

Taste, or the chemical sense which we associate with the presence of chemical substances in the mouth, is essentially the facility to perceive the presence of chemical substances and in that respect resembles the sense of smell. It differs from the sense of smell in that the receptor organs for taste are receptor cells innervated by dorsal root nerves, i.e. by sensory nerves whose cell bodies are in the dorsal root ganglia. Since taste buds may be innervated by the facial (VIIth), glossopharyngeal (IXth) or vagus (Xth) nerves, the ganglia concerned are the geniculate, glossopharyngeal and vagus ganglia. Although taste organs are confined to the alimentary canal in terrestrial animals they may be found on various, mainly anterior, parts of the body in fishes.

The traditional sense of 'feeling' is perhaps better called cutaneous sensitivity and heat, cold, touch and pain can be discriminated by the skin nerve endings. There are also receptor organs in muscles, joints and tendons which give rise, in man, to no particular sensation but which supply information to the central nervous system about the state of contraction of muscles and the positions of joints, and which provide a 'muscle sense' that is just as important for the correct functioning of the limbs as is the sensory information received from outside for the functioning of the body in its environment.

Sight

A description of the eyes of the dogfish, frog and mammal have already been given in the chapters dealing with those animals. A brief description of the way in which the eye develops will be found in the section of embryology, and we have just seen that the relation between the brain and the eye is different from that of all the other sense organs and that the eye can really be regarded as a part of the brain. How, may we ask, is seeing accomplished? By the removal of the sclerotic at the back of a fresh bull's eye and its replacement with ground glass it can be shown that the cornea, lens and humours together form a real, inverted image on the retina. Somehow this is recognized as corresponding to the object in form, colour and relationships in man, and presumably in many other animals. It will be recalled that the light receptor units of the human eye are the so-called rods and cones of which the rods are scattered over the retina between the more numerous cones, except at the central fovea where cones alone are present. It is believed that the intensity of light necessary to stimulate a rod is less than that required for a cone. This can be supported by the observation that in light of low intensity, for example in moonlight, when an attempt is made to look directly at an object and by so doing to focus it on the fovea, it is impossible to see the object. If the gaze is not directed at the object it comes into view again. In general the relative number of rods and cones in the eyes of mammals is correlated with their ways of life. For example, the nocturnal rat has a retina composed chiefly of rods, whereas the squirrel, which is active in the day, has a retina composed entirely of cones.

The way in which a rod receives a light stimulus is believed to depend upon a chemical reaction, activated by light, involving a substance known as visual purple. This is a protein conjugated with a carotenoid (a substance allied to vitamin A and to the yellow pigment of carrots, butter, etc.) and in the presence of light is broken down from a reddish pigment to a yellow substance. Thus, extraction of pigment from the eye of an animal which has been kept in the dark yields a reddish solution, whereas if the eyes of the animal had been strongly illuminated, only a yellowish solution would have resulted. Exposure of the visual purple solution to light turns it yellow. It is believed that the rods respond in this way in the eye, and this is in agreement with the observation that the ability to perceive a dimly lit object is increased by staying in the dark. 'Dark adaptation' consists, in fact, of the re-synthesis of visual purple which has been broken down in the light; although it is known that the effect of light is to cause the breakdown of visual purple, it is not known how this process causes a nerve impulse to be initiated.

The way in which the cones of the retina receive light stimuli is different from that of the rods because they possess no visual purple. They respond in some other unknown way, and although the response mechanism is not understood, various of the properties of the cones are well established. For example, at light intensities higher than that of bright moonlight, rods cease to be effective owing to the bleaching of their visual purple but at this intensity cones are just stimulated. Cones are effective at high intensities and are also believed to provide the means whereby colours (i.e. lights of different wavelength) are perceived. Many cones may be connected to a single bipolar cell in the peripheral region of the retina but at the fovea only one cone is connected to one bipolar cell. This implies that these two adjacent cones may respond to different light intensities and hence there is great discrimination of fine details. Since the distance between adjacent cones at the fovea of man is about $2\frac{1}{2}$ μ, only points whose image on the retina is further apart than $2\frac{1}{2}$ μ are seen as separate points. A distance of $2\frac{1}{2}$ μ on the retina corresponds to an angular separation of points of a little less than 1 minute. Visual acuity is only as great as this over a very small area, the fovea itself subtending an angle of no more than about 1 degree. At an ordinary reading distance of 1 foot or 30 cm. this corresponds to a separation of two points by 5 mm. Many theories have been put forward to account for the way in which the normal man perceives light of all wavelengths from violet to red and it is believed that although no morphological difference can be perceived between one cone and another they differ from one another in the colour of light to which they respond most readily. Just as the primary pigments can be mixed to yield a large variety of colours, so appropriate stimulation of the cones with their various sensitivities can lead to the perception of different colours. Just as printing a coloured plate by means of a varying distribution of dots of three or four colours can lead to a whole range of tones, so, it may be imagined, the eye perceives colours by the different intensities of stimulation given to cones which are sensitive to different regions of the spectrum. This is a very crude picture and certainly a great over-simplification, but it is probably correct to assume that colour discrimination takes place at the retina whereas many other aspects of vision depend to a large extent on happenings in the brain rather than the eye.

For example, it is clear that the perception of objects in their right relationships depends on the brain rather than the eye, since the image formed on the retina is inverted but the object nevertheless appears the right way up. It is believed that this ability is learnt during the early perception of the external world by the young animal.

This discussion of sight has, of necessity, drawn upon information obtained from man as well as from other animals, but it is believed that the essential features of the vertebrate eye are the same throughout the sub-phylum. There are, however, considerable differences in the optical parts of the eye correlated with the way of life of the animal and with the distribution of the sensitive cells of the retina, colour vision occurring in bony fishes, some reptiles, birds and primates.

Hearing

Although we all know what we ourselves mean when we say that we hear a sound, we cannot be certain that other animals have the same powers of perception, particularly so because only in mammals is the organ traditionally associated with hearing, namely the cochlea, fully developed. Nevertheless there is little doubt that vertebrates lower than mammals do hear, and hearing is perhaps best defined by saying that an animal hears when it behaves as if it has located a sound source which is not in contact with it. A sound for this purpose can be regarded as any mechanical disturbance which is not actually in contact with the animal. We have already seen in the chapter on the dogfish that the lateral-line system of neuromast organs is able to locate the source of vibrations in the water. Although the functions of the inner ear which are most clearly understood are the perception of the animal's position in relation to the direction of gravity and the perception of pitching, yawing and rolling movements, it is probable that some of the sensory spots may also respond to sound vibrations.

The inner ear of the frog resembles that of the dogfish in general structure but the animal is adapted for the reception of aerial vibrations by the presence of an ear drum and transmission device, the columella. Unless such a device were present there would be great loss of energy of the sound waves when they passed from air to the fluid of the labyrinths. This is avoided by collecting the sound vibration in air over the relatively large area of the tympanum and transmitting them by the solid columella to the relatively small area of the fenestra ovalis.

The mammal possesses in the cochlea an outgrowth from the sacculus accompanied by perilymphatic channels, a unique mechanism for the reception of sounds. (See Fig. 16.35.) Birds are able to hear almost as well as mammals but the outgrowth from the sacculus is not coiled and the arrangement of the receptor cells is not so complex.

The mechanism of hearing is best understood in man but is believed to be of much the same type in all mammals. The tympanum of man has an area nearly thirty times that of the stapes where it fits into the fenestra ovalis. Since the amplitude of movement of the centre of the tympanum is reduced by the chain of ossicles to a half at the stapes, the pressure differences which are actually communicated to the fluid in the membranous labyrinth are about fifty times those incident on the tympanum allowing for some loss in the mechanism.

The vibrations of the tympanum, transferred to the stapes by the malleus and incus, are in turn transferred to the perilymph contained in the so-called *scala vestibuli*. This is one of the three canals of the cochlea. Another perilymphatic duct, the *scala tympani*, runs parallel to the *scala vestibuli* and communicates with it only via a very small opening, the *helicotrema*, at the apex of the spiral into which the cochlea is coiled. The *scala tympani* ends against the fenestra rotunda. Perilymph can flow from one duct to the other and back again via the helicotrema. Pushing in the stapes thus causes the fenestra rotunda to bulge and pulling the stapes causes it to be sucked in. When, however, rapidly alternating movements such as sound waves actuate the stapes and are transmitted to the fluid in the scala vestibuli, they are not only transmitted via the connexion at the apex but are also transmitted from the scala vestibuli to the scala tympani along the length of these channels and *across the intervening cochlea duct*. This, the third canal of the cochlea, is filled with endolymph and is part of, and communicates with, the membranous labyrinth. The ductus cochlearis is separated from the scala vestibuli by the vestibular membrane (Reissner's membrane) and from the scala tympani by the basilar membrane. Reissner's membrane and the basilar membrane are thus caused to vibrate. The basilar membrane bears the organ of Corti which consists of a series of paired rods of Corti and hair cells on either side of them. The hairlike processes of these touch a projecting flap, the tectorial membrane, which is fixed at the base and has a free inner edge. The hair cells are receptor cells around which the endings of sensory nerve fibres are wrapped. The sensory neurons have their cell-bodies in a ganglion on the auditory (VIIIth) nerve. It is believed that stimulation of the receptor cells of the organ of Corti results from their vibration against the tectorial membrane and that those at the base of the cochlea respond to the highest audible frequencies (about 20,000 c.p.s. in man), while those at the apex respond to the lowest frequencies (about 16 c.p.s.).

Chemical sense

It can be said at once that the essential features of the olfactory sense are the same in all vertebrates and consist of an epithelium in which there are many neuro-sensory cells, receptive to chemical stimuli at one end and drawn out into a nerve fibre at the other. This passes directly into the olfactory lobe of the brain. There is no satisfactory theory of the way in which the whole gamut of smells can be perceived and distinguished, nor is there any satisfactory classification of smells except in a very approximate fashion, and chemical substances of widely different chemical composition may have similar odours, e.g. benzaldehyde, nitrobenzene and hydrocyanic acid. The minimum amount of material required to stimulate the olfactory organ varies greatly from one substance to another, but is in general much smaller than is required to stimulate the organs of taste. The part normally played by smell in the enjoyment of food, and the difficulty of distinguishing the effects of taste from those of smell, are well known and are revealed when the olfactory organs are put out of action by a 'cold in the head'.

Taste

The sense of taste differs from that of olfaction in that the receptor cells are innervated with nerve fibres whose cell bodies lie in the dorsal root ganglia of the VIIth and Xth and especially the IXth cranial nerves. In mammals the taste receptor cells, grouped together with supporting cells as taste buds, are confined to the tongue but in some bony fishes similar taste buds may occur in other parts of the buccal cavity, in the pharynx and particularly in the barbels around the mouth. The classification of tastes is nearly as difficult as that of smells, although a rough grouping may be made into sweet, sour, bitter and salt flavours. In man the tip of the tongue is most sensitive to sweet tastes, the anterior edges to salt, the posterior edges to sour and the back to bitter.

Touch

The skin is richly innervated in many animals both with fine free nerve endings and also with nerve fibres which end in small sense organs such as the Pacinian corpuscles, or Meissner's corpuscles. Cutaneous sensitivity has been investigated most fully in man but no undisputed relation between any one sensation, e.g. hot, cold or pain, and a particular type of nerve ending has been found. The sensitivity of the skin in man varies in different parts of the body from the nose and tongue which require only 2 gm./sq. mm. to elicit a sensation of touch, to the sole of the foot where 250 gm./sq. mm. are required. Similarly two points of stimulation can be distinguished when separated by 1 mm. at the tip of the tongue but only when separated by more than 65 mm. in the middle of the back.

Position

The way in which the membranous labyrinth of the inner ear functions in the perception of position in space and the detection of angular movements has already been described for the dogfish. There is little doubt that the same mechanism exists throughout the vertebrates as the parts of the inner ear, comprising the utriculus, sacculus and semicircular canals are of similar construction throughout the subphylum Craniata.

Proprioception

The proprioceptor organs are internal receptor organs which are stimulated by actions of the body and capable of registering tensions of other stresses set up. The best known are the 'muscle spindles' of mammals. These usually consist of three muscle fibres enclosed in a fine connective tissue sheath (such as usually covers each individual muscle fibre), the sheath being expanded in the middle of the fibres

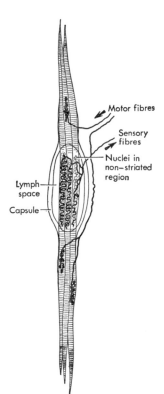

Fig. 30.2. A mammalian muscle spindle composed of three fine fibres on which there are sensory nerve endings enclosed by a capsule. (Based on *Barker*.)

Motor fibres

Sensory fibres

Nuclei in non-striated region

Lymph space

Capsule

and enclosing a capsule containing lymph. Each muscle spindle is innervated by both sensory and motor nerves, the latter ending in ordinary motor end-plates. The sensory nerve terminations, however, lie around the muscle fibres or in the capsule walls and are doubtless stretched or compressed when the muscle is stretched or contracts. Such proprioceptors signal information about the state of contraction of the muscle in which they lie to the central nervous system by variations of the number of impulses sent per second, much as do other sense organs. Since nearly half the fibres in a nerve supplying a skeletal muscle of a vertebrate are sensory, it is apparent that the proprioceptors are of great importance in the working of the body, although it may fairly be said that their study has lagged behind that of the sense organs which respond to stimuli from outside and which are termed collectively the exteroceptors.

31. *Reproduction*

Introduction

Until quite recent times living things were thought to arise spontaneously from non-living matter. Worms and eels were believed to grow from the mud of ponds. The putrefaction of meat and the fermentation of wine were taken to show that the minute living organisms which cause it could arise from the material itself. Pasteur, in the nineteenth century, showed by clear-cut experiments that if all the micro-organisms in a meat broth were killed by prolonged boiling and that if no air was admitted to the container, then no putrefaction took place. He went on to show that when air was admitted putrefaction took place but he finally demonstrated that if the air admitted was very carefully filtered, again no putrefaction occurred. This demonstration of the necessity for some small particles to enter the broth before putrefaction began (bacterial spores, in fact) convinced most people that living organisms could not arise spontaneously from non-living matter but could only arise by reproduction of existing organisms. The ability of living organisms to produce more organisms almost exactly like themselves is a necessary property of life. It may entail a mechanism for passing on from the parents to the offspring the means whereby a minute zygote develops into a large adult like its parents. That such a process could work over a single generation is marvellous, but that it could be repeated over and over again during many millions of years would be incredible were it not demonstrably true by the existence in the world today of animals such as the fish *Latimeria* and the lamp-shell *Lingula* which very closely resemble their ancestors found as fossils in rocks which are 300,000,000 and 400,000,000 years old respectively.

In many ways the simplest sort of reproduction is that shown by bacteria where the organism increases in size by the absorption and transformation of necessary material from the solution in which it is living until it reaches a certain size, whereupon it becomes cut into two, each of which in turn grows and itself becomes two. Many non-cellular plants and animals such as *Euglena*, *Chlorella*, *Amoeba* and

Paramecium grow and multiply in a similar fashion but with the added complexity which results from their larger size and visibly more complex structure. It seems that this simplest type of reproduction commonly follows a period of growth in which increase in the number of molecules incorporated into the living organism takes place. Division of the body into two then occurs, and each of these grows and again divides. However, it is clear from everyday observations that the reproduction of most animals is far more complex than this and involves not only the division of one animal into two but the union of the whole or parts of two separate individual organisms, followed by a complex process of development by which the reproductive body comes in the end to resemble its parents. Such a type of reproduction, involving two separate organisms, is known, of course, as sexual reproduction and it is of great importance in the animal and plant kingdom not only because it leads to the formation of new organisms (asexual reproduction does that) but also because it causes the formation at each generation of organisms which are not identical with their parents but differ very slightly from them. The detailed study of the way in which the gametes are formed and unite is part of the province of cytology, the study of the way in which the zygote develops is known as embryology, and the relation between the characters of the parents and offspring constitutes the study of heredity. Not only are these sciences concerned with the reproduction of organisms but the changes in the parents, connected with reproduction and varying with their state of nutrition and age or with the season of the year, constitute the study known as reproductive physiology. Since only one aspect of reproduction can be dealt with at a time, the reader is referred to Ch. 33 for an account of the cytology of gametes; to Chs. 33 and 34 for an account of development, and to Ch. 35 for an account of inheritance. The present chapter will be concerned only with the general physiology of reproduction. As such it must be concerned with asexual as well as with sexual reproduction.

Asexual reproduction

In bacteria and in many Protozoa, asexual reproduction takes place by the division of the whole organism into two parts, each of which goes on to develop the full structure typical of the species. In *Paramecium* the nuclei divide followed by the cytoplasm and the separate daughter animals develop those adult organelles which they lack as a result of the division. For example, each will have one contractile vacuole instead of two and one will lack a gullet. They soon gain adult size and eventually themselves divide. It is not known exactly how this process is controlled but it is well known that growth precedes reproduction which only occurs when the animal has attained a certain size. This is not true for all types of asexual reproduction for it will be recalled that each zygote of *Monocystis* forms eight sporozoites and each ookinete or zygote of *Plasmodium* forms many thousands of minute sporozoites.

Although sexual reproduction occurs in *Hydra* and *Obelia*, the rapid multiplication of the polyps of these species and of many other types of coelenterate is brought about by a form of asexual reproduction which is difficult clearly to distinguish from growth. *Chlorohydra viridissima* forms buds which eventually leave the parent and live separately. When liberated they may even have buds of their own. A colony of *Obelia* may, in fact, be likened to a *Hydra* from which the buds have not separated and in which it is impossible clearly to state what constitutes an individual. But as was seen in the chapter on coelenterates, *Obelia* colonies give rise not only to hydranths but also to medusae which are released from the colony and lead a free-swimming life. These organisms clearly *are* individuals and they are formed only in an asexual manner. In turn they reproduce sexually and the resulting planula larva founds another hydroid colony. This succession of sexual and asexual reproduction is sometimes called alternation of generations but should not be confused with the haploid and diploid generations of plants and indeed may be distinguished by being termed metagenesis.

The Platyhelminthes as a phylum are notable for their powers of asexual reproduction, as shown by the formation of rediae and cercariae in *Fasciola*. Although free-living platyhelminths do not generally reproduce asexually to any extent, they have very great powers of regeneration when injured and of the production of monsters if the head region is cut in two or the head of another specimen grafted on.

Higher in the animal kingdom the powers of asexual reproduction by a process similar to growth are not so well developed, although many marine annelids produce new individuals by budding. Molluscs do not reproduce asexually and neither do echinoderms to any great extent, although the process does occur in that phylum.

In general it may be said that animals which occupy a relatively lowly position in the animal kingdom often reproduce by asexual means which are similar to the processes of growth in that new individuals are gradually formed and organized from a mass of undifferentiated cells. As such, asexual reproduction resembles in some ways the process of development of an embryo after fertilization of the egg by the sperm in sexual reproduction but it differs from it in being reversible. Thus 'degrowth' and 'de-differentiation' of a partially formed bud may take place in hydra if conditions are unfavourable for its further growth.

Asexual reproduction is typically found in the life history of an animal during seasons of favourable environmental conditions or in circumstances where very rapid multiplication is advantageous as it is in the lives of parasites in intermediate hosts.

From the evolutionary point of view the disadvantage of asexual reproduction is believed to be the absence of variation in the offspring. Even if a mutation (p. 669) should take place in the cell of a multicellular organism undergoing asexual reproduction (e.g. in an interstitial cell of hydra), its effects are only on the cells produced by its division and these make up only a small part of the whole daughter organism. If this be compared with the effects of a mutation which occurs during the formation of a germ cell, it will readily be seen that all the cells of an organism produced by a sexual process from a single ovum and a single sperm will contain the new gene complement which will result in the formation of a slightly different organism. In addition, as has been seen in the section on heredity, sexual reproduction makes it possible for various combinations of characters to appear in the offspring even of the same parents. Some of these may enable more of their possessors to survive than other combinations and so may be selected and after many generations become the 'standard model' of the organism.

It can be argued against this that there are many examples of organisms which have reproduced in a sexual manner almost without change for many millions of years, e.g. *Latimeria*, mentioned above. No satisfactory explanation has been advanced to explain how this may happen while the evolution of other species has been rapid. Although it would appear that the mutation rate of species which have persisted virtually unchanged for 400,000,000 years must be low, it is by no means certain that this is so, since in a variety of animals and plants tested mutation rates have been found to be much the same. Their stability may perhaps be accounted for by the stability of their environment, as in *Latimeria*, or their excellent adaptation to it, but it is not obvious why *Latimeria* or *Lingula* are so much better adapted than other organisms dwelling in the same situation or why they have not been ousted by later and presumably more 'efficient' competitors. Why some organisms persist for vast ages of geological time and others come and go on the evolutionary scene is still a problem which requires a solution.

It will be apparent that it is difficult to distinguish between the type of asexual reproduction shown by hydra and the regeneration of lost parts. For example, a beheaded hydra can grow anew its crown of tentacles in fact, as well as in Greek mythology. It has been a favourite animal for such experiments for 200 years. A planarian when cut in half can regenerate the appropriate head and tail ends. This results in two planarians being formed. Likewise a starfish can regenerate a lost arm and a separate arm can even re-grow the other four. Again, this results in the presence of two starfishes where one lived before. The process of regeneration is distinguishable from asexual reproduction only if the process does not occur spontaneously and is not a normal means of reproduction of the animal. Some species of starfish can, and do in fact, reproduce asexually by breaking into two parts, each of which regenerates a complete animal.

In the majority of animals, however, regeneration is a more limited process than it is in planarians and starfishes and is confined to the regrowth of a relatively small part of the body after accidental or self-inflicted injury. For example, a crab can sever a limb at the base by a special autotomy muscle and a new limb can be grown to replace it. This is useful because it may enable the crab to escape from a predator at a small sacrifice. A lizard can grow anew a tail lost in the same way, although the replacing structure is not as well developed as was the original. Throughout its life a newt can regenerate a limb which has been cut off but although a frog can regenerate a limb while still in the tadpole stage, the power is lost at metamorphosis.

In birds and mammals the power of regeneration is confined to the healing of wounds. The blood clot which is formed shortly after injury is gradually replaced by connective tissue and the Malpighian layer of the epidermis slowly grows across the surface of the soft blood clot which has become separated by a film of fluid from the dry superficial scab. Although this process is adequate and obviously has survival value, the healed wound is never as good as the uninjured region. The whiteness of the scar denotes the presence of a greater amount of collagen and fewer blood vessels than normal. The epidermis may also remain thinner and weaker.

It will readily be appreciated that asexual reproduction by a growth process, the regeneration of limbs and the healing of wounds are all processes in which the power of forming organized structures of the appropriate sort are shown, e.g. a newt's limb and not a tail, a crab's swimming leg and not its chela. The processes are alike in that respect but animals differ in the amount to which they possess them. The power may be likened to the retention into adult life of the abilities possessed by the undifferentiated embryo and which are normally inactive in the adult but which can be brought into operation by an appropriate stimulus such as injury.

Sexual reproduction

The essential feature of sexual reproduction—the fusion of haploid male and female pronuclei, and the processes leading to it—have already been described for many types of animals. In the insects the phenomenon of parthenogenesis (virgin birth) will be described (page 614) and although it might be called asexual reproduction in that no fusion of nuclei takes place, it is quite different from the type of asexual reproduction to which budding belongs and which involves many cells. It can be looked upon rather as a type of modified sexual reproduction in that the new individuals develop from an unfertilized egg. As is well known, unfertilized eggs of the bee, possessing a haploid set of chromosomes (16) develop only into males, while fertilized (diploid—32 chromosomes) eggs develop into females (queens or workers). The parthenogenesis of aphids is different in that the eggs which develop without fertilization are diploid, having been formed without meiosis. Later generations can produce males and females and these in turn produce haploid eggs and sperm which undergo a normal sexual process, thereby restoring the diploid condition.

The sexual reproduction of the majority of animals is a seasonal process and this is, of course, most marked in those living in the temperate and polar regions and, in general, least marked in the tropics where the seasons are least noticeable. Good examples of seasonal reproduction are found in many phyla and several examples will be given. *Nereis*, the ragworm, spawns in the spring in southern England, and *Arenicola*, the lugworm, spawns in the autumn. The gametes are formed in the coelom and mature gradually until spawning is due. Most of the breeding population liberate their gametes within a day or two of one another, although how this coincidence is brought about is not understood. Frogs spawn in the early spring and the tadpoles hatch and begin to feed as the vegetation begins to grow. The Emperor penguin of the Antarctic incubates its single egg during the total darkness of the antarctic winter and the young are hatched at a time when the ice begins to melt and the parents can again begin to find food. The red deer mates in the autumn and the young are born in the following summer. The mating or rutting period lasts only for a few weeks and hence the majority of the calves are born during the same month. By contrast the common rat can breed at all times of the year, although the season of greatest activity is from March to June. Finally man himself breeds at all times of the year with very little seasonal fluctuation.

One may well ask how these complex processes are regulated and how they are related to the seasonal changes of the environment. A few examples will illustrate what is known of the answers to these questions.

FEMALE SEXUAL CYCLE

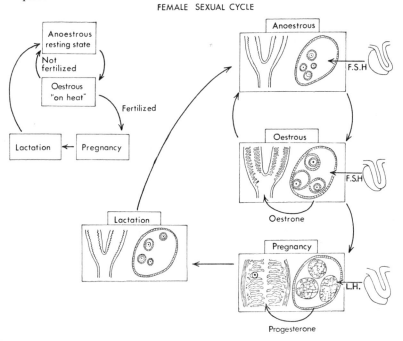

Fig. 31.1. Diagram illustrating the cycle of sexual activity in a female mammal.

The variations in the condition of the uterus and ovary are shown in the rectangles. F.S.H. = follicle stimulating hormone. L.H. = luteinising hormone.

A young mammal is possessed of gonads from birth, but during its early growth these remain quiescent. When the adult size is approached the gonads enlarge and the germ cells mature (see page 611). Secondary sexual characters develop, such as the mammae in the female and the antlers of male deer. These changes are thought to be started by the secretion of hormones from the anterior portion of the pituitary gland. In the female, a follicle-stimulating hormone is carried by the blood stream but acts only on the ovaries where it stimulates the growth of Graafian follicles. In the male, a corresponding hormone stimulates the maturation of spermatozoa in the

MALE SEXUAL CYCLE

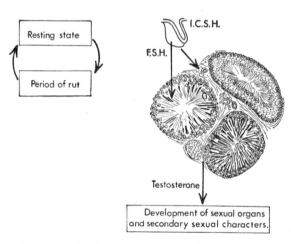

Fig. 31.2. The sexual cycle in the male mammal.

I.C.S.H. = interstitial cell stimulating hormone. F.S.H. = Gonadotrophic hormone corresponding to the follicle stimulating hormone in the female.

tubules of the testis. In the female the maturing follicles in turn pass a hormone (an *oestrogen*) into the blood stream which stimulates changes in the uterus and vagina and also in the behaviour of the animal, which, instead of being indifferent to or even hostile to the male, becomes receptive to his approaches and finally permits copulation to occur. The oocyte which is discharged from the Graafian follicle when sexual activity is at its height is replaced by cells which form a yellow glandular body known by its Latin name of *corpus luteum*. The growth of this body is stimulated by a hormone liberated by the anterior pituitary gland and the corpus luteum in turn secretes a hormone, *progesterone*, which acts on the uterus and causes great growth of its epithelial lining and increase in size as the embryo develops in it.

In the male not only are spermatozoa stimulated by an anterior pituitary hormone but also another hormone stimulates activity of the interstitial cells of the testis which pack the spaces between the cylindrical tubules. These interstitial cells in turn (like the cells of the corpus luteum) secrete a hormone, testosterone, which stimulates growth of accessory reproductive structures such as the seminal vesicles and the prostate gland.

In some mammals such as the deer there is one period in each year of sexual activity or oestrus. In others, such as the dog, there are two—one in the spring and one in the autumn. In the cow the period of activity and readiness to mate is repeated every 21 days if fertilization and pregnancy do not result. In the wild rabbit the female is always in a condition to mate during the breeding season, which lasts from about January to June. The release of the oocyte from the follicle of the ovary in this animal takes place only as a result of the stimulus of copulation, whereas in many mammals ovulation is spontaneous during the period of oestrus.

Man has no cycle of sexual activity which can be compared exactly with the period of oestrus and anoestrus (sexual inactivity) of most other mammals but nevertheless regular cyclical changes in the reproductive organs of women take place between puberty, when sexual maturity begins, and the menopause at 45–50 years of age when reproductive activity ends. The mucous membrane lining the uterus becomes very much more corrugated and its blood vessels congested until, at the end of the cycle, the lining and blood are shed and pass out through the vagina during the course of four or five days. This constitutes the monthly or menstrual period which is followed by a time during which the uterine mucous membrane begins to grow and again becomes complex in its folding and very vascular. At about 13–15 days after the onset of the menstrual period, ovulation takes place. If fertilization occurs and the young embryo becomes implanted in the wall of the uterus, the lining is not shed and the menstrual cycle does not take place during the ensuing nine months of pregnancy. If fertilization does not take place, the monthly breakdown of the uterine tissue occurs and the cycle is repeated. Although this cycle of changes in the reproductive organs appears to resemble the oestrus and anoestrus periods of other mammals, it differs in that copulation may occur at any time and is

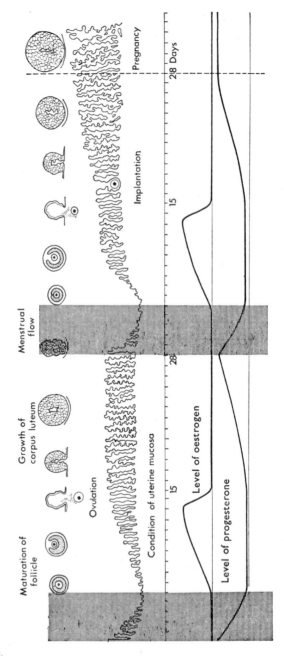

Fig. 31.3. Diagram illustrating the changes in the reproductive organs and their hormonal control during the human menstrual cycle.

In the cycle on the left the oocyte is not fertilized, but on the right hand fertilization has taken place and has been followed by implantation, the continued existence of the corpus luteum, and the beginning of pregnancy.

not restricted to the time of maximum congestion of the uterine lining. Uterine bleeding does not occur at the time of ovulation as it does, for instance, in the dog, and at no time between the beginning and end of reproductive life are the sexual organs in a non-functioning state. The menstrual cycle of women resembles the oestrous cycle of other mammals, however, in that the maturation of the ovarian follicle, the proliferation of the uterine lining and the formation of the corpus luteum in the event of pregnancy are all known to be controlled by hormonal changes (Fig. 31.3).

No corresponding cyclical changes occur in the male, and after the onset of puberty sexual activity continues during life but with diminishing vigour in later years.

In wild birds, in general, there is very great difference in size between the gonads in the breeding season and during the other parts of the year. It has been clearly shown that the chief external agent which influences the reproductive cycle is the amount of light received by the bird. With increasing day length after the shortest day of winter (the winter solstice), the pituitary is stimulated to produce a hormone which brings about the growth of the gonads and reproductive tracts. Changes of behaviour are also produced and birds such as starlings or rooks, which have associated in flocks during the winter, pair off, nest, lay and incubate their eggs and tend their young. By the time this is complete the gonads have gone back to their resting winter condition.

Both birds and mammals being warm blooded might well be expected to be relatively unaffected by the external temperatures inasmuch as their internal organs are all maintained at a nearly constant temperature. As we have seen, particularly in birds, it is believed that the most important factor influencing their reproductive cycle is the amount of light received. This, however, can hardly be the case with the Amphibia, since they hibernate in winter in dark places. Being cold-blooded animals and at the same temperature as their environment, it is believed that they are influenced in their seasonal sexual activity by the rise in temperature which occurs in the spring. It has been shown as well that sexual activity can be increased by increased light, and it may well be that in a state of nature a succession of stimuli such as rise in temperature and increased illumination are necessary to bring about spawning.

Among the fishes there is a great variety of reproductive habits and less is clearly understood about the hormonal control of the reproductive cycle. Many fishes such as the trout and stickleback have an annual spawning season of relatively short duration but others, such as the dogfish, may breed during most of the year and are only a little more active in spring than at other times.

We have already seen that it is a characteristic of invertebrates, as with most of the lower vertebrates, to have a cycle of changes in the reproductive organs which are active at one or more periods of the year and quiescent at others. Little is known of the way in which these changes are controlled within the bodies of these animals but there is little doubt that temperature is an important factor, especially for those living in regions of the globe where there are well-marked seasons. Breeding is clearly related to temperature in some animals such as oysters, which only liberate their larvae when the temperature rises above 18°C. On the other hand, the sea urchins of the Red Sea spawn chiefly at full moon. The famous Palolo worm of the Pacific (*Eunice viridis*) spawns twice a year on the day of the last quarter of the moon in October and November at dawn. Such regularity is remarkable and it is hard to believe that the lunar cycle and spawning are not related as cause and effect, or at least that the stimulus to release of gametes is not provided by lunar changes. It is thus highly probable that a variety of mechanisms have been evolved among the invertebrates which play a part in the control of sexual reproduction, and it would seem that, for many animals, seasonal fluctuation in the temperature of the environment is of dominant importance but that in many species some additional stimulus is required for the animals to go through their mating behaviour and for the release of gametes.

32. *The Endocrine Organs (Ductless Glands)*

IN A preceding chapter co-ordination of the activities of the body of a vertebrate by means of the nervous system has been described but there is another way by which the functions of the various parts of the body are controlled and integrated. In the body of a vertebrate occur several so-called ductless glands, or *endocrine organs*. These produce secretions which are not conveyed from the glands by ducts leading to a surface as in the case of those glands associated with the alimentary canal, or with the skin or respiratory tract, but which pass into the blood stream for distribution to all parts of the body. Hence the name 'ductless gland' originally applied to these organs. The secretions consist of definite chemical compounds which may in some circumstances affect the general metabolism or in others produce specific effects. These compounds are called *hormones* or 'chemical messengers' and certain of them produce co-ordinated action of various parts of the body. This type of action is known as *chemical co-ordination* to distinguish it from that effected by means of the nervous system (*nervous co-ordination*). An outstanding example of chemical co-ordination is that produced by a hormone called *adrenalin* produced by the *adrenal bodies* situated near the kidneys. Adrenalin when secreted into the blood stream produces a number of effects directed to the preparation of the body for muscular exertion. It accelerates the rate of heart-beat, diverts blood from the alimentary canal and the skin to the muscles by producing constrictions of the blood vessels in those organs (i.e. the gut and the skin), dilates the blood vessels in the muscles and causes the discharge into the blood of sugar derived from the glycogen stores in the liver—all these effects being directed towards the greater efficiency of muscular action by supplying the muscles with adequate amounts of sugar and oxygen and the removal of the breakdown products associated with muscular action.

The term 'hormone' (derived from a Greek word meaning 'to excite') was first applied to a substance called *secretin*, discovered in

1902 by Bayliss and Starling, who found that when the acid chyme of the stomach passes into the duodenum, the mucous membrane of the duodenum is stimulated to produce secretin. This is carried by the blood stream to the pancreas where it 'excites' the pancreas to secrete pancreatic juice more copiously. The acid chyme also causes the production by the mucous membrane of the duodenum of another hormone called *gastrin* which is conveyed by the blood to the gastric glands of the stomach causing further secretion of gastric juice by those glands which are, however, primarily stimulated by nervous reflex action produced by the presence of food in the buccal cavity and also by gastrin secreted by the mucous coat of the stomach in contact with certain chemical substances in food—notably in meat. This gastrin also travels in the blood to reach the gastric glands.

The principal endocrine organs are (1) the thyroid and para-thyroids, (2) the pituitary body, (3) the adrenals, (4) the islets of Langerhans in the pancreas, (5) the interstitial cells of the gonads (testis and ovary).

The thyroid

In mammals this is a bilobed gland straddling the ventral side of the larynx; in Amphibia, the homologous organ consists of two yellow spherical bodies situated beneath the roots of the lingual arteries, while in the dogfish it is a pear-shaped organ beneath the anterior end of the ventral aorta.

The thyroid in mammals is composed of a mass of spherical vesicles whose walls consist of a single layer of cubical cells. These cells secrete into the cavities of the vesicles a yellow colloid containing the thyroid hormones. From the vesicles the hormone diffuses into the blood flowing through the capillaries penetrating the connective tissue binding the vesicles together. Two compounds have been isolated from the thyroid—(1) thyroxine and (2) tri-iodothyronine. Both contain iodine and are derivatives of the amino-acid tyrosine. Their chemical formulae are:

Thyroxine $HO\langle\rangle-O-\langle\rangle-CH_2.CHNH_2.COOH$

Triiodothyronine $HO\langle\rangle-O-\langle\rangle-CH_2.CHNH_2.COOH$

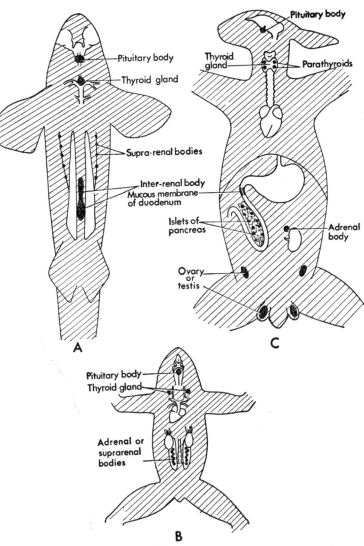

Fig. 32.1. Diagrams to show the positions of the principal endocrine organs in (*A*) the dogfish, (*B*) the frog and (*C*) the rabbit.

The latter compound is regarded as the more effective hormone of the two.

The iodine in these compounds is supplied to the body in the form of iodides in food or in drinking water. Should these salts be deficient in the diet, the gland is unable to synthesise the thyroid hormones and the deficiency causes a condition known as *hypothyroidism*, characterized by the following features.

(1) Cretinism. This condition occurs in young mammals. Cretins are undeveloped and remain infantile even if they survive to an adult age. Human cretins have a vacant expression and eyelids devoid of eyelashes.

(2) Myxoedema. This is normally found in adults as a result of thyroid deficiency later in life. The skin, particularly in the facial region, develops a 'puffy' condition and the sufferer is lethargic owing to a low rate of tissue respiration.

In both cases the gland may enlarge considerably, causing a bulge at the base of the neck known as a goitre. Provided the gland is capable of producing the hormones, both conditions can be remedied or alleviated by the addition of iodides to the diet, usually in the form of iodized salt. If the gland itself is defective, thyroid extracts from the thyroids of animals slaughtered for food may be given as a remedy.

(3) In Amphibia hypothyroidism delays the onset of metamorphosis. Conversely the addition of thyroid extract to the food of young amphibian larva accelerates metamorphosis and leads to the production of miniature adults. The axolotl (*Ambystoma*)—an aquatic newt-like amphibian living in certain lakes in Mexico—fails to metamorphose owing to lack of iodine in its native waters. It retains throughout its life external gills and a finned tail, but unlike other amphibian larvae becomes sexually mature and can breed, a condition known as *paedomorphosis*. When transferred to water containing sufficient iodine or when given a thyroid extract, the axolotl develops lungs, loses its gills and tail fins, and becomes terrestrial.

The opposite condition to hypothyroidism is *hyperthyroidism* due to an over-active thyroid gland. Here the metabolic rate is heightened, muscular weakness and nervous prostration is experienced and the eyes often protrude (exophthalmic goitre).

The parathyroids

Embedded in the thyroid gland of mammals are two pairs of small bodies known as the parathyroids. Their secretion controls the amount of calcium in the blood. Removal of the parathyroids causes a rapid fall in the calcium content of the blood, accompanied by severe spasmodic muscular contractions.

The pituitary body

This has a double origin. During the development of a vertebrate, a downgrowth of the floor of the diencephalon called the infundibulum (page 638) meets an evagination of the roof of the stomodaeum known as the hypophysis. In the lamprey these remain separate from each other but in all higher vertebrates from the fish upwards the hypothysis becomes constricted off from the roof of the stomodaeum and partly surrounds the lower end of the infundibulum. The fully developed pituitary body consists of the stalk, an anterior lobe (*pars anterior*) formed from the hypophysis, and a posterior lobe formed partly of nervous tissue (*pars nervosa*) and partly from the posterior border of the hypophysis (*pars intermedia*). It has recently been agreed that the anterior portion of the pituitary body consisting of the pars anterior and the pars intermedia shall be referred to as the *adenohypophysis* and the hinder portion as the *neurohypophysis*. Both secrete hormones, some of which act directly on various bodily functions while the remainder stimulate the secretions of other endocrine organs. For example, the adenohypophysis secretes a growth hormone which directly controls the rate of growth of young vertebrates—a dwarf and a giant being extremes resulting from an under-normal and an over-normal rate of secretion of this hormone; while another (*thyrotropic hormone*) stimulates the secretion of the thyroid. Other pituitary hormones acting indirectly are the *adrenotropic hormone* stimulating the adrenal cortex (page 604) and the *gonadotropic hormones* affecting the secretions of the interstitial cells of the gonads (pp. 594 and 606). It is thus seen that the pituitary exercises a considerable amount of control over the functioning of the body either through its own direct action or through the medium of the other endocrine organs. In addition to the above hormones, the adenohypophysis produces others regulating the carbohydrate and fat metabolism of the body. That concerned with carbohydrates (diabetogenic hormone) raises the sugar content of the blood by causing the glycogen reserves to be converted to glucose—an effect opposite to that of insulin (page 605).

The secretion of the neurohypophysis known as *pituitrin* produces contraction of unstriped muscle in all parts of the body and thus plays a part in the maintenance of the blood pressure by causing constriction of the arteries whose walls contain unstriped muscle fibres (page 458). It is used in medicine to produce contraction of the walls of the arteries when required. In those vertebrates, e.g. certain fish, Amphibia and lizards, whose skin contains chromatophores (pigment cells), e.g. the melanophores of the frog's skin, the effect of pituitrin is to cause the pigment to extend from the body of the pigment cell into its branches. In its absence the pigment recedes into the centre of the cell. In the case of the melanophores this produces a darkening of the skin. In darkness or in dim light the secretion of pituitrin by the pituitary body is continuous but in bright light its secretion is diminished as the result of nervous reflex action. Light falling on the retinas of the eyes sets up nervous impulses which are relayed to the pituitary body to inhibit or reduce the secretion of pituitrin. In this way the colour or hue of the skin may be made to harmonize with the colour of the environmental background of the animal so as to produce a certain degree of protective coloration.

The suprarenals and adrenals

These are two distinct organs of different origin which remain separate in the Elasmobranch fish but are united in the mammal to form a pair of bodies (the adrenal bodies) adjacent to the kidneys. The suprarenals in the dogfish consist of small patches of cell tissue accompanying the ganglia of the sympathetic chains and derived from the neural crest cells of the embryo (page 630) while the inter-renal body develops from the same rudiments which give rise to the gonads, i.e. are formed from part of the coelomic epithelium. In the mammals the suprarenals form the central portion (or *medulla*) and the inter-renals the outer portion (*cortex*) of the so-called adrenal bodies. The medulla and the cortex have different functions.

The medulla secretes *adrenalin* which is a compound having the formula:

$$OH\underset{OH}{\overset{OH}{\diagdown}}CHOH.CH_2.NH.CH_3$$

The rate of secretion is under the control of the central nervous system via the sympathetic system which relays nervous impulses set up in the brain by emotions such as fear or anger from the C.N.S. to the adrenal bodies. The effects of this hormone have already been given (page 599). Normally small amounts of the hormone are continuously secreted into the blood and maintain the muscle tone (i.e. slight contraction) of the arterial walls to keep up the pressure of the blood in the arteries and so to assist the circulation. In the condition known as 'shock' following an operation or an accident, the reaction of adrenalin is much diminished, causing a fall in the blood pressure and a state of general collapse. Injections of adrenalin are employed to overcome 'shock'. (In passing it may be mentioned that substances producing effects similar to those of adrenalin but more specific in their action are liberated from the terminals of sympathetic nerve fibres under nervous stimulation. These substances are known as '*sympathins*'.)

The cortex produces a hormone which controls the water and the sodium chloride content of the blood. In its absence an excessive amount of excretion of water and sodium chloride by the kidneys occurs. A deficiency in the amount of secretion of this hormone produces in human beings a discoloration of the skin owing to the deposition in it of melanin (Addison's disease). It is probable that other hormones may be secreted by the adrenal cortex but their precise effects are only beginning to be understood.

The islets of the pancreas

Embedded in the connective tissue binding together the alveoli of the pancreas occur isolated clumps of cells known as the islets of Langerhans, which secrete a hormone called *insulin*. Normally this passes continuously into the blood stream and enables the oxidation of sugar to proceed to completion in the tissues. It also promotes the formation of glycogen from the sugar in the blood in the liver and in the muscles—in this respect it has an effect directly opposite to that produced by adrenalin. Should the hormone cease to be produced by the islets for one cause or another (e.g. a condition which sometimes follows an accident resulting in injury to the cerebellum, pons or floor of the fourth ventricle in the brain), *diabetes* occurs. Since the sugar is not utilized in the normal way, it accumulates in the blood to such an extent that the kidneys excrete it in the urine. The body then draws on the fats and proteins of the tissues to provide energy, causing wasting away of the muscles and fatty tissues with the formation of poisonous breakdown products, e.g. aceto-acetic acid, leading to coma and eventual death.

The Gonads

Both the testis and the ovary begin to function as endocrine organs in mammals at the onset of puberty (sexual maturity). The hormones appear to be produced by the interstitial cells, i.e. cells in the connective tissue of the gonads.

In the testis, the interstitial cells secrete hormones such as *testosterone* or *androsterone*, which are sterols. These cause the development of the secondary sexual characteristics of the male, e.g. the beard and deepened voice in man and the well-developed horns and muscles of stags and bulls. If young mammals are castrated (i.e. operated on for removal of the testes), the secondary male characters fail to appear and the bodily form becomes more feminine. The practice of castration of domesticated male animals is employed to suppress their sex instincts and to render them more docile. Farm animals (pigs, cattle and sheep) grow and fatten more rapidly after castration.

In the ovary, the follicle cells secrete a hormone (an oestrogen) which is responsible for the onset of oestrus ('heat') at the mating seasons. Oestrogen produces changes in the uterine wall in preparation for the possible reception of a fertilized ovum (or ova). The uterine wall thickens and becomes more vascular (i.e. its blood supply is increased). Ovulation (shedding of ova from the Graafian follicles of the ovary) occurs at some time during the period of oestrus. If the ovaries are removed from a female mammal the oestral changes do not occur. This operation is known as 'spaying' and is used to prevent female cats from breeding. After an ovum has been discharged from a Graafian follicle, the cells of the follicle multiply to form a temporary endocrine organ called the corpus luteum. Its duration as such depends on whether a fertilized ovum is implanted in the uterine wall or not. In the former case it continues to enlarge and to secrete a hormone called progesterone during the period of pregnancy. Progesterone causes the uterus to enlarge to accommodate the developing foetus and stimulates the growth and development of the placenta (page 662). In the later stages of pregnancy it also stimulates the enlargement of the mammary glands and the secretion by them of milk. As previously mentioned (page 603), the pituitary gland produces gonadotropic hormones which stimulate the production of the male and female hormones, and also *lactogenic* hormones which also stimulate directly the mammary glands.

In the vertebrates other than mammals the production of the secondary sexual characters is also under the control of the 'sex' hormones produced by the gonads. In birds, whose genetical sex mechanism is the opposite to that in mammals (page 682), removal or atrophy of the ovaries in the hen bird produces the assumption by the female of the male characteristics, i.e. the brighter-hued male plumage and male sex instincts. Removal of testes from young male birds merely inhibits the sexual instincts of the male without producing any suppression of the male secondary sexual characteristics, i.e. the male type of plumage develops. A subsidiary effect is a prolongation of the growing phase so that the castrated male bird eventually reaches a larger size than the normal. In the domestic fowl such birds are known as *capons*. It would therefore appear that the ovarian hormone (or hormones) suppress in the hen bird the development of the male secondary sexual characteristics.

The thymus

This is derived from patches of cells associated with the visceral clefts. In the mammal these form a pinkish mass in the thorax anterior to the heart and ventral to the roots of the large blood vessels connected with the heart. It reaches its greatest development in the early, infantile life of the mammal and then degenerates as maturity comes on. This body is regarded as an endocrine organ though little is known of its functions. There is some evidence that secretions of the thymus may be connected with the onset of sexual maturity, and it is also likely that it plays a part in resistance to infection and the immunity reactions of the body.

Invertebrate hormones

Less is known regarding the action of hormones in the invertebrates but they have been shown to exist, for example, in certain marine Crustacea. In the hypodermis of prawns occur chromatophores of two types similar in structure to that of the melanophores of Amphibia (page 314). One type contains red and yellow pigments and the other red and white ones. In response to changes in the colour of the background, changes in hue of the animal are produced to harmonize with them so as to provide the animal with a marked degree of protective coloration. These changes in hue result from movements of the pigments in and out of the branching processes of the chromatophores under the control of hormones produced by the nervous system and possibly by the eye-stalks, though these may merely be reservoirs for the storage of hormones. Removal of the eyes and their stalks causes expansion of the pigment in the chromatophores with consequent darkening of the skin owing to removal of the hormones, while injecting a sea-water extract of the eye-stalks into animals with excised eyes produces lightening of the skin by reintroducing the hormones, causing contraction of the pigments. The existence of other hormones controlling ecdysis (page 167), growth and maturation of the eggs, and the level of the sugar content of the blood, has also been demonstrated.

IV. THE DEVELOPMENT OF THE INDIVIDUAL

33. Gametes, Fertilization and Segmentation

SEXUAL reproduction, which is the commonest method of reproduction among the Metazoa, involves the production of germ cells or *gametes*. The formation of these cells occurs by a process called *gametogenesis* accompanied by a special type of nuclear division known as *meiosis* (page 435) during which the homologous chromosomes pair together and then separate after interchange of certain segments. The member chromosomes of each pair then proceed to opposite poles of the nuclear spindle so that the two new nuclei formed contain the haploid number of chromosomes (i.e. half the number of chromosomes originally present in the parent nucleus). Hence the nuclei of the gametes ultimately produced contain the haploid number of chromosomes, the diploid number being restored when the gametes unite. In this way the somatic cells of each generation of any particular species of animal have nuclei with a constant number of chromosomes.

Gametogenesis

In the gonads of the Metazoa, whether in the testes or the ovary, the cells of the germinal epithelium undergo divisions with mitotic divisions of their nuclei. The cells thus 'budded off' from the germinal epithelium form the *spermatogonia* or the *oogonia*—a process easily visible in the seminal vesicles or ovaries of the earthworm. The spermatogonia or oogonia, with or without further divisions, give rise to the *primary gametocytes* (*primary spermatocytes* or *primary oocytes*). Each of these in turn undergo *maturation divisions* to form the gametes. It is during these maturation divisions that meiosis occurs.

Spermatogenesis

Each primary spermatocyte divides to form two *secondary spermatocytes* and these divide to produce four *spermatids* (Fig. 33.1). The spermatids then develop into mature spermatozoa, whose structure is shown in the accompanying diagram (Fig. 33.2A).

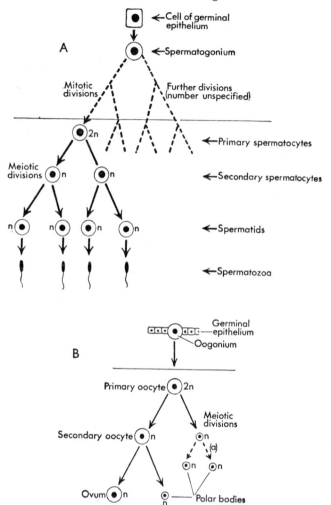

Fig. 33.1. Gametogenesis *A* Spermatogenesis; *B* Oogenesis

$2n$ = diploid number of chromosomes
n = haploid number of chromosomes

[(a) this division does not always occur]

Oogenesis

Each primary oocyte divides into two cells of very unequal size: the *secondary oocyte* and the first *polar body*. The former undergoes a second division to produce the mature *ovum* and a *second polar body*. Occasionally the first polar body also divides. The polar bodies get

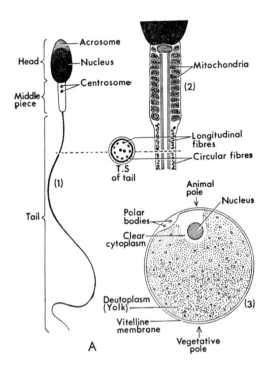

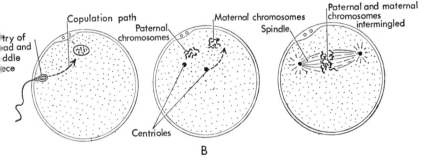

Fig. 33.2.

A Gametes. (1) a mammalian spermatozoon; (2) microscopic structure of middle piece and tail of a spermatozoon; (3) a mature ovum.

B Stages in the fertilization of an ovum by a spermatozoon.

their name from the fact that they were first seen as small objects extruded at the upper (animal) pole of the hen's egg. They are actually abortive ova. This type of division into cells of unequal size is due to the necessity for providing as much as possible of the available food for storage in the yolk (or *deutoplasm*) of the primary oocyte for the future needs of the embryo developing from the egg. The spermatozoon, on the other hand, needs but a small amount of food to provide the energy needed for swimming to the egg at the time of fertilization of the egg.

In chordates, the first polar body is extruded from the 'egg' when ovulation (discharge of the 'egg' from the ovary) occurs, and the second one at fertilization.

The ovum is an undifferentiated cell enclosed in a thin membrane called the *vitelline membrane* within which lie the polar bodies after their extrusion (Fig. 33.2A). The amount of deutoplasm (or yolk) varies in different types of ova, that of the ovum of *Amphioxus* being much less in amount than that of the hen's egg. In chordates the deutoplasm tends to gravitate to the lower region of the ovum and this gives to the ovum a *polarity*. The upper pole is known as the *animal pole*, the lower one being the *vegetative pole*. The nucleus lies in the region of the animal pole but there is no centrosome.

(The word 'egg' is loosely used. It may be used indiscriminately to refer to secondary oocytes, ova, or even to complex structures such as the hen's egg which may even contain early embryonic stages.)

Fertilization

Before an ovum can develop into an embryo, it must normally be fertilized by a spermatozoon. Exceptions occur, as, for example, in the honey-bee where unfertilized ova can develop into the male bees (drones), whose cells have haploid nuclei and which produce spermatozoa by maturation divisions which do not involve meiosis, or in the aphids where a number of successive generations in the life cycle arise from unfertilized ova. These are cases of *parthenogenesis*. Mechanical stimuli (e.g. pricking) and certain chemical stimuli may sometimes cause an ovum to develop into an imperfect embryo. Immersion of sea urchins' ova in sea water containing small amounts of lithium chloride will produce this effect.

The process of fertilization necessitates the discharge of eggs and spermatozoa in close proximity. In aquatic animals the 'eggs' and spermatozoa are merely shed into the water where the spermatozoa swim actively until either their small store of energy-producing food is exhausted or they meet and fertilize 'eggs' floating passively in the water. To render the fertilization of the 'eggs' of bisexual aquatic animals more probable, the male may deposit spermatozoa in the neighbourhood of the eggs laid by the female, as in the case of the salmon, while in bivalve molluscs ciliary currents are used to draw the spermatozoa to the vicinity of the 'eggs'. Land animals, however, by an act of *coitus* introduce the spermatozoa, usually suspended in a seminal fluid (the *semen*) either into the oviducts of the female or into special receptacles known as *spermathecae* (as in the earthworm and cockroach) to be stored until required for the fertilization of the 'eggs'. In any case fertilization requires the presence of water for the spermatozoa to swim to the eggs. There is little, if any, evidence of the attraction by chemical means (*chemotaxis*) of the sperm to the 'eggs' but if a spermatozoon in its movements happens to touch an 'egg', the head (acrosome and nucleus) and the middle piece containing the centrosome penetrate it, leaving the tail outside. So many spermatozoa are produced in comparison with the 'eggs' that even in the absence of any specific attraction of the spermatozoa by the 'eggs', fertilization is highly probable by random contact of the spermatozoa with the 'eggs'.

The energy available for the swimming activity of the spermatozoa is provided either by the very small amount of food stored in their cytoplasm or by nutrient materials in the seminal fluid which in mammals includes fructose, citric acid and phospholipids. As soon as fertilization has occurred, the vitelline membrane becomes more obvious and separates from the surface of the 'egg'. It then becomes known as the *fertilization membrane*. Usually only one spermatozoon enters each 'egg' but when *polyspermy* (i.e. the entrance into the cytoplasm of the egg of several spermatozoa) occurs, the nucleus of one spermatozoon only fuses with that of the 'egg' and the remainder of the spermatozoa degenerate.

Segmentation (cleavage) of the fertilized egg

As the nucleus of the spermatozoon after entry into the 'egg' approaches that of the 'egg', the chromosomes of each nucleus become visible while the nuclear membranes disappear. The centrosome introduced by the sperm divides into two and a spindle is formed between the two new centrosomes. The chromosomes of the nuclei of the egg and the spermatozoon intermingle and become attached to the equator of the spindle by their centromeres. The chromatids of the individual chromosomes then separate following the divisions of the centromeres and, proceeding to opposite poles of the spindle, form two new nuclei having the diploid number of chromosomes. Further divisions of these nuclei follow, together with cleavages of the cytoplasm, to form separate cells known as *blasto-meres*. These divisions result in the formation of an embryonic structure called the *blastula*. The actual form of the blastula is usually conditioned by the amount of yolk in the egg, as will be seen from the following brief accounts of the segmentation (cleavage) of the 'eggs' of different animals.

1. THE CRAYFISH. The 'egg' is relatively large (about 4 mm. in diameter) and contains a fair amount of yolk. After fertilization, the dividing nuclei arrange themselves around the periphery and cleavage of the cytoplasm is limited to their proximity. The blastula so formed consists of a 'shell' of cells (the *blastoderm*), one cell in thickness, surrounding an undivided mass of yolky cytoplasm (Fig. 33.3). The 'egg' is said to be *centrolecithal* owing to the yolky cytoplasm being central in position.

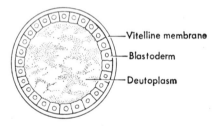

Fig. 33.3. The crayfish. Cleavage of the fertilized egg. (Diagrammatic.)

2. AMPHIOXUS. The 'egg' is *microlecithal*, i.e. it contains relatively little yolk. The segmentation is *holoblastic* and *equal*, i.e. following the nuclear division, the whole of the cytoplasm undergoes cleavage and the blastomeres are of approximately the same size, though those of the vegetative pole are slightly larger and fewer in number than those of the animal pole. The stages in segmentation are shown in Fig. 33.4. The final stage or completed blastula is a hollow sphere of which the wall (blastoderm) is one cell thick and surrounds a central cavity called the *blastocoele*. Since the yolk (deutoplasm) after fertilization gravitates towards the vegetative pole, the 'egg' is

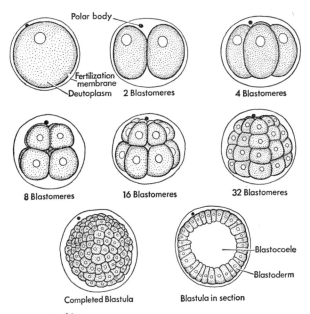

Fig. 33.4. *Amphioxus.*
Cleavage of the fertilized egg leading to the formation of the blastula. (Diagrammatic.)

telolecithal and it is on account of this accumulation of yolk in the lower portion of the 'egg' that the rate of cleavage is slower in that region and the blastomeres are larger and fewer in number than at the animal pole.

3. THE FROG. The frog's 'egg' is larger and contains more yolk than that of *Amphioxus* which it resembles in being telolecithal but the cleavage while holoblastic is much more *unequal*. The blastoderm is more than one cell thick and the blastocoele is confined to the upper hemisphere of the blastula. The cells of the animal pole are much smaller and more numerous than the large yolky cells of the vegetative pole forming the floor of the blastocoele. The superficial cells of the blastoderm of the animal pole contain a black pigment (melanin). Fig. 33.5 shows the segmentation and the completed blastula in section.

4. THE FOWL. The fowl's egg is *macrolecithal*, containing a large amount of yolk. Cleavage is confined to a small region at the animal pole, resulting in the formation of a small cap of cells (blastoderm)

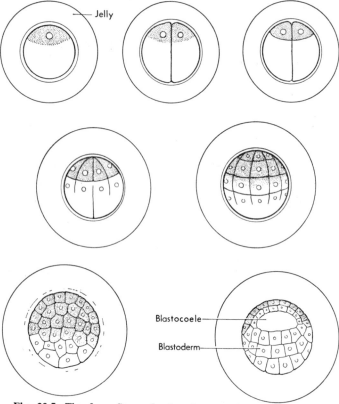

Fig. 33.5. The frog. Stages in the cleavage of the fertilized egg leading to the formation of the blastula. (Diagrammatic.)

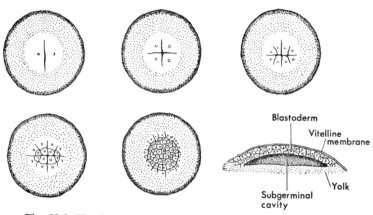

Fig. 33.6. The fowl. Stages in the cleavage of the fertilized egg. (Diagrammatic.)

known as a *blastodisk* separated from the mass of non-nucleated, undivided deutoplasm by a narrow cavity (the *sub-germinal* cavity). The large amount of yolk prevents the whole of the 'egg' from undergoing cleavage and the segmentation of the 'egg' is only partial (*meroblastic*). The sub-germinal cavity is held to be the equivalent of a blastocoele. Fig. 33.6 shows the stages in cleavage of this 'egg'.

5. THE MAMMALS. The mammalian egg is minute and contains only a small amount of yolk, i.e. it is microlecithal like that of *Amphioxus*. Cleavage is holoblastic but results in the formation of a *solid* ball of cells known as a morula instead of a hollow blastula (Fig. 33.7).

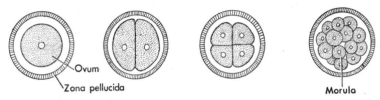

Fig. 33.7. The mammal. Cleavage of the fertilized egg. (Diagrammatic.)

As a result of further development following the completion of the cleavage of the fertilized 'egg', there is formed a young organism which in its earliest stages is known as an *embryo*. The subsequent history of the embryo differs in various types of animals but broadly follows two possible lines of development.

(a) The embryo may gradually acquire the form of a miniature adult and at some stage becomes a free-living, independent animal. Up to this stage its development depends on food supplied by the parent in the form of yolk stored in the 'egg', though in mammals this is sufficient only for the very early stages, being supplemented further by food supplied from the maternal blood during the later stages of development when the embryo, now recognizable as a miniature of the adult, is known as a *foetus*. This type of development is called *direct development*.

(b) The embryo may develop into a free-living self-supporting organism known as a *larva*. This usually differs in form to a greater or lesser degree from the adult stage into which it finally changes by a process called *metamorphosis*. For examples of this see the chapters on *Obelia*, annelids, insects and the frog (Chapters 3, 6, 9, 15). Only rarely is the larva capable of reproduction. The example of the axolotl, a permanently larval amphibian which becomes sexually mature and reproduces, has already been given (p. 602).

34. *The Embryology of Amphioxus, the Frog, the Fowl and the Rabbit*

Gastrulation

WHEN the segmentation of the egg has been completed, a process called *gastrulation* commences. This results in the formation of a *gastrula*—a hollow structure whose cavity, known as the *archenteron*, is surrounded by a wall of two distinct layers of cells. The archenteron primitively has an opening to the exterior at the posterior end of the gastrula called the *blastopore*. In chordates the blastoderm of the blastula (page 616) consists of definite regions (the *presumptive areas*) which are destined to give rise to various tissues and organs in the later embryo, namely the three primary germinal layers: the ectoderm, endoderm and mesoderm, the neural plate (rudiment of the future central nervous system) and the notochord. In the egg of *Amphioxus* the presumptive areas (Fig. 34.1A) originate from separate

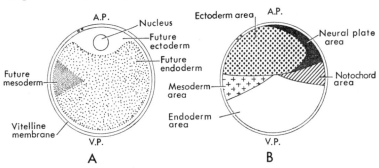

Fig. 34.1. *Amphioxus.*
 A presumptive areas of fertilized egg; *B* presumptive areas of the blastula. (Based on *Conklin.*)

regions of the cytoplasm of the egg, such an egg being known as a mosaic egg, but the frog's egg is a non-mosaic one in which no such demarcation of the cytoplasm exists. It follows that if the first two blastomeres of the segmenting egg of *Amphioxus* are separated, neither can produce by further cell division a perfect embryo, since each blastomere will lack certain regions of the cytoplasm already destined to form specific presumptive areas. In the case of the frog the first two blastomeres, if separated, can each develop into a perfect embryo, the presumptive regions of the cytoplasm not having yet been delineated. During gastrulation the cells of the presumptive areas are moved or actively migrate to their appropriate positions in the gastrula. Just as the process of segmentation is affected by the amount of yolk in the egg, so that of gastrulation is modified by the same factor, as will be seen in the following accounts of gastrulation in the various chordate types.

Amphioxus

The egg of *Amphioxus* (Fig. 33.4) is fertilized by a sperm entering the lower hemisphere and, following this, a rearrangement of the contents of the cytoplasm occurs, the yolk gravitating towards the vegetative pole. The region of the yolky cytoplasm is the presumptive area from which the future endoderm is formed while the clear cytoplasm of the animal pole gives rise to the future ectoderm. A crescentic area of denser cytoplasm (Fig. 34.1) to one side of the yolky cytoplasm is the area from which the future mesoderm will arise. The stages in the segmentation of the egg are shown in Fig. 33.4 and described on page 616.

Gastrulation is effected by the invagination ('buckling-in') of the yolky cells of the vegetative pole produced by the more rapid rate of division of those of the animal pole. The invagination of the yolky cells leads to the obliteration of the blastocoele and to the formation of a cup-shaped gastrula (Fig. 34.2). The hollow of this cup is the archenteron and its rim the margin of the blastopore. Further division of the cells of this margin produce an elongation of the gastrula and at the same time a narrowing of the blastopore due to unequal rates of growth around its edges, the maximum rate being in its most dorsal region. The invaginated cells include those of the endodermal mesodermal and notochordal areas, while the cells remaining on the exterior are those of the ectodermal and neural plate areas. In the completed gastrula, the archenteron is bounded by the notochordal cells in the centre of its roof, flanked on either side by a strip of mesodermal cells and by the endodermal cells forming its floor and lower sides. Externally to the wall of the archenteron is a layer of ectodermal cells with a strip of neural plate cells lying over the notochordal cells (Fig. 34.2). During the elongation of the gastrula further extensions of all these layers are produced as the result of cell

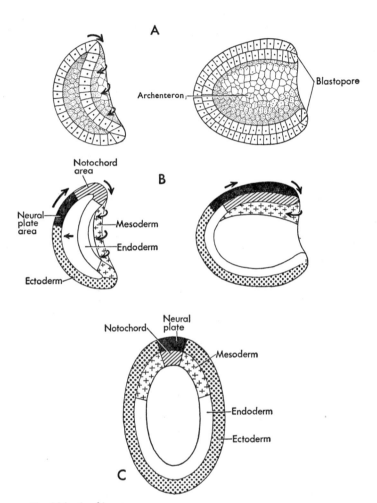

Fig. 34.2. *Amphioxus.*

Stages in gastrulation: *A* Sectional views of developing gastrula; *B* Movements of the presumptive areas during gastrulation; *C* Transverse section of gastrula to show the final positions of the presumptive areas. (Diagrammatic.)

(Note that the embryos are not orientated in the same way as in Figs. 33.4 and 34.1, i.e. with the animal pole towards the top of the page, but are shown here after the rotation which accompanies gastrulation and have the future *anterior* of the animal to the left and the *posterior* to the right (except *C*).)

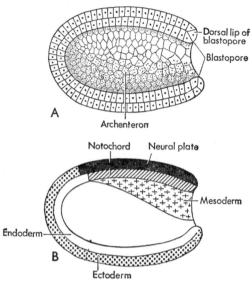

Fig. 34.3. *Amphioxus.*

A Longitudinal section of completed gastrula. *B* Diagram of longitudinal section of completed gastrula to show distribution of the various presumptive areas. (Diagrammatic.)

division around the margin of the blastopore which now marks the position of the posterior end of the gastrula.

Three processes now follow, proceeding side by side:

(1) notogenesis (the formation of the notochord from the noto-
    chordal cells);

(2) neurogenesis (the formation of the neural tube from the neural
    plate cells);

(3) the separation of the mesodermal cells from the roof of the
    archenteron and the formation from them of the mesodermal
    somites.

NOTOGENESIS. The cells of the notochordal region develop into large disk-shaped cells arranged in linear order and separated by alternating fibrous bands.

NEUROGENESIS. The neural plate starts to sink in and to become rolled upwards to form a tube, commencing at the posterior end. At the same time the ectodermal cells at the lateral borders of the neural plate detach themselves from it and form the neural folds which, advancing towards the mid-line, meet and fuse to cover over the neural tube (Fig. 34.4). The formation and fusion of the neural folds also begins at the posterior end. Eventually the enclosed neural tube opens to the exterior at the anterior end by the *neuropore* and communicates with the archenteron at its posterior end by the *neurenteric canal* formed by an extension backwards of the neural folds to roof over the blastopore (Fig. 34.5).

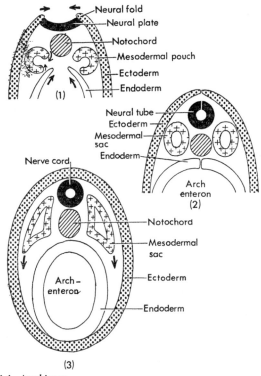

Fig. 34.4. *Amphioxus.*

(1), (2), (3) Successive stages in neurogenesis, notogenesis and formation of the mesodermal sacs. (Diagrammatic.)

THE FORMATION OF THE MESODERMAL SOMITES. The cells of the mesodermal regions on either side of the notochordal region separate from it and from the adjacent endodermal cells. At the anterior end each mesodermal strip arches upwards and constricts to form a pair of *mesodermal (enterocoelic) pouches* with their apertures directed downwards. Behind these pouches the remainder of the mesodermal strips also arch upwards forming longitudinal grooves which by means of further constrictions form a series of pairs of

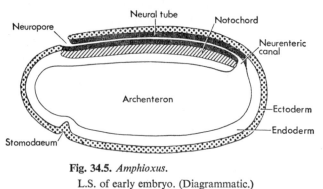

Fig. 34.5. *Amphioxus.*
L.S. of early embryo. (Diagrammatic.)

mesodermal pouches (Fig. 34.4) The pouches close up to form the *mesodermal sacs*, while the upper edges of the endodermal walls of the archenteron extend upwards to meet in the mid-line beneath the notochord to re-form the roof of the archenteron after the separation of the mesodermal regions. The archenteron thus acquires a complete lining of endoderm and forms the future gut. The cavities of the mesodermal sacs are *coelomic* since they are spaces surrounded by mesoderm.

The embryo (as the gastrula may now be termed) continues to grow in length, additions being made to all three germinal layers (the ectoderm, mesoderm and endoderm) and to the notochord and neural tube, by cell division at the posterior end. The number of pairs of mesodermal pouches likewise increases with the elongation of the embryo, fresh pairs being constricted off from the new, undifferentiated mesoderm formed at the posterior end.

THE FURTHER DEVELOPMENT OF THE MESODERMAL SACS. Each sac elongates in a downward direction, insinuating itself between the ectoderm and the endoderm until it meets its fellow of the opposite side in the mid-ventral line (Figs. 34.4(3), and 34.6). The walls of the sacs break down where they touch so that the cavities of each pair of sacs become continuous. The upper portions of the sacs retain their separate identities and form the *mesodermal somites*, but below the level of the base of the notochord the adjacent walls of the sacs break down so that a continuous longitudinal cavity (the *splanchnocoele*) is formed (Fig. 34.6). The continuous layer of mesoderm thus formed next to the endoderm is known as the *splanchnic layer* and the corresponding layer next to the ectoderm as

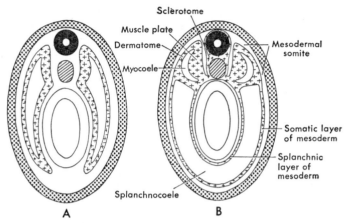

Fig. 34.6. *Amphioxus.*
Diagrams to show the further development of the mesodermal sacs:
A downward elongation of the mesodermal sacs; *B* formation of
mesodermal somites and the splanchnocoele.

the *somatic* (or *parietal*) *layer*. The inner wall of each somite thickens
to form a *myotome* (muscle plate). From the myotomes of somites are
formed the V-shaped striped muscle blocks of the larva and the
adult. The outer wall of each somite becomes a *dermatome* separated
for a time from the myotome by a narrow cavity—the *myocoele*. The
dermatomes give rise to the sub-epidermal connective tissue separating the muscles from the ectoderm. From the base of each somite on
its inner side arises a *sclerotome* which spreads to ensheath the notochord and the neural tube, later becoming fibrous in nature (Fig. 34.6).

From the anterior end of the gut a pair of diverticula push forward. That on the left separates from the gut, acquires an opening
to the exterior and becomes known as Hatschek's pit (page 246). The
other enlarges to form the cavity of the head.

The ectoderm of the fully formed gastrula (embryo) becomes
ciliated, the vitelline membrane is shed and the embryo is now a free-
swimming *larva*. An ingrowth of the ectoderm (the *stomodaeum*) at
the head end on the ventral side to meet the endoderm becomes perforated at its inner end together with the endoderm in contact with
it to form the *enterostome* ('mouth'). An anus is formed similarly
on the left side at the posterior end by another inturning of the ectoderm (the *proctodaeum*) followed by perforation. Beyond the anus
further growth occurs to produce the post-anal tail. In the pharyngeal
region of the gut paired *visceral clefts* are formed partly by lateral

pouch-like outgrowths of the endoderm and partly by corresponding slight depressions of the ectoderm, perforations occurring where the two meet. The subsequent development of these visceral clefts gives rise to the gill clefts separated by the primary and secondary gill bars with their associated skeletal structures and blood vessels (page 237). The whole of the endoderm including that of the gill slits becomes ciliated while in the floor of the pharynx develops, as a longitudinal groove, the *endostyle* in which bands of mucus-secreting cells alternate with tracts of ciliated cells.

As the larva develops, it becomes asymmetric, the somites of one side alternating in position with those of the other side. Similarly the roots of the segmental nerves arising from the dorsal tubular nerve cord formed from the neural tube alternate in position except at the very anterior end. Longitudinal folds of the body wall (*metapleural folds*) grow downwards from the level of the top of the pharynx to enclose a space (the *atrium*) into which the gill slits open and which has a ventral opening at its hinder end leading to the exterior and known as the *atriopore* (page 232). Other structures, e.g. the oral hood, fins, 'liver' diverticulum, ectodermal nephridia, and finally the mesodermal gonads appearing in their turn complete the metamorphosis of the larva into the adult form, which, unlike the freeswimming larva, spends much of its time burrowing in the sand at the bottom of the sea.

The Frog

The blastula (Fig. 33.5) cannot be converted into a gastrula by the simple process of invagination as in *Amphioxus* owing to the thickness of the blastoderm of the vegetative pole. At the time of fertilization a sperm enters the egg at some point just above the equator of the egg, and diametrically opposite to this point of entry of the sperm a re-arrangement of the pigment of the animal pole causes the appearance of a grey crescent, the plane of cleavage of the egg into the first two blastomeres passing through the centre of it. This grey crescent marks the site of the dorsal lip of the future blastopore and when gastrulation commences a small crescentic groove appears in the lower margin of this region (see Fig. 34.7, which also shows the presumptive areas). At the same time, the rapidly dividing cells of the animal pole break away from the yolky cells of the vegetative pole at their junction with the latter and proceed to spread downwards over their surface. This process of over-growth is known as *epiboly* and is visible to the naked eye by the downward spread of the black

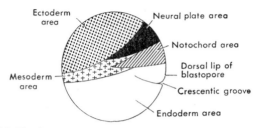

Fig. 34.7. The frog.
Diagram to show the presumptive areas of the blastula. (After *Pasteels.*)

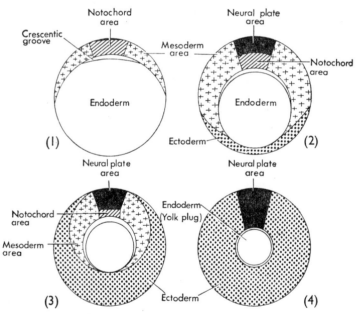

Fig. 34.8. The frog.
(1)–(4) Successive stages in gastrulation as seen from below. (Diagrammatic.)

pigment. At the upper margin of the crescentic groove, however, the advancing cells of the animal pole turn inwards and spread upwards beneath the surface cells of the animal pole. The sides of the crescentic groove extend until it becomes a complete circle (the blastopore). The first cells to turn in on reaching the crescentic groove are those of the presumptive area of the notochord (*chorda* cells). Following these cells, proceed those of the neural plate area. These do not turn in on reaching the crescentic groove but remain on the surface, while the chorda cells extend inwardly beneath them. As the crescentic groove extends sideways, the advancing cells of the mesoderm area also turn in on reaching its margins and proceed to occupy positions internally on either side of the chorda cells. As a result of the inturning of the chorda and mesoderm cells, the yolky cells (the future endoderm) of the vegetative pole are rotated inwardly causing the obliteration of the blastocoele while a new cavity (the *archenteron*) is formed. The roof of the archenteron is composed of the chorda and mesoderm cells while its floor consists of a heaped-up mass of yolky cells visible through the blastopore as the *yolk plug*. The exterior of the completed gastrula consists of the pigmented cells of the ectoderm and neural plate areas (Figs. 34.9 and 34.10).

NOTOGENESIS. The chorda cells separate from the adjacent meso-derm cells and form the notochord which consists of vacuolated cells. The notochord does not extend so far forwards as in *Amphioxus*, its anterior end lying beneath the future mid-brain.

NEUROGENESIS. The process differs from that in *Amphioxus* in that the ectodermal cells bordering the edges of the neural plate (the *neural folds*) do not break away from it but in growing towards the mid-line roll up the neural plate to form the neural tube (Fig. 34.11). This process of formation of the neural tube commences just in front of the middle region of the neural plate and extends forwards and back-wards. Certain of the cells at the lateral margins of the neural plate do not become incorporated in the neural tube but remain outside it. These form the *neural crests*. They are at first continuous bands of cells but later segment to form the dorsal root ganglia of the cranial and spinal nerves. In the head region, too, they give rise to the anterior parts of the *trabeculae* (page 638) and to the skeletal elements of the visceral arches. The neural tube has for a short time an anterior opening to the exterior—the *neuropore*—but this soon closes. As in *Amphioxus*, the neural folds extend backwards to roof over the blastopore but only enclose its dorsal portion. Before this happens

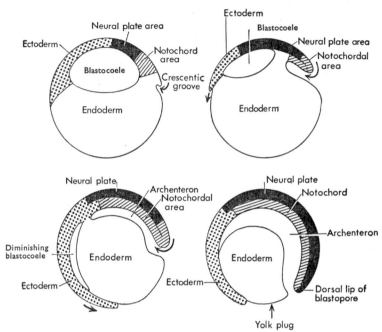

Fig. 34.9. The frog.

Stages in gastrulation as seen in vertical section showing movements and extensions of the presumptive areas. (Diagrammatic.)

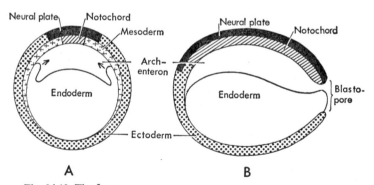

Fig. 34.10. The frog.

A T.S. of completed gastrula; *B* L.S. of completed gastrula. (Diagrammatic.)

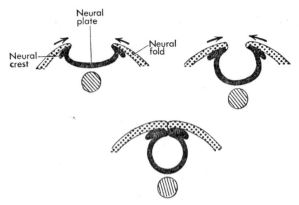

Fig. 34.11 The frog. Stages in neurogenesis. (Diagrammatic.)

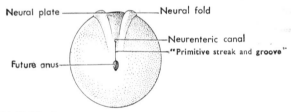

Fig. 34.12. The frog.

External view of earlier embryo to show primitive streak and groove at posterior end. (After *Borradaile*.)

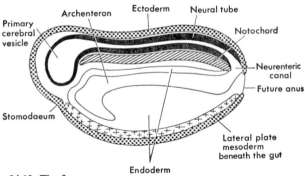

Fig. 34.13. The frog.

Longitudinal section of the embryo after closure of the neuropore. (Diagrammatic.)

the lateral margins of the blastopore extend inwards to meet and fuse in the mid-line except at its upper and lower ends. The upper aperture so formed becomes the *neurenteric canal* after the neural folds have enclosed it. The lower aperture marks the site of the future anus. The region of fusion of the margins of the blastopore is equivalent to the *primitive streak and groove* of the chick (Fig. 34.25), and it is by the proliferation of the cells of this that the post-anal tail is developed, with the result that the anus becomes ventral in position while the neurenteric canal retains its dorsal position. After the closure of the neuropore, the anterior end of the neural tube enlarges to form the *primary cerebral* vesicle (Fig. 34.13). From this develop by constriction the fore-, mid- and hind-brain vesicles.

THE FORMATION OF THE MESODERMAL SOMITES AND THE LATERAL PLATE MESODERM. After the inturning of the mesodermal cells at the lateral margins of the crescentic groove (page 628) these cells form two *solid* blocks, one on either side of the notochord (cf. the *hollow* mesodermal sacs of *Amphioxus*). The edges of the endoderm cells forming the floor of the archenteron (page 630) now extend upwards beneath the mesodermal cells and the notochord to form a new roof to the archenteron, while the mesoderm extends downwards on either side between the ectoderm and the endoderm (Fig. 34.14). Eventually the mesoderm forms a continuous layer beneath the archenteron. The upper portions of the mesoderm on either side of the notochord segment to form pairs of *mesodermal somites*, the process commencing at the head end. In the lower portion (the *lateral plate mesoderm*) no segmentation occurs, but on each side a split appears, extending downwards to meet the one from the other side. A cavity, continuous throughout the length of the lateral plate mesoderm and U-shaped in section, is thus formed. This is the *splanchnocoele*, separating the outer somatic (parietal) mesoderm from the inner splanchnic mesoderm. A narrow slit appears for a short space of time in each somite. This is a *myocoele* dividing a thin outer layer of cells (the *dermatome*) from the inner thicker *myotome (muscle plate)*. A *sclerotome* arises as in *Amphioxus* to ensheath the notochord and neural tube. At the junction of the somites with the somatic mesoderm occurs a thickened longitudinal ridge (the *nephrotome*) in which arise the excretory tubules and their ducts (Fig. 34.15).

Further development of the tadpole and its organogeny

1. THE TAIL. In the later embryonic stages prior to the hatching of the larva, the embryo elongates and this elongation is mainly due to

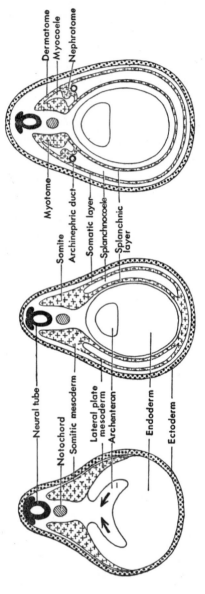

Fig. 34.14. The frog.
Stages in the development of the mesoderm. (Diagrammatic.)

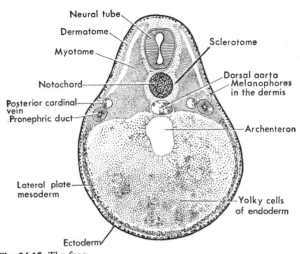

Fig. 34.15. The frog.

A transverse section through the middle of a newly hatched tadpole. (From a prepared slide.)

the formation of a post-anal tail. As previously mentioned (page 633) this is produced as a result of the multiplication of the cells in the region of the primitive streak and groove. The tail bud so formed extends backwards differentiating into ectoderm and mesoderm, while the hinder ends of the neural tube and notochord also grow into it. The mesoderm on either side of these segments form pairs of somites whose myotomes form the V-shaped muscles visible through the ectoderm. The tail also develops the thin dorsal and ventral fins continuous around the tip of the tail. Around the edges of the ventral anus formed from the unclosed portion of the blastopore at the lower end of the primitive streak and groove (page 633) a certain degree of inturning of the ectoderm occurs to form a shallow proctodaeum which becomes the cloaca. The bladder of the adult frog develops as a ventral ingrowth of the cloaca into the splanchnocoele.

2. THE ALIMENTARY CANAL. (a) *The mouth and buccal cavity.* On the ventral side of the anterior end of the embryo an ingrowth of the ectoderm forms the stomodaeum, which later becomes the mouth and the buccal cavity. Some hours after hatching, the stomodaeum becomes perforated at its inner end, together with the endoderm at its point of contact with the latter, so that its cavity becomes continuous with that of the archenteron. Until this happens, the larva—as the embryo may now be termed—remains attached to some external object by means of the secretion of the mucous glands on the underside of the head end (Fig. 34.17).

(b) *The visceral clefts and the visceral arches.* The archenteron, with its endodermal wall, forms the gut. At the time of hatching, the rudiments of the visceral clefts appear on either side of the anterior end of the gut (i.e. the future pharynx). These are produced by lateral outgrowths of the endoderm towards the ectoderm to form the visceral pouches, while the ectoderm overlying them grows in to meet

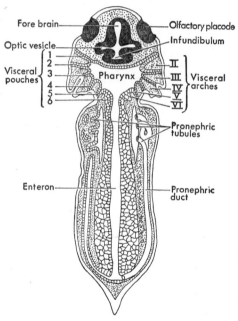

Fig. 34.16. A horizontal longitudinal section through a young tadpole shortly after hatching. (After *Marshall* and *Kellicott*.)

them forming vertical furrows. In all, six pairs of visceral pouches are formed, the posterior pair being rudimentary. When the mouth is formed, the visceral pouches become perforated, with the exception of the first and sixth pairs, the first (*hyomandibular*) pouches ultimately forming the 'ear tubes'. The second, third, fourth and fifth pairs after perforation become known as the *branchial clefts*. The regions of the body wall between the visceral pouches together with the anterior borders of the first pair of pouches form the *visceral arches*: the mandibular, hyoid and branchial arches. The mandibular arches lie anterior to the first pair of pouches, the hyoid between these and the first of the branchial pouches and the remainder (the branchial arches) between the succeeding pouches. Within all these visceral arches and in the floor of the pharynx develop the skeletal elements which make up the *visceral skeleton* and also blood vessels. Above the third, fourth and fifth visceral arches, superficial outgrowths form three pairs of branching gill filaments—the *external gills*. These function for a short time after the larva hatches while *internal* gill filaments are being formed within the branchial clefts as filamentous outgrowths of the endodermal linings. These internal gills take over the respiratory functions of the external gills which are absorbed into

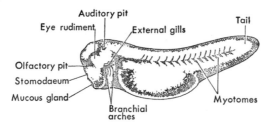

Fig. 34.17. The frog.
External features of a newly-hatched tadpole.

the body. A pair of outgrowths from the posterior borders of the hyoid arch extend backwards to form the *operculum*, covering the external gills and the branchial clefts. These folds unite with the body wall and meet beneath the pharynx to enclose an *opercular cavity* into which the branchial clefts open. On the left side an opening from this cavity to the exterior is formed—the so-called 'spiracle'. The current of water flowing in through the mouth as a result of the respiratory movements performed by the visceral skeleton and its muscles passes out of the pharynx via the branchial clefts into the opercular space and then through the 'spiracle' to the exterior. When the larva metamorphoses to the adult, the branchial clefts close up and the forelimbs develop as outgrowths into the opercular space. The right forelimb bursts through the operculum while that of the left side emerges through the 'spiracle'.

(c) *The liver and the pancreas.* The liver develops from a diverticulum of the anterior floor of the gut, burrowing into the yolky cells which gradually diminish as they yield up their stores of food. The gut elongates and becomes coiled. Its various regions: the stomach, intestine and rectum appear, the pancreas being formed as a diverticulum of the duodenum.

THE MUCOUS GLANDS. Just before hatching, on the ventral side of the region of the mandibular arches, the ectoderm becomes glandular to form the mucous glands by which, after hatching, the larva attaches itself for a time to some external object (Fig. 34.17).

THE LUNGS. In the later stages of the tadpole when the branchial clefts have been completely covered over by the operculum, the lungs develop as downgrowths of the floor of the pharynx. The tadpole now begins to come to the surface frequently to take in air into the buccal cavity whose lining becomes respiratory in function and the lungs eventually also function as respiratory organs in place of the gills.

THE SKELETON. The first appearance of the cartilaginous skeleton of the larva is marked by the formation of two cartilaginous rods—the *parachordals*—one on either side of the anterior end of the noto-chord. Anterior to these beneath the developing fore- and mid-brain regions of the neural tube appear two curved rods—the *trabeculae*—the anterior portions of which are derived from neural crest tissue (page 630). These rods fuse to form a plate with a small gap in the centre (Fig. 34.18) through which there grows downwards from the

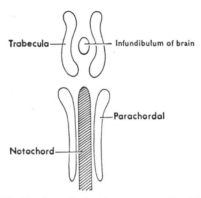

Fig. 34.18. The frog. Trabeculae and parachordals.

ventral side of the hind region of the fore-brain the stalk-like *infundi-bulum* to meet the *hypophysial sac* formed by an upgrowth of the roof of the buccal cavity. From these two structures develops the *pituitary body*.

The trabeculae and the parachordals fuse to form the base of the *chondrocranium* whose walls and roof are completed by further developments of cartilage in the mesoderm surrounding the brain.

The roof, however, is very incomplete with large gaps in it—the *fontanelles*. The cartilaginous sense capsules—olfactory, optic and auditory—form independently of the chondrocranium. The optic capsules later form the sclerotic coats of the eyeballs and do not join on to the chondrocranium as do the others (Figs. 15.11 and 15.12).

The cartilaginous visceral skeleton is formed from tissues produced by downward extensions of the anterior ends of the neural crests. It develops as a series of arches partly encircling the anterior part of the gut and situated between the visceral clefts with the exception of the first which lies in front of the first visceral cleft and the last behind the sixth. The first or mandibular arch, together with the anterior portions of the trabeculae which are also formed from neural crest tissue, forms the jaws: the upper jaw (or palato-ptery-go-quadrate bars) and the lower jaw (or Meckel's cartilages). The upper jaw bars become attached to the cranium at the anterior and posterior ends so that the suspension of the jaws is *autostylic*, the lower jaw articulating with the underside of the quadrate regions of the upper jaw bars. The second arch is the hyoid arch and the succeeding ones the branchial arches. The muscles attached to the visceral arches develop from the splanchnic mesoderm and hence become innervated by the dorsal roots of certain cranial nerves.

The bony vertebrae developed from mesodermal tissue later replace the notochord except in the tail region while parts of the cranium and the jaws become ossified. Also in the mesoderm of the head region dermal bones are formed which become applied to the cranium and the jaws (page 322). When the limbs appear, the girdles and limb bones are first formed of cartilage which is later replaced almost entirely by bone. A dermal bone (the clavicle) arises in the mesoderm anterior to the precoracoid of the pectoral girdle. During the later stages of metamorphosis, the visceral skeleton apart from the jaws is reduced until it is represented only by the hyoid plate in the floor of the buccal cavity, the columella bones of the middle ear formed from the upper ends (*hyomandibulas*) of the hyoid arch and the larynx.

THE BLOOD VASCULAR SYSTEM. The heart rudiment early develops in the undivided mesoderm beneath the anterior region of the gut. It is at first a straight tube, the stages of its formation being shown in the accompanying diagram (Fig. 34.19).

The heart tube next extends forwards and backwards. Its central region elongates and assumes the form of an S. From this S-shaped tube, a single auricle and a single ventricle develop, while its hinder

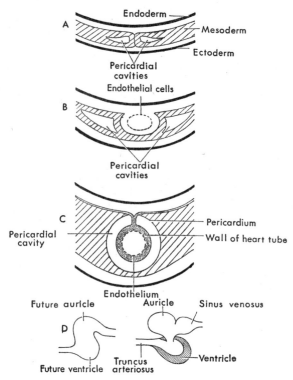

Fig. 34.19. The frog. Diagrams to show the formation of the heart.

A Appearance of the pericardial cavities by splitting of the lateral plate mesoderm beneath the fore-gut.

B Commencement of the heart tube as a groove produced by the folding of the upper (splanchnic) layer of the mesoderm, with the formation of the endothelial lining from cells separated from the upper side of the mesoderm.

C Completion of the heart tube by the approximation of the edges of the groove. *A–C* in transverse section.

D Elongation of the heart tube with the assumption of the shape of an S and the subsequent formation of the heart chambers.

region forms a sinus venosus from which a pair of *vitelline veins* extend back into the yolky cells. The anterior end of the tube develops into a conus arteriosus and ventral aorta from which arise successively in the visceral arches six pairs of vessels (aortic arches). At their upper ends these vessels join the longitudinal dorsal vessels which appear one on each side above the visceral clefts. The longitudinal dorsal vessels unite posteriorly and extend backwards as a single dorsal aorta beneath the notochord. The first two pairs of vessels ascending the mandibular and hyoid arches have only a fleeting existence and soon disappear. The third, fourth and fifth pairs function as branchial vessels and become connected with the capillaries of the external gills but these are later replaced by the internal gills and then these branchial vessels develop capillary networks in connexion with the latter. The sixth pair of vessels are the last to appear, making up a total of four pairs of branchial vessels (Fig. 34.20). When the gills cease to function the courses of the branchial vessels again become continuous. The most anterior pair (3rd aortic arches) form the carotid arches, the next (4th aortic arches) the systemic arches, the next (5th aortic arches) degenerate while the last pair (6th aortic arches) form the pulmo-cutaneous arches.

On each side the portion of the longitudinal dorsal vessel between the carotid and systemic arches degenerates to a mere fibrous band (the *ductus caroticus*) and so, too, does the upper portion of each of the fourth pair of branchial vessels forming a fibrous band known as the *ductus arteriosus*, and resulting in the pulmo-cutaneous arches losing their connexions with the longitudinal dorsal vessels. All the ducts are sometimes referred to collectively as the *ducts of Botalli*. The conus arteriosus and ventral aorta become the truncus arteriosus of the adult frog. With the disappearance of the gills and the disappearance of the lungs, the single auricle becomes divided into two by a septum, the left auricle becoming connected to the lungs by a pair of pulmonary veins and acquiring a separate opening into the ventricle.

The venous system when first formed broadly resembles that of a fish (p. 277) with the addition of vitelline veins. During metamorphosis, a median posterior vena cava replaces the two posterior cardinal veins while the Cuvierian sinuses become the anterior venae cavae (Fig. 15.18).

URINOGENITAL ORGANS. Just beneath the somites a region of the lateral plate mesoderm on either side becomes the *nephrotome*. Within this a longitudinal duct (the *archinephric duct*) appears, while adjacent to it coiled kidney tubules are formed. Each kidney tubule opens into the splanchnocoele by a ciliated funnel (*nephrostome*) while its other end leads into the archinephric duct. The formation of the kidney tubules begins at the head end, where are formed three pairs of tubules segmentally arranged in conjunction with the first three pairs

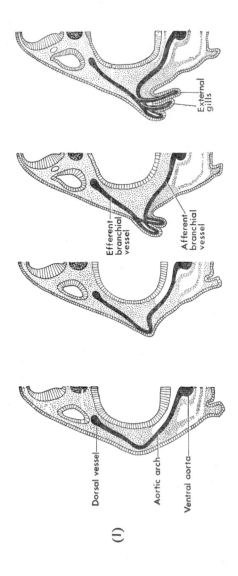

(I)

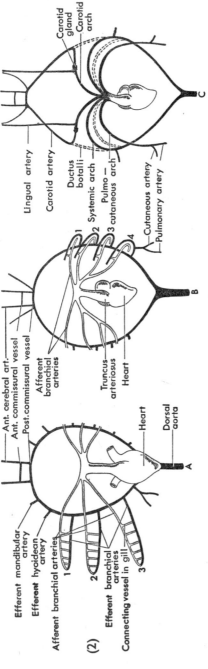

Fig. 34.20. The frog. Stages in the development of the arterial system.
(1) Formation of the branchial vessels. (After *Kellicott.*)
(2) Changes in the arterial system during metamorphosis: *A* external gills stage; *B* internal gills stage; *C* adult stage. (After *Borradaile* from *Bourne.*)

of somites. They are known collectively as the *pronephros*. The prone-phros and anterior end of the archinephric duct do not persist but in the abdominal region numerous tubules, which are segmentally arranged, appear and join the archinephric duct which extends backwards to the cloaca where it opens to the exterior. These later-formed tubules constitute the *opisthonephros* and the persistent portion of the archinephric duct connected with it, the *Wolffian duct*. The opisthonephric tubules acquire at their inner ends Malpighian bodies (page 378) while the nephrostomes become detached and remain as functionless vestiges on the lower surfaces of the kidneys. (See Figs. 34.14, 34.15 and 34.16.)

The testes and ovaries develop as the result of the proliferation of certain patches of mesodermal cells in the dorsal wall of the abdomen on either side of the mid-line. In the male, the anterior opisthonephric kidney tubules join on to the ends of the seminiferous tubules of the testes, losing their excretory function and acting as vasa efferentia to convey sperm to the Wolffian duct which thus combines the functions of a vas deferens and a ureter. In the female, the Wolffian duct acts solely as a ureter and all the opisthonephric tubules retain their excretory function. The oviducts (*Müllerian ducts*) develop as grooved longitudinal ridges in the lateral walls of the abdomen. These then become tubular and detached from the abdominal wall, elongating and developing the ciliated oviduct funnels at their inner ends while leading to the cloaca posteriorly.

The central nervous system and the Sense organs

As previously mentioned, after the closure of the neuropore, the brain is formed from the front end of the neural tube which enlarges to form the primary cerebral vesicle. This by constriction forms the three primary fore-, mid- and hind-brain regions. The remainder of the tube forms the medulla and the spinal cord. The cerebrum, optic lobes and the cerebellum arise as dorsal upgrowths of these regions and the paired nerves, with the exception of the olfactory and optic nerves, as segmental outgrowths.

SENSE ORGANS. 1. *The olfactory organs.* In the early tadpole stage, even before hatching, a pair of olfactory pits produced by ingrowth of the ectoderm appear at the front of the head (Fig. 34.17). These eventually reach the lining of the buccal cavity and become per-forated to form the internal nares. Patches of sensory epithelium in the linings of the nostrils so formed become connected with the olfactory nerves, which grow out from the ventral side of the fore-brain.

2. *The eyes.* The eye rudiments also appear at an early stage in the development of the tadpole. On each side of the base of the hinder part of the fore-brain an optic vesicle grows out with its cavity continuous with that of the fore-brain. The vesicle then develops into a hollow, stalked cup with the obliteration of its cavity to form a double-layered wall to the cup. At the same time the ectoderm overlying the vesicle becomes invaginated to form the rudiment of the lens. The stalk of the optic cup forms the optic nerve and the outer layer of its wall the pigment layer lying behind the retina which is formed from the inner layer. The lens rudiment becomes constricted off from the ectoderm to lie in the mouth of the optic cup and forms a solid structure (the *crystalline lens*), while the ectoderm, which closes over it, becomes the conjunctiva. The coats of the eye, i.e. the sclerotic and choroid with their various regions: the cornea, iris, ciliary processes, etc., are laid down from the surrounding mesoderm. The three pairs of antagonistic muscles which become attached to the eye develop from the three anterior (pro-otic) pairs of somites. The recti muscles (excepting the rectus externus) and the inferior oblique muscles become innervated by the oculomotor nerves (the ventral roots of the nerves of the first or premandibular segments), the superior oblique muscles by the trochlear nerves (ventral roots of the nerves of the second or mandibular segment) and the rectus externus muscles by the abducens nerves (ventral roots of the nerves of the third or hyoidean segment).

3. *The auditory organs.* At the hinder end of the head on each side a thickening of the skin forms the *auditory placode*. This sinks inwardly to form the inner ear (Fig. 15.25) which becomes encased in the auditory capsules (page 262). From the adjacent first visceral pouch—the hyoid pouch—is formed the middle ear with its external auditory meatus and Eustachian tube. The ectoderm overlying the pouch is not perforated and together with the underlying mesoderm forms the drum (tympanum) of the ear flush with the surface. As previously stated, at metamorphosis the columella bone is formed by the ossification of the hyomandibular cartilage of the hyoid arch to bridge the gap between the underside of the drum and the fenestra ovalis in the wall of the auditory capsule, and to convey vibrations set up in the drum by sound waves to the inner ear, which becomes innervated by a branch of the seventh cranial (facial) nerve—the *auditory nerve* (eighth cranial nerve). In the tadpole stage patches of

ectoderm along the flanks give rise to the fish-like lateral line organs which disappear when the tadpole changes to the adult frog.

Some of the changes visible externally from the commencement of the segmentation of the egg to the end of metamorphosis are shown in Figs. 33.5, 34.17 and 34.22.

In the early stages of development the food needed is provided by the yolk stored in the yolky cells of the endoderm. Later, after the mouth has opened, the tadpole develops horny edges to the jaws and feeds on algae and other water plants. The intestinal portion of the alimentary canal elongates considerably and becomes coiled like a watch spring, but when the final stage in the metamorphosis is reached the intestine shortens, the horny edges of the jaws are shed and teeth develop on the upper jaw. The diet is also changed, the young frog becoming carnivorous and feeding on slugs, worms and insects.

Locomotion in the tadpole stage is effected by wriggling movements produced by undulations of the tail but when the young frog migrates to the land, it progresses by means of its limbs and the tail is absorbed with the body by a process of internal digestion.

Gaseous exchange for respiration in the tadpole occurs through the skin, the lining of the buccal cavity and the gills. After the closure of the gill clefts, the tadpole can be seen to come to the surface of the water frequently to gulp in air into the buccal cavity or to discharge it, the lining of the buccal cavity and the developing lungs playing an increasing part in respiration.

The Fowl

As stated on page 617, the hen's egg is macrolecithal with the nucleus situated at the animal pole surrounded by a little yolk-free cytoplasm, and after fertilization, segmentation (cleavage) is confined to this region. The egg normally takes about 24 hours to descend the oviduct before being laid, and segmentation is completed during this period. When the 'egg' is laid, its structure is complex, as shown in Fig. 34.23. During the descent the egg acquires a coating of albumen enclosed in two thin shell membranes external to which is a porous shell of calcium carbonate, all these additions being secreted by the walls of the oviduct. At the top (animal pole) of the egg is the plate of cells—the *blastodisk*—produced by cleavage of the fertilized nucleus and its surrounding cytoplasm. Beneath the centre of the blastoderm forming the blastodisk, is the *sub-germinal cavity* representing the blastocoele (Fig. 33.4). This causes the blastoderm above it to appear

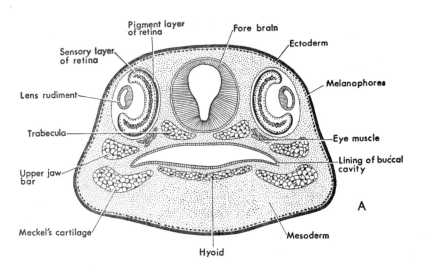

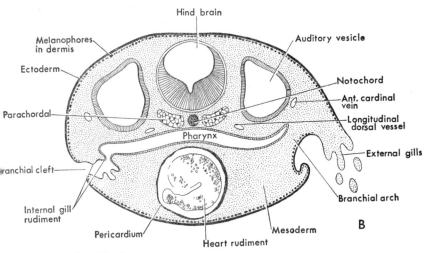

Fig. 34.21. The frog.

A Diagram of a transverse section through the region of the eyes of an early tadpole (external gills stage).

B Diagram of a transverse section through the region of the ears of an early tadpole (somewhat oblique). (From prepared slides.)

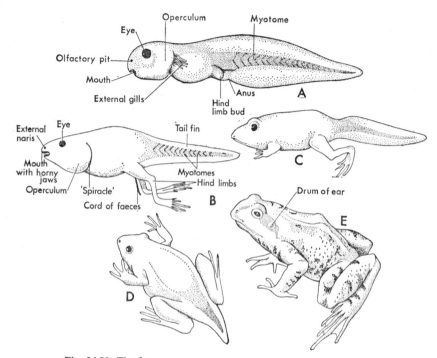

Fig. 34.22. The frog.

Stages in the development and metamorphosis of the frog: *A* a tadpole – age, about one week after hatching; *B* a tadpole – age, about 9 weeks; *C* a tadpole – age, about 12 weeks; *D* young frog – age, about 14 weeks migrating to the land; *E* adult frog. (Not drawn to scale.)

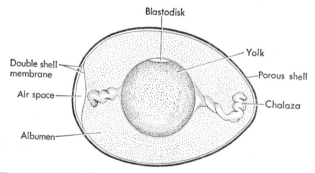

Fig. 34.23. The fowl.

Diagram of the egg of a fowl in sectional view at the time of laying.

translucent—the so-called *area pellucida*, while the blastoderm surrounding it and resting on the surface of the yolk forms the ring-like whitish *area opaca*. (A few cells also occur in the yolk beneath the sub-germinal cavity, but their existence is transitory.) Further development is arrested when the egg is laid, owing to the drop in temperature, and is not resumed until the temperature of the egg is again raised to approximately 38°C. when gastrulation normally commences. (The actual stage of development reached when the egg is laid depends on the time taken for the egg to pass down the oviduct.) After incubation for about 20 hours at this temperature, the blastodisk is seen to be pear-shaped and in the narrow portion of the area pellucida appears a *primitive streak* and *groove* with a dense spot (the *primitive knot*) at its anterior end. At this stage the presumptive areas of the blastoderm of the area pellucida can be mapped as shown in Fig. 34.24. The primitive streak and groove are

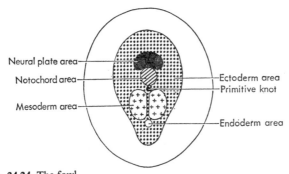

Fig. 34.24. The fowl.
Diagram of the presumptive areas of the blastoderm. (After *Pasteels*.)

considered to be the equivalent of the blastopore of the frog and the primitive knot to represent the dorsal lip of the blastopore, although there exists no aperture. It is towards the primitive streak and groove that the cells of the presumptive areas migrate during gastrulation. The cells bordering the primitive streak and groove are those of the presumptive endoderm, and these sink in and spread out beneath the blastoderm as a single layer of flattened cells, which eventually joins up with the endoderm of the area opaca which is formed by delamination from the underside of the blastoderm of that region. The presumptive mesoderm cells follow next, migrating to the edges of the primitive streak and groove where they turn down and spread out between the endoderm and the superficial blastoderm—now the ectoderm—as two wing-like masses of cells extending beyond the area pellucida into that of the area opaca. The first of the presumptive mesoderm cells to migrate inwards form the lateral plate mesoderm; those which succeed them move so as to form two narrow strips on either side of the notochord to give rise to the somites. The sub-germinal cavity may now be regarded as the archenteron. (Fig. 34.25.)

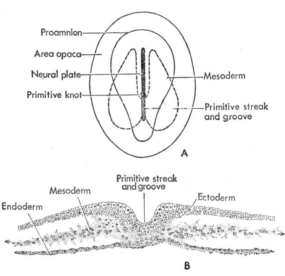

Fig. 34.25. The fowl.

A Diagram of a surface view of an early embryo. *B* Transverse section of an early embryo through the primitive streak and groove to show the formation of the mesoderm. (From a stained preparation.)

NOTOGENESIS. A narrow strip of the blastoderm anterior to the primitive knot forms the presumptive notochordal cells. These travel backwards, turn in at the primitive knot and then move forward to occupy a central position beneath the neural plate and between the two strips of somitic mesoderm mentioned above. They then form the notochord.

NEUROGENESIS. The neural plate cells extend backwards in the wake of the notochordal cells but stop at the primitive knot. The formation of the neural tube from the neural plate follows the same course as in the frog but the meeting of the neural folds occurs first in the region of the future mid-brain and extends forwards and backwards from that point. Also the primitive streak and groove do not become roofed over by the neural folds for a considerable time, since the primitive streak and groove are seen to travel backwards owing to cell division in the region just anterior to the primitive knot, forming additions to all the germinal layers and causing the embryo to grow in length. The neuropore at the anterior end of the neural tube closes during the second day of incubation and the front end of the latter enlarges to form the primary cerebral vesicle which by constrictions becomes divided into fore-, mid- and hind-brain regions. A cranial flexure then develops in the region of the mid-brain, causing the fore-brain to bend downwards.

DEVELOPMENT OF THE SOMITES AND LATERAL PLATE MESO-DERM. The mesoderm, whose origin has been given on page 649, consists of a pair of sheets of solid tissue. On either side of the notochord

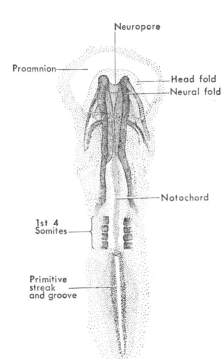

Fig. 34.26. The fowl.

Surface view of a developing embryo at the four-somite stage. (From a prepared slide.)

the mesoderm forms thickened strands—the *somitic* mesoderm—flanked externally by the thinner *lateral plate* mesoderm. The somitic mesoderm segments to form pairs of somites, the first pair being formed by two transverse splits appearing some little distance in front of the primitive knot (Fig. 34.26A). The parts of the somitic mesoderm anterior to these splits form the first pair of somites. Successive pairs are formed posteriorly to these by the appearance of more transverse splits. The time of appearance of the first and subsequent pairs of somites varies with the temperature at which incubation is taking place and also to some extent with the time taken by the egg to descend the oviduct (see note on page 649). Hence it has become customary to relate any particular stage of development of the embryo after the formation of the first pair of somites to the number of somites actually present at that stage, rather than by reference to the time interval since the commencement of incubation. As the primitive streak and groove retreat backwards with the growth in length of the embryo, more pairs of somites are added in the rear of those already formed. The lateral plate mesoderm separates into the outer somatic and inner splanchnic layers by the appearance of the splanchnocoele. The formation of myotomes, sclerotomes, dermatomes, and nephrotomes takes place as in the tadpole (page 633).

The folding-off of the embryo

Unlike the frog, the whole of early embryonic structures so far described do not give rise to the actual embryo. This is formed from the central region only, i.e. that part which was first represented by the area pellucida, by a process of 'folding-off'. The outer region (area opaca) gives rise to the *extra-embryonic region*, which later forms the *yolk sac* and the *foetal membranes*: the *amnion* and the *allantois* to which the embryo is eventually attached by a narrow hollow stalk called the *umbilical cord*. The 'folding-off' of the embryo commences by the appearance at the front end of the area pellucida of the *head fold* (Fig. 34.27). (Just in front of this is a region devoid of mesoderm, often referred to as the *pro-amnion*.) As the head fold develops, the anterior part of the archenteron (the space between the endoderm and the yolk in the central region) becomes included in it to form the so-called 'fore-gut' lined by endoderm. Lateral folds next appear, followed by a tail fold which includes the 'hind-gut'. The embryo is now perched above the extra-embryonic region to which it is joined by the umbilical cord, the floor of the archenteron being open towards the yolk in the region of the cord. The

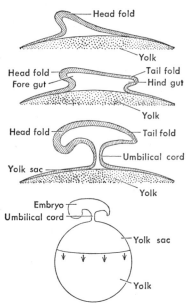

Fig. 34.27. The fowl.
Diagrams to show the formation of the head fold and the 'folding off' of the embryo from the yolk sac.

brain region of the neural tube is included in the head fold which flops over on to its left side with its right side uppermost and produces a twist in the embryo at its anterior end. Through all stages of its development, the embryo depends on the food stored in the yolk and this, consisting as it does of protein and lipoid, has to be digested and absorbed by the endoderm, but after the 'folding-off' of the embryo only the endoderm of the extra-embryonic region is in contact with the yolk. This region extends downwards to enclose the dwindling yolk in a structure called the *yolk sac*, the endoderm of which continues to digest and absorb the yolk. To transport this absorbed food to the embryo necessitates the early appearance of a blood system both within the embryo and in the extra-embryonic region, the two parts being connected via the umbilical cord. The formation of the blood system is dealt with in the next section.

Organogeny

It is usual to study the development of the embryo only as far as the end of the third day of incubation since most of the organ systems have made their appearance by this time.

1. THE GUT. The formation of the fore- and hind-guts has already been mentioned. A stomodaeum is formed beneath the head and a proctodaeum beneath the end of the hind-gut by inturnings of the ectoderm. In the side walls of the fore-gut are formed four pairs of visceral pouches, but only the anterior three become perforated to form visceral clefts. The first (hyomandibular) cleft remains open as the future 'ear tube' but the remainder soon close up. At no stage are gill filaments or their capillary networks formed. These clefts are visible during the third day of incubation.

2. THE BLOOD VASCULAR SYSTEM. Within the embryo, the blood system develops along the same lines as in the tadpole (page 639) except that the branchial vessels are at no stage interrupted by gill capillaries. The heart is formed in the mesoderm in the floor of the fore-gut, and increases in size rapidly. Even during the second day of incubation it can be seen bulging from the underside of the embryo and to consist of a single auricle and a single ventricle. Meanwhile in the extra-embryonic region there appears in the mesoderm a large number of blood-filled spaces (*lacunae*) which unite to form a network of capillaries and small vessels. From the back of the heart two vitelline veins diverge and extend through the umbilical cord to connect up with this network, while from the dorsal aorta two *vitelline arteries* branch off to connect likewise with it. A circulation of blood from the embryo to the extra-embryonic region via the vitelline arteries and back again to the embryo via the vitelline veins is thus set up as soon as the heart commences to beat. The venous system of the embryo, like that of the tadpole, resembles that of a fish.

3. THE CENTRAL NERVOUS SYSTEM AND THE SENSE ORGANS. The formation of the brain has already been described (page 650) and during the second and third days of incubation the optic vesicles and the lens rudiments can be seen to develop; also the inner ear rudiments as ingrowing pits in the ectoderm adjacent to the hind-brain.

4. THE URINARY ORGANS. Transverse sections through the embryo at an early stage after the formation of the somites reveal the formation in the nephrotome on each side of the archnephric duct and of the kidney tubules of the pro- and meso-nephric tubules connected with it.

5. THE EMBRYONIC (FOETAL) MEMBRANES: THE AMNION AND THE ALLANTOIS (Fig. 34.28). The *amnion* arises as an upgrowing

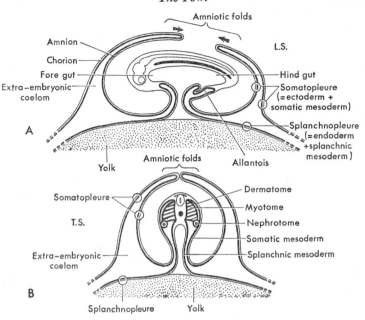

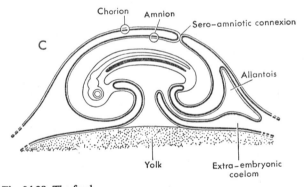

Fig. 34.28. The fowl.
Diagrams to show the formation of the amnion and the allantois.
A early stage in L.S.; *B* later stage in T.S.; *C* later stage in L.S.

fold of the *somatopleure* (ectoderm+somatic mesoderm) of the extra-embryonic region commencing in front of the head end of the embryo and extending posteriorly along the sides of the embryo and around the tail end. The upgrowth of this fold continues until the embryo is enclosed in a double-walled hood. Where the various parts

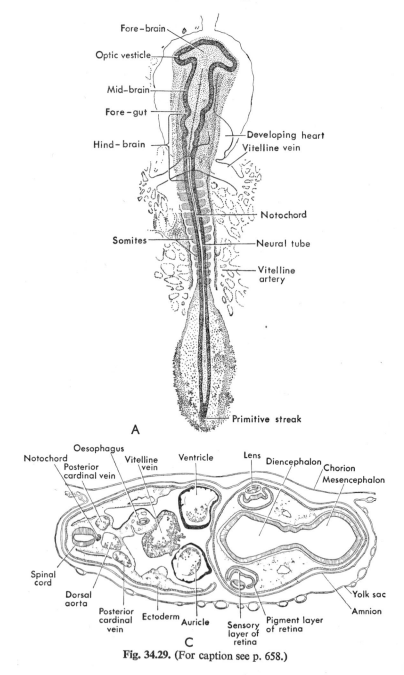

A

C

Fig. 34.29. (For caption see p. 658.)

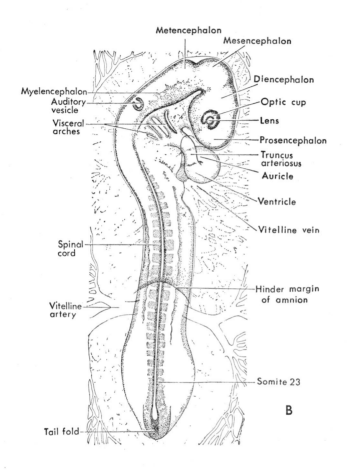

Metencephalon
Mesencephalon
Diencephalon
Myelencephalon
Auditory vesicle
Optic cup
Lens
Visceral arches
Prosencephalon
Truncus arteriosus
Auricle
Ventricle
Vitelline vein
Spinal cord
Hinder margin of amnion
Vitelline artery
Somite 23
B
Tail fold

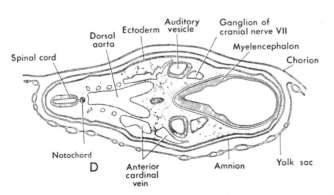

Auditory vesicle
Dorsal aorta
Ectoderm
Ganglion of cranial nerve VII
Myelencephalon
Spinal cord
Chorion
Notochord
D
Anterior cardinal vein
Amnion
Yolk sac

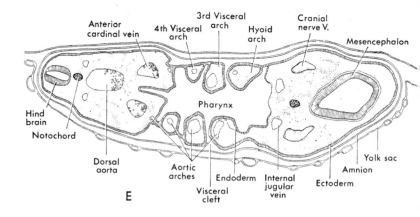

E

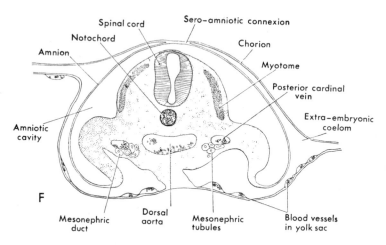

F

Fig. 34.29. The fowl.

A Surface view of an embryo (13-somite stage).

B Surface view of an embryo (23-somite stage).

C Transverse section of the anterior end of a 68-hour embryo passing through the eyes and the heart.

D Transverse section of the anterior end of a 68-hour embryo passing through the myelencephalon and the roof of the pharynx.

E Transverse section of the anterior end of a 68-hour embryo passing through the mesencephalon and the pharynx.

F Transverse section through the trunk region of a 68-hour embryo.

(From prepared slides.)

of the fold meet above the embryo, the outer ectodermal layer becomes continuous but the mesoderm and the inner ectodermal layers form a dividing layer—the *sero-amniotic connexion*. The outer wall of the hood is known as the *chorion* or *false amnion*, while the inner wall is the *true amnion*. The space between the chorion and the amnion is continuous with the splanchnocoele of the extra-embryonic region (the *extra-embryonic coelom*); that between the amnion and the embryo is the amniotic cavity and is filled with the amniotic fluid which serves as a water cushion to protect the embryo from damage when the incubating hen disturbs the position of the egg as she frequently does while sitting on the eggs. The development of the amnion commences during the second day of incubation and is completed during the third day.

The allantois. This arises later than the amnion, at about the 28 somite stage (third day of incubation). It is formed as a blind downgrowth of the *splanchnopleure* (endoderm+splanchnic mesoderm) of the floor of the hind-gut into the coelom of that region. It ultimately lengthens and extends down the coelomic cavity of the umbilical cord, its head entering the extra-coelom, where it later enlarges to form a mushroom-headed structure whose outer wall becomes applied to the chorion. The fusion of the outer wall with the chorion forms the *allanto-chorion*. This becomes highly vascularized and its network of capillaries and larger blood vessels connected with a pair of allantoic arteries and a pair of allantoic veins running in the walls of the stalk of the allantois. The allantoic arteries arise as branches of the sciatic arteries while the allantoic veins are connected to the Cuvierian ducts. The cavity of the allantois serves as a receptacle for the excreta produced by the embryo and the allantochorion as a respiratory organ, gaseous exchange taking place between the blood circulating in it and the external air through the porous shell.

The Mammal

The egg is surrounded by a thin striated membrane (the *zona pellucida*) within which, after fertilization, segmentation produces a solid ball of cells (the *morula*) as previously described (page 619). Numerous divisions of the cells of the morula convert this into a hollow spherical body (the *blastocyst*) whose wall consists of a single layer of cells (the *trophoblast*) enclosing a mass of cells within its cavity attached to the trophoblast at the animal pole. In the rabbit

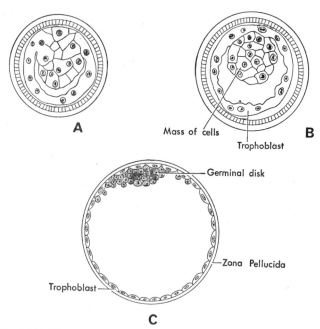

Fig. 34.30. The mammal.

A, B, C Successive stages in the formation of the blastocyst. (After *Kellicott.*)

—though not in all mammals—the cells of the trophoblast overlying this mass of cells, and known as the cells of Rauber, soon degenerate and the mass of cells then forms the *germinal disk*. The blastocyst (or *blastosphere* as it is sometimes called) is *not* the equivalent of a blastula, nor is its cavity a blastocoele. In fact the lower portion of the blastocyst and its cavity are rather to be regarded as a *functionless* yolk sac whose wall becomes double-layered by cells separating from the underside of the germinal disk and spreading downwards to form a single layer of flattened cells beneath the trophoblast. The trophoblast may now be regarded as the ectoderm of the yolk sac and the inner layer as its endoderm. Gastrulation now commences. The germinal disk flattens and at this stage is the equivalent of the area pellucida of the blastoderm of the chick and consists of the same presumptive areas except for that of the endoderm, whose cells have, as stated above, arisen independently by delamination from the underside of the germinal disk. A primitive streak and groove appear at the future posterior end and migration of the chordal and

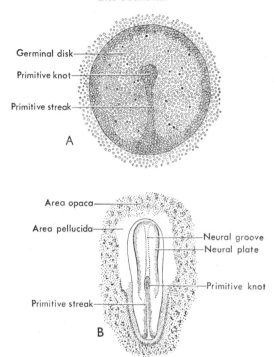

Germinal disk

Primitive knot

Primitive streak

A

Area opaca

Area pellucida

Neural groove

Neural plate

Primitive knot

Primitive streak

B

Fig. 34.31. The mammal.

A Appearance of the primitive streak and groove in the blastodisk.
B Surface view of early embryo. (After *Kellicott*.)

mesodermal cells occurs as in the fowl, followed by the 'folding off' of the embryo from the lower 'yolk sac'. The extension and further development of the mesoderm proceeds in the same manner as in the chick with the formation of the somites and of the lateral plate mesoderm with its splanchnocoele, but the mesoderm does not penetrate all round the 'yolk sac', of which the wall of the lower region consists therefore solely of trophoblast and endoderm. The foetal membranes, the amnion and allantois, have similar origins and develop on the same lines as in the chick except that the allantois gives rise to the *placenta* (page 662). The organogeny is also similar.

The nutrition, respiration and excretion of the developing embryo and foetus

When the developing blastocyst after descending the oviduct reaches the uterus, the lower region of the trophoblast forms small finger-like outgrowths called *trophoblastic villi*. These penetrate into the uterine wall, which at this time thickens and becomes more vascular, i.e. its blood vessels dilate. At this stage, the blastocyst is nourished by secretions of the uterine wall and by food absorbed from it by means of the trophoblastic villi. With the formation of the amnion and chorion, larger villi arise from the chorion and the embryo sinks deeper into the *decidua*, formed by multiplication of the cells of the epithelium of the uterus. These *chorionic villi* have a temporary existence except in the region of the *placenta*—an organ formed by the fusion of the outer wall of the allantois with chorion and corresponding to the allanto-chorion of the chick. The villi of this region

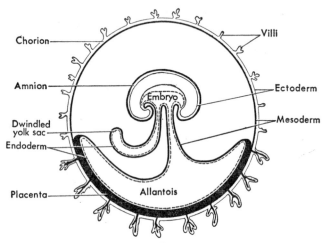

Fig. 34.32. The mammal.

Diagram to show the relationships of the embryo (or foetus) and the embryonic (or foetal) membranes.

enlarge still further to form the *placental villi*, which become vascularized and contain blood vessels and capillaries connected with the extra-embryonic circulation which is continuous with that of the embryo via the allantoic arteries and veins in the umbilical cord (cf. those of the chick, page 652). The tissues of the uterine wall in contact with these villi break down to form spaces (*lacunae*) through which flows the maternal blood to bathe the villi. The foetal blood circulating through the capillaries in the villi is separated from the maternal blood by the intervening ectoderm and mesoderm of the walls of the villi but exchange of substances in solution between the two blood streams is easily effected by diffusion. Oxygen and food in the maternal blood diffuse into the foetal blood stream while excreta and carbon dioxide produced by the foetus diffuse in the reverse direction. The foetus therefore utilizes the digestive system, lungs and kidneys of its mother. The heart of the foetus soon becomes four-chambered but the pulmonary circulation is hardly established since the lungs are unexpanded and no breathing movements occur. The blood returning to the right auricle does not pass in any quantity via the right ventricle to the lungs but is largely short-circuited into the left auricle through the *foramen ovale*—an aperture in the partition left between the two auricles—and hence via the left ventricle into the general circulation. When the period of gestation (i.e. time spent in the uterus by the developing young) is complete, the un-striped muscle of the uterine wall contracts rhythmically, forcing the young rabbits towards the vagina. As they pass through the passage, the foetal membranes burst so that each of the young rabbits in turn emerges into the outer world freed from its enclosing membranes, though at this stage still attached to them by the umbilical cord which has considerably lengthened since it was first formed. The young rabbit now takes its first breath, expanding its lungs and, with the consequent increase in the volume of the pulmonary circulation, withdrawing much of the blood from the placenta into the body. The foramen ovale and the ductus arteriosus (page 366) rapidly close up so that a truly double circulation is established. (This does not happen in 'blue' babies so that much of the blood still by-passes the lungs and suffers from lack of oxygenation.) The umbilical cord then ruptures or is bitten through by the mother, the part attached to the young rabbit soon shrivelling and dropping off to leave a scar (the navel or *umbilicus*) in the centre of the abdominal wall. The placenta separates from the uterine wall together with the decidua and is expelled by further contractions of the uterine wall as the 'after-birth'.

The control of embryological development

The development of an embryo from a fertilized egg follows—as has been seen from the foregoing examples—an orderly pattern in each case, and this must obviously result from some kind of direction. In the first instance this direction would seem to be provided by the action of the genes inherited from the parents by the fusion of the nuclei of the spermatozoon and the egg at the time of fertilization. The differentiation of the cells of the blastoderm resulting from the segmentation of the eggs to form specific types of cells, e.g. ectoderm, endoderm, mesoderm, etc., may be due to the formation of different types of protein peculiar to each type. The genes act enzymically to produce the proteins of the cytoplasm through the intermediate production of ribose nucleic acid (RNA) and in this way determine the 'pattern' of the proteins present. What is not clear, however, is why—since all the nuclei of the cells of the blastoderm contain the same gene complement—the operation of the genes should vary in the different cell groups. Environmental factors, however, cannot entirely be ruled out. For example, when cells from the presumptive area of the ectoderm are removed and cultured in a suitable medium, they develop into typical ectoderm cells, but if transplanted into the presumptive area of the neural plate, they form nervous tissue instead of ectoderm. The only certain factor controlling development so far discovered is the existence of specific 'organizers' which, once they commence to operate, determine the course of development of cells in their immediate neighbourhood. The earliest of these 'organizers' to appear lies in the group of cells forming the dorsal lip of the blastopore. This organizer causes the cells of the blastoderm anterior to the dorsal lip of the blastopore and in the mid-line of the embryo to form the notochord and the neural plate. If the cells forming the dorsal lip of the blastopore are transplanted into the ectoderm of the flank of another or of the same embryo, the ectoderm anterior to the graft is induced to form a second notochord and neural plate. The existence of a second organizer has been recognized in the optic vesicles developed from the fore-brain. This organizer causes the ectoderm cells overlying the optic vesicles to invaginate to form the lens rudiments. The formation of the optic vesicles themselves, however, does not appear to be the result of the action of a previous organizer, so that the various stages in the development of an embryo cannot be wholly ascribed to the formation of a series of 'organizers'. It can only be stated in conclusion that very little is at present known concerning the causative factors underlying embryological develop- ment.

V. THE EVOLUTION OF ANIMALS

35. *Variation and Inheritance*

IT IS a truism that 'like begets like' and although this is true in that the offspring of dogs (say) are always dogs and not animals of any other species, nevertheless it does not require very close observation to see that in any litter of puppies, even of so-called pure-bred, 'pedigree' parents, slight differences in size, length of tail and other minor characteristics are shown by the individual members of the litter. Should the parent dogs be of different breeds, very marked differences may be seen among the puppies of a single litter—not only in size but in coat colour or pattern, curliness or straightness of the hairs, etc.

There are, in fact, two distinct types of variation: (1) *Continuous variation* and (2) *discontinuous variation*. In continuous variation the differences appear to 'shade' one into another and are not sharply marked off as they are in discontinuous variation. Thus, in a litter of pure-bred puppies slight variations in weight occur, some being heavier and others lighter than the average (or norm) for that particular litter, and the individual weights can be arranged in a linear series beginning with the lightest and ending with the heaviest. In discontinuous variation, there is no average (or norm) from which divergence can be seen. For example, in a litter of puppies of mixed parentage some may be brown in colour, while the others are all black with no intermediate shades.

The term 'continuous variation' owes its origin to the fact that if it is possible to measure a large number of individual adult members of the same species for a particular character such as height or length, the data so obtained can be treated in a graphical way. Such a variation is known as a meristic variation (i.e. one which can be measured) and its graphical representation is an approximation to a mathematical curve known as a probability curve (Fig. 35.1).

In actual practice, the heights of a very large number of adult men are first obtained. The heights are then classified in steps differing by (say) 1 in. The number of individuals in each step-range, e.g. 5 ft. 0 in.–5 ft. 1 in., is then recorded. By plotting the results as shown in the above figure a histogram is obtained (Fig. 35.2).

The smaller the step-range chosen, the greater will be the number

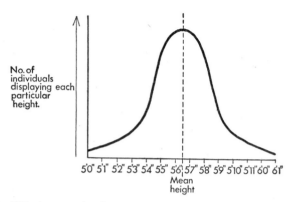

Fig. 35.1. An example of a normal curve of frequency in heights of an adult human population.

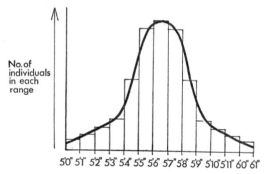

Fig. 35.2. Histogram of frequency of heights in an adult human population.

of steps and the closer will be the approximation to the normal curve of variation. It will be noticed that the classes (step-ranges) which are nearest the mean (or norm) contain a larger number of individuals than those which diverge more widely.

Continuous variation is shown by the members of any particular animal species, though naturally it is more obvious in higher animals owing to their greater complexity and size; it is not possible for *Amoeba* to display variation to the same degree as man. A prominent feature of continuous variation is that, provided the environment remains stable, each generation displays very much the same range and type of continuous variation about a norm which itself shifts very little. However, should the environment change, the norm and the range of variation around it may also change. For example, the mean height of the present-day Australian population is greater than that of the early settlers, many of whom belonged to the underfed and badly housed strata of the population of England of the early days of the Industrial Revolution.

As stated previously, discontinuous variation is shown when a particular member of an animal species, as, for example, when a white or black coated mouse or rabbit appears in a litter of normal-coloured mice or rabbits. Such 'freaks' or 'sports'—more scientifically called 'mutations'—are relatively infrequent in nature and do not usually survive for various reasons, such as the hostility of the normal members of their kind. Man, however, has frequently preserved such occasional mutations either for arbitrary reasons of choice or for utilitarian ones, and, by breeding from them, has produced the varieties found today in most domesticated species. The pug-nosed Pekinese dog is an example of an arbitrary choice or 'fancy', while the hornless breed of cattle known as the Aberdeen-Angus has been developed on utilitarian grounds. The outstanding feature of discontinuous variation is that it is capable of being inherited and passed on to future generations, whereas variation of the continuous type is not. Children of very tall parents are not necessarily so tall as their parents—in fact the members of a sizeable family of tall parents often show considerable variation in height.

Our basic knowledge of the mechanism of inheritance is due in the first place to the work of Gregor Mendel (published 1865) who studied the inheritance of discontinuous variations in garden peas. His conclusions were shown to be equally applicable to inheritance of discontinuous variations in animals, and are best illustrated by reference to breeding experiments carried out by Morgan in America in the earlier part of this century using mutations found in the fruit fly (*Drosophila melanogaster*). Morgan selected *inter alia* a mutation known as 'vestigial wing' in which the wings are only partly developed. In mating a normal-winged female with a vestigial-winged male (or *vice versa*), he found that all the offspring (known as the F_1 (1st filial) generation in Mendel's parlance) were winged. By allowing these F_1 hybrid flies to mate, he obtained an F_2 (2nd filial) generation in which both normal-winged and vestigial-winged flies appeared. Approximately three-quarters of the flies of this generation were normal-winged and the other quarter, vestigial-winged (Fig. 35.3). These results were in line with those obtained by Mendel experimenting when crossing round and wrinkled garden

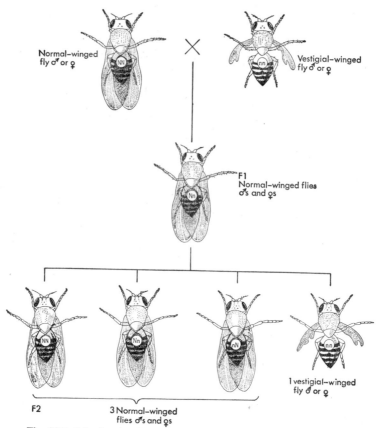

Fig. 35.3. Inheritance of wing characters in the fruit fly (*Drosophila melanogaster*).

peas, and could be explained in terms of his hypothesis on the following lines:

(1) Opposed (or contrasted) characters (e.g. normal wings and vestigial wings) are produced by the action of *factors* (now called *genes*) handed on in the germ cells (sperm and eggs) of the parents to the individuals of the next generation.

(2) In all the cells of an individual animal, with the exception of the germ cells, the genes exist in pairs, but in the germ cells they occur singly. A pure-bred (*homozygous*) normal-winged fly contains in its cells only those genes which produce normal wings, while those of the pure-bred vestigial-winged fly contain only those genes which produce vestigial wings. The cells of the hybrid F_1 (heterozygous)

flies produced by crossing a normal-winged fly with a vestigial-winged fly contain both types of gene. We may now denote the gene for producing normal wings by N and the gene for producing vestigial wings by n.

(3) When the hybrid F_1 fly produces its germ cells, the two types of genes separate (or segregate) so that two kinds of sperm (or eggs) are produced, one kind containing the gene (N) producing normal wings and the other the gene (n) producing vestigial wings, but not both. This principle is known as Mendel's First Law, or his Law of Segregation.

(4) When the F_1 flies mate, all four possible combinations of the two types of sperm and eggs will occur in approximately equal numbers as the result of random meetings of the sperm and the eggs. Thus:

Sperm		Egg		Fertilized egg (zygote)
N	$\longrightarrow$	N	$\longrightarrow$	NN
n	$\longrightarrow$	N	$\longrightarrow$	nN
N	$\longrightarrow$	n	$\longrightarrow$	Nn
n	$\longrightarrow$	n	$\longrightarrow$	nn

(5) Following Mendel's 'Principle of Dominance', gene 'N' is assumed to be *dominant* in its effect, with the result that gene 'n' cannot affect the wing character in its presence. It is therefore known as the *recessive* gene while gene N is called the *dominant* gene. Since three of the above zygotic combinations contain the dominant gene, while only one contains the recessive genes alone, it follows as an average result that of every four of the F_2 flies, three will be normal-winged and one vestigial-winged.

Members of pairs of genes which separately produce opposite (or dissimilar) characters are known as *allelomorphs*. In the vast majority of cases one member of each pair of allelomorphs is dominant, and the other recessive, but instances of incomplete dominance are known in which the F_1 hybrid shows a character which is intermediate between those of the parents. An example of this occurs in a breed of fowls known as the Andalusian. Two varieties of this breed occur, (1) black and (2) splashed white (i.e. white with a few black specks on the feathers). On crossing, the following result is obtained:

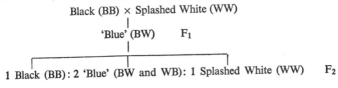

Black (BB) × Splashed White (WW)

'Blue' (BW) F_1

1 Black (BB) : 2 'Blue' (BW and WB) : 1 Splashed White (WW) F_2

The heterozygous F_1 fowls are called 'Blue'—an appearance produced by a mixture of black and white specks on their feathers, giving the birds a colour intermediate between those of the parents.

The foregoing principles are often referred to as Mendel's Laws of Dominance and Segregation (First Law) and to these Mendel added another, known as his Second Law—the Principle of Independent Assortment. This states that when more than one pair of contrasted characters (allelomorphs) are involved in inheritance, the members of each separate pair segregate independently of those of the other pairs so that all possible combinations may appear in the F_2 generation (excluding, of course, those which would violate his First Law). An example of this is the result obtained when a pure-bred grey-bodied, red-eyed fruit fly is crossed with a black-bodied, pink-eyed fly. The F_1 flies are all grey-bodied with red eyes, but when these are allowed to mate among themselves, the F_2 offspring consist of grey-bodied red-eyed flies, grey-bodied pink-eyed flies, black-bodied, red-eyed flies, and black-bodied, pink-eyed flies, in the approximate ratio of

9 grey-bodied, red-eyed flies
3 grey-bodied, pink-eyed flies
3 black-bodied, red-eyed flies
1 black-bodied, pink-eyed fly.

The characters shown by the F_1 hybrid flies indicate that the gene B producing a grey body is dominant to gene b producing a black body, while gene R producing a red-coloured eye is dominant to gene r producing a pink-coloured eye. The genetic constitution (genotype) of the pure-bred grey-bodied, red-eyed fly is therefore represented by BBRR, and of the pure-bred black-bodied, pink-eyed fly, bbrr, producing respectively gametes of the constitution BR and br. On crossing, hybrid flies of the genotype BbRr will be produced.

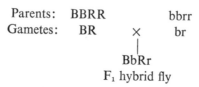

In accordance with Mendel's Second Law, the F_1 flies will form four types of gametes in approximately equal numbers, with the gene complements BR, Br, bR and br respectively, and when mated, give F_2 offspring in which 16 possible combinations of these four types of

gametes will appear. These are most easily determined by a checker-
board method as follows:

	BR	Br	bR	br	♂ gametes
♀ gametes BR	BR BR	Br BR	bR BR	br BR	
Br	BR Br	Br Br	bR Br	br Br	
bR	BR bR	Br bR	bR bR	br bR	
br	BR br	Br br	bR br	br br	

Nine of the above combinations include both dominant genes B and
R, and will produce grey-bodied, red-eyed flies; three contain one
dominant gene (the gene B) only, giving grey-bodied, pink-eyed flies;
three contain the other dominant gene (R) only, giving black-bodied,
red-eyed flies, and one with no dominant genes, producing a black-
bodied, pink-eyed fly.

Glossary of terms used in Genetics (Study of inheritance)

1. GENE (formerly called a factor): a 'unit particle' producing and/or
controlling the appearance of a character in an individual during
development from the fertilized egg and handed on from one
generation to the next in the nucleus of a gamete.

2. ALLELOMORPH: one of a pair of opposed (or contrasted)
characters which are alternative in inheritance, e.g. the normal-
winged character in *Drosophila* or its opposed vestigial-winged
character. This term may be applied to the corresponding gene
which is often also called an *allele*.

3. DOMINANCE: a dominant gene is one which alone produces or
affects the production of a particular character in the presence of its
allelomorphic partner.

4. RECESSIVENESS: a recessive gene is one which does not produce
or affect the production of a particular character in the presence of
its allelomorphic partner.

5. HOMOZYGOTE (adj. homozygous): a zygote (or an individual developed from it) which possesses only one of a pair of allelomorphs e.g. a pure-bred normal-winged fly (NN).

6. HETEROZYGOTE (adj. heterozygous): a zygote (or an individual developed from it) which possesses both members of a pair of allelomorphs, e.g. a hybrid normal-winged fly (Nn).

7. GENOTYPE: an individual or zygote with a particular complement of genes.

8. PHENOTYPE: the particular external appearance of an individual or a collection of individuals displaying a character or characters common to them all. A phenotype may include a number of separate genotypes, e.g. the phenotype: grey-bodied, red-eyed fly may include the following genotypes:

BRBR   BrBR   bRBR   BRbr   bRBr

9. BACK CROSS: when an F_1 hybrid is mated with either of the parental types, a *back-cross* is said to be made. In a monohybrid (i.e. a hybrid for one pair of allelomorphs), when the F_1 hybrid is mated with the recessive parent, the F_2 generation consists of the hybrid type and the recessive type in the ratio of 1:1.

Example:

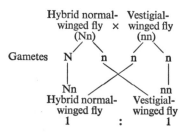

Examples of dominant and recessive characters:

	Dominant	*Recessive*
In cattle:	Absence of horns	Presence of horns
	Hereford coat pattern	Self-colour
In sheep:	Presence of horns	Absence of horns
In rabbits and mice:	Agouti (wild type) coloration	Plain colours, e.g. black or white (albino)
In man:	Right-handedness	Left-handedness
	Brown eyes	Blue eyes
In Drosophila:	Normal wings	Vestigial wings
	Wild type body colour	Black body colour
	Red eyes	White eyes

The chromosome hypothesis

Mendel's account of his discoveries passed almost unnoticed until roughly 35 years had elapsed, and by the time their importance was realized (about 1900) the mechanisms of cell division, both mitotic and meiotic, had been demonstrated. It was soon realized by a number of research workers, including T. H. Morgan in America, that the behaviour of the chromosomes during the meiotic divisions which occur at gametogenesis provided a physical basis for the operation of Mendel's laws provided that it could be assumed that the genes were borne on the chromosomes. On this assumption the separation of homologous chromosomes during the first meiotic division explains Mendel's First Law (the Law of Segregation).

In each of the somatic nuclei of the fruit fly there become visible during cell division four pairs of homologous chromosomes. Each pair consists of two identical (homologous) chromosomes usually differing in length from those of the other pairs. One of the homologous chromosomes in each pair is of paternal and the other of maternal origin, being descendants of those originally contributed by the nucleus of the sperm and of the egg and whose identity of structure has been preserved by the orderly and repeated longitudinal divisions of the chromosomes through all the mitotic divisions occurring during the development of the individual animal from the fertilized egg. In the somatic nuclei and in the nuclei of the primary spermatocytes and oocytes, it may be assumed that the genes producing the wing characters—normal and vestigial—are borne on the homologous chromosomes of one of the four pairs, and that the gene N (producing normal wings) and its allelomorph n (producing vestigial wings) are borne at the same corresponding sites or *loci* on the two chromosomes. At the first division of the nuclei of the primary gametocytes (spermatocytes and oocytes), the homologous chromosomes bearing these genes separate, so that each sperm or egg contains in its nucleus only one of these chromosomes and hence only one of the 'wing' genes N or n (Fig. 35.4).

In the second meiotic division, the homologous chromosomes divide longitudinally so that each of the four potential germ cells formed from the primary gametocyte still contain only one homologous chromosome bearing one gene. In the hybrid F_1 fly produced by mating a normal-winged fly with a vestigial-winged fly, the primary gametocytes contain both homologous chromosomes of the pair in question but one will bear the gene N and the other the gene n (Fig. 35.5). These will be separated at the first meiotic division so

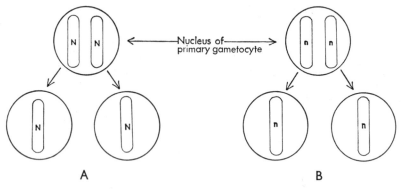

Fig. 35.4. *Drosophila.*

A First meiotic division in the homozygous normal-winged fly.
B First meiotic division in the homozygous vestigial-winged fly.

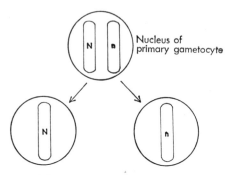

Fig. 35.5. *Drosophila.*

First meiotic division in the heterozygous normal-winged fly.

that ultimately there will be found two types of sperm or egg (see page 671).

Random combination of these produces the F_2 generation (see page 671).

When two pairs of homologous chromosomes A^1A^2 and B^1B^2 are considered, it is a matter of pure chance whether at the first meiotic division of the nucleus the primary gametocyte, chromosome A^1, is accompanied by chromosome B^1 or by chromosome B^2, or A^2 by B^1 or B^2, so that four possible associations of these chromosomes occur in the gametes, i.e. A^1B^1; A^1B^2; A^2B^1; A^2B^2. In the case of a heterozygous dihybrid fly produced by mating a grey-bodied, red-eyed fly with one having a black body and pink eyes (see page 672), it may be assumed that the genes B and b are borne on one pair of homologous chromosomes (A¹ and A²), while the genes R and r are borne on another pair (B¹ and B²). Following the behaviour of these chromosomes at the first meiotic division of the nucleus of the gametocyte, it can easily be seen how, on this assumption, four different gene combinations can alternatively occur in the four types of gametes produced (Fig. 35.6).

Thus Mendel's Second Law of Independent Assortment can also be explained in terms of the chromosome hypothesis that the genes are borne on the chromosomes of the nuclei.

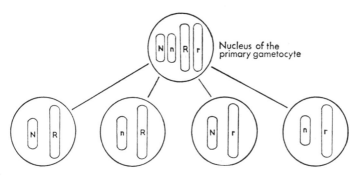

Fig. 35.6. *Drosophila.*
First meiotic division in the heterozygous dihybrid fly.

Linkage.

Mendel's First Law (the Law of Segregation) has been found to be valid in all cases of inheritance which have been investigated, but his Second Law (the Law of Independent Assortment) has only a limited application. Since in any individual there are far more genes than there are chromosomes, and since chromosomes behave as entities during cell division, it follows that each chromosome must carry more than one gene and that the genes borne on any particular chromosome must be associated (or linked together) in heredity.

In the fruit fly, the genes B (grey body) and N (normal wings) occur in the same homologous chromosome. Genes b (black body) and n (vestigial wings) are similarly linked together, occupying when present the same loci as those of B and N. (Fig. 35.7.)

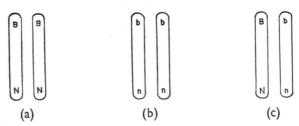

Fig. 35.7. *Drosophila.* Linkage.

(a) Homologous chromosomes of the homozygous grey-bodied, normal-winged fly.

(b) Homologous chromosomes of the homozygous black-bodied, vestigial-winged fly.

(c) Homologous chromosomes of the heterozygous grey-bodied, normal-winged fly.

The gametes of the heterozygous fly (Fig. 35.8) will contain either

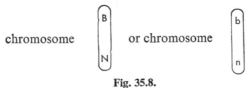

Fig. 35.8.

and the zygotes in F_2 the following combinations (Fig. 35.9).

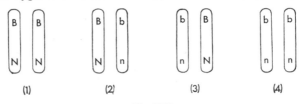

Fig. 35.9.

Since B is dominant to b and N to n, we should expect the F_2 generation to consist of grey-bodied, normal-winged flies and black-bodied, vestigial-winged flies in the ratio of 3:1, i.e. 75% grey normal and 25% black vestigial. Actual experiment, however, shows that the linkage is not absolute, so that a small proportion of grey-bodied, vestigial-winged flies and black-bodied, normal-winged flies appear in the F_2 generation. In some way the linkage of characters provided by their association on the same chromosome has been broken.

Here again the explanation is provided by the behaviour of the chromosomes in the first meiotic division of the nucleus of the primary gametocyte. Prior to the separation of the homologous chromosomes, a certain amount of 'crossing-over' occurs (see page 435). If the breaking and rejoining of the chromatids takes place between the loci occupied by the genes B, N, b and n, then recombinations, as they are called, will be formed and a small proportion of the gametes will contain the genes B and n and b and N respectively (Fig. 35.10).

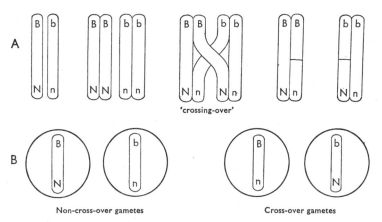

Fig. 35.10. *Drosophila.*

   A The behaviour of a pair of homologous chromosomes involving 'crossing-over' prior to their separation.
   B The resultant gametes.

Union of two gametes each with a chromosome bearing B and n will produce a grey-bodied fly with vestigial wings, and of two with b and N, a black-bodied fly with normal wings.

Breakage of linkage due to 'crossing-over' is the more frequent the further two linked genes are apart. From the percentages of recombinations, it is possible to map out the relative positions of the genes in a chromosome.

Sex linkage

Certain characters are more commonly found in one sex than in the other. For instance, red-green colour-blindness is much more common in men than in women. Moreover, a woman with normal colour vision may have red-green colour-blind sons, though her daughters have normal colour vision. Inability of the blood to clot (haemophilia) is a similar case. Such characters are said to be sex-linked and the manner of their inheritance is explained by the mechanism by which certain eye colours are inherited in the fruit fly.

One pair of the four pairs of homologous chromosomes in this fly are known as the sex chromosomes. In the female fly the individual chromosomes of this pair are identical in shape and length and are known as X chromosomes. In the male, one of the chromosomes is an X chromosome but the other has a different shape and is known as a Y chromosome. All the eggs are similar, possessing one X chromosome, but the sperm are of two kinds, one with an X chromosome and the other with a Y chromosome. This follows from the separation of the X and Y chromosomes at the first meiotic division of the primary spermatocyte. If an egg is fertilized by a sperm having an X chromosome, it will develop into a female, but if fertilized by one with a Y chromosome it will develop into a male. The dominant gene which produces red eyes, and its recessive allelomorph producing white eyes, are borne at the same locus on the X chromosome but are absent from the Y chromosome.

If a homozygous red-eyed female is mated with a white-eyed male,

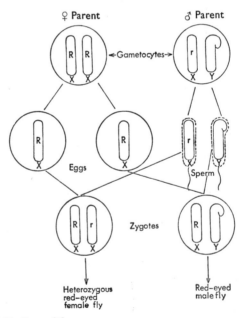

Fig. 35.11. *Drosophila.*

Sex-linked inheritance. The result of crossing a homozygous red-eyed female with a white-eyed male. R = gene for red eyes; r = gene for white eyes.

all the F_1 flies, both male and female, have red eyes. Mated together, these produce an F_2 generation consisting of red-eyed and white-eyed flies in the ratio of 3:1, but all the white-eyed flies, like their grandfather, are males. The explanation will be evident from the following diagrams in which only the sex chromosomes are considered (Figs. 35.11 and 35.12).

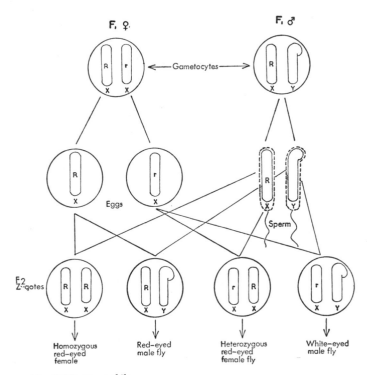

Fig. 35.12. *Drosophila.*

Sex-linked inheritance (continued). The result of crossing a heterozygous red-eyed female with a red-eyed male, both from the F_1 generation of the previous cross (Fig. 35.11).

The sex determination mechanism of man is similar to that of *Drosophila,* and the inheritance of colour vision is sex-linked. The genes C and c (C = dominant gene for normal colour vision; c = recessive allelomorph producing red-green colour blindness) are borne on the X chromosomes but not on the Y chromosomes. So too are the allelomorphic genes for the normal clotting of the blood and for its inability to clot. The inheritance of these genes follows therefore the same course as the inheritance of red and white eye colour in the fruit fly.

While in the Diptera and the mammals the male is the heterozygous form for sex, possessing an X and a Y chromosome, and the female is homozygous for sex, having two X chromosomes, in the Lepidoptera and in the birds the reverse is the case. In these latter groups, sex-linked characters are passed from the grandmother to the granddaughters via the male line, instead of from grandfather to grandsons through the female line.

So far it has been assumed that each character displayed by an individual is produced or affected by the operation of a single gene or its allelomorph, but it must be emphasized that it is more likely that a gene does not operate by itself but in association with other genes in the same '*gene-complex*'—as the total gene complement of an individual is called. Thus the action of one gene may be modified by the presence of another, as illustrated by the following example.

A number of different types of comb are displayed by the various breeds of the domestic fowl (see Fig. 35.13).

PEA COMB

ROSE COMB

SINGLE COMB

WALNUT COMB

Fig. 35.13. Types of combs in fowls. (Based on *Bateson*.)

The pea comb is produced by the operation of a dominant gene P. Its recessive allelomorph by itself produces a single comb. The rose comb is produced by another dominant gene R, whose recessive allelomorph r also by itself produces a single comb. The genotype of a homozygous pea-combed fowl is PPrr and of a homozygous rose-combed fowl is RRpp. A cross between these two types produces an F_1 genotype PpRr.

$$\begin{array}{ccc}
\text{PPrr} & & \text{RRpp} \\
| & & | \\
\text{Gametes Pr} & \times & \text{Rp} \\
& | & \\
F_1 & \text{PpRr} &
\end{array}$$

This F_1 type has a comb described as a walnut comb (Fig. 35.13). In other words, the two genes P and R produce a character which differs from that produced by either of them in the absence of the other. If the F_1 generation is allowed to interbreed, the F_2 generation has the composition: nine walnut-combed fowls; three pea-combed fowls; three rose-combed fowls; one single-combed fowl, as may easily be seen by the checker-board method.

♀ gametes	PR	Pr	pR	pr ♂ gametes
	PR	Pr	pR	pr
PR	PR	PR	PR	PR
	PR	Pr	pR	pr
Pr	Pr	Pr	Pr	Pr
	PR	Pr	pR	pr
pR	pR	pR	pR	pR
	PR	Pr	pR	pr
pr	pr	pr	pr	pr

Inspection of the above shows that there are nine combinations in which occur both P and R and which produce fowls with walnut combs; three with one dominant gene (the gene P) only, producing fowls with pea combs; three with the other dominant gene (R) only, producing fowls with rose combs, and one with neither dominant, thus producing a fowl with a single comb.

The tortoiseshell cat is another example of the combined action of two distinct genes together with sex linkage. The tortoiseshell type of coat appears in a hybrid obtained by mating a homozygous female black cat (BB) with a homozygous yellow male (YO). Incidentally, all the hybrid tortoiseshell cats (BY) are female. The reason for this is that the coat colours (black and yellow) are sex linked, the genes B and Y being borne on the X chromosomes, the Y chromosome bearing neither of them. Since in the male there is only one X chromosome in any of its cells, only gene B or gene Y can be present,

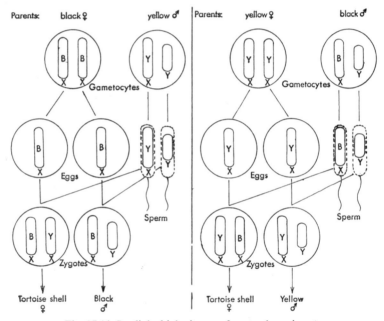

Fig. 35.14. Sex-linked inheritance of coat colours in cats.

whereas in the female, where there are two X chromosomes in the nuclei, it is possible for both genes to be present, B on one of the X chromosomes and Y on the other (Fig. 25.14).

Many other instances of the interaction of genes in a given gene-complex can be quoted. However, while it is the *major* effect of a gene which is most easily detected, minor ones which it may exert on the effects of other genes may pass almost unnoticed. (It is also true that each gene may produce more than one effect, e.g. the 'vestigial-wing gene' not only affects the size and development of the wings but also alters the shape of the spermatheca of the female and reduces the length of life and fecundity.) In short, so many genes may contribute to the mode of development of an individual from a fertilized egg, and so much interaction among them may occur, that it is difficult to analyze all the factors involved. While it is known that the mode and rate of development of the whole or parts of the body and the control of chemical processes in it are largely under genetical control, it must not be overlooked that the environment of a developing individual may also condition the action of the genes. For example, the action of the gene 'n' which in *Drosophila* prevents the normal wing development, resulting in the vestigial-wing character, is markedly reduced if homozygous vestigial-winged flies are kept at a temperature of 30–32°C during their development instead of 25°C—the temperature at which experiments with *Drosophila* are usually carried out. It may therefore be said that the final form of an individual is the product of its genes and of its environment.

36. *Classification and Evolution*

It is an innate characteristic of the human mind to detect similarities and differences, and associated with this habit is a tendency to group together similar things—in other words, to classify. The first well-authenticated system of classification was that of Aristotle (fourth century B.C.), and, following the Renaissance, later ones were proposed, notably that of John Ray (1628–1705). All these systems were to a greater or lesser extent artificial in the sense that they were based on arbitrary divisions on the part of the classifier as to what groupings should be made. It was not until the middle of the eighteenth century that Linnaeus (Carl von Linné) in 1757 produced a system of classification (called his Systema Naturae) based on relationships. Using structural features as the criterion of relationship, he included in one *genus* or family all those types of animals which on broad lines showed obvious similarities. For example, he included all the cat-like animals: lions, tigers, pumas, wild and domestic cats, in the genus *Felis*, and he further gave the name *species* to the various types. Under his system, each type of animal was given a double name: the name of the genus, followed by the name of the species. Hence he called the lion: *Felis leo*; the tiger: *Felis tigris*; the leopard or panther, *Felis pardus*, and so on. (This system is sometimes referred to as the binomial nomenclature.) Linnaeus held the medieval doctrine of the Fixity of Species, i.e. that all the individual members of a particular species, e.g. those of *Felis tigris*, were lineal descendants of a single pair of animals created in a form which has remained virtually unchanged to the present day. While he recognized that minor individual differences occurred among members of the same species, he ignored these deliberately in devising his system of classification. Nevertheless, it soon became obvious that such a view was not logical and that it was more likely that the existence of present-day variation among the members of a particular species pointed to the possibility of variation in the past and that, in consequence, the original characters of a particular species have undergone change and have not remained fixed. It is but a step further to assume that the differences which distinguish the members of one species from those of another species of the *same* genus have arisen as the result of past variation in the descendants of an ancestral type common to both species. *All* the existing species of this genus in fact could have originated from an ancestral type common to them all. Moreover, distinct genera can show certain similarities, e.g. the dentition of the dog-like animals of the genus *Canis* is similar to that of the cats belonging to the genus *Felis*, and hence these genera may have arisen from a common ancestral type even more remote in time. This idea of descent accompanied by variation from common ancestral types can be projected still further to embrace the larger classificatory groups: the classes and the phyla (see Outline Classification of the Animal Kingdom, p. 708). This constitutes the doctrine of Evolution, of which the roots can perhaps be traced back to classical times, but which only became generally accepted towards the end of the last century—mainly as the result of the work of Charles Darwin (1809–82). To recapitulate—the doctrine of Evolution supposes that the earliest animal life on this planet consisted of simple forms from which, by a continuous process of variation, later and more complex and specialized types arose. The *general* trend of evolution has been towards the production of animal forms showing an increasing complexity of structure accompanied by an increasing degree of organization of the body with integration of the body as a whole. At the same time, ability to survive in diverse habitats became evident, so that while the earlier forms were undoubtedly aquatic, later others appeared adapted for life on land and in the air. While it is unlikely that any of the primeval types exist today even in the form of animals of such simple structure as that shown by amoeba, it is natural to assume that the Protozoa are more nearly related to the primeval types than are the multicellular animals (or Metazoa). Evolutionary series have also been traced through the invertebrate Metazoa starting with the diploblastic coelenterates and leading on through the acoelomate, triploblastic, free-living Platyhelminthes to the coelomate, triploblastic members of the superphylum Annulata with its two main branches: the Annelida and the Arthropoda. Within these phyla, the various classes again present possible evolutionary series especially in the class Insecta (see p. 185) where not only has the life history become more complicated as evolution has proceeded from the primitive types, e.g. springtails and silverfish, to the 'higher' ones represented by the Holometabola (Lepidoptera, Hymenoptera, Coleoptera, etc.), but at the same time diversity of structure, particularly with regard to the mouthparts, has occurred resulting in the appearance of a number of types, each showing adaptation to particular types of food and environments. At this juncture, it should be stressed that evolutionary changes may have led to a secondary simplification of

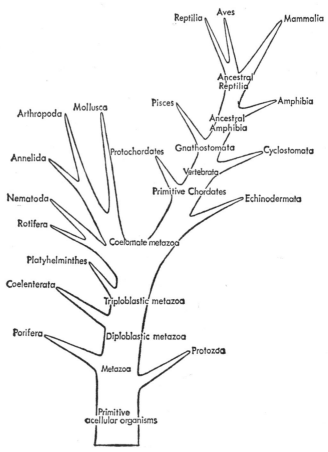

Fig. 36.1. A hypothetical tree of descent of the Animal Kingdom.

structure as shown by the parasitic Arthropoda, e.g. *Sacculina*, or the sedentary ones, e.g. barnacles. *Sacculina* in the adult stage is parasitic on crabs and is devoid of appendages and sense organs. At the same time these secondarily simplified types often show adaptive modifications of certain structures to befit them for the parasitic mode of existence. It must be admitted, however, that even within a limited range of genera a complete series of evolutionary changes often cannot be traced owing to the dying out of intermediate forms. These extinct intermediate forms are sometimes referred to as 'missing links'. Probably the best representation of evolutionary descent is that of a tree in which many of the branches have died and which has become buried in drifting sand so that only the tips of the living branches are seen. These living branches—some older, others younger—represent the main lines of descent, while their emergent tips represent the living representatives of the phyla, genera and species which make up the Animal Kingdom as it is known today.

Evidence in support of evolution

1. THE NATURAL SYSTEM OF CLASSIFICATION. As previously pointed out, the system of classification adopted by zoologists and based on that of Linnaeus tacitly supports the doctrine of evolution in that the existence of the resemblances and differences used as criteria for classification are most easily explained as being due to evolutionary change in the descendants of the original ancestral forms.

2. THE GEOLOGICAL EVIDENCE. Many fossilized remains of animals have been found in those geological strata known as the sedimentary rocks in which during their formation remains of plants and animals have been wholly or partially preserved as fossils. If evolution has actually occurred, various assumptions regarding these fossils could be made: (i) the older strata should contain fewer *types* of animal remains than the younger ones and only the more primitive types should be present; (ii) in passing from the oldest to the youngest strata, a geological succession should be found, the *types* of the fossils not only becoming more numerous but also showing the successive appearance of more and more complex forms; (iii) the time of appearance of representatives of the various phyla or classes should be correlated with their evolutionary status, e.g. fossils of fish should appear in earlier strata than those in which those of amphibia first appear, and these in turn in earlier strata than those in which reptilian fossils are found, while only in the later strata should fossils of mammals be found; (iv) fossils of extinct animals, some of them intermediate between various types of living (extant) animals should exist.

Reference to the adjoining table of geological succession shows

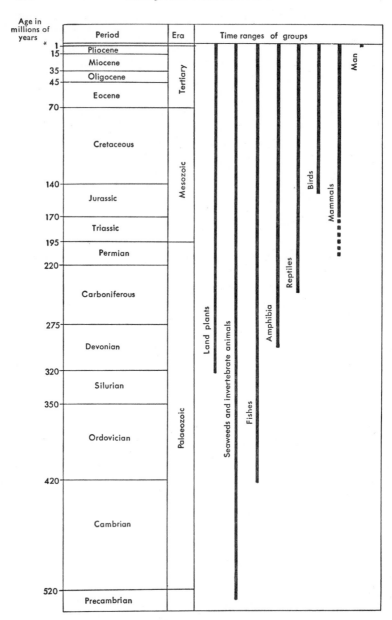

* Quaternary (Pleistocene and Holocene)

Fig. 36.2. Table of geological succession. (Adapted from *Short guide to the Exhibition Galleries,* British Museum (Natural History). By permission.)

that assumptions (i), (ii) and (iii) above are supported by the evidence of the fossils through the later appearance of birds as compared with that of the earliest mammals appears to be an exception, but the birds may be regarded as a separate branch of the 'reptilian tree' which early became specialized and static, whereas the early egg-laying mammals, though originating before the birds, gave rise in turn to more specialized mammals, first the marsupials and then to the placentals whose origins are later in geological time than those of the birds. In a somewhat comparable way, the earlier Amphibia probably arose from fish which were more ancient than the majority of the fish extant today, though this does not appear in the fossil record. As regards assumption (iv) above—there is abundant fossil evidence to show that many animals have become extinct, particularly reptiles such as the dinosaurs (large lizard-like types), pterodactyls (flying reptiles) and ichthyosaurs (fish-like reptiles), and the trilobites (ancestral types of arthropods). While fossils of intermediate forms now extinct are not common, there are several outstanding examples, notably that of *Archaeopteryx*—an extinct bird which although it possessed feathers like those of the modern birds, also, unlike them, possessed teeth of the homodont reptilian type and a less modified forelimb than those of the birds, indicating that it represents a stage in the evolution of birds from reptilian ancestors. Fossil evidence also exists to show a progressive series of evolutionary changes in the shells of certain Mollusca, e.g. *Paludina*, and in the feet of the horse. The fossil remains of the horse show a progressive increase in size accompanied by a reduction in the number of digits (Fig. 36.3).

3. THE EXISTENCE OF LIVING INTERMEDIATE TYPES. Mention of the existence of fossils of animals intermediate in structure between those of ancient and present-day types naturally suggests that certain intermediate forms may also occur. A few of these do in fact exist today, one of the most outstanding examples being that of *Peripatus*, a small slug-like animal found widely distributed in isolated localities in the tropical regions of America, Africa and Australasia. *Peripatus* displays both annelid and arthropod characteristics, suggesting that it may be a type intermediate between the annelids and the tracheate arthropods (myriapods and insects). Its wide distribution coupled with the fact that its range in each continent is limited to small localities suggests that it was once much more widely dispersed but has largely been ousted by later-evolved and more successful competitors. The Dipnoi (lung fishes) have a

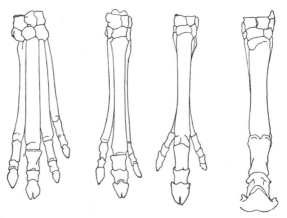

Fig. 36.3. Stages in the evolution of the foot of the horse. (Based on *Gregory*.)

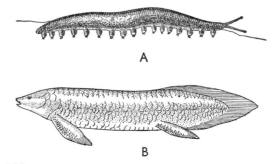

A

B

Fig. 36.4.

A Peripatus. (After *Sedgwick*.) *B* A dipnoan fish, *Ceratodus*. (*By permission*.)

similar kind of distribution, being found in a few rivers only in each of the above continents. Their structural features (p. 406) suggest that they form a link between the ancient fish and the ancestors of the modern Amphibia.

4. THE MORPHOLOGICAL EVIDENCE. Two types of evidence may be deduced from a study of the morphology of animals: (i) the variations shown by homologous organs and (ii) the existence of vestigial structures.

(i) The variations shown in homologous organs indicate evolutionary changes in those organs to adapt them for new uses. A clear example of this is shown by a comparison of the forelimbs of a variety of vertebrates, such as the whales and dolphins, the birds and bats, and the ungulates. All these limbs are modifications of the basic pentadactyl limb (see p. 317). In the whales and dolphins, the limb is shortened and the number of the phalanges of the digits

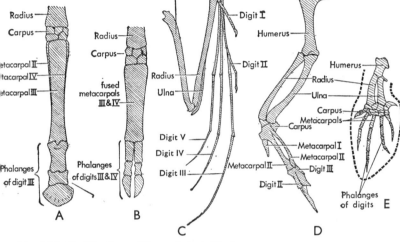

Fig. 36.5. Modifications of the pentadactyl limb.

A Horse; *B* Cow; *C* Bat; *D* Bird; *E* Whale. (From various sources.)

increased to produce a paddle-like limb comparable to the pectoral fins of the fish. In the birds and bats, the forelimb is modified for flight, though in different ways. In the ungulates (hoofed mammals) the forelimbs, and the hind-limbs as well, have been modified to enable the animals to progress at relatively high speeds.

(ii) Vestigial structures. In man a number of these occur, as, for example, the functionless muscles connected with the pinna of the ear; a few people can use them to a limited degree. In the horse and many other mammals these muscles are used to direct the pinnae towards the source of a sound, but in man they have lost that function and occur in an undeveloped form. In the inner angle of each eye is a pinkish triangular flap which is a vestige of the nictitating membrane or third eyelid of the reptiles. It is better developed in the cat, where is can be partially drawn across the eye but not completely so, as in birds. The caecum and its appendix is another vestigial structure in man, but is well developed in rodents and in the horse where it plays an important part in digestion (vide p. 489). The pineal body projecting from the roof of the third ventricle of the brain may be a vestige of a median eye, since in a primitive lizard—the tuatara of New Zealand (*Sphenodon*)—such an eye occurs. All these vestigial structures indicate degenerative evolutionary changes.

5. THE PHYSIOLOGICAL EVIDENCE. Through their descent from common ancestors, the members of closely related genera and species are likely to display certain physiological characters in common. This is exemplified in the Primates by the existence of 'blood groups' in the various races of man and in the higher apes. A 'blood group' consists of individuals whose blood is similar in that a transfusion of blood can be made from one individual to another without the red blood cells becoming agglutinated (stuck together), whereas blood from another individual belonging to a different blood group may result in agglutination of the red cells causing blockages of the blood vessels which may be fatal. There are four *main* blood groups in man. These are designated as O, A, B and AB. Two distinct substances called agglutinogens (or antigens) A and B may be present separately or together on the red cells while two other substances known as agglutinins (or antibodies) α and β may be present in the plasma.

Blood of group O contains neither A nor B on the red cells but both α and β are present in the plasma.

In the blood of group A, A is present on the red cells and β in the plasma.

In the blood of group B, B is present on the red cells and α in the plasma.

In the blood of group AB, both A and B are present on the red cells but neither α nor β occurs in the plasma.

Persons belonging to group O are known as 'universal donors', since individuals of this group can donate their blood to those of all the other groups without the occurrence of agglutination, since neither antigens A nor B are present on the red cells. Blood from individuals of group A is agglutinated when transferred into the blood of those belonging to groups O and B, since the blood of both contain the antibody α which reacts with the antigen A to produce agglutination. Similarly blood from individuals of group B cannot be given to members of groups O and A since the antibody β is present in their blood and this reacts with the antigen B. Blood from members of group AB which contains both antigens A and B cannot be given to members of the three other groups, all of which contain one or other or both of the antibodies α and β.

Another well-known blood group is called the Rhesus group

because it occurs in the Rhesus monkey as well as in Man. The blood of Rhesus-positive individuals contains the Rhesus antigen (Rh) but this is absent from the blood of a Rhesus-negative person. Neither Rhesus-positive nor Rhesus-negative blood normally contains the antibody. If, however, Rhesus-positive blood is transfused into the blood vessels of a Rhesus-negative person, then the blood of the latter is stimulated to form the antibody. A subsequent transfusion of Rhesus-positive blood then produces haemolysis (destruction of the red cells). In certain cases, therefore, Rhesus-negative blood has

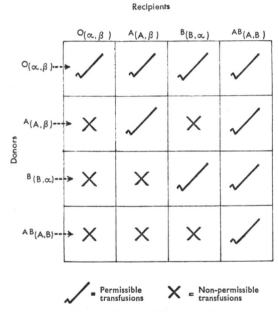

Fig. 36.6. Table of blood transfusions.

to be used for blood transfusions since this can produce no formation of the antibody. When a Rhesus-positive foetus is developing in the uterus of a Rhesus-negative woman, the blood of the mother is stimulated to form the antibody by the diffusion of the Rhesus antigen from the foetus into her blood via the placenta. Diffusion of the antibody in the reverse direction produces haemolysis in the blood of the foetus, usually with fatal results to the foetus. If, however, the child is born alive, though suffering from severe haemolysis, its life can often be saved by replacing its blood by a transfusion of blood from a suitable donor, thus removing the antibody. The mother, having developed the antibody, must therefore always be given Rhesus-negative blood should a transfusion of blood subsequent to the birth of the child be necessary.

The existence of the various blood groups is conditioned by certain controlling genes inherited from former generations. These have been studied in greatest detail in man, but it is known that similar genes affect the inheritance of the various blood groups in the higher apes. The existence of similar blood groups in man and in the higher apes would therefore seem to suggest relationship due to descent from a common ancestral source.

6. THE EMBRYOLOGICAL EVIDENCE. The life history of the frog (q.v.) could possibly be explained by assuming that the ancestors of the frog were fish which evolved lungs and pentadactyl limbs to enable them to live on land. It can be suggested that each generation of frogs repeats, as it were, the history of the evolution of the frog species. During its development from the egg, each frog passes through stages similar to those which produced the adult form of the frog during its evolution from a fish-like ancestor similar to those fish known as the Dipnoi. These Dipnoi (lung fish) have in their adult form lungs as well as gills, with a corresponding modification of the blood system including the presence of two auricles and of pulmonary vessels similar to those of the frog. Moreover they have larvae very much like the tadpoles of the frog, at first with external gills and later with internal ones. Though the modern Amphibia have scale-less skins, unlike the Dipnoi, it is interesting to note that the earlier, now-extinct Amphibia (the Stegocephalia) did, from the fossil evidence, possess a complete covering of dermal scales.

A common basic plan of development can be traced through all the embryos and foetal stages of the vertebrates, all of which possess visceral clefts and a visceral skeleton—though not used for respiration in those of the true land vertebrates, the reptiles, birds and mammals. Among the invertebrates certain larval types common to various groups are also found, such as the trochosphere larva of the annelids and the Mollusca, and the *nauplius* larva of the Crustacea which is common to many of the orders of this class.

It was from a consideration of such examples which led von Baer (1792–1867) and Haeckel (1834–1919) to support the principle that 'ontogeny repeats phylogeny', i.e. that the development of an individual recapitulates to a greater or lesser extent the evolutionary history of the race to which it belongs. This principle cannot, however, apply universally since the larval and pupal stages of the holometabolous insects (see p. 185) and the larval stages (other than the miracidium) of *Fasciola* (p. 79) would seem to be later interpolations into the life histories of these animals, since they are absent from those of the more primitive (non-specialized) members of their respective groups (i.e. the springtails and silverfish in the insects and the free-living forms in the Platyhelminthes). The environmental conditions under which the early stages of development occur can obviously lead to alterations in the pattern of development, while the different modes of gastrulation in the early embryonic stages of the vertebrates have been undoubtedly produced by the differing amounts of yolk present in the eggs. Thus departures from the common plan of development may occur and these have to be borne in mind in attempting to evaluate the reliability of this type of evidence in support of the evolutionary doctrine. It may also be pointed out that the mode of development of the functionless yolk sac of the mammalian embryos is so different from that of the functional ones of the reptiles and birds that it is difficult to relate it to the common pattern which should be present on the assumption that mammals evolved from a reptilian stock.

7. THE EVIDENCE FROM THE EXISTENCE OF ADAPTATIVE, CONVERGENT AND PARALLEL EVOLUTION. Granted that evolution has occurred, it is reasonable to suppose that some, at any rate, of the evolutionary changes which have taken shape will show adaptations to the environment in which the animal lives, since without such adaptative features survival in a particular environment would be difficult, if not impossible. Examples of adaptative evolution are seen, as already stated, in the modifications of the forelimb for flight in birds and bats and in the streamlined body and paddle-like forelimbs of the dolphins and whales for propulsion in water, or in the spade-like hands and feet of the moles suited for tunnelling through the earth. Many other examples can be quoted. Where non-homologous organs (i.e. those of different origin) have become adapted for the same function (i.e. have become *analogous*), then shape and form approximate, as in the case of the fins of fish and of the dolphins. Such instances are often referred to as examples of *convergent* evolution.

It is through adaptative evolution that certain groups of animals, notably the insects and the mammals and, in the past the reptiles, include so many diverse types adapted for life in different environments. Such adaptative evolution is called *Adaptative Radiation* since it has resulted in radiation into different environments (subterranean, arboreal, aerial or aquatic) from the ordinary land habitat.

Example of Adaptative Radiation:

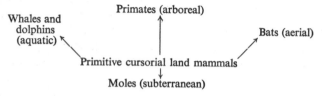

The best example of parallel evolution is seen in the history of the mammals. The earliest mammals showed certain affinities with the reptiles, such as the possession of an interclavicle bone and the habit of laying eggs with calcareous shells. There are only two surviving types of these—the duck-billed platypus (*Ornithorhynchus*) and the spiny ant-eater (*Tachyglossus*), both of Australasia and New Guinea. They are included in the group of mammals known as the Prototheria (or monotremes). Later appeared the Metatheria (or marsupials). These, e.g. the kangaroos, wombat, koala bear, Tasmanian wolf, are viviparous. The young are born alive but in so immature a condition that they are carried for a period in a pouch on the ventral side of the abdomen of the female known as the marsupium. Finally arose the Eutheria (true or placental mammals) which by means of the organ known as the allantoic placenta (p. 662) are able to retain and nourish the unborn young in the uterus for a considerably longer period than in the marsupials so that when born the young mammals are in a more advanced state of development. One of the marsupials (*Perameles*, the bandicoot) has, however, a small functional allantoic placenta and the absence of this organ in the other marsupials is thought by some zoologists to be a degenerative feature. The Eutheria displaced the marsupials in all parts of the world except in Australasia which appears to have been separated from Eurasia before the placental mammals appeared, and in the Americas where two examples, the opossum and *Coenolestes*, still exist. The remarkable feature in the evolution of the mammals is that the marsupials and the placental mammals display parallel evolution. A large number of placental types have their counterparts among the marsupials, e.g. the Tasmanian wolf (*Thylacinus*), the marsupial mole (*Notoryctes*) and the rabbit-like bandicoot (*Perameles*).

8. PRESENT-DAY EXAMPLES OF VARIATION. In the preceding paragraphs, variation in the past has been quoted as evidence for

the progress of evolution but it is reasonable to look for evidence of its continuing today. If it is granted that evolution has occurred over long periods of time, it follows that it has been a comparatively slow process and that therefore rapid changes cannot be expected today. Nevertheless, evidence of the formation of new species by variation has been detected in recent times, though more so among plants than among animals. The underlying causes will be discussed in a later section of this chapter (p. 703). It is sufficient to say at this stage that new variants have been observed to appear from time to time in certain species and that these new variants have displaced the normal members of the species. A recent example is that of the melanic form of the scalloped hazel moth (*Gonodontes bidentata*). This dark-coloured variant which was hardly known to exist a hundred years ago has now replaced the pale-coloured normal type in industrial areas, particularly in the Black Country.

Evolutionary Theories

While zoologists are agreed that evolution has taken place, considerable divergence of opinion exists as to the mechanism by which it has occurred. The first serious attempt to provide a theory as to the causes of evolution was that of Lamarck (1744–1829).

LAMARCK'S THEORY. Lamarck assumed that *heritable* variations were produced in animals by a change of habit or by a change in the environment, though the latter he considered applied more to plants than to animals. Hence he thought that the elongated neck of the giraffe had been produced by the short-necked horse-like ancestors of the giraffe ceasing to feed on grass and feeding instead on the leaves of trees. Constant stretching of the necks to reach leaves high up on the trees ultimately produced, in his view, the long necks of the present-day giraffes, each generation acquiring slightly longer necks and transmitting this acquired character to the off-spring. On this account Lamarck's theory is often referred to as the theory of Inheritance of Acquired Characters. He stressed the effect of use and disuse as agents in modifying certain structures in the animal body. The effects of use and disuse, he would argue, are to be seen in the long powerful legs and the poorly developed wings of the ostrich, which no longer flies but relies on its speed of running to escape from its enemies. The main objections to his theory are (a) the absence of experimental evidence in support of it, (b) the lack of evidence that modifications of structure acquired during the life of an animal can affect the germ cells in such a way that the modification can be transmitted to the offspring. These objections were first raised by Weismann in the latter part of the last century. He pointed out that mutilations practised by man on domestic animals, e.g. the 'docking' of tails of sheep and horses, though continued through many generations, has produced no heritable effect. He also postulated that the potentially immortal germ plasm which is handed on from each generation to the succeeding one is housed by the mortal body or soma and that no mechanism existed by which any modification of the soma could alter the constitution of the germ plasm.

DARWIN AND WALLACE. In 1858 Charles Darwin, jointly with Wallace, produced before the Linnaean Society a paper embodying a new theory of evolution based on conclusions reached by him and Wallace as the result of observations spread over a long period on the differences between closely related species. Darwin had studied the fauna of the Galapagos Islands and that of the near-by Continental regions of South America when he visited that area as a naturalist on board H.M.S. *Beagle* during a nautical survey in 1831–36. Wallace studied the fauna of the Amazon basin and of the Malay Peninsula. The main points of their theory may be summarized briefly as follows.

(1) Animals and plants display variation in their characters, i.e. no two individuals of any particular species are exactly alike.

(2) Animals and plants show in the vast majority of cases a high degree of fecundity and tend to produce numerous offspring.

(3) As a result of this high rate of increase, a *struggle for existence* occurs.

(4) This struggle for existence will lead to the survival of the fittest (i.e. those individuals which display characters which benefit them in the competition for food and living space) and to the elimination of the unfit.

(5) This selection of the fittest by the struggle for existence was called by the authors of this theory *Natural Selection*.

(6) The advantageous characters displayed by the fittest are transmitted to their offspring and enhanced in succeeding generations.

To quote one example: The long neck of the giraffe would in their view have come into existence in the following way. In the early days of the giraffes, the necks of the animals were short but, even so, some had slightly longer necks than others. These had an advantage over the shorter-necked giraffes in that they were able to reach higher for leaves. In the competition for food these longer-necked giraffes would tend to survive, particularly in times of drought, while the shorter-necked ones starved (a parallel case is that of sheep and bullocks—the sheep can graze closer to the ground than bullocks, so that when herded together in the same field, the bullocks in time starve while the sheep survive). The same process repeated through succeeding generations would account, on the theory of Natural Selection, for the long-necked giraffe of the present day.

Darwin, in the following year (1859), published a fuller account of this theory in a book entitled *The Origin of Species by means of Natural Selection*. In this book, while further elaborating the idea that Natural Selection is the main directing agent of evolution, he also included secondary ones such as sexual selection, the effect of geographical isolation, and, like Lamarck, the effect of use and disuse on certain organs.

Sexual selection, Darwin considered, was responsible for the brighter plumage of male birds as compared with that of the hen of the same species owing to the hen birds always choosing the more brightly coloured cock birds as mates in each generation. On the other hand, the more sober coloured plumage of the hen birds could be due to a process of elimination of the brighter coloured ones. The sitting hen is liable to be seen and attacked by predatory birds, e.g. the hawks, so that the less conspicuous ones stand a greater chance of escaping observation. In this manner, generation by generation the plumage of the hen birds has become less and less conspicuous. (*N.B.* This is due to Natural Selection and *not* Sexual Selection.) In polygamous species, e.g. the deer, the stronger males with the best developed antlers overcome their weaker rivals and mate with the females, so that their male offspring inherit those features which in their turn enable them to overcome their rivals. In this way, progressive increase in the size of the antlers of the male deer has taken place.

Geographical isolation, due to mountain and sea barriers, could induce, in Darwin's view, increased variation and hence favour the production of new species owing to the absence of the 'swamping effect', as he called it, by interbreeding with other variations so as to produce a less varied population. He believed that if all the various varieties of pigeons produced by man's selective action were allowed to interbreed, reversion to the original type of wild pigeon would result. Geographical isolation also increased speciation (formation of new species) by reducing competition. Under such conditions new varieties which might not be able to survive in competition with existing species could be preserved from extinction. The dodo, a type of pigeon with reduced powers of flight, until recently an inhabitant of the island of Mauritius, could not have survived on the mainland of Africa, since its capture by predatory enemies would be easily accomplished owing to its inability to fly. No such enemies existed on the island of Mauritius until the arrival of the crews of sailing ships visiting the island to obtain fresh water. Indiscriminate killing of the dodos for food occurred during their visits, resulting eventually in their complete extermination. Darwin's theory would have accounted for the diminished power of flight and the poorly developed wings by Natural Selection. Mauritius is exposed to high winds and those birds with well-developed wings which flew well were liable to be swept out to sea, while those with poorly developed wings and unable to fly were preserved from this danger. In this way Natural Selection by the agency of high winds evolved a breed of flightless dodos. On Lamarckian lines the absence of enemies could account for the diminished size of the wings as the result of their disuse over a long period of time, since the need to escape by flight from enemies was not present.

The theories of both Lamarck and Darwin require the transmission of advantageous characters to the members of succeeding generations. Though Mendel published his work on the mechanism of heredity within a year or so of the publication of the theory of Darwin and Wallace, Darwin remained in ignorance of Mendel's work. He felt, however, compelled to produce a theory of inheritance to counter criticisms on the lines of those of Weismann (p. 700). According to this theory of his, the organs of the body during the lifetime of the individual produced heritable particles called gemmules which were carried by the blood stream to the gonads and stored in the germ cells. The nature of these gemmules was influenced, in his view, by variations, however produced, in the organs themselves and through the operation of the gemmules these variations could be reproduced in the same organs of the individuals of succeeding generations. Darwin called this idea *Pangenesis* but it is clearly discredited today in the light of modern knowledge of the mechanism of heredity.

  As previously stated, Lamarck considered variation to be due to the operation of certain factors such as change of habit, leading to use and disuse of organs or to the effect of the environment, but Darwin accepted the fact that variations occurred among the members of a species and did not attempt to account for their existence. In his view, variations provided the raw material for the operation of Natural Selection and other selective agencies, the sole exception being the effects of use and disuse. The *type* of variation which Darwin considered provided this raw material was the *continuous* type (see p. 667). Discontinuous variations ('sports' or mutations) were, he considered, so infrequent as to play but little part in the evolution of new species.

Since the publication of 'The Origin of Species' by Darwin, much criticism has been levelled at his theory. Even Natural Selection has been challenged on various grounds. It is sufficient to mention in this connexion the work of Johannsen, who practised the effect of selection on the mean weight of beans. He originated the idea that in many races of animals and plants there is a mixed population consisting of 'pure lines' with different means for particular characters. Selection, in his view, merely eliminates certain of the 'pure lines' while preserving others. Beyond this preliminary selection no further effect can be obtained by continuing the process of selection and hence he concluded that *continuous* evolution by Natural Selection was not possible. Others have pointed out that the struggle for existence does not begin to operate in a particular environment until the population has reached a high density and that, moreover, selection by this means may be invalidated by epidemic diseases or sudden climatic changes. A particular type selected by the struggle for existence as being the most fit to survive in competition with the other members of its species might prove the least fit to survive during a period of epidemic disease or during a severe winter. Darwin considered evolution to be a slow process but changes in environment can be comparatively rapid and adjustment of a species to survive in the changed environment might not occur quickly enough by such a slow process of evolution as that produced by Natural Selection.

With these criticisms in mind, it is now possible to proceed to a consideration of the present-day views of zoologists on the subject of Evolution. These may be summarized briefly as follows.

Evolution, past and present, is accepted as a fact but any theories as to how it occurs must be subjected, if possible, to experimental test and must be explicable in the light of modern knowledge of cytology and of the mechanism of inheritance. Experimental testing of selection has not produced much evidence in favour of Natural Selection but most zoologists are reluctant to abandon this causative agent owing to its plausibility and the unlikelihood of any better agent being forthcoming. Moreover, if the process of evolution has been a slow one, then—unless selection can be practised over many years—it is not likely to produce marked results in the lifetime of the experimenter. More light on the mode of speciation can be gleaned from cytological studies of closely related species and of those species which are known to have arisen in recent times. Gene mutation, i.e. an alteration in the chemical constitution of a gene leading to an alteration in the character conditioned by it, produces a new heritable variation. If, as generally happens, the new gene is recessive, the new character it produces will not immediately appear and, until the gene has been multiplied by successive cell division and has spread into a number of individuals by interbreeding, the character cannot appear since it will only be produced in individuals which are homozygous for this gene. Should the new character be disadvantageous to the individuals possessing it, then, by Natural Selection (or Sexual Selection), such individuals will not survive and the gene can only survive as hidden in the recessive form distributed among the individuals of the population. Should, however, the new character confer an advantage, the homozygous individuals will tend to multiply since they will be preserved and not eliminated by Natural (or Sexual) Selection. The new mutants will therefore in time displace the original types. Continued mutation of genes of different allelomorphic pairs will eventually produce a race of individuals which show so marked a deviation in appearance from the original type that the systematist —basing his classification on observation of character differences— will identify this race as a new species. There exists, however, a more fundamental basis for recognizing the race as a new species if we accept the Linnaean conception of a species as a unit (or collection) of individuals of similar characters, fertile *inter se* but not with those of other species and producing similar inter-fertile offspring. By this conception a 'sterility barrier' exists between members of different species and this is precisely what continued gene mutation will ultimately produce. It will be recalled (p. 435) that, at the first division of the gametocytes, the homologous chromosomes pair together at the zygotene stage of the meiotic nuclear division and exchange parts of themselves by 'crossing over'. This in itself leads to increased variation owing to the recombinations of the genes (p. 679) and this provides more raw material for the operation of selective agencies. However, this pairing of homologous chromosomes is held to be dependent on the mutual attraction of *similar* genes. When as a result of gene mutation a large number of the genes on the two homologous chromosomes have become dissimilar, then the chromosomes fail to pair owing to the lack of a sufficient number of *similar* genes to hold them together. This results in a breakdown of the process of meiosis and viable gametes are not formed—in other words, sterility occurs. Thus in a large population of inter-fertile individuals, gene mutations occurring in different ways in the chromosomes of the individual members may lead eventually to the splitting up of this population into a number of groups, the members of which do not interbreed successfully with those of other groups since their hybrid offspring are sterile. At this stage, following the Linnaean conception of a species, a number of new species may be said to have arisen and these will be recognized as such by the systematists on the basis of their different characters produced by gene mutation. The establishment of these new species will be facilitated if the original population was spread over a number of different environments, since variations produced by gene mutation will be subjected to the selective conditions of the separate environments. A number of 'ecological' races, each fitted to its particular environment, will thus result by selection and these will form self-breeding species when gene-mutation has proceeded far enough to establish a sterility barrier between the members of one race and those of the others. The donkey and horse may have arisen in this way from a common equine ancestral type, the donkey being adapted for life under more rigorous conditions, e.g. mountainous regions, than the horse which lived in the wild state on the open grasslands (the steppes and the prairies). The hybrids between the donkey and the horse—the mules and the hinnies—are sterile owing to the failure of the 'donkey' and 'horse' chromosomes to pair at gametogenesis.

In addition to gene mutation, alterations in the actual structure of the chromosomes and in the number of chromosomes found in the nuclei appear also to have played a part in speciation. The first of these two alterations has been due to 'accidents' to the chromosomes during nuclear division and the second to *polyploidy*. Accidents to the chromosomes include (a) loss of whole chromosomes, (b) breakage of one or more of the chromosomes, followed by (1) loss of a part or parts (*deletion*), (2) reunion of the broken parts in an inverted order (*inversion*), (3) union of the part of one chromosome with another chromosome or with part of it (*translocation*), (4) duplication of parts of a particular chromosome. All these accidents lead to the production of gametes which differ from the normal ones and result either in the appearance of new varieties owing to the disturbance of the previously existing gene-complexes or to the establishment of sterility barriers owing to the inability of the altered chromosomes to pair with the normal type of homologous chromosomes. Chromosome alterations on the above lines coupled with gene mutation have apparently led to the formation of certain wild species of the genus *Drosophila*, notably *Drosophila pseudo-obscura* and *Drosophila miranda*.

Polyploidy—the second of the two alterations mentioned above —is the name given to an increase in the number of chromosomes in the nuclei of an individual as compared with that in the nuclei of the normal individual of the same species. The increase is produced by the failure of chromatids or chromosomes to separate at the meta-phase stage of mitosis or meiosis (pp. 429, 435). As a result, all the chromatids or chromosomes enter the nucleus of one of the new cells so that that particular nucleus has a double set of chromosomes. If a gamete with such a 'diploid' (or unreduced) set of chromosomes unites with one having the usual 'haploid' set, the individual produced is a 'triploid', the nuclei of each of its cells having an extra 'haploid' set of chromosomes in addition to the 'diploid' set. When such an individual produces gametes, the presence of this extra set of chromosomes upsets the normal process of nuclear division and causes sterility. Cases of 'triploid' rabbits have been described. They are larger than the normal type, but sterile. Should two 'diploid' gametes unite, the individual they produce is a 'tetraploid' having two complete 'diploid' sets of chromosomes in each of the nuclei of its cells. A 'tetraploid' can *theoretically* produce gametes—since each chromosome has an homologous one to pair with at meiosis— even if the individual is a hybrid between two distinct species. Whereas in the mule or hinny produced by the union of a 'haploid' donkey gamete with a 'haploid' horse gamete, gametogenesis cannot occur owing to the inability of the 'donkey' and the 'horse' homolo-gous chromosomes to pair for reasons stated above, such would not be the case if a 'diploid' donkey gamete could meet a 'diploid' horse gamete to produce a tetraploid hybrid. While new hybrid species in plants have arisen in this way, it is not possible for such to occur in animals which possess, as the majority do, a chromosome sex-mechanism (p. 680). Investigations with *Drosophila* have shown that individuals with more than the usual number of X chromosomes either fail to develop or are sterile. Polyploid animals can only exist in certain types of animals (e.g. Coelenterata) which are capable of reproduction by non-sexual methods. Polyploidy does not therefore appear to have played a significant part in evolution in the *animal* kingdom. The operative factors must therefore be gene mutation and chromosome modifications, such as deletions, inversions, translocations and duplications.

Finally, it may be said that the factors just mentioned either are spontaneous in origin or may be due to some fortuitous circumstance such as X-ray or cosmic ray bombardment which induce either gene mutations or chromosome alterations. These facts raise questions in the mind as to whether the course of evolution has been a purely circumstantial chain of events dependent on random factors or has been directed by a series of changing environmental conditions whether external or internal. If it is accepted that changes in the genetic constitution of individual animals are the basic cause of evolution—and without such changes, evolution could not occur—then no theory can satisfactorily explain the course of evolution both past and present which cannot account for these changes. The modern tendency is therefore to look for the causes of evolution *within* the individual and not to possible ones *outside* it, as did Lamarck, Darwin and Wallace. One puzzling series of evolutionary changes yet to be explained is that which leads or has led to a progressive increase in size either of the whole body or of certain organs, as exemplified by the huge extinct reptiles or the mandibles of stag beetles. These increases in size confer no advantage to their possessors in the struggle for existence but rather the reverse, and seem to have followed a predetermined course known as Orthogenesis.

37. An Outline Classification of the Animal Kingdom

REFERENCE has already been made in Chapter 36 to the principles of classification, and it is now desirable to draw up a table of classification of the whole Animal Kingdom to include the main phyla with their subdivisions: classes, sub-classes and orders, together with a few representative genera of each order, enumerating such features as are necessary for the purpose of assigning any particular animal to its proper position in the classificatory scheme, or, in other words, to give its systemic place. Taking the rabbit, for example, it would be classified as follows:

Kingdom: Animalia
Sub-Kingdom: Metazoa
Phylum: Chordata
Sub-Phylum: Vertebrata (Craniata)
Class: Mammalia
Sub-Class: Eutheria
Order: Lagomorpha
Genus: Oryctolagus
Species: cuniculus

A TABLE OF CLASSIFICATION OF THE ANIMAL KINGDOM

1. *Sub-Kingdom:* PROTOZOA. The bodies (somata) of these animals are acellular, i.e. *not* divided into units called cells. Each soma consists of a small mass of protoplasm consisting of cytoplasm and, usually, a single nucleus, though in a few (e.g. *Paramecium*) more than one nucleus may be present.

Phylum: Protozoa. This is the only phylum in the sub-kingdom Protozoa and its characteristics are the same as those of the sub-kingdom.

Class I: Flagellata (Mastigophora). Protozoa possessing generally one or two flagella as organs of locomotion. They do not form pseudopodia, having firm cuticles which permit of but small changes in shape. Flagellates display various types of nutrition: some are

708

holozoic ingesting solid food through a gullet (e.g. *Peranema*), some are saprophytic (e.g. *Polytoma*), others are holophytic (e.g. *Euglena*), while some are parasitic (e.g. *Trypanosoma*). Reproduction is asexual only—by binary fission.

Sub-class: Phytomastigina. Flagellates with a maximum number of four flagella. They contain chloroplasts or chromatophores containing a brown pigment. Nutrition is holophytic, e.g. *Euglena*.

Sub-class: Zoomastigina. Flagellates which do not possess chloroplasts or chromatophores. A few have more than four flagella. Nutrition is holozoic, saprophytic or parasitic, e.g. *Peranema, Polytoma, Bodo, Trypanosoma*.

Class II. Sarcodina. Protozoa forming pseudopodia for locomotion and feeding.

Sub-class: Rhizopoda.

Order 1. Amoebina. Rhizopods with blunt pseudopodia. Mostly freshwater but some parasitic, and reproducing by binary or multiple fission, e.g. *Amoeba proteus, Amoeba histolytica*.

Order 2. Foraminifera. Rhizopods with fine interlacing pseudopodia. All are marine and form part of the plankton (floating organisms in the surface layers of the sea). They secrete shells of calcium carbonate usually with many small apertures (foramina) through which the pseudopodia protrude. Reproduction by multiple fission or by isogamy or anisogamy, e.g. *Globigerina, Polystomella* (= *Elphidium*).

Sub-class: Actinopoda.

Order 1. Radiolaria. Rhizopods with stiff pointed pseudopodia and highly sculptured shells of silica (SiO_2). They are all marine and often contain in their cytoplasm yellow unicellular algae (zooxanthellae) living in symbiosis. Reproduction by multiple fission, e.g. *Actinomma*.

Order 2. Heliozoa. Freshwater rhizopods with stiff pointed pseudopodia supported by horny fibres, e.g. *Actinophrys*.

Class III. Ciliophora. Protozoa with a firm cuticle, possessing cilia for locomotion and food capture.

Sub-class: Protociliata. Ciliates with one or more nuclei but without differentiation into micro- and macronuclei and no gullet, e.g. *Opalina*. This group also has affinities with the Flagellata.

Sub-class: Ciliata. Ciliates with a gullet and with a double nucleus (micronucleus and macronucleus). The majority display a high degree of organization with division of labour, possessing organelles, e.g. cilia, a gullet, kinetodesmata. Reproduction: asexual by binary fission and sexual by conjugation.

Order 1. Holotricha—without adoral zone of membranellae, others with cilia of equal length distributed all over the body, e.g. *Paramecium*. This is the largest order of ciliates.

Order 2. Spirotricha. With adoral zone of membranellae and with clockwise arrangement of cilia leading to cytostome, e.g. *Spirostomum, Stentor, Stylonichia.*

Order 3. Chonotricha. Ciliates with one nucleus and a spiral ciliated funnel at the anterior end, attached by posterior end to bodies of Crustacea, e.g. *Spirochona.*

Order 4. Peritricha. Ciliates with a spiral anticlockwise ciliated groove leading to the cytostome. Sessile on a contractile stalk, e.g. *Vorticella.*

Class IV. Suctoria. Ciliophora with no cilia in the adult form but possessing suctorial tentacles, e.g. *Acineta*—feeds on *Paramecium* and other ciliates.

Class V. Sporozoa. Parasitic protozoa lacking organelles and with no or very limited powers of movement. Many form dormant sporelike bodies for the purpose of dispersal. Reproduction by either sexual or asexual methods with profuse multiplication, e.g. *Monocystis, Plasmodium* (the malaria parasite).

2. *Sub-Kingdom:* METAZOA. Animals whose bodies are constructed of units called cells, each consisting of a nucleus surrounded by cytoplasm. The cells are differentiated to form tissues and the body is divided into organs composed of various tissues, with division of labour to a greater or lesser degree.

Phylum: Porifera. Metazoa of radial symmetry or irregular form. The body consists of a mesenchyme with an outer and inner epithelium, the inner made up of collar cells or choanocytes. With many inhalant pores and internal canals. The main body opening or openings are exhalant, a mouth being absent.

Class I. Calcarea. Marine and freshwater sponges with a skeleton of calcium carbonate spicules, e.g. *Grantia, Sycon.*

Class II. Hexactinellida. With skeleton of six-rayed siliceous spicules, e.g. *Euplectella,* Venus' flower basket.

Class III. Demospongia. With skeleton of siliceous spicules or collagen fibres or both, e.g. *Euspongia,* the bath sponge.

Sub-class I. Branchiopoda. Free-living Crustacea with compound eyes. A carapace is usually present. Broad, thin limbs fringed with bristles used for producing a current of water for food capture and respiration, e.g. *Chirocephalus, Daphnia.*

Sub-class II. Ostracoda. Free-living Crustacea with or without compound eyes, possessing a bivalved carapace with an adductor muscle, e.g. *Cypris.*

Sub-class III. Copepoda. Free or parasitic Crustacea without compound eyes or carapace; antennules enlarged and used for swimming, e.g. *Cyclops.*

Sub-class IV. Cirripedia. Crustacea with a free-swimming larval stage but sedentary in the adult, e.g. *Lepas* (the goose barnacle), *Balanus* (the acorn barnacle), *Sacculina* (parasitic on the crab).

Sub-class V. Malacostraca. Crustacea with compound eyes, usually stalked. Body divided into a cephalo-thorax and an abdomen usually with a carapace covering the cephalo-thorax partially or entirely. Abdomen bears appendages and a terminal 'tail fan' formed of the next posterior pair of appendages—the uropods and the telson (terminal segment). There is a large group containing a number of orders including the following orders: Amphipoda, e.g. *Gammarus*; Isopoda, e.g. *Asellus* (water slater), *Oniscus* (wood louse); Decapoda, e.g. *Astacus* (crayfish), *Cancer* (crab), *Homarus* (lobster), *Crangon* (shrimp).

Class II. Insecta. Terrestrial arthropods breathing by tracheae and possessing one pair of antennae, a pair of compound eyes, three pairs of legs and usually two pairs of wings. (For classification of insects into orders, see pages 185, 187.)

Class III. Myriapoda. Terrestrial arthropods with tracheae, one pair of antennae, numerous legs and no wings—the centipedes (e.g. *Lithobius*) with one pair of legs per segment, and the millipedes (e.g. *Julus*) with two pairs of legs per *apparent* segment.

Class IV. Arachnida. Terrestrial arthropods with a few exceptions (e.g. the king crab and the water spider). Respiration by gill books, lung books or tracheae. The body is divided into (i) the prosoma, bearing two pairs of appendages, the chelicerae and the pedipalpi, and (ii) the mesosoma with *four* pairs of walking limbs and the metasoma. In some arachnids, e.g. the spiders, the mesosoma and metasoma are fused to form the opisthosoma. Examples of arachnids are the scorpions, e.g. *Scorpio*, the king crabs, e.g. *Limulus*[1], the spiders, e.g. *Epeira*, and the mites, e.g. *Tyroglyphus.*

1 Sometimes placed in a separate class – Merostomata.

Class VI. Onchyophora. Primitive terrestrial arthropods breathing by tracheae and possessing nephridia—a link between the annelids and the arthropods, e.g. *Peripatus.*

Phylum: Mollusca. Triploblastic coelomate Metazoa either bilaterally symmetrical or asymmetrical. There is no obvious metameric segmentation though certain organs, e.g. nephridia and gonads, may be paired. The body is typically divided into three regions: the head, the muscular foot and the visceral hump. A mantle (a projection from the visceral hump) usually houses within its cavity a pair of comb-like gills (the ctenidia). The ectoderm of the visceral hump and of the mantle often secrete a calcareous shell. The blood system is an 'open' one with a definite heart dorsal to the gut enclosed in a coelomic pericardium. The nervous system consists of a ganglionated nerve collar around the fore-gut connected to outlying ganglia by commissures. A larval stage resembling the trochosphere of the Annelida may be presented in the life history.

Class I. Amphineura. Marine Mollusca whose body plan is nearest the 'ideal' mollusc, being bilaterally symmetrical. The mantle and visceral hump bear a linear series of calcareous plates, e.g. *Chiton.*

Class II. Gastropoda. Mollusca with an asymmetric twisted visceral hump covered by a spiral univalve shell (absent or reduced in slugs) into which the flat-soled foot can be withdrawn. A head is present, often bearing simple eyes on retractable stalks. In the floor of the buccal cavity is a rasp-like radula. The gills, if present, are comb-like or feathery. Both aquatic and terrestrial types occur, e.g. periwinkles (*Littorina*), *Patella* (limpet), *Buccinum* (whelk), *Limnaea* (pond snail), *Helix* (snail), *Limax* (slug).

Class III. Lamellibranchiata. Aquatic Mollusca with a laterally compressed bilaterally symmetrical body encased in a bivalved shell from which a wedge-shaped foot may be protruded. No head or radula present. The gills are plate-like. Ciliary currents produced by cilia on the linings of the mantle and gills used for feeding, respiration, excretion and reproduction, e.g. *Anodon* (the freshwater mussel), *Mytilus* (the sea mussel), *Ostrea* (oyster), *Pecten* (scallop), *Cardium* (cockle).

Class IV. Cephalopoda. Marine Mollusca with a well-developed head bearing a pair of large eyes and tentacles with suckers. The shell is absent or enclosed in the visceral hump. The mantle cavity communicates with the exterior by a funnel (part of the foot) through which water can be forcibly ejected for jet propulsion. The nervous system is well developed, e.g. *Sepia* (the cuttlefish), *Octopus*.

Phylum: Echinodermata. Marine triploblastic coelomate Metazoa with secondarily radial symmetry—the larval stages being bilaterally symmetrical. The body is built on a five-rayed plan. Calcareous plates occur in the dermis, sometimes fused to form a shell (e.g. sea urchin). No definite blood system or excretory system is present. The coelom is divided into three parts with different functions; one of these parts is the hydrocoele connected with the numerous tube feet used for locomotion. There is no central nervous system, e.g. Asteroidea (star fish), Echinoidea (sea urchins), Holothuroidea (sea cucumbers), Ophiuroidea (brittle stars), Crinoidea (sea lilies).

Phylum: Chordata. Bilaterally symmetrical metamerically segmented triploblastic Metazoa whose body plan differs fundamentally from that of the foregoing invertebrate metazoan phyla (pages 227, 229). Chordates are characterized by the following features: (1) a dorsal tubular nerve cord with paired nerves, each nerve having a dorsal and a ventral root, (2) an axial skeletal rod called the notochord lying between the nerve cord and the gut and present at least during the early developmental stages, though wholly or partly replaced in the adult in the majority of the chordates by the vertebral column, (3) visceral clefts in the region of the pharynx, (4) a closed blood system with a dorsal and a ventral vessel connected in the pharyngeal region by pairs of vessels running in the walls of the visceral clefts, the direction of blood flow being forwards in the ventral vessel and backwards in the dorsal vessel, (5) an hepatic portal vessel, (6) a post-anal tail.

Sub-phylum: Acrania (Protochordata). Primitive chordates with no definite heart or skull or brain. The excretory organs are not kidneys.

Class I. Enteropneusta (Hemichordata). Burrowing aquatic worm-like Acrania with a proboscis anterior to the mouth and a collar. The pharynx has numerous perforations and there is a dorsal nerve cord in the region of the collar, e.g. *Balanoglossus* (an acorn worm).

Class II. Urochordata. Acrania, mostly sedentary except in the larval stage (with notochord). The body of the adult is enclosed in a covering of a cellulose-like material—hence the name tunicates often applied to them. Numerous apertures occur in the enlarged pharynx opening out into a space (atrium) enclosed by atrial folds.

A number of the typically chordate organs, e.g. notochord, post-anal tail, dorsal tubular nerve cord, occur only in the larva, except in one order. Ciliary currents used for feeding, respiration, excretion and reproduction, e.g. *Ascidia* (sea squirt).

Class III. Cephalochordata. Acrania whose notochord extends to the anterior tip of the body beyond the front of the central nervous system. Numerous gill slits, a pronounced endostyle and an atrium are present. Ciliary currents are used for feeding, etc. Excretion occurs by means of numerous nephridia with solenocytes. Free swimming, though often burrowing in sand, e.g. *Amphioxus* (*Branchiostoma*)—the lancelet.

Sub-phylum: Craniata. These are also called vertebrates, the notochord of the embryonic stage being wholly or partially replaced by a vertebral column. The head is well developed with a definite brain encased in a cranium and sense organs: olfactory, optic and auditory housed in capsules. The visceral clefts are restricted in number and do not open into an atrium. A well-developed muscular heart is present, maintaining a high blood pressure. The organs of excretion are kidneys composed of mesodermal tubules.

Branch Agnatha—Jawless vertebrates.

Class: Cyclostomata. Cold-blooded aquatic vertebrates breathing by gills; with smooth skins devoid of scales. Jaws and limbs are absent. The nasal aperture is single and median. The larva (ammocoete) is a ciliary feeder with an endostyle secreting mucus, e.g. *Petromyzon* (the lamprey).

Branch Gnathostomata—Vertebrates with jaws developed from the 2nd visceral (mandibular) arch.

Class: Pisces. Cold-blooded aquatic vertebrates breathing by gills situated in the visceral clefts. The skin is covered by dermal scales. Paired pectoral and pelvic fins present together with median and tail fins, usually supported by horny rays. The tail is muscular and used for propulsion. No amnion or allantois present in the embryonic stage.

Sub-class I: Chondrichthyes (Elasmobranchs). Fish with a cartilaginous endoskeleton but devoid of an air bladder and usually having no operculum (gill cover), e.g. *Scyliorhinus* (dogfish), *Raia* (the skate).

Sub-class II: Osteichthyes (Teleostomi). Fish with a bony endoskeleton wholly or partly replacing the cartilaginous one of

Phylum: Coelenterata. Radially symmetrical, diploblastic Metazoa with a single body cavity (the digestive enteron) enclosed in a wall of two cellular layers, each one cell in thickness—the outer ectoderm and the inner endoderm separated by a jelly-like layer—the mesogloea. There is only one aperture into the enteron and this serves as both mouth and anus. There is usually a ring of tentacles used in food capture surrounding the mouth. In the ectoderm are structures used for defence and food capture known as nematocysts. An elementary nervous system is present in the form of a nerve net of nerve cells adjacent to the mesogloea and having connection with sensory cells in the ectoderm and endoderm and with the 'muscle' tails of the musculo-epithelial cells of both layers. There are often two phases in the life history—the sedentary, asexual polyp (hydroid) stage and the motile, sexual medusoid stage which alternate with each other.

Class I. Hydrozoa. Colonial Coelenterata with both hydroid and medusoid phases present. Gonads are ectodermal. The medusae have four unbranched radial canals.

Order 1. Calyptoblastea. Marine colonial forms with the common stalk (coenosarc) of the hydroid stage surrounded by a horny perisarc which forms cup-like hydrothecae in which the hydranths are seated. The medusae produced from modified polyps called blastostyles, are saucer-shaped, e.g. *Obelia.*

Order 2. Gymnoblastea. Marine colonial forms in which the perisac does not form hydrothecae. The medusae are bell-shaped and in some forms are not detached but are modified to form gonophores which bear the gonads, e.g. *Tubularia.*

Order 3. Hydrida. Freshwater solitary hydroids reproducing both asexually by budding and sexually by producing gonads, the medusoid phase being absent, e.g. *Chlorohydra.*

Order 4. Siphonophora. Hydrozoa whose colonies are pelagic and display a high degree of polymorphism and division of labour among the polyps and medusae, e.g. *Physalia* (Portuguese Man-of-War).

Class II. Anthozoa. Marine coelenterates either solitary or colonial, in which the polyp stage only occurs. The mouth lies at the bottom of an internal 'gullet' lined by ectoderm and called the stomodaeum. The enteron is divided up by mesenteries composed of inwardly projecting partitions of mesogloea lined by endoderm and bearing endodermal muscle bands. The gonads are endodermal and positioned on the mesenteries. Both solitary and colonial types occur. The Anthozoa include the sea anemones and the corals.

Order 1. Alcyonaria (Octactinia). Anthozoa with eight feathery tentacles and eight mesenteries. To one side of the stomodaeum is a ciliated groove—the siphonoglyph. Skeleton if present, composed of spicules of calcium carbonate embedded in the mesogloea, e.g. Dead men's fingers (*Alcyonium*) and the organ-pipe coral (*Tubipora*).

Order 2. Zoantharia (Hexactinia). Anthozoa with numerous unbranched tentacles. There are numerous mesenteries, primaries and secondaries, the primaries arranged in six pairs. The stomodaeum has two siphonoglyphs, e.g. *Actinia* (sea anemone, solitary) and the madreporarian corals (colonial).

Class III. Scyphozoa: the jelly fish. Marine coelenterates in which the medusoid stage is the dominant one. The medusae differ from those of the Hydrozoa in having numerous branching radial canals, a stomodaeum and endodermal gonads, and are formed by strobilization from the hydroid stage (hydratuba).

Class IV. Ctenophora—the sea combs or sea gooseberries. Solitary forms swimming by means of comb-like bands of cilia. No nematocysts occur and hence these coelenterates are sometimes included in a separate phylum.

Phylum: Platyhelminthes (Flatworms). Bilaterally symmetrical Metazoa with three layers in their body walls—the single cell-layered ectoderm and endoderm separated by a solid mass of cells (the mesoderm), i.e. are triploblastic and acoelomate. The only body cavity (if present) is the enteron which is much branched and has only one aperture serving as mouth and anus. Longitudinal and transverse muscles lying beneath the epidermis are present. There is a more centralized nervous system than that of the coelentarates, consisting of a nerve ring at the anterior end of the body and lateral nerve cords. Also an excretory system consisting of a branching system of tubes whose ultimate branches end in flame cells embedded in the mesoderm. These animals are usually hermaphrodite with complicated sexual organs.

Class I. Turbellaria. Free-living aquatic platyhelminths of a leaf-like shape, with a ciliated ectoderm, the action of whose cilia produces a gliding movement, e.g. *Dendrocoelum*, *Procerodes*.

Class II. Trematoda. Parasitic platyhelminths with hooks or suckers or both and a non-ciliated ectoderm with a tough external cuticle with spines.

Order 1. Monogenea—ectoparasites with a simple life history and attached to one host, e.g. *Polystoma* (found in bladder or rectum of frog).

Order 2. Digenea—endoparasites with a complicated life history involving two alternative hosts. Polyembryony and larval stages common, e.g. *Fasciola*.

Class III. Cestoda (tapeworms). Internal parasites lacking the enteron and endoderm and possessing a very thick cuticle. Suckers and/or hooks present. Strobilization usually present. Polyembryony does not occur but the larval stage (the hexacanth) gives rise in an alternative host to a bladderworm (cysticercus) which may multiply by asexual means, e.g. *Taenia*, *Echinococcus*.

Phylum: Rotifera (wheel animals). Minute, aquatic, triploblastic, acoelomate animals showing no segmentation but possessing an alimentary canal with a mouth and anus. Anterior to the mouth is a ciliated disk used for feeding and locomotion, giving the appearance of a revolving wheel—hence their name. No blood system or respiratory organs are present but there is an excretory system including flame cells. The sexes are separate. The females produce either fertilized or parthenogenetic eggs, e.g. *Rotifer*.

Phylum: Nematoda (Round worms). Bilaterally segmented triploblastic Metazoa. The body is covered by a tough cuticle secreted by the epidermis. The body cavity in which lie the viscera is not a true coelom. The enteron has two openings: the mouth at the anterior end and the anus at the posterior end. A layer of muscle cells lies beneath the epidermis. The nervous system is a simple nerve collar around the anterior end of the gut with a number of longitudinal nerve cords. Excretory cells connected with two lateral canals are present. Nematodes are unisexual. Both free-living forms and forms parasitic on animals and plants occur, e.g. *Rhabditis* (free living), *Ascaris* (parasitic).

Phylum: Annelida (Ringed worms). Bilaterally symmetrical, metamerically segmented, triploblastic Metazoa whose body cavity is a true coelom dividing the mesoderm into an outer somatic and an inner splanchnic layer. The epidermis is glandular, moist, covered by a thin cuticle and used as a respiratory organ. The enteron has two openings: the anterior mouth leading into a stomodaeum of inturned ectoderm and the posterior anus opening into a short proctodaeum also lined by ectoderm. The gut is straight and unbranched; longitudinal and circular muscle bands occur in both layers of the mesoderm. A closed blood system is present and the circulation is maintained by contractile vessels. The nervous system consists of two suprapharyngeal ganglia connected by commissures to a ventral nerve cord with the neurones scattered along its length. The excretory organs are usually ectodermal nephridia terminating internally in the coelom by flame cells or ciliated funnels. Chitinous bristles (chaetae) set in sacs in the body wall are typically present although absent in one class—the leeches.

Class I. Polychaeta. Annelids with lateral projections of the segments (parapodia) bearing numerous chaetae. There is present a head bearing tentacles and palps and often simple eyes. The sexes are usually separate with gonads segmentally arranged. All polychaetes are marine and many have a larval stage—the trochophore, e.g. *Nereis* (the ragworm), *Arenicola* (the burrowing lugworm).

Class II. Oligochaeta. Annelids with no parapodia and with few bristles per segment. The head is not well developed and devoid of tentacles, etc. (cf. polychaetes). These annelids are hermaphrodite, with the gonads confined to a few segments only. They are either terrestrial or fresh water and have no larval stage (direct development), e.g. *Lumbricus, Allolobophora, Eisenia.*

Class III. Hirudinea—the leeches. These are ectoparasites provided with suckers and chitinous teeth. Chaetae are absent. Each segment bears externally a number of ring-like markings (annuli). They are hermaphrodite with direct development.

Phylum: Arthropoda. Bilaterally symmetrical metamerically segmented Metazoa. Each segment typically bears a pair of jointed appendages, one or more of which are gnathites (jaws). The cuticle forms a firm exoskeleton, to the inside of which the muscles are attached. The head is well developed and includes a number of segments, the mouth being ventral and not in the anterior segment though the anus is in the terminal one. The blood system is an 'open' one, with a definite dorsal valved heart and the main body cavity is a haemocoele and not a coelom, the pericardial space being part of the haemocoele. The nervous system consists of a pair of cerebral ganglia dorsal to the oesophagus joined by a pair of circum-oesophageal commissures to a double ventral chain of ganglia connected by commissures. The sexes are separate. Cilia are absent.

Class I. Crustacea. Aquatic arthropods with two pairs of antennae, usually breathing by gills.

Sub-class I. Branchiopoda. Free-living Crustacea with compound eyes. A carapace is usually present. Broad, thin limbs fringed with bristles used for producing a current of water for food capture and respiration, e.g. *Chirocephalus, Daphnia.*

Sub-class II. Ostracoda. Free-living Crustacea with or without compound eyes, possessing a bivalved carapace with an adductor muscle, e.g. *Cypris.*

Sub-class III. Copepoda. Free or parasitic Crustacea without compound eyes or carapace; antennules enlarged and used for swimming, e.g. *Cyclops.*

Sub-class IV. Cirripedia. Crustacea with a free-swimming larval stage but sedentary in the adult, e.g. *Lepas* (the goose barnacle), *Balanus* (the acorn barnacle), *Sacculina* (parasitic on the crab).

Sub-class V. Malacostraca. Crustacea with compound eyes, usually stalked. Body divided into a cephalo-thorax and an abdomen usually with a carapace covering the cephalo-thorax partially or entirely. Abdomen bears appendages and a terminal 'tail fan' formed of the next posterior pair of appendages—the uropods and the telson (terminal segment). There is a large group containing a number of orders including the following orders: Amphipoda, e.g. *Gammarus*; Isopoda, e.g. *Asellus* (water slater), *Oniscus* (wood louse); Decapoda, e.g. *Astacus* (crayfish), *Cancer* (crab), *Homarus* (lobster), *Crangon* (shrimp).

Class II. Insecta. Terrestrial arthropods breathing by tracheae and possessing one pair of antennae, a pair of compound eyes, three pairs of legs and usually two pairs of wings. (For classification of insects into orders, see pages 185, 187.)

Class III. Myriapoda. Terrestrial arthropods with tracheae, one pair of antennae, numerous legs and no wings—the centipedes (e.g. *Lithobius*) with one pair of legs per segment, and the millipedes (e.g. *Julus*) with two pairs of legs per *apparent* segment.

Class IV. Arachnida. Terrestrial arthropods with a few exceptions (e.g. the king crab and the water spider). Respiration by gill books, lung books or tracheae. The body is divided into (i) the prosoma, bearing two pairs of appendages, the chelicerae and the pedipalpi, and (ii) the mesosoma with *four* pairs of walking limbs and the metasoma. In some arachnids, e.g. the spiders, the mesosoma and metasoma are fused to form the opisthosoma. Examples of arachnids are the scorpions, e.g. *Scorpio*, the king crabs, e.g. *Limulus*[1], the spiders, e.g. *Epeira*, and the mites, e.g. *Tyroglyphus.*

1 Sometimes placed in a separate class – Merostomata.

Class VI. Onchyophora. Primitive terrestrial arthropods breathing by tracheae and possessing nephridia—a link between the annelids and the arthropods, e.g. *Peripatus.*

Phylum: Mollusca. Triploblastic coelomate Metazoa either bilaterally symmetrical or asymmetrical. There is no obvious metameric segmentation though certain organs, e.g. nephridia and gonads, may be paired. The body is typically divided into three regions: the head, the muscular foot and the visceral hump. A mantle (a projection from the visceral hump) usually houses within its cavity a pair of comb-like gills (the ctenidia). The ectoderm of the visceral hump and of the mantle often secrete a calcareous shell. The blood system is an 'open' one with a definite heart dorsal to the gut enclosed in a coelomic pericardium. The nervous system consists of a ganglionated nerve collar around the fore-gut connected to outlying ganglia by commissures. A larval stage resembling the trochosphere of the Annelida may be presented in the life history.

Class I. Amphineura. Marine Mollusca whose body plan is nearest the 'ideal' mollusc, being bilaterally symmetrical. The mantle and visceral hump bear a linear series of calcareous plates, e.g. *Chiton.*

Class II. Gastropoda. Mollusca with an asymmetric twisted visceral hump covered by a spiral univalve shell (absent or reduced in slugs) into which the flat-soled foot can be withdrawn. A head is present, often bearing simple eyes on retractable stalks. In the floor of the buccal cavity is a rasp-like radula. The gills, if present, are comb-like or feathery. Both aquatic and terrestrial types occur, e.g. periwinkles (*Littorina*), *Patella* (limpet), *Buccinum* (whelk), *Limnaea* (pond snail), *Helix* (snail), *Limax* (slug).

Class III. Lamellibranchiata. Aquatic Mollusca with a laterally compressed bilaterally symmetrical body encased in a bivalved shell from which a wedge-shaped foot may be protruded. No head or radula present. The gills are plate-like. Ciliary currents produced by cilia on the linings of the mantle and gills used for feeding, respiration, excretion and reproduction, e.g. *Anodon* (the freshwater mussel), *Mytilus* (the sea mussel), *Ostrea* (oyster), *Pecten* (scallop), *Cardium* (cockle).

Class IV. Cephalopoda. Marine Mollusca with a well-developed head bearing a pair of large eyes and tentacles with suckers. The shell is absent or enclosed in the visceral hump. The mantle cavity communicates with the exterior by a funnel (part of the foot) through which water can be forcibly ejected for jet propulsion. The nervous system is well developed, e.g. *Sepia* (the cuttlefish), *Octopus*.

Phylum: Echinodermata. Marine triploblastic coelomate Metazoa with secondarily radial symmetry—the larval stages being bilaterally symmetrical. The body is built on a five-rayed plan. Calcareous plates occur in the dermis, sometimes fused to form a shell (e.g. sea urchin). No definite blood system or excretory system is present. The coelom is divided into three parts with different functions; one of these parts is the hydrocoele connected with the numerous tube feet used for locomotion. There is no central nervous system, e.g. Asteroidea (star fish), Echinoidea (sea urchins), Holothuroidea (sea cucumbers), Ophiuroidea (brittle stars), Crinoidea (sea lilies).

Phylum: Chordata. Bilaterally symmetrical metamerically segmented triploblastic Metazoa whose body plan differs fundamentally from that of the foregoing invertebrate metazoan phyla (pages 227, 229). Chordates are characterized by the following features: (1) a dorsal tubular nerve cord with paired nerves, each nerve having a dorsal and a ventral root, (2) an axial skeletal rod called the notochord lying between the nerve cord and the gut and present at least during the early developmental stages, though wholly or partly replaced in the adult in the majority of the chordates by the vertebral column, (3) visceral clefts in the region of the pharynx, (4) a closed blood system with a dorsal and a ventral vessel connected in the pharyngeal region by pairs of vessels running in the walls of the visceral clefts, the direction of blood flow being forwards in the ventral vessel and backwards in the dorsal vessel, (5) an hepatic portal vessel, (6) a post-anal tail.

Sub-phylum: Acrania (Protochordata). Primitive chordates with no definite heart or skull or brain. The excretory organs are not kidneys.

Class I. Enteropneusta (Hemichordata). Burrowing aquatic worm-like Acrania with a proboscis anterior to the mouth and a collar. The pharynx has numerous perforations and there is a dorsal nerve cord in the region of the collar, e.g. *Balanoglossus* (an acorn worm).

Class II. Urochordata. Acrania, mostly sedentary except in the larval stage (with notochord). The body of the adult is enclosed in a covering of a cellulose-like material—hence the name tunicates often applied to them. Numerous apertures occur in the enlarged pharynx opening out into a space (atrium) enclosed by atrial folds.

A number of the typically chordate organs, e.g. notochord, post-anal tail, dorsal tubular nerve cord, occur only in the larva, except in one order. Ciliary currents used for feeding, respiration, excretion and reproduction, e.g. *Ascidia* (sea squirt).

Class III. Cephalochordata. Acrania whose notochord extends to the anterior tip of the body beyond the front of the central nervous system. Numerous gill slits, a pronounced endostyle and an atrium are present. Ciliary currents are used for feeding, etc. Excretion occurs by means of numerous nephridia with solenocytes. Free swimming, though often burrowing in sand, e.g. *Amphioxus* (*Branchiostoma*)—the lancelet.

Sub-phylum: Craniata. These are also called vertebrates, the notochord of the embryonic stage being wholly or partially replaced by a vertebral column. The head is well developed with a definite brain encased in a cranium and sense organs: olfactory, optic and auditory housed in capsules. The visceral clefts are restricted in number and do not open into an atrium. A well-developed muscular heart is present, maintaining a high blood pressure. The organs of excretion are kidneys composed of mesodermal tubules.

Branch Agnatha—Jawless vertebrates.

Class: Cyclostomata. Cold-blooded aquatic vertebrates breathing by gills; with smooth skins devoid of scales. Jaws and limbs are absent. The nasal aperture is single and median. The larva (ammocoete) is a ciliary feeder with an endostyle secreting mucus, e.g. *Petromyzon* (the lamprey).

Branch Gnathostomata—Vertebrates with jaws developed from the 2nd visceral (mandibular) arch.

Class: Pisces. Cold-blooded aquatic vertebrates breathing by gills situated in the visceral clefts. The skin is covered by dermal scales. Paired pectoral and pelvic fins present together with median and tail fins, usually supported by horny rays. The tail is muscular and used for propulsion. No amnion or allantois present in the embryonic stage.

Sub-class I: Chondrichthyes (Elasmobranchs). Fish with a cartilaginous endoskeleton but devoid of an air bladder and usually having no operculum (gill cover), e.g. *Scyliorhinus* (dogfish), *Raia* (the skate).

Sub-class II: Osteichthyes (Teleostomi). Fish with a bony endoskeleton wholly or partly replacing the cartilaginous one of the embryo and composed of cartilage and dermal bones. An operculum and an air bladder are usually present. The scales are dermal. This sub-class contains a number of orders, some of them, e.g. Coelacanthii and Dipnoi (lung fishes) including living but apparently ancient types near to ancestral forms, e.g. *Latimeria* (a coelacanth), *Ceratodus* (a dipnoan). The majority (modern fishes) belong to the order Teleostei, e.g. *Gadus* (the cod), *Salmo* (the salmon), *Anguilla* (the eel).

Class: Amphibia. Cold-blooded vertebrates with aquatic fresh-water larvae breathing by means of gills. The larvae are fish-like but have no paired fins and metamorphose to an adult form with penta-dactyl limbs, breathing by lungs and the scaleless, glandular moist skin. Endoskeleton mainly of bone. The adults usually return to the water to lay their eggs which are fertilized externally and the hyomandibula of the larva becomes in the adult the columella of the ear. No amnion or allantois are present in the embryonic stage.

Order 1. Stegocephalia—extinct Amphibia with dermal bones in the skin forming a more or less complete armour.

Order 2. Urodela—amphibians with scaleless skins, short limbs and persistent tails. Some members retain their gills in the adult stage, e.g. *Triton* (the newt), *Salamandra* (the sala-mander), *Ambystoma* (the axolotl) in which the larval stage persists and becomes sexually mature (paedogenesis).

Order 3. Anura—amphibians with a scaleless skin, short bodies, long hind limbs and no tail, e.g. *Rana* (the frog), *Bufo* (the toad).

Order 4. Gymnophiona (Apoda)—Burrowing Amphibia with-out girdles or limbs and with worm-like bodies, e.g. *Coecilia*.

Class: Reptilia. Cold-blooded vertebrates with pentadactyl limbs and a covering of horny epidermal scales. Air-breathing by lungs. Teeth, if present, of a simple uniform type (homodont). Columella in ear. Fertilization internal. The eggs are heavily yolked and encased in a calcareous shell. Inside this the embryo develops enclosed in foetal membranes, the amnion and chorion. An allantois is also present. Visceral clefts present in the embryo only but gills are absent. Reptiles were once the dominant race of animals on the earth, though now supplanted by the mammals, and showed, like the mammals, adaptive radiation (page 697). Many types of reptiles (e.g. the pterodactyl) are now extinct. Living reptiles belong to the following orders:

Order 1. Lacertilia—the lizards.

Order 2. Ophidia—the snakes.

Order 3. Chelonia—the tortoises and turtles.

Order 4. Crocodilia—the crocodiles.

Order 5. Rhynchocephalia—*Sphenodon* (the tuatara of New Zealand).

Class: Aves (Birds). Warm-blooded vertebrates, air breathing by means of lungs and possessing feathers derived from the epidermis. The limbs are pentadactyl, the forelimb skeletons being modified to form the bases of the wings which are used for flight. The hind limbs used for walking have their lower portions encased in horny epidermal scales. The jaws form the horny bills and are devoid of teeth (*Archaeopteryx*, page 411, now extinct, however possessed them). A columella is present. Only one aortic arch—the right one —occurs in the adult. Fertilization is internal. The eggs resemble those of the reptiles.

Class: Mammalia. Warm-blooded vertebrates with pentadactyl limbs breathing air by means of lungs. The skin is covered by hairs derived from the epidermis of the skin and contains sweat glands and sebaceous glands. Certain of the skin glands are modified to form the milk-producing (mammary) glands of the female—rudimentary in the male. Teeth of several types (heterodont) and set in sockets in the jaw bones. The body cavity is divided into an anterior cavity (thoracic cavity) and a posterior one (the abdominal cavity) by a muscular partition, the diaphragm. External ears are present and in place of the single columella there is a chain of three auditory ossicles. The nasal passage is separated from the buccal cavity by a palate. In the adult the left systemic arch only is present. Epiphyses (separate centres of ossification) occur at the ends of many of the bones. The optic lobes are divided to form four corpora quadrigemina. Fertilization is internal. Mammals are divided into three sub-classes:

(i) *The Prototheria (Monotremata)*. Primitive mammals with certain reptilian features in their skeleton (e.g. separate precoracoid and coracoid bones with an interclavicle as well as a clavicle) and laying shelled eggs in which the young develop. After hatching the young are nourished with milk produced from modified skin glands of the female, e.g. *Ornithorhyncus* (the duck-billed platypus of Australia) and *Tachyglossus* (the spiny anteater of Australasia and New Guinea).

(ii) *The Metatheria* (*Marsupials*). A later type of mammal than the Prototheria. They are viviparous, the young developing inside the uterus though in only one example (*Perameles*—the bandicoot) is there a true allantoic placenta. After being born in an immature state, the young are carried for a time in an external pouch (the marsupium) on the abdomen of the female, where they are nourished with milk produced by definite mammary glands with mammae (teats). Like the later eutherian mammals, the marsupials have undergone evolution accompanied by adaptative radiation (page 697) and present today a number of different forms adapted for life in various habitats and closely resembling their eutherian counterparts, e.g. the marsupial wolf, rabbit, mole and bear, from which they can be distinguished by such minor characters as the absence of a tympanic bulla and an inturned edge of the rear of the mandible. Apart from the arboreal opossums of America, all are confined to Australasia in the present epoch.

(iii) *The Eutheria* (*or Placental Mammals*). These represent the culminating stages in the evolution of the mammals. The brain is more highly developed than in the 'lower mammals', especially in the region of the cerebrum. The young are born alive in a more advanced stage and during the major part of the prolonged gestation are nourished by means of an allantoic placenta which also serves for respiration and excretion by exchanges between the maternal and foetal blood streams. The dentition is modified to suit the feeding habits. These mammals are divided into a number of orders which have already been listed and briefly described on pp. 414–416.

INDEX

(References to figure pages are printed in bold type)